Winton and Bayliss

HUMAN PHYSIOLOGY

SIXTH EDITION

Revised and Edited by

O. C. J. LIPPOLD
M.B., B.S.(Lond.)

Reader in Physiology, University of London (U.C.L.)

and

F. R. WINTON
M.D., D.Sc.

Sometime Professor of Pharmacology University of London (U.C.L.); Reader in Physiology, University of Cambridge

With 267 Illustrations

J. & A. CHURCHILL LTD.
104 GLOUCESTER PLACE, LONDON

1968

First Edition	.	.	1930
,, ,,	Reprinted		1932
Second Edition	.	.	1935
,, ,,	Reprinted		1936
Third Edition	.	.	1948
,, ,,	Reprinted		1949
Fourth Edition	.	.	1955
Fifth Edition	.	.	1962
Sixth Edition	.	.	1968

Standard Book Number
7000 1374 1

Printed in Great Britain

The Editors are grateful to the following colleagues for writing or revising chapters, as indicated in the Table of Contents.

H. BARCROFT, M.A., M.D., F.R.S.
  Professor of Physiology, St. Thomas' Hospital Medical School, London, S.E.1.

H. M. CHARLTON, D.Phil.
  Lecturer, Dept. of Human Anatomy, The University, Oxford.

M. DE BURGH DALY, M.A., M.B., B.Ch., SC.D.
  Professor of Physiology, St. Bartholomew's Hospital Medical College, London, E.C.1.

M. G. EGGLETON, D.SC., M.R.C.S., L.R.C.P.
  Fellow and formerly Reader in Physiology, University College, London, W.C.1.

J. A. B. GRAY, M.A., SC.D., M.B., B.Chir.
  Secretary, Medical Research Council; Formerly Professor of Physiology, University College, London, W.C.1.

R. A. GREGORY, M.SC., D.SC., Ph.D., M.R.C.S., L.R.C.P., F.R.S.
  Professor of Physiology, The University, Liverpool 3.

G. W. HARRIS, M.A., SC.D., F.R.S.
  Professor of Anatomy, University of Oxford.

B. R. JEWELL, Ph.D., B.SC., M.B., B.S.
  Lecturer in Physiology, University College, London, W.C.1.

P. A. MERTON, M.B.
  Lecturer in Physiology, University of Cambridge.

D. H. SMYTH, M.D., M.SC., F.R.S.
  Professor of Physiology, The University, Sheffield 10.

PREFACE TO SIXTH EDITION

THIS text-book of "Human Physiology" is written for students of medicine, dentistry and the biological sciences. Human physiology, particularly as the basis for modern medicine, is best understood in terms of the principles of comparative and general physiology, and the experimental evidence obtained in other species has always been very important in synthesizing an account of the way in which the human body normally functions. For students, it is necessary to limit the subject matter; in this book the authors have aimed at a balanced exposition of the general principles of physiology and the experimental research which has led to the establishment of these principles. Where possible, proof is given in support of statements made and clinical examples are described. The choice in this matter has been left to the authors of the different parts of the book.

The authors are mostly active research workers in various fields of physiology, and this sixth revision of "Winton and Bayliss" is a lively and up to date presentation. Most of the sections have been completely rewritten and rearranged, whilst the illustrations have been thoroughly revised with the aim of making the students' task in comprehending the subject as easy as possible. A further modification, to help the reader, is the subdivision of the text into much shorter chapters, the chapters themselves being grouped into sections. Throughout, the intention has been to inculcate the habit of critical thought, and to avoid the inducement of that unreasoning state in which the student passively absorbs unsupported facts and plausible theories derived from them.

London,   O. C. J. Lippold
July, 1968.   F. R. Winton

EXTRACTS FROM THE PREFACE TO THE FIRST EDITION (1930)

. . . the problems of human disease called for a survey of the normal functions of the human body and this inspired the development of experimental human physiology and supplementary observations on the frog when the choice of a cold-blooded animal rendered the technique simpler . . . Developments of chemistry in the direction of biochemistry, and of zoology in that of comparative physiology, have intermingled with classical physiology, and the composite science of general physiology is now concerned more with the furtherance of natural knowledge than with applications to medicine . . .

The medical student is expected to know too much and to think too little. He has two chief needs, a training in scientific methods and a knowledge of the properties of the human body. They can, it seems, be best satisfied . . . by . . . eliminating from his curriculum those parts of physiology which have no immediate bearing on the happenings in the body of man.

The book has been kept short by omissions rather than by compression. Much anatomy, histology and biochemistry that is commonly included in text-books of physiology is now so admirably treated in special books on these subjects that duplication here has been deemed unnecessary, and only an outline of the immediate facts needed to complete the description or argument under consideration has been included.

HISTORICAL NOTE

IN 1928, Professor (now Sir Charles) Lovatt Evans proposed to two younger members of his staff in the Department of Physiology at University College London that they should write a comparatively short textbook of Physiology, to run as a companion to the longer textbook by Professor E. H. Starling who died in 1927. Lovatt Evans had begun his first revision of "Starling", to appear in 1930 as the fifth edition, as did the first edition of "Winton and Bayliss". Both were tactfully and very effectively helped through teething troubles by the late Mr. J. Rivers of J. & A. Churchill Ltd. The two authors wrote all of the shorter book except for the chapter on special senses, written by their fellow lecturer, the late Dr. R. J. Lythgoe. Dr. Grace Eggleton, in the same department, read the proofs and prepared the index, as she has nobly done for all editions since.

Physiology developed quickly in every direction, and in subsequent editions certain chapters or parts of chapters were contributed by colleagues with corresponding experience. Warm appreciation is due to them for the ready way in which they allowed the authors to edit and particularly to curb the length of their contributions.

Then, alas, Leonard Bayliss died in 1965. Son of Sir William Bayliss ("General Physiology") and nephew of Starling, Leonard was one of the most thoughtful and original physiologists and had put an immense amount of work into preparation of successive editions of "Human Physiology". His co-author has retired from University work and was fortunate in inducing Dr. O. C. J. Lippold to join him in preparing the sixth edition and indeed, to take the lead in doing so. Happily the appearance of post-war austerity which had persisted since the 1949 edition has been replaced by a welcome "new look" which accounts for much of the increase in the number of pages.

F. R. W.

ACKNOWLEDGEMENTS

WE would like to record our thanks to the many individuals who have helped in the production of this edition, particularly students and their tutors who have made many valuable suggestions regarding both the general layout and specific items in the text. Several colleagues have been involved in reading part of the manuscripts and proofs; to them we are most grateful.

This edition contains many new illustrations; some of these have been specially prepared, while others have been taken unchanged from original publications. For all these, whether modified or unchanged, we would like to thank the authors concerned and record our gratitude for the co-operation of the editors of the following journals *Acta physiologica Scandinavica; American Journal of Physiology; Brain; British Journal of Anæsthesia; British Medical Bulletin; British Medical Journal; Bulletin of the Johns Hopkins Hospital; Clinical Science; Nature; Journal of the Acoustical Society of America; Journal of the American Medical Association; Journal of Biophysical and Biochemical Cytology; Journal of General Physiology; Journal of Neurophysiology; Journal of Physiology* and the *Proceedings of the Royal Society.*

The D. Appleton-Century Co.; Edward Arnold (Publishers) Ltd.; Baillière, Tindall & Cox; G. Bell & Sons; Cambridge University Press; W. Heffer & Sons Ltd.; Hinrichsen Editions; Lloyd-Luke (Medical Books) Ltd.; Longmans, Green & Co. Ltd.; Macmillan & Co. Ltd.; The Macmillan Co., New York; Oxford University Press; The W. B. Saunders Co.; Shaw & Sons; Charles C. Thomas; and The Williams and Wilkins Co. have all been good enough to grant permission for the use of certain illustrations from their publications and we thank them for this facility.

Finally, we must again express our appreciation of the courtesy and patience maintained by our publishers, and particularly by Mr. J. A. Rivers and by Mr. A. S. Knightley.

CONTENTS

PROLOGUE

THE dead and the living body differ. How they differ and how the living body sees, moves, digests, keeps warm, and so on, is the province of physiology. We see a man lift an arm or walk without staggering and as physiologists we wonder what is going on in his muscles and nervous system. To discover things of this kind, we have first to take the machine to pieces, much as we should have to take a motor car to pieces to explain its varied performance on the road. You cannot, of course, take a man to pieces, so the corresponding tissues of animals, say the limb muscles, intestine or heart, have to be examined one by one after removal from animals immediately after death. If the property of an organ is found to be much the same in a number of animals, such as the frog, rabbit, cat, dog and monkey, we presume that it may well be much the same in man. This basic knowledge about individual organs can be extended to a study of their functions and interactions in anaesthetised animals. Only then, as a rule, can painless methods be devised for similar and further studies on unanaesthetised animals and man. Thus physiology extends from physical and chemical processes in cells and tissues to elaborate performances of whole animals, but it does not extend very far into studies of behaviour or mental affairs which are the province of psychology.

Physiology has another boundary; it is primarily concerned with normal animals. Disease processes belong to the subject matter of pathology and medicine. Practising physicians, however, need a vivid awareness of physiological processes in the body for both diagnosis and treatment. Normally they lack the leisure to submit disorders presented by individual patients to extensive physiological analysis; moreover, the treatment of of the sick cannot be delayed till the outcome of such analysis is known. Treatment depends on speedy diagnosis which is based on the symptoms reported by the patient, on physical signs observed by the physician and perhaps on a few simple tests such as X-ray, histological or biochemical examinations. Such slender elements of evidence must be fitted into the whole relevant knowledge of physiological processes in the body before they have much value beyond rule-of-thumb indicators, yielding "slot-machine diagnosis." So it happens that important advances in physiology are made in the research departments of medicine, particularly in fields somewhat neglected by physiologists who may be preoccupied with studies without such applications to medicine. Certain diseases such as diabetes mellitus have, however, been extensively studied by physiologists sometimes with dramatic improvements in treatment as a consequence.

The most noticeable and measurable sign of deterioration in ill-health is often the reduction of the amount of muscular exercise that can be endured without excessive breathlessness and thumping of the heart. If a sedentary clerk and an athlete run side by side to catch a train, the first may arrive panting, sweating and exhausted and take quite some time to recover, while the second may suffer little discomfort and that soon over. Neither would be regarded as ill unless his performance deteriorated to the point of interfering with his normal occupation. A third person may find that, for example, climbing slowly up a staircase may engender such breathlessness as to demand a rest on reaching each floor, yet the physiological mechanisms controlling breathing are much the same in all three. Thus, physiology is essential to the understanding of both normal and disease processes.

The line dividing the living and the dead is not easy to draw. If you prod a live animal it is apt to move, but neither anaesthetised animals nor most plants move actively when disturbed. Growth and reproduction are regarded as characteristic of the living state, but many adults past growth and beyond child-bearing are far from dead and still appear irritable to prodding.

Men and large animals are certainly dead when the heart has stopped beating for so long that there is no hope of recovery. In them, the blood pumped by the heart is essential for carrying foodstuffs and their products in the intestine to organs like muscles, to which, also, oxygen is carried by blood from the lungs. Energy derived from chemical reactions resembling burning can then be converted into mechanical or other forms of useful energy, while the waste products of the combustion are carried away, again by the blood, the carbon dioxide to the lungs and most soluble products to the kidneys, where they are eliminated from the body. Perhaps the continued use of oxygen as part source of chemical energy is one of the more widespread features of life, but anaerobic organisms provide exceptions; moreover, power for industry and traffic is still derived from fuels oxidised in apparatus which is indubitably dead.

In animals of microscopic size, in contrast to larger animals, blood circulation is not needed. Every part is so near the surface of the cell or organism that it can derive oxygen and foodstuffs by direct diffusion from the surface. A blood circulation is, however, essential in larger animals and this may be illustrated by some features of muscular exercise in man.

Muscle occupies much of the total body weight and when active, each gram of muscle uses oxygen and produces waste products more rapidly than any other tissue. The large output of carbon dioxide itself is one of the factors producing the well-known increase in breathing during strenuous exercise, and this also secures the increase in oxygen intake. A large increase in blood flow is needed to carry the extra carbon dioxide and oxygen to and from the lungs and is produced by the heart which accordingly beats at a higher rate and puts out more blood per beat. Moreover, muscles resemble man-made engines in being unable to convert more than, at best, about one quarter of the chemical energy into mechanical work. Three-quarters or more, therefore, of the chemical energy is converted to heat. Again, the blood is essential for transporting the extra heat from muscles to the skin from which the heat can be lost by radiation and conduction. Indeed, in healthy people the severity of the exercise they can take is generally limited, not by their muscles, but by the rate at which the heart can pump blood round the body.

Cardiac output can be measured in man, but not easily enough to be a useful test in clinical practice. Heart-rate, easily measured as the pulse of the radial artery at the wrist, is a most useful quick guide to change in cardiac output, but when the frequency reaches about 180/minute the time available for the heart to refill between contractions becomes too short and the output per beat falls. Below this limit, pulse-rate can be used as a guide to the degree of physical fitness in two ways. First, during moderate exertion the pulse-rate will rise more in sick people than would be expected in normally fit people. Secondly, during rest following exertion, the pulse-rate will return to normal more slowly.

Undue fatigue is well known to accompany ill-health. Fatigue is a state which may reduce or end longer-lasting muscular exercise or other forms of activity. It is said to supervene when an activity, which has been sustained for some time, diminishes although the incentive to maintain it remains unchanged and effective, the standard of performance being completely restored after a period of rest. Formerly, fatigue was attributed to the accumulation in the body of metabolic products of activity known as "fatigue products." Though this may happen in a few kinds of activity, it is now considered incapable of explaining most forms of fatigue. Different kinds of activity may be impaired by different processes which may concern primarily almost any of the physiological systems in the body.

An isolated frog muscle contracts less and less in response to repeated electrical stimulation of constant strength : if given a rest, the contractions regain their original size. By analogy, it is said to have become "fatigued." This is attributed to inadequate supply of oxygen diffusing from the surface of the muscle to the fibres and leading to an accumulation of lactic acid. Accordingly, it is difficult to fatigue a single muscle in an anaesthetised mammal by repeated electrical stimulation because it is well-provided with oxygen from its own blood circulation. In very severe exercise in man involving many muscles, however, the oxygen supply to muscles is restricted by the cardiac output, as mentioned earlier, and lactic acid correspondingly accumulates in the body and reduces muscular activity. In less severe exercise the lactic acid is oxidised to carbon dioxide and water; but if such exercise continues till the animal, say a dog running on a treadmill, is exhausted, the fatigue is due to lack of fuel. If glucose is administered periodically, the dog can continue to run for much longer without exhaustion.

Another factor which produces fatigue after even short spells of moderate exercise is the undue rise in body temperature which occurs in a hot moist atmosphere, or if evaporation is reduced by wearing a rubber or oilskin coat. Reduction in blood volume which reduces blood circulation in the brain often makes people feel tired and "go slow" accordingly. When men stand strictly to attention for half an hour or so, they may even faint. The loss in blood volume is here due to high blood pressure in the veins and capillaries of the immobile legs with outward filtration of water into the tissue fluid. There are many ways other than blood or oxygen lack in which the brain can become fatigued, mental work among them as some students know from experience.

The activity, and even survival, of the cells and tissues of an animal or man depend on the properties of the fluids surrounding them. For example, chemical processes in cells are catalysed by enzymes, at varying rates according to temperature and acidity; but some vary more than others. Particularly in the more complex species, therefore, body temperature, the acidity and osmolar concentration of body fluids and many other factors must remain nearly constant if physiological processes are to continue in normal balance. Such ideas were crystallised by Claude Bernard (1830) ; the higher animals were said to have an *internal environment* which is maintained remarkably constant, even during great changes of the external environment, such as climate, the amount and kinds of food and water taken in, and the extent of muscular activity. The pattern of regulatory processes in the body which operate to control the internal environment within so narrow a range of variation was called *physiological homeostasis* by W. B. Cannon (1929) and is one of the essential factors in maintenance of health and, indeed, in survival.

The following chapters include many descriptions of such regulatory processes appertaining to the physiological systems concerned. The interactions between these processes, to achieve homeostasis, will be considered further in the epilogue following the chapters devoted to the individual physiological systems.

Section 1
CELLS, THEIR COMPOSITION
AND THEIR ENVIRONMENT

CHAPTER 1

THE CELL AND ITS MEMBRANE

Cells

Nearly all tissues and organs in the body are composed of *cells*, held together by various intercellular supporting substances. The cells of the body have certain basic characteristics common to all kinds of cell but apart from these, cells display an enormous variety in form, each type being specially adapted to carry out its particular function. Red blood cells, for example, are specialized in structure to enable them to carry oxygen from the lungs to the tissues. Muscle fibres are cells which have the ability to contract. Although the various cells of the body have such diverse functions and structure, they all consist basically of a fluid system, proto-plasm, and are surrounded by a membrane which acts as a barrier between the fluid within the cell and the fluid outside it.

During the course of normal cellular activity molecules and ions pass across this membrane and there is a dynamic interchange between substances in solution in the extracellular and intracellular spaces.

The Cell Membrane

Cell function depends on the integrity of the cell membrane and its property of allowing certain molecules and ions to cross it whilst preventing the passage of others. The membrane, on analysis, is found to consist largely of proteins and lipids. The protein is a fibrous substance called *stromatin* and the lipids are *cholesterol*, *lecithin* and *cephalin*. The lipoid substances form a bi-molecular layer round the cell as shown in Fig. 1.1. Since the membrane is largely lipoid in composition, fat-soluble substances penetrate into the cell easily, whereas non-fat-soluble ones enter only slowly or not at all. Lipids are good electrical

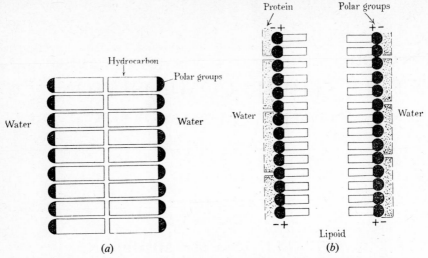

Fig. 1.1. Hypothetical structure of the cell membrane. (a) Red cell membrane, (b) General pattern. (Davson & Danielli (1952). *Permeability of Natural Membranes*. Cambridge Univ. Press.)

insulators, a fact that we will discuss later in connection with the high electrical impedance of membranes, characteristic of all cells.

One can visualize the membrane as having a sieve-like or porous structure, the openings (or pores) being of molecular size, so that small molecules will travel through them. The pores have not been seen under the electron microscope—indeed they probably do not exist in a simple form—but rather they represent preferential pathways within the complex molecular structure of the membrane along which diffusion can take place.

Membrane Permeability

Many substances enter and leave the cell whilst it is active by passing through the membrane. A membrane which allows materials to pass through it is termed *permeable* (to the materials). A membrane which will let only water through is called *semi-permeable*; it must be noted that in fact such membranes do not exist in biological systems. Most cell membranes are *selectively permeable*, a term denoting that in addition to water, certain substances can traverse the membrane whilst others cannot. The reader will soon discover that common usage tends to confuse the distinction between the latter two terms. The word "permeability" is also applied to describe the properties of blood vessel walls, intestinal cells and other regions which separate two fluid compartments.

Permeability of the cell membrane either is *active*, i.e. metabolic processes are involved, carrier mechanisms are used and energy is consumed in the process, or it is *passive*, i.e. no energy is required to move particles across the membrane, only a concentration gradient being involved.

PASSAGE OF WATER AND SOLUTES ACROSS MEMBRANES

It is a fundamental law of physical chemistry, based on universal experience of the properties of matter and energy, that the components of a solution tend to move from regions where they are in high concentration, to regions where they are in low concentration. They will, in fact, move in this direction unless they are prevented from doing so by some obstruction, or are driven in the opposite direction by some other force. This force may be electrical; it may be mechanical, such as a hydrostatic pressure; or it may be chemical, such as would be produced by interactions with other substances present in the solution or in contact with it. This general law applies to the water as well as to the substances dissolved in it. The concentration of the water becomes smaller as the concentration of the dissolved substances becomes larger, since, in a given volume, water molecules are replaced by solute molecules. But when we refer to the "concentration" of a solution, we ordinarily mean the *solute* concentration: water will thus move from a *less* concentrated solution (in this sense) to a *more* concentrated solution. The concentrations, however, must be expressed in terms of "osmolarity", that is, of the sum of the (molar) concentrations of *all* the solutes present, each ion of an electrolyte being considered as a separate substance. Unless the solution is very dilute, we must then multiply by the appropriate value of the "osmotic coefficient", which may be found in tables of physical and chemical constants. For mammalian body fluids, the value is about 0·9. The osmolar concentration of any solution may be measured directly in terms of its freezing point, or vapour pressure.

The fact, as indicated in Fig. 2.1, that the fluids in the different compartments have different compositions, shows that there must be obstructions, or barriers of some kind at their junctions. Such barriers exist between the intracellular and interstitial fluids (cell membranes) and between interstitial fluid and plasma (walls of capillary blood vessels). The properties of these barriers determine the nature of the interchanges which take place between these different compartments.

The Donnan Membrane Equilibrium

Suppose we have two solutions of sodium chloride, and add to one of them the sodium salt of a protein or of any of the organic anions found within living cells, as mentioned above. The two solutions are now put one on each side of a boundary, or membrane, through which sodium and chloride ions can penetrate but the organic anions cannot. The concentration of sodium ions is greater on one side of the membrane than on the other, but their natural tendency to diffuse in the direction of the concentration gradient is immediately opposed by an electrical force set up by the in-diffusible anions which are left behind; this pulls them in again. Chloride ions, on the other hand, are driven out, so as to create a concentration gradient by the same electrical force; a force which pulls in positively charged ions will push out negatively charged ions. The freely diffusible ions thus become distributed unevenly between the two solutions, and an electrical potential difference is developed across the membrane. In these conditions, all freely diffusible ions which may be present (sodium, potassium, chloride and bicarbonate, for example) will move from one solution to the other until, for each kind of ion, the concentration in one solution is related to that in the other by a general equation defining what is known as the "Donnan Membrane Equilibrium". Using plasma (pl) and interstitial fluid (int) separated by the capillary wall as concrete examples, the equation is:—

$$\frac{[Na^+]pl}{[Na^+]int} = \frac{[K^+]pl}{[K^+]int} = r; \quad \text{and} \frac{[Cl^-]pl}{[Cl^-]int} = \frac{[HCO_3^-]pl}{[HCO_3^-]int} = \frac{1}{r}$$

the square brackets indicating concentrations. The electrical potential difference between the two fluids is given by the Nernst equation:

$$E = \frac{RT}{ZF} . \ln . r = 61 \cdot 5 \log . r \text{ at } 37°C \text{ (millivolts)}*$$
$$= 57 \cdot 2 \log . r \text{ at } 15°C \text{ (millivolts)}$$

The value of the "distribution ratio", denoted by r, increases if the concentration of the indiffusible (e.g. protein) ions is increased, or if the concentration of the diffusible (e.g. chloride) ions is decreased. In the plasma, the indiffusible ions are anions, and r is greater than 1, the concentrations of sodium and potassium are greater in the plasma than in the interstitial fluid (by about 5 per cent) and the concentrations of chloride and bicarbonate are smaller; the plasma is electrically negative to the interstitial fluid by about 1 millivolt.

The equation, as just given, is an approximation only, since instead of concen-trations we should, strictly, use "activities". By direct analysis of plasma and of interstitial fluid, or of a simple solution in equilibrium with plasma at a membrane impermeable to proteins (an "ultra-filtrate" or "dialysate" of plasma), it is found that the value of r for sodium ions is 1·06, and that for chloride ions is 1·04. The apparent discrepancy is due to the fact that the activity coefficients of sodium and chloride ions are slightly smaller in the plasma than in a protein-free fluid.

* Precise details of this equation are unimportant at the present juncture but for information, R is the gas constant (·08 L/atmos/°C/mole), T is absolute temperature, F is the Faraday (96,500 coulombs/mole) and Z is the charge on the ion. When substituted, at 18°C, these values give the relation:

$$E(mV) = \frac{60}{Z} \log . r.$$

(natural log has been converted to the base 10).

Hence potential in mV across a membrane is directly proportional to the ratio of the concentrations of the ions across it. (See also p. 261.)

Membrane Transport

We are still far from understanding the nature and properties of the cell membranes. Certain facts, however, which are of importance in the present connection are well established. Water can penetrate relatively freely into and out of the cells; certain substances in solution, notably oxygen and carbon dioxide, can penetrate nearly as freely; other substances such as urea and certain organic compounds (known as "non-polar" or "lipoid-soluble" compounds) whose molecular weight is not too large, and small univalent ions, can penetrate, but much less freely.

The non-polar substances are those which are soluble in ether, benzene and other liquid hydrocarbons, in which the "lipoid" materials, such as long-chain fatty-acids, cholesterol and lecithin, are also soluble. It is partly because of the relative ease with which non-polar substances penetrate, that the cell membrane is thought to be composed chiefly of lipoid material. For this reason, also, non-polar substances are used for determining the total volume of water in the body.

From the compositions of the intracellular and extracellular fluid we see that the concentration gradients of potassium ions and of chloride ions are in the direction which is to be expected if there is a *Donnan equilibrium* (see p. 3) set up by the presence of indiffusible anions within the cells. There is no reason to suppose that these ions (and bicarbonate ions) cannot penetrate the cell membranes. Indeed, the use of radioactive isotopes and the existence of the "chloride shift" in the red blood cells (as discussed in Chapter 11) show that they do penetrate. There is also an electrical potential difference across the cell membranes of the sign to be expected (intracellular fluid negative to extracellular fluid) and of about the right size (10 to 100 millivolts). But the concentration gradient of sodium ions is in the opposite direction from that of potassium ions and it might seem, at first sight, that the cell membranes must be totally impermeable to sodium ions. But the use of isotopes has shown that this is not so, and it is impossible to avoid the conclusion that sodium ions are being expelled from the interior of the cell by come active process, the "sodium pump", which is only kept going by a continuous supply of energy from metabolic reactions. In effect, the cell membranes behave as if they were impermeable to sodium ions, since any that enter are immediately expelled.

The Sodium Pump

A "sodium pump" which expels positively charged ions will generate an electrical potential difference between the intracellular fluid and the extracellular fluid, and this will draw out chloride ions as well. The concentration ratios of all the ions which can diffuse freely will still be defined by the membrane equilibrium equation, and the value of the distribution ratio r will be related to the electrical potential difference across the membrane whether this is due to the presence of indiffusible ions or to the action of the "sodium pump". But the outward movement of sodium ions through the membranes of most kinds of cell is at least partly "coupled" to the inward movement of potassium ions, one potassium ion going in for each sodium ion "pumped" out. (Such a "pump" will not generate an electrical potential difference.) Owing to this restraint on the movement of potassium ions, the concentration ratio (intracellular fluid)/(extracellular fluid) is not precisely the inverse of that of chloride ions, nor precisely that to be expected from the electrical potential difference across the cell membrane. The distribution of potassium ions, as well as that of sodium ions, between the intracellular fluid and the extracellular fluid is not that to be expected if there were a Donnan equilibrium between the fluids, and the left-hand part of the membrane equilibrium equation does not apply. In red blood cells, the discrepancy is large, for both sodium ions and potassium ions, as may be seen in Fig. 2.1; but in muscle and nerve cells the discrepancy is small for potassium ions, though large for sodium ions.

The cell membranes thus allow many substances in solution to pass through them. But if there is a change in the total osmolar concentration of either the intracellular fluid or of the extracellular fluid, water is found to pass from one to the other much more rapidly than any of the substances in solution. The cells swell or shrink until the two fluids are once more in equilibrium with one another. Since the cells are not rigid, and can swell or shrink quite freely, changes in the concentration of the extracellular fluid are accompanied by equal changes in the concentration of the intracellular fluid, and *vice versa*; the consequent shifts of water from one to the other may, even in the normal living animal, be of quite considerable magnitude. For example, the activity of almost any organ is accompanied by the production of metabolites which are mainly of smaller molecular weight than the parent substances from which they are derived; the osmolar concentration of the active cells rises, therefore, and the cells swell. Muscular exercise, in particular, causes a rise in the volume of the intracellular fluid which can be observed, in man, by the methods of measurement already described.

Owing to the maintenance of osmotic equilibrium between the intracellular and extracellular fluids by a shift of water from one to the other, it is important that the substances used for measuring the volume of the extracellular fluid should be such that they can be analysed accurately even in low concentration. If the substance added to the extracellular fluid increases the osmolar concentration significantly, enough water will be drawn out from the intracellular fluid to produce a significant error in the estimated volume of the extracellular fluid. Indeed, by suitable calculation, it is possible to deduce the *total* volume of water in the body from the concentration of an added substance which does not enter the cells at all.

Isotonic Solutions

A solution is defined as being "isotonic" if, when placed in contact with living cells, no water passes into or out of the cells, "hypertonic" if it draws water out of the cells, and "hypotonic" if water goes into the cells. If two solutions are separated by a membrane permeable only to water, and impermeable to all the substances in solution, water will move from the solution with the smaller total molecular (osmolar) concentration to the solution with the larger osmolar concentration. But if the membrane is permeable to some of the substances in solution, these substances will move from one solution to the other until their concentrations are the same in both, and they will then have no effect on the movement of water. In calculating whether a solution is isotonic or not, the concentrations of all those substances to which the cell membranes are permeable must be left out of consideration. (This may not be strictly true if the substances are electrolytes, owing to the effect of the Donnan equilibrium, but it is very nearly true.) For example, the red blood corpuscles

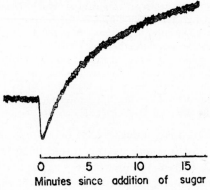

Minutes since addition of sugar

Fig. 1.2. Swelling and Shrinking of Human Red Blood Cells.

Changes in the average volume of the cells were recorded directly in terms of the amount of light transmitted through a very dilute suspension in a saline solution. At time 0, 2 ml of a solution of sorbose was added to 10 ml of the suspension, the final concentration of sorbose being 0·3 M. The total osmolarity of the suspending solution was thus approximately doubled. The optical transmittance decreased suddenly, indicating an almost instantaneous shrinkage of the cells: movement of water between the cells and the outside solution is very rapid.

The sorbose then penetrated slowly into the cells, raised the concentration of the intracellular fluid, water was drawn in, and the cells swelled. The final optical transmittance is greater than the initial, since (a) the whole suspension has been diluted to 5/6 (the effect of the initial shrinkage is partly masked by this); and (b) the suspending solution has been made hypotonic, since water was added as well as sorbose and the cells have swelled accordingly. (Lefevre and Davies.)

are impermeable to sodium chloride, but permeable to urea, oxygen and carbon dioxide, so that the addition, of, say, urea to an isotonic solution of sodium chloride will not make this solution hypertonic with respect to the red blood corpuscles. Again, the ordinary collodion membrane, like the glomerular membrane in the kidney, is permeable to all crystalloidal substances, so that only the concentrations of the colloidal ones (such as proteins) need be considered. All these membranes, however, are more permeable to water than to any solute, so that transient osmotic effects may be observed even with solutions that are, in the long run, isotonic with respect to these membranes. In physiology, we often use the word *"isotonic"*, without further specification, to mean "isotonic with respect to the red blood corpuscles". For mammalian cells, a solution containing 0·90 to 0·95 g of sodium chloride in 100 ml of water is "isotonic".

The movements of water and dissolved substances into and out of the intra-cellular fluid are very conveniently studied by using suspensions of red blood corpuscles. Changes in their volume can be measured by the use of the haematocrit (Chapter 10) or, as in Fig. 1.2 in terms of the amount of light transmitted by the suspension. Records from an experiment which illustrates the points just discussed are given in Fig. 1.2. If a solution of the hexose sugar sorbose, of such a concentration as to be apparently hypertonic, is added to a suspension of red blood cells in an isotonic saline solution, there is initially a very rapid withdrawal of water from the cells, which therefore shrink. The sorbose then slowly penetrates into the cells, drawing water with it. Finally the cells are more swollen than they were initially, since the saline solution has been diluted by the water added with the sorbose, while the sorbose, having the same concentration inside and outside the cells, is osmotically inactive.

An isotonic solution may, alternatively, be defined as a solution which has the same osmotic pressure as the intracellular fluid, a hypertonic solution as one with a greater osmotic pressure, and a hypotonic solution as one with a smaller osmotic pressure. But it must be remembered that the osmotic pressure exerted by a solution depends on the nature of the membrane at which it is developed as well as on the concentration of the solution. The *"tonicity"* of a solution must therefore be defined in terms of the osmotic pressure exerted at the particular membranes considered— e.g. the membranes of certain kinds of cell, the glomerular membranes, etc.—and not necessarily in terms of the "ideal" osmotic pressure exerted at a membrane permeable only to water.

Haemolysis

If the cell membranes are destroyed, or sufficiently damaged, the cell contents pass into the surrounding solution. The red blood cells, again, are very useful for studying the conditions in which this occurs; the haemoglobin which they contain has a strong red colour and is thus easily detected in the external solution; and the cells themselves are easily removed by centrifugation.

There are three general ways in which haemolysis may be brought about. In the first, the cells are placed in a solution which has a salt concentration less than that of the plasma; water passes into them and they swell up and finally burst. In the second, the cell membranes are damaged by means of a solution of ether, saponin, bile salts or other surface active substances. In the third, the blood is repeatedly frozen solid and thawed as rapidly as possible.

When placed in a hypotonic salt solution, the red cells, owing to their biconcave shape (Chapter 10), can increase in volume very considerably before the surface membrane becomes stretched. The amount of further swelling which can take place without rupture of the membrane and haemolysis, varies from one cell to another, even in the same sample of blood from the same individual person; in normal human blood, while the great majority of cells are just haemolysed in about 0·4 per cent NaCl, a small proportion (5 to 10 per cent) burst in stronger solutions, and about the same proportion are unaffected unless the concentration is reduced to less than 0·4 per cent. In this way a *resistance* or *fragility curve* can be constructed, showing the proportion of corpuscles haemolysed, against the concentration of the solution in which they are placed.

The proportion of cells with small resistance is greatly increased in the blood of patients suffering from certain diseases such as familial haemolytic jaundice; when these patients have their spleens removed, their red cells attain a resistance which is normal, or even greater than normal. During recovery from anaemia (e.g. pernicious, or after haemorrhage), on the other hand, the proportion with a large resistance is greatly increased. The resistance to haemolysis of a given cell probably depends upon its age, the membrane becoming steadily weaker during its life in the circulation until it finally gives way altogether.

The surface active substances do not necessarily destroy the cell membrane entirely, but make it permeable to sodium and potassium—perhaps only in certain places. The concentrations of sodium, potassium, chloride and bicarbonate then become more nearly the same inside and outside the cells, and there is an excess osmotic concentration of haemoglobin within the cells: these then take up water, swell, and eventually burst, allowing the haemoglobin to escape

Chapter 2

THE FLUID COMPARTMENTS OF THE BODY

Body Fluids

The greater part of any animal consists of watery solutions; the structural part, which gives the animal its solidity, has less than one-half the weight of the fluid part. It is in the body fluids that most of the chemical reactions involved in metabolism take place, and it is by means of diffusion in these fluids, and by their movement as a whole from place to place, that the metabolites reach and enter the active cells and the products of the metabolic reactions leave and are carried away. Changes in the volume and composition of these fluids may thus affect the activities of most of the organs and tissues of the body, and it is becoming increasingly apparent that the study of these changes in health and disease is an important branch of physiology.

The composition of this fluid matrix is not uniform throughout, and variations in the concentrations of different kinds of dissolved substances are found in different parts of the body. It is useful to think of the animal body as divided into distinct fluid compartments which are more or less separated by various barriers, but at the same time are in equilibrium with each other—or if not in true equilibrium, in a "steady state", maintained by appropriate metabolic reactions. The whole body fluid may be conveniently divided into two major compartments: (1) the intracellular fluid enclosed by the cell walls, and (2) the extracellular fluid between and around the cells; this latter can be again divided into (*a*) the interstitial, or tissue, fluid and (*b*) the blood plasma. The interstitial fluid, which lies between the cell walls and the walls of the blood vessels, forms the "internal environ-

TABLE 2.1

Body Fluids
(*in an average man, weight 70 kg*)

	Kilogram	Per cent of body weight
Total Body Fluids . .	49	70
(1) Intracellular Fluid .	35	50
(2) Extracellular Fluid .	14	20
(*a*) Interstitial Fluid .	11·2	16
(*b*) Blood Plasma . .	2·8	4

ment" for the cells, and provides the connection between the intracellular fluid, where the metabolic reactions occur, and the plasma. The plasma, by virtue of its circulation, distributes the local changes in the composition of the interstitial fluid which are produced by metabolic activity, and enables those produced in the muscles, liver, etc., to be offset by those produced in the lungs, kidneys and alimentary tract.

Each of the different fluid compartments has its characteristic volume and composition. Their relative sizes are given in Table 2.1, and their compositions are discussed in a later section.

Methods of Estimating the Fluid Volumes

A known quantity of some suitable substance is added to the fluid whose volume is to be estimated and its concentration measured: the quantity added, in grams for example, divided by the concentration, in grams per litre, is the volume of the fluid in which it is dissolved, in litres. The principle of the method is thus simple, but discovering the "suitable substance" is not so simple.

The substance chosen must be harmless and without pharmacological effects which would change the amount or distribution of body fluids. In practice, it must be injected into the blood stream, allowed to become distributed throughout the body, and its concentration estimated in a sample of venous blood, usually taken from an arm vein. Corrections must be made for any production or destruction of the substance in the body, as for example by metabolic processes, and for the quantity eliminated e.g. in the urine, during the interval between injection and collection of blood for analysis. It is obvious that these corrections should be small if possible. Many of the most accurate methods depend on the use of radioactive isotopes; special facilities for handling and estimating radioactive substances are needed and proper precautions must be taken against radiation hazards.

The Volume of the Blood

The "reference substance" must be retained within the blood vessels for a period at least long enough to allow it to become uniformly distributed. This is ensured by using a substance which is attached either to the plasma proteins, the volume of the plasma being measured; or to the red blood cells, the total volume of these cells, or that of the whole blood, being measured. The volume of the plasma, of the red cells and of the whole blood are related to each other by the *haematocrit value* (volume of red cells as per cent of volume of whole blood—Chapter 10), so that any one may be calculated from any other. The volume of the whole blood, however, is best measured by adding together the volume of the plasma and the volume of the red cells. Three methods have been used most frequently.

(a) *Plasma Volume.* A known quantity of the non-toxic dye Evans Blue T 1824, which becomes bound to the serum albumin, or a known quantity of serum albumin which has been iodinated with radioactive iodine (^{131}I), is injected intravenously. The blood sample is centrifuged and the concentration of dye, or of "labelled" protein, in the plasma is estimated.

(b) *Red Cell Volume.* A quantity of red blood cells which have been "labelled" by means of radioactive isotopes of iron, phosphorus or chromium and of known radioactivity, is injected. The radioactivity of a known volume of red cells, packed by centrifuging at high speed, is measured.

(c) *Total Blood Volume.* A known amount of carbon monoxide mixed with oxygen is re-breathed until all the carbon monoxide is absorbed and combined with haemoglobin. The amount of CO-haemoglobin in unit volume of blood is estimated by means of the reversion spectroscope.

The Volume of the Extracellular Fluid

The substance injected must be able to pass through the walls of the blood capillaries, but unable to pass through the cell membranes. Many different substances have been used, but none satisfies the criteria perfectly and all have some disadvantages. Reliable values seem to have been obtained by the use of inulin, mannitol, sucrose (in man only), sodium sulphate (containing the radioactive isotope of sulphur for ease of analysis), sodium thiosulphate and sodium thiocyanate. The volume which is measured is that of all the water in which the reference substance is dissolved; the volume of the whole extracellular space is larger than this, since there are microscopic and ultra-microscopic structures into which the substance does not penetrate.

The Volume of the Intracellular Fluid

This can only be measured as the difference between the total volume of the body fluids and the volume of the extracellular fluid (apart from the volume of the red blood cells, as already described. The measurements are thus subject to considerable uncertainty. The intracellular fluid contains substances of large molecular weight and its total volume is greater than that of the intracellular water.

The Total Volume of the Body Fluids

Fundamentally, the most perfect method of measuring the volume of water in an animal is to weigh it, kill it, dry the body in an oven, and weigh it again. But if the animal, or man, is not to be destroyed by the method of estimation, a reference substance must be used which penetrates into all the water of the body—i.e. into all three compartments. Very few substances have yet been discovered which are at all suitable. Water containing the isotopes of hydrogen (deuterium, or radioactive tritium) is theoretically the best, but the analyses require elaborate apparatus, and tritium is not easily obtained. Urea may be used, although the corrections for metabolism and excretion are rather large and certain other organic compounds (the drug antipyrin, for example) have been found which are better.

The Composition of the Body Fluids

Water is the largest single component of the body fluids. Its presence in the proper quantity is important for two reasons: first, to maintain the total volume of the body fluids, and the volumes of the various compartments, and secondly, to maintain the concentrations of the solutes in these fluids. A great many different substances are dissolved in the water, and in general, the different compartments have different compositions. Some substances are present in all the compartments, but few of them have the same concentration in all.

The processes by which the water content of the body is maintained, and a "water balance" achieved have been discussed in Chapter 1. We shall be concerned here with the nature of the dissolved substances in the various compartments and with the movements of these, and of the water, from one compartment to another.

Extracellular Fluid

Apart from proteins, the interstitial fluid has very nearly the same composition as the blood plasma and, since enough plasma for chemical estimation can easily be collected, its composition is usually taken as equivalent to that of the extracellular fluid. The concentrations of the diffusible electrolytes (sodium, potassium, chloride and bicarbonate), however, are not quite the same in the plasma as in the interstitial fluid, as will be discussed later.

The peritoneal, **pleural and pericardial fluids**, although separable anatomically from the bulk of the interstitial fluid, all have much the same composition and may be regarded as parts of it. Their particular function is largely one of lubrication, enabling the intestines, lungs and heart to move freely in their respective enclosures. Lubrication of the articular surfaces of the bones is performed by the **synovial fluid**; this differs from the other fluids in containing mucin, which helps in the lubricating action.

The **cerebro-spinal fluid** and the **intra-ocular fluids** are usually regarded as part of the extracellular fluid, but differ quantitatively in composition from the general interstitial fluid. They will, therefore, be considered separately, the cerebro-spinal fluid at the end of this chapter, and the intra-ocular fluids as essential parts of the eye in Chapter 25. Fluid is also present in the inner ear and labyrinth; that which lies between the bony wall and the membranous labyrinth—the **perilymph**—has the composition of the interstitial fluid, but that which lies within the membranous labyrinth—the **endolymph**—has a very different composition.

In spite of the fact that there is no difficulty in obtaining quite large quantities of human blood, a full and exact description of its chemical composition cannot be given. It contains many substances whose identity is known, but in too small a concentration for accurate estimation; and other substances whose presence can be inferred only from their actions, many of them not having been isolated or chemically identified, for example some hormones and enzymes.

Intracellular Fluid

The cells which make up the various organs and tissues are intimately surrounded by connective tissue and interstitial fluid; an organ or tissue which has been dissected out, however cleanly, includes both intracellular and extracellular fluids. In order to discover the composition of the intracellular fluid from the gross composition of the whole organ or tissue, it is necessary, therefore, to discover the fraction of the whole organ or tissue which consists of extracellular fluid. This can be done by the use of a reference substance which cannot penetrate into the cells, but since complete accuracy is impossible, we know even less about the exact composition of the intracellular fluid than about that of the extracellular fluid. Moderately complete analyses are available for mammalian striated muscle and much less complete analyses for some other mammalian organs and tissues. The red blood corpuscles do not present this complication, since they can be obtained practically free from plasma by centrifuging the blood, but in some respects their composition is not typical of intracellular fluid in general.

Proteins

The blood plasma contains some 7 to 8 g of protein in solution in each 100 ml. This protein can be split into many different fractions, but for most purposes it is sufficient to consider it as being composed of two parts, serum globulin and serum albumin, accounting for 2 g and 5 g per 100 ml plasma respectively, in addition to which there is about 0·3 g to 0·4 g of fibrinogen. The functional significance of these proteins will be considered in later chapters. The interstitial space, on the other hand, contains only small quantities of protein in solution; but, particularly in the connective tissues, there are substantial quantities of proteins of various kinds, chiefly collagen and elastin, in the form of fine fibres visible under the microscope, which provide rigidity and elasticity to the whole structure. These are surrounded by the "ground substance" which contains muco-poly-saccharides (polymerized amino-sugars), notably hyaluronic acid, as well as proteins. The "intercellular cement" lies between, and holds together, the individual cells of an organ or tissue, and has the same (or a very similar) composition. The presence of extracellular material which is not in solution is particularly obvious, of course, in such structures as hairs, finger- and toe-nails, tendons, teeth, cartilage and bone.

Proteins in quite considerable concentration also occur within the cells, both in solution and as microscopically visible structures; the distinction, however, is bound to be somewhat vague, since the electron microscope reveals fibrils for example, as structures invisible in the light microscope. Some kinds of protein, notably the nucleo-proteins and those which form many kinds of enzyme, are found in all kinds of cell. The nucleo-proteins in many kinds of cell appear ordinarily to be in solution, since they are invisible: but during mitosis, when the cell divides and becomes two cells, some of the nucleo-proteins become visible as chromatin threads and chromosomes. Other kinds of protein are peculiar to the particular kind of cell considered, and are essential to the function of those cells. The red blood cells, for example, contain haemoglobin in large concentration but apparently

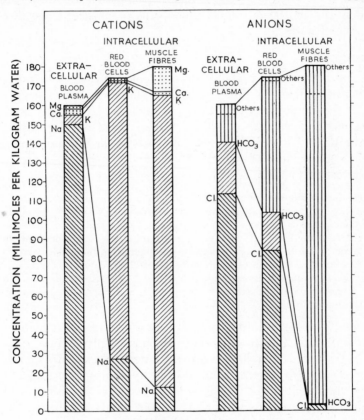

FIG. 2.1. The Concentration of Electrolytes in the Extracellular and Intracellular Fluids of Man.

The values plotted may be taken as representative, but there are appreciable variations between one individual and another, and in any one individual according to circumstances.

The concentrations are given in millimoles per kilogram of water; those of the "other anions" are deduced from the necessity for the total anion concentration to be electrically equivalent to the total cation concentration. The intracellular fluid appears to be more concentrated than the extracellular fluid; but actually the two fluids are osmotically equivalent, as some of the intracellular constituents are not osmotically active.

in solution; this is essential to their function of transporting oxygen and carbon dioxide. Muscle cells contain special kinds of protein, in relatively small concentration, but in the form of fibrils and filaments; these are essential for the shortening and development of tension characteristic of muscle cells.

The concentration of the proteins, in the intracellular fluid and in the blood plasma, in terms of grams per unit volume of fluid, is quite large; the weight (and volume) of the water present is thus correspondingly less than that of the whole fluid. In 100 ml. of blood plasma, there are 90 to 93 g of water, and in 100 ml of red blood cells or muscle fibres, there are 70 to 80 g of water.

Electrolytes

All the body fluids contain salts, and electrolytes, in solution, but their concentrations in the intracellular fluid are very different from those in the extracellular fluid and it is necessary to consider separately the cations and the anions which together make up these salts. The concentrations of the chief cations and anions in the blood plasma and in the intracellular fluid of red blood cells and muscle fibres are plotted diagrammatically in Fig. 2.1.

When considering the chemical properties and osmotic and electrical equilibria of a solution, the concentrations should be expressed in terms of gram-molecules rather than in grams, and per kilogram of water, rather than per litre of solution; the substances are dissolved in the water and not in the proteins or other colloidal constituents which may occupy an appreciable fraction of the whole volume of the fluid. A millimolar solution of a substance, say sodium chloride, contains 1/1,000 of its molecular weight in grams (e.g. 58·5 mg) in 1 kg (or approximately 1 litre) of water. Concentrations are commonly estimated, and expressed, nevertheless as mg/100 ml of solution.

Cations. The greatest difference between the extracellular fluid and the intracellular fluid is that the former contains chiefly sodium, the molar ratio Na/K being about 30, whereas the latter contains chiefly potassium, the molar ratio Na/K being about 0·18 in the red blood cells, and about 0·08 in the muscle fibres. This very large excess of potassium is characteristic of muscle and nerve fibres, but other kinds of cell may be more similar in this respect to the red blood cells.

In some kinds of animal other than man, the red blood cells do not contain an excess of potassium, the Na/K ratio in the cells of the cat and the dog, for example, being about 15.

The only other cations present in significant, though relatively small, concentration are calcium and magnesium. The calcium concentration of the intracellular fluid is somewhat less than that of the extracellular fluid and the magnesium concentration is definitely greater; both are present within the cells largely in combination with organic substances, and not in the free state as ions.

Anions. In the extracellular fluid the most important anions are chloride and bicarbonate, the other anions which are present, sulphate, phosphate and lactate, together making up only some 2 per cent of the total concentration. Within the cells, however, the combined concentration of chloride and bicarbonate is far too small to be equivalent to that of the cations. It is necessary to suppose, therefore, that other kinds of anion are present in substantial concentration. In red blood cells, these are provided almost entirely by haemoglobin; in muscle fibres, they consist mainly of hexose phosphates, creatine phosphate, adenosine triphosphate and the substance carnosine (β-alanyl histidine), some also being provided by proteins. The concentration of protein ions will depend on the acidity (or pH) of the fluid, since this will affect the strength of the protein as an acid; there will then be inverse changes in the bicarbonate concentration. This effect is of considerable importance in the regulation of the acidity of the blood and the carriage of carbon dioxide.

Other Substances

The extracellular fluid contains, in easily analysable concentration, glucose, urea, and "lipids" such as lecithin and cholesterol. Urea is the only normal constituent of the body fluids which is present in the same concentration (about 0·03 g/100 ml or 5·5 mM) in both intracellular and extracellular fluids; its concentration depends on the amount of protein taken in the diet, so that there may be quite large differences between different individuals. The glucose concentration in the blood (about 0·1 g/100 ml or 5·5 mM) is maintained relatively constant. It is converted in the intracellular fluid into hexose phosphates and glycogen, for example, but glucose may be present in some kinds of cell.

CHAPTER 3

INTERCHANGES ACROSS CAPILLARY WALLS

FORMATION OF TISSUE FLUID AND LYMPH

THE walls of the capillary blood vessels are very much more permeable to dissolved substances than are the cell membranes. Of the substances ordinarily present in the extracellular fluid all, except the plasma proteins, can penetrate freely and will diffuse to and fro between the blood and the interstitial fluid. Now the plasma proteins, like any other substances in solution, will contribute to the total osmolar concentration of the plasma. This, therefore, will be a little greater than that of the interstitial fluid, even though the concentrations of the crystalloidal substances are very nearly the same in both. Water will tend to pass into the plasma, accompanied by those substances to which the walls of the capillaries are freely permeable. As already mentioned, however, the tendency of water to move from solutions whose osmolar concentration is small to those whose concentration is large, may be opposed by the application of a hydrostatic pressure. Such a pressure, however, cannot be effective in practice unless there is a rigid membrane separating the two solutions concerned and impermeable to some, at least, of the dissolved substances. If this pressure is just sufficient to prevent any net movement of the water, it is equal to that part of the total osmotic pressure which is contributed by those substances which cannot penetrate the membrane. In the blood vessels there is such a hydrostatic pressure, produced by the action of the heart, and necessary for the circulation of the blood. If the capillary blood pressure exceeds the osmotic pressure due to the proteins (about 25 mm Hg in mammals), fluids will pass out from the plasma into the interstitial fluid. At the arterial ends of the capillaries the pressure is high enough (about 35 mm Hg) for this to occur. At the venous ends of the capillaries, the hydrostatic pressure (about 20 mm Hg) is less than the osmotic pressure due to the proteins, and fluid will be drawn in again. The net difference between (1) the capillary pressure (less the hydrostatic pressure in the interstitial spaces), and (2) the osmotic pressure difference between the plasma and the tissue fluid, is known as the *effective filtration pressure*. If this is positive, fluid leaves the blood stream; if it is negative, fluid enters.

This filtration and absorption can be seen in the capillaries of the frog's mesentery. The mesentery is observed under a binocular microscope; a capillary with a rapid circulation is chosen and blocked by pressing a fine blunt glass rod on it by means of a micro-manipulator. In some cases the mass of corpuscles remaining in the capillary moves towards the block, indicating that filtration is taking place, and in some cases they move away from the block, indicating absorption. A very fine glass pipette is now inserted into the capillary, connected with a water manometer, and the capillary pressure is measured, the block being still in place. The results of a large number of such experiments are shown in Fig. 3.1, in which the rate of passage of fluid through the capillary wall is plotted against the capillary pressure. It will be seen that, on the average, fluid passes out when the pressure is greater

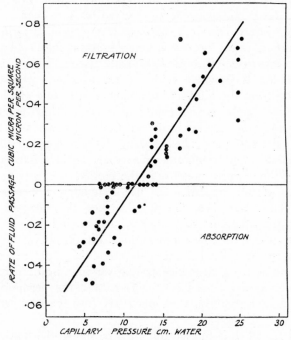

FIG. 3.1. The effect of the Pressure within a Capillary on the Passage of Fluid through its Walls.

Positive values of the rate of fluid passage indicate filtration of fluid; negative values indicate absorption.

The observations were made on several different frogs, and the straight line, representing the average, passes through the line of zero flow at a hydrostatic pressure of 11·5 cm of water (about equal to the colloid osmotic pressure of the plasma); fluid passes neither in nor out at this pressure and the rate of flow is directly proportional to the pressure both above and below it. (Landis.)

than 11·5 cm of water, and in when it is less than this; independent measurements of the colloid osmotic pressure of frog's plasma indicate that it normally lies between 10 and 12 cm of water.

The same general relation between the rate of filtration or absorption of interstitial fluid, and the excess or deficit of the mean capillary pressure above or below the protein osmotic pressure, can be demonstrated in preparations of the hindlimbs of cats or dogs; but the experimental procedure is more elaborate and the evidence less direct.

Formation of Lymph

In all the organs of the body, therefore, there is a flow of interstitial fluid out of the capillaries in the parts near the arterioles, and back into the capillaries in the parts towards the venules. The fluid would be expected to collect in the tissue spaces, and build up a hydrostatic pressure, until the inflow and outflow are equal. But in fact, the pressure in the tissue spaces is not ordinarily more than 1 or 2 mm of mercury; the return flow into the plasma is in general rather less rapid than the outflow from the plasma and the excess fluid—which is known as **Lymph**—is carried off by the lymphatic system. This consists of very thin-walled vessels provided with valves, which all run towards the thorax, those from the hind-limbs, abdomen, left side of chest and left arm all joining together to form the *thoracic duct*, which empties into the venous system at the junction of the left internal jugular vein with the left subclavian vein. Fluid is propelled along the lymphatics partly by means of the pumping action of muscular movement, as in the veins, and partly by reason of the negative pressure in the thorax.

The walls of the capillaries are not completely impermeable to the plasma proteins. But since the proteins pass through very much less readily than the water and salts, they get left behind during the filtration of the interstitial fluid; the more rapid is the filtration, the more, proportionately, are they left behind. The interstitial fluid, therefore, usually contains some proteins, the concentration varying in different parts of the body, according to the capillary pressure and the permeability of the capillary walls for proteins. Both may vary from part to part and from time to time.

The protein which is filtered off with the interstitial fluid tends to be left behind again when the fluid is reabsorbed into the venous capillaries. Lymph, therefore, has a higher concentration of protein than has the fluid filtered off from the capillaries, the actual value being very variable (1 to 6 per cent); lymph from the intestines and liver has a higher protein concentration (6 per cent) than that from the muscles (2 per cent). Otherwise lymph contains the same substances as does the plasma, and in about the same concentrations. It usually clots if left to stand, but not so rapidly as the blood, owing to the absence of platelets. After a meal there is often a considerable quantity of fat present, giving it a milky appearance; the lymphatic system is the chief route for the absorption of fats from the alimentary canal. It normally contains, also, considerable numbers of lymphocytes.

Factors Affecting the Flow of Lymph

In the steady state, as already described, any excess of interstitial fluid is carried away in the lymphatics; but any change in the rate of lymph flow is ordinarily associated with an inverse change in the volume of fluid in the interstitial spaces. If, in any organs or tissues, there is a large increase in the rate of production of interstitial fluid, or a large decrease in the rate of its removal, these organs or tissues become swollen and puffy, and a condition of *oedema* is said to have developed. Such an accumulation of interstitial fluid in any part of the body is likely to occur, of course, if there is any obstruction to the lymphatic drainage from that part. It will occur also, more generally, in response to any changes in the difference between the rate of filtration out of the capillaries and the rate of absorption into them.

The factors which influence this may be grouped under three headings: (1) the capillary pressure; (2) the difference between the osmolar concentration of the plasma and that of the tissue fluid; and (3) the permeability of the capillary wall.

(1) Any rise in *capillary pressure* occasioned either by dilatation of the arterioles or obstruction of the veins, increases the rate of production of tissue fluid. Such a rise is a common accompaniment of activity in any organ.

(2) Two factors come into the consideration of the *osmolar concentration*: (*a*) the concentration of the colloids, and (*b*) the concentration of crystalloids.

(*a*) The concentration of the plasma proteins, and hence the colloid osmotic pressure of the plasma, can be reduced to a very low value by repeatedly bleeding an animal and re-injecting the blood corpuscles suspended in physiological salt solution; the plasma proteins are thus removed, but not the corpuscles, so that the blood can still carry oxygen and carbon dioxide in a more or less normal manner. This process leads to a large increase both in the volume of the interstitial fluid and in the rate of flow of lymph. Such a condition is, of course, highly artificial.

(*b*) If the concentration of crystalloids is suddenly increased by injecting a hypertonic solution intravenously, the absorption of tissue fluid is increased. Although the crystalloids can pass through the walls of the capillaries quite rapidly, water can pass through even more rapidly. Equalization of the crystalloid concentration in the blood and the interstitial fluid is brought about by a simultaneous passage of water into the blood and passage of crystalloids out of it. The flow of lymph practically ceases for a short time while this is occurring. The total volume of the blood is increased as a result of the inflow of water and thus the concentration of the proteins, and their omotic pressure, is decreased; the rate of filtration is increased, the lymph flow starts again and continues at a rate larger than normal until the excess fluid has been removed. The net result, therefore, of introducing a hypertonic salt solution is the same as that of removal of the proteins: both act as *lymphagogues* (from "lymph", and the Greek word for "to lead"). The excess fluid is not all returned to the blood by the lymph, however, but mainly stays in the tissues until it is excreted by the kidneys.

The action of the crystalloid concentration is of importance, also, during the activity of any organ. The metabolites produced by the active cells will diffuse out into the tissue spaces, raise the osmotic pressure of the interstitial fluid and draw fluid from the capillaries. This, together with the rise in capillary pressure, accounts for the mild degree of oedema that often occurs in muscles after exercise.

(3) When a capillary dilates excessively, it allows more fluid to pass through its walls at a given effective filtration pressure and holds back protein less completely. Whether the physiological dilatation of the capillaries that occurs during activity of the organ supplied by them plays a part in the increased flow of lymph, is disputed, but it is of importance in connection with certain abnormalities. Histamine is one of the most powerful capillary dilators known, and it also injures the capillary endothelium, making it more permeable to large molecules. Histamine, therefore, increases the rate of formation of tissue fluid and of lymph. Its introduction below the surface of the skin through a needle prick results in the formation of a wheal, just as if the skin had been burnt. Similar reactions result from contact with the skin of the leaves of the poison ivy, or the stings of stinging nettles or jelly-fish; these are known to inject small quantities of histamine (among other substances) into the skin. The release of histamine, or of some substance with similar actions, by damaged tissues will be referred to again in a later chapter, in relation to the "immunity reactions".

The increased permeability of damaged capillaries has been observed by the method described above. When alcohol or mercuric chloride was added to the blood flowing through them, fluid passed out much more rapidly, and there was practically no reabsorption except at very low pressures; they had thus become almost completely permeable to proteins.

There are several pathological conditions in which the rate of elimination of fluid is diminished, and the general water balance of the body disturbed. An excess of fluid accumulates and this is held chiefly in the interstitial spaces, giving rise to oedema. This occurs not only when the excretion of water fails, but also, and more commonly, when the excretion of salts fails; the control systems which preserve the constancy of the osmolar concentration of the body fluids bring about a simultaneous retention of water. An inadequate elimination of fluid will occur, most obviously, when there is a failure of the kidneys themselves, due to disease (nephritis); oedema, also, not infrequently accompanies disease of the heart. Heart failure is likely to produce a rise in venous pressure, but the consequent direct action on the rate of filtration from the capillaries is only partly responsible for the salt retention and oedema, the origin of which has not yet been explained.

Oedema also occurs in cases of severe malnutrition, when the supply of protein in the diet is grossly inadequate (*hunger oedema*). The plasma proteins are among the last to be sacrificed for the supply of energy or nitrogen to the rest of the body, so that the oedema is not due, to any considerable extent, to a simple reduction of the colloid osmotic pressure of the plasma. But the proteins of the less essential tissues are broken down to supply energy and to replace proteins unavoidably lost from the essential tissues; the fluid in which they were previously held thus becomes, as it were, "surplus to requirement". For some reasons, which are not obvious, this fluid is not completely eliminated, and accumulates in the interstitial spaces.

FORMATION OF CEREBRO-SPINAL FLUID

There are four membranes covering the central nervous system. They are (1) the pia mater, which closely invests the nervous substance and carries the blood vessels to it; (2) the arachnoid, separated from the pia by the sub-arachnoid space, which contains the *cerebro-spinal fluid*; (3) the meningeal layer of the dura mater; and (4) the periosteal layer of the dura mater. The venous sinuses are situated between the two layers of the dura and delicate processes known as the *arachnoid villi* arise from the arachnoid and penetrate into the venous sinuses. The relations between these structures are essentially similar in the skull and in the spinal column; but since the pia ends, with the spinal cord, at the first lumbar vertebra, and the dura and arachnoid extend as far as the second sacral vertebra, the sub-arachnoid space is of considerable size in this region. Cerebro-spinal fluid can, therefore, be readily obtained by inserting a hollow needle (usually between the fourth and fifth lumbar vertebrae) into this space; this procedure is called *lumbar puncture*, and the fluid usually emerges at a rate of about one drop per second.

The cerebro-spinal fluid is formed by the plexuses of blood capillaries, known as the *choroid plexuses*, in the ventricles of the brain. This can be shown by the facts that (*a*) fluid can be collected from a tube inserted into either of the ventricles; (*b*) blocking the outflow of a ventricle leads to its distension (hydrocephalus); and (*c*) if the choroid plexus is first removed, subsequent blocking of the outflow no longer leads to a distension of the ventricle. From the ventricles, the cerebro-spinal fluid passes to the *cisterna magna*, an enlargement of the sub-arachnoid space at the base of the brain, and thence out and up in the sub-arachnoid spaces around the cerebellum and the cerebral cortex. It returns to the blood by absorption into the venous sinuses through the arachnoid villi. Flow up and down the spaces in and around the spinal cord probably results chiefly from changes in pressure in different parts of the system produced by movements of the head, or sudden changes in blood pressure.

Composition of CSF

The composition of the cerebro-spinal fluid is, in most respects, not far from that of an ultra-filtrate of plasma, containing a little protein (0·03 per cent), and is thus very similar to that of the extracellular fluid shown in Fig. 2.1. The actual concentrations of the various constituents are subject to considerable variation, as are those of the blood plasma; but the changes in the two fluids tend to run hand in hand, so that the values of the concentration *ratios* remain relatively constant. Careful and precise analyses of the fluids drawn from one and the same animal show, however, that the values of these ratios are not quite those to be expected if the fluid were an ultra-filtrate; the choroid plexuses must be regarded as secretory organs, and not merely as membranes which act as simple filters impermeable to proteins. Chloride ions, and to a less extent sodium ions, appear to be actively secreted into the cerebro-spinal fluid, while potassium ions, urea and glucose are kept out. (The relatively low value of the glucose concentration may be due merely to the fact that it is metabolized by the tissues of the brain, and cannot diffuse out from the plasma very rapidly.)

The Blood—Brain Barrier

That the structures which divide the cerebro-spinal fluid from the blood plasma have properties unlike those of the walls of the capillary blood vessels, is shown by the rate at which substances pass across them. Substances with relatively small molecules pass very rapidly through the walls of the capillaries in muscles, for example, and their concentrations in the plasma and the interstitial fluid become sensibly identical in a matter of seconds. Passage from the plasma to the cerebro-spinal fluid occurs very much more slowly; it takes several minutes for the most rapid of the substances studied, ethyl alcohol, to attain equality of concentration; and after 4 hr the concentration of creatinine in the cerebro-spinal fluid is only about 1/10th of that in the plasma. We are thus led to the idea of the *blood—cerebro-spinal fluid barrier* which controls the passage of substances from one to the other. The rate of penetration of this barrier, moreover, depends markedly on the lipoid solubility of the substance used, so that in its properties it resembles the cell membranes more than the capillary walls. There is also the *blood—brain barrier* between the plasma and the interstitial fluid of the brain, with properties similar to those of the blood—cerebro-spinal fluid barrier. Between the interstitial fluid and the cerebro-spinal fluid, however, the barrier is less restrictive and substances pass from one to the other relatively freely. It is difficult to get penicillin, for example, into the interstitial fluid of the brain in a useful concentration by injecting it into the blood; it is relatively easy to do so by injecting it into the cerebro-spinal fluid.

The total volume of the cerebro-spinal fluid in man is about 140 ml, and its rate of formation is about 0·5 ml per minute. The pressure, measured by lumbar puncture, is about 150 mm water when the subject is lying down, and rises to about 280 mm water when he sits up. All these values may vary within wide limits.

Lumbar Puncture

Lumbar puncture is a procedure of considerable medical importance, for not only may it relieve increased intracranial pressure by providing an escape for excessive cerebro-spinal fluid, but it may yield valuable information enabling a distinction to be made between those diseases which exhibit characteristic changes in the nature and amount of the fluid. Inflammation of the membranes of the brain (meningitis), for example, is accompanied by an abnormally high rate of production of the fluid, by an increase in its protein content (which may be tenfold), by its composition approaching that of an ultra-filtrate of the plasma (except that the glucose concentration falls), and by an enormous increase in the content of leucocytes. Normal fluid contains about 1 to 5 lymphocytes per cubic millimetre; meningitic fluid contains hundreds of cells per cubic millimetre, which are mainly neutrophil leucocytes or lymphocytes.

Local anaesthetics may be injected by lumbar puncture into the sub-arachnoid space to produce spinal anaesthesia. Air, or lipiodol (a heavy liquid opaque to X-rays) may be injected into the cisterna magna and the site of a tumour or inflammatory adhesion may then be discovered by the use of X-rays.

Raised Intracranial Pressure

If the volume of the brain increases, as by the formation of a cerebral tumour, the intracranial pressure rises. This rise is transmitted to all points within the rigid brain-case by the cerebro-spinal fluid, with the result that the veins are compressed and the capillary pressure rises. The first structure to suffer is the optic nerve, and the obstruction of the veins running along it causes oedema of the optic disc, which can be observed with an ophthalmoscope; this condition is known as *papilloedema*. The intracranial pressure is also increased in the condition known as *hydrocephalus*, which results from an excessive accumulation of cerebro-spinal fluid. This may be caused by obstruction to the fluid pathway from ventricles to sub-arachnoid space, or by blocking or maldevelopment of the arachnoid villi.

Rise in the pressure of the cerebro-spinal fluid is also caused by injections of isotonic or hypotonic saline into the blood, showing that its production does depend to some extent upon physico-chemical factors. Injections of hypertonic saline, on the other hand, cause a fall in the pressure, probably due chiefly to an osmotic withdrawal of fluid from the brain itself, with consequent diminution in volume. This is a procedure commonly used in brain surgery, where it is often advisable to reduce the volume of the brain before the skull is opened.

CHAPTER 4

PHYSIOLOGICAL SALINE SOLUTIONS

Isolated Preparations of Tissues

A great deal may be learnt about the way in which the various organs and tissues of animals perform their functions, by removing them from the whole animal and examining their behaviour in isolation. They will not then be surrounded by their normal interstitial fluid and this must be replaced by some artificial solution; the substances which must be present in such a solution have been discovered largely by trial and error.

Owing to its automatic rhythmic activity, the heart is the most convenient indicator of responses to changes in its perfusion fluid, and the classical experiments of Ringer on this organ form the basis of our knowledge of the subject. If a frog's heart is isolated and placed in a solution, of whatever composition, of which the total osmolar concentration is substantially different from that of the blood, it soon ceases to beat. The requirement that solutions outside cells should be isotonic with the intracellular fluid has already been discussed, and is made obvious by the haemolysis of the red blood cells in hypotonic solutions. That the solution should be isotonic is not, however, sufficient. The heart will not beat in solutions of non-electrolytes, such as glucose. It will do so, however, for a little time in an isotonic solution of sodium chloride (0·65 per cent for the frog); but soon the beats cease, and the heart remains relaxed. If, now, a small amount of calcium chloride is added to the solution, the beats begin

TABLE 4.1

Compositions of Blood Plasma and of Physiological Saline Solutions

	Ringer's Solution (Frog's heart)	Frog's blood plasma	Locke's Solution (Mammalian heart)	Mammalian blood plasma
	g	g	g	g
NaCl	0·65	0·55	0·9	0·7
KCl	0·014	0·023	0·042	0·038
$CaCl_2$*	0·012	0·025	0·024	0·028
$NaHCO_3$.	0·02	0·1	0·02	0·23
NaH_2PO_4*	0·001	0·02	—	0·036
Glucose	—	0·04	0·1–0·25	0·07
Water	to 100	(100)	to 100	(100)

* The weights given refer to the anhydrous salts. Appropriately greater weights of the hydrated forms, which are in common use, should be employed in making up Ringer's solutions.

again; but after a short while, the relaxation after each beat becomes progressively less complete, until, at last, the heart remains fully contracted, and ceases to beat. If at this stage a suitable small amount of potassium chloride is added to the solution, contractions begin again, and the heart may continue to beat fairly normally for many hours. These observations are illustrated in Fig. 4.1. It is clear, therefore, that at least three salts must be present in an adequate physiological solution—sodium,

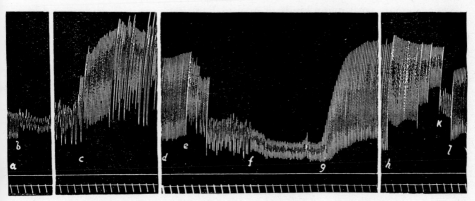

FIG. 4.1. The Action of Electrolytes on the Heart of the Tortoise.

a–b: Beat of excised heart before perfusion.

b–c: Perfusion with *sodium chloride* solution, 0·75 g/100 ml with sodium bicarbonate 0·01 g/100 ml.

c–d: Addition of *calcium chloride* (3 ml of 0·1 M to 100 ml of solution of sodium salts). Contraction improved but relaxation incomplete.

d–e: Addition of *potassium chloride* (6 ml of 0·1 M to 100 ml of solution of sodium and calcium salts). Relaxation improved and beats more regular.

e–f: Perfusion with solution of *sodium* salts again.

f–g: Addition of *potassium chloride* (6 ml of 0·1 M to 100 ml. of solution of sodium salts). Beats more regular but contractions small.

g–h: Addition of *calcium chloride* (3 ml of 0·1 M to 100 ml of solution of sodium and potassium salts). Contraction greatly improved, with good relaxation.

h–k: Addition of excess calcium chloride. 3 ml of 0·1 M solution added to 100 ml of solution of sodium, calcium and potassium salts at each step in the record. Progressive impairment of relaxation.

k–l: Potassium chloride added in amount to correspond to the calcium chloride present—i.e. 2 ml 0·1 M KCl for each 1 ml 0·1 M $CaCl_2$. Improved relaxation but poor beat.

l onwards: Perfusion with normal Ringer's solution.

The smallness of the beat initially is due to the action of acid metabolites, which are formed during the anoxaemia accompanying dissection; they are rapidly removed by the perfusion fluid. Recording: systole is upstroke. (From Bayliss "Principles of General Physiology", Longmans, Green & Co.)

potassium, and calcium chlorides—and the heart survives longer still if the solution is made slightly alkaline by adding sodium bicarbonate. Ringer, in his series of experiments, found the concentration of each of these salts which favoured longest survival of the heart-beat of the frog and tortoise. Locke, working with isolated mammalian hearts, found the addition of glucose an advantage, and the compositions of these "physiological fluids" are given in Table 4.1. The addition of a small quantity of a magnesium salt (0·01 per cent $MgCl_2$, for example) is beneficial in experiments with many kinds of mammalian tissue (as in Tyrode's, and in Krebs', modifications of Ringer's solution), but has little effect on the heart. The concentrations of potassium and calcium may be varied slightly to suit the particular tissue in use.

On the whole, therefore, the necessary composition of an artificial environment for contractile (and other) tissues, as discovered empirically, is very similar to that of the interstitial fluid; this, of course, is hardly surprising. Ringer's, and Ringer-Locke's solutions contain smaller concentrations of sodium bicarbonate, and in compensation, greater concentrations of sodium chloride, than do the corresponding frog's plasma and mammalian plasma, respectively. Such differences are necessary because the artificial solutions are in equilibrium with room air containing only very small amounts of carbon dioxide, whereas the plasmas contain much larger quantities of free carbon dioxide, mammalian arterial plasma, for example, being in equilibrium with 5 per cent of carbon dioxide. The acidity of the solution is related to the ratio of the concentration of carbon dioxide to that of bicarbonate; reduction in the former, therefore, must be compensated by a reduction in the latter if the solution is not to be too alkaline. In some kinds of experiment, it is possible to keep the artificial saline solutions in equilibrium with 5 per cent of carbon dioxide (usually in pure oxygen) without great inconvenience; the bicarbonate concentration is then increased, and the chloride concentration decreased, to about the values found in the plasma (as in one form of Krebs-Ringer solution). Alternatively, the bicarbonate and carbon dioxide may be omitted and replaced by an equivalent concentration of a sodium phosphate buffer mixture adjusted to pH 7·4 (as in the other form of Krebs-Ringer solution).

The Action of Ions on Tissues

The subject of the action of individual ions on contractile tissues is inevitably a confused one, owing to the fact that different tissues respond in different fashion to excess or deficiency of any particular ion. There are, however, certain general rules. (1) Sodium salts occupy a unique position. The amount present in Ringer's solution is greatly in excess of the minimal amount necessary. Muscles cease to contract when more than 9/10 is replaced by some non-toxic substance such as glucose or sucrose. (2) The concentrations of calcium and potassium salts are interdependent, and must be in about the right ratio, though the absolute values may vary considerably. (3) Anions are relatively unimportant so long as they are not toxic; chlorides are usually employed, as these salts are all soluble, but the presence of sulphates, bromides, nitrates, bicarbonates, etc., has little influence on the survival of activity of an isolated tissue. (4) The hydrogen ion concentration must be not far removed from that of a neutral solution. Most tissues are favoured by a hydrogen ion concentration slightly on the alkaline side of neutrality. Slight acidity produces slowing or arrest of the heart-beat, relaxation of the tone of most unstriated muscles and phenomena analogous to fatigue in striated muscles.

If a muscle or nerve is placed in a solution which contains too high a concentration of potassium ions (say Ringer's solution modified to contain about three times the normal amount of potassium chloride), it becomes inexcitable; the excitability can be restored by washing it with ordinary Ringer's solution. This effect accounts for the practical necessity of washing isolated muscles and nerves with Ringer's solution; this removes the excess of potassium salts which diffuse out of those few fibres which are injured during dissection.

These, and many other kinds of experimental study make it clear that for proper functioning of the cells, the electrolyte composition of the fluid bathing them must be quite different from that of the fluid within them. The cells contain potassium ions and practically no sodium ions, while the fluid outside them must contain sodium ions and very little potassium ions. Many cells, also, contain practically no chloride, while the outside solution ordinarily contains chloride, although this can be replaced by other univalent ions.

Section 2
THE CIRCULATION
OF THE BLOOD

CHAPTER 5

PHYSICAL PRINCIPLES OF FLOW IN TUBES
AND HAEMODYNAMICS

Introduction: The Circulation

We owe to Harvey (1628) the conception and proof of the idea that the blood circulates, and as this step marks the beginning of modern physiology, it is of more than usual interest to note his argument. Harvey was able to show that the valves in the heart are so arranged as to allow the passage of blood in only one direction. Further, by watching the motion of the heart in the living animal he concluded that blood is expelled from the ventricles into the pulmonary artery and aorta during systole, and enters the heart from the venae cavae and pulmonary veins during diastole. He calculated that if only a drachm* of blood were expelled at each beat, the heart would in half an hour use up all the blood in the body, and so empty the veins completely and distend the arteries; from this he concluded that the blood must move in a circle, entering the veins from the arteries. Proof that the blood flows continuously in one direction he found in the cutaneous veins of the human arm (Fig. 5.1). It had been shown previously by Fabricius (1603) that if a ligature is tied around the arm the veins swell up distally, and present along their course little swellings which mark the position of valves allowing the passage of blood in only one direction, towards the heart. The significance of this discovery was lost on Fabricius, but was appreciated by Harvey, who made a further observation, which anyone may repeat on his own arm. The middle finger of the left hand is pressed firmly on a prominent cutaneous vein of the right forearm, and blood is massaged out of the vein proximally by rubbing the fore-finger firmly up the vein past the next valve. If the forefinger is lifted, the vein fills from above only as far as the valve, but when the middle finger is lifted the

* *A drachm (or ʒ fl) is 60 minims; ⅛ ounce; or* 3.55×10^{-6} *m³.*

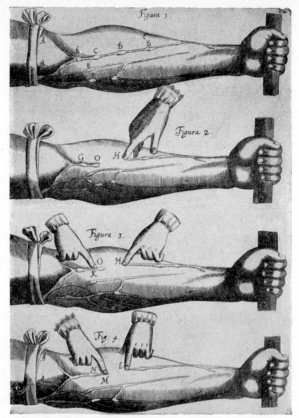

FIG. 5.1. Harvey's Figures Illustrating the Unidirectional Flow of Blood in the Veins.

(1) The bandage A A is tied round the arm above the elbow, constricting the veins which become distended. The position of each valve is indicated by a swelling or knot, B, C, D, E, F. (2) The blood is pressed out of a vein from H to O with one finger, while another keeps the vein closed at H. No blood runs back past the valve at O. (3) If the vein is pressed by another finger at K, no blood can be forced backwards past the valve at O. (4) The vein is closed with one finger at L, as before, and emptied by stroking with another finger, M, towards the valve at N; the vein continues empty until the finger at L is removed, when it rapidly fills up from the periphery.

whole stretch of collapsed vein rapidly fills from below. This process may be repeated indefinitely, blood always entering from the periphery; we must conclude with Harvey that blood is always entering the veins from the distal side, and the only source of this blood is the arterial system.

The missing link in Harvey's argument, namely, the connection between the arteries and veins, was supplied forty years later by Malpighi, when he discovered the capillaries.

The General Arrangement of the Circulation

This is shown in Fig. 5.2. In man, as in all mammals, the circulation consists of two circuits connected in series, the greater or systemic, and the lesser or pulmonary circuit; accordingly the heart consists of two pumps, one for the lungs and the other for the rest of the body. Blood is pumped by the right heart into the pulmonary artery and on through the pulmonary capillaries to the pulmonary veins, and so enters the left heart. The left

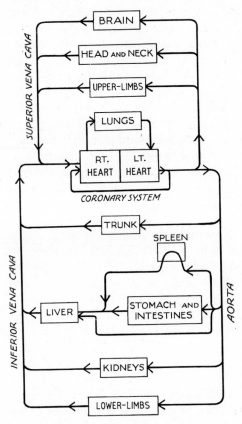

FIG. 5.2. Scheme of the Human Circulation.

heart ejects the blood into the aorta, and then into the branching arteries which distribute it to the various organs of the body. From the capillaries of these organs, the blood is collected into veins, and then returns to the right side of the heart *via* the inferior and superior venae cavae. During its passage through the pulmonary capillaries, the blood takes up oxygen from the air in the lungs, and loses carbon dioxide; in the capillaries of the other organs, supplied from the left side of the heart, the blood gives up oxygen to the tissues, and takes up carbon dioxide from them.

The blood flow to the various organs and tissues depends on the total output of the heart per minute, and on the proportion of this output which is sent to each of them. The regulation of the cardiac output, and of the eventual distribution of the blood, are thus the central problems of the physiology of the circulation.

The Blood Vessels

On each contraction of the heart, blood is expelled from the ventricles at high pressure into the aorta and pulmonary artery. The *aorta* is a wide tube, the thick walls of which are largely composed of elastic tissue; like any other elastic structure, its capacity is determined largely by the pressure of the blood it contains. When blood is expelled during ventricular systole, the aortic pressure rises, the aorta is distended and so accommodates a large part of the blood expelled, the remainder escaping through the arteries. During ventricular diastole, the tension in the aortic walls maintains the flow of blood onwards through the arteries, and the aorta diminishes in size until it is again distended at the next heart beat. In this purely passive way the aorta (and to a less extent its larger branches, which are similar in structure) converts the intermittent flow from the heart into a continuous, though pulsating flow in the arteries.

Arteries

The *arteries* have smooth muscle in their walls, which, on suitable stimulation, will contract actively or relax. The proportion of muscular to elastic tissue is greater in small arteries than in large, and the diameter, particularly of the smallest branches, or *arterioles*, can change over a wide range independently of the pressure within the lumen. The state of constriction or dilatation of the arterioles supplying any particular organ largely determines the proportion of the total cardiac output which is sent to it.

Capillaries

The *capillaries* are about 10μ in diameter and the blood they contain is separated from the tissues by a single layer of flat endothelial cells which forms the capillary wall; it is accordingly here that the interchange of substances between the blood and the tissues takes place. In spite of their thin walls and the absence of muscle cells, the capillaries are capable of active contraction, and of exerting pressure of 60 mm Hg or more when contracted. In some resting tissues the majority of the capillaries are closed; during activity they open, and thus they also play a part in regulating the distribution of the blood to the organs. Although the capillaries are under nervous control, they are pre-eminently the vessels which react to chemical substances released during the activity of tissues which they supply.

Veins

The blood from the capillaries is collected into *venules*, which join up to form *veins*. These are wide and relatively thin-walled, and offer little resistance to the flow of blood. They are capable of active variation of calibre and are under nervous control. All but the smallest and largest veins contain valves, consisting of a number of semi-circular folds of the intima projecting into the lumen. As a rule two such folds are placed opposite one another, and are so formed that when the blood is forced in a direction away from the heart, the folds float out into the blood-stream and block the vein. When the muscles contract the thin-walled veins are squeezed and blood is forced in the only direction it is free to travel, namely towards the heart. When the muscles relax, blood can enter the veins, but only from the arterial side. This "muscle pump" is an important mechanism for facilitating the venous return to the heart, as will be discussed later.

The artery which supplies an organ, and the vein which drains it, may be some 2 to 5 mm in diameter; there will be 10,000 to 100,000 arterioles and venules, 0·02 to 0·05 mm in diameter; tens of millions of capillaries, some 0·01 mm in diameter. As the vascular tree branches, the total cross sectional area of the vessels increases: that of all the arterioles is around 10 times that of the artery, and that of all the capillaries some 10 times greater again. Thus the velocity of blood, about 10 centimetres per second in the artery, decreases progressively until, in the capillaries, it is less than 1 mm/sec; it then rises again and reaches several centimetres per second in the vein. Even though each capillary is very short (less than 1 mm long) the average particle of blood spends enough time in one (about 1 sec, or less if the organ **is a**ctive) for interchange to take place with the tissues. (All these figures are very approximate, for purposes of illustration only.)

The Physics of Pressure and Flow in Fluids

Blood is a fluid, forced by the pumping action of the heart through a series of tubes, the blood vessels. In order to understand the working of the circulation it is necessary to know the physical laws which govern the behaviour of fluids. In applying these laws to conditions as they exist in the living circulation, complexities arise because blood is a fluid having unusual properties while the vessels through which it flows are distensible and often contractile. Moreover, the rates of flow and pressures are by no means uniform since the output of the heart itself is pulsatile.

Poiseuille's Experiments

In 1836 and the following years, Poiseuille, performed experiments on animals with a view to discovering the relations between blood pressure and flow in the circulation. He found his observations so bewilderingly variable that he turned his attention to the simpler problems concerned with the flow of pure liquids like water through glass tubes. For our purposes, the results of his experiments—which are embodied in Poiseuille's Law—may be summarized by the following statements.

(1) The rate of flow of a fluid through a tube is proportional to the pressure driving it.

The ratio of the pressure to the rate of flow is, of course, the *resistance* of the tube to the flow of the fluid through it.

Mathematically, this is

$$\dot{Q} = \frac{\varDelta P}{R}$$

where $\dot{Q}$ is the flow in ml/min; $\varDelta P$ is the pressure gradient (i.e. $P_1 - P_2$) in mm Hg and R is the resistance in mm Hg/ml/min.

A little thought convinces one that this equation,

$$\dot{Q} = \frac{\varDelta P}{R}$$

is basically analogous to Ohm's Law,

$$I = \frac{E}{R}$$

This relationship ceases to be true if the rate of flow is very large and the flow becomes "turbulent". Local turbulence may occur in the blood vascular system, but it is not sufficient to affect the pressure—flow relations.

If we have a number of tubes with different resistances arranged in such a way that all the fluid goes through all of them in succession (in "series"), the pressure drop across each will be proportional to its resistance, and the total resistance of the whole will be the sum of the separate resistances. If the tubes are arranged in such a way that the flow is divided among them (in "parallel"), and all have the same pressure across them, the flow through each will be inversely proportional to its resistance, and the reciprocal of the total resistance of the whole—i.e. the total *conductance* —will be the sum of the separate conductances. Any complicated system of tubes in series and in parallel (such as the blood vascular system) will thus have a resistance to flow, the *total peripheral resistance* (TPR), which will depend on the separate resistances of its component parts; but it may always be measured in terms of the ratio of the pressure applied to the total rate of flow produced.

As a rule, the venous pressure is considerably lower than the arterial pressure and in calculating the TPR the former can usually be ignored.

(2) The resistance to flow of any particular fluid is directly proportional to the length of the tube (*l*), and inversely proportional to the fourth power of its radius (*r*): the resistance thus increases very rapidly as the radius becomes smaller. This accounts for the fact that the resistance of the arterioles is much greater than that of the arteries (see p. 50), in spite of

the fact that the total cross sectional area is greater and the velocity of flow smaller.

Flow resistance is therefore a property of the tube (mainly its size), and can be expressed as the *hindrance*, H.

$$H = \frac{8l}{\pi r^4}$$

For a given pressure gradient then, fluid will flow faster through a short tube; flow is inversely proportional to the length of the tube.

(3) For any given tube, the flow resistance depends a great deal also on the nature of the fluid driven through it. Clearly, the "thicker" the fluid, i.e. the more *viscous* it is, the greater will be the resistance to flow.

Viscosity

The ratio of the viscosity of a fluid at any temperature, to the viscosity of water at the same temperature is termed the *relative viscosity*, η of that fluid. The relative viscosity of most simple fluids such as water or alcohol does not alter, even if the length or diameter of the tube, the rate of flow, or the pressure gradient are varied over wide limits.

Resistance to flow is proportional to the relative viscosity.

We can now write the whole of Poiseuille's Law as an equation:

$$R = \frac{8\eta l}{\pi r^4}$$

$\left(\text{or in a more convenient form, since } \dot{Q} = \dfrac{\varDelta P}{R}\right.$

$$\dot{Q} = \frac{\varDelta P \pi r^4}{8\eta l}\bigg)$$

(see Fig. 5.3).

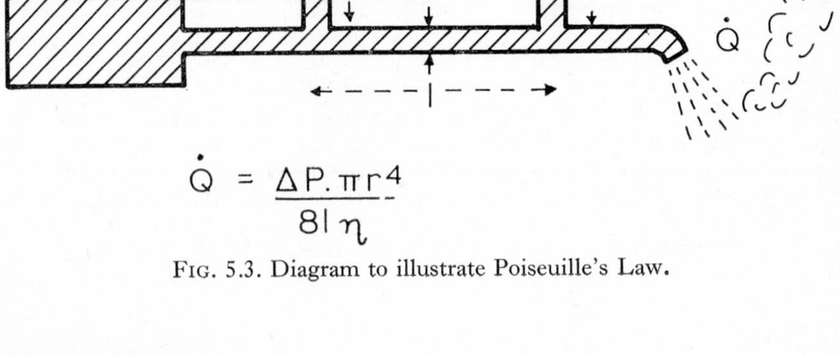

$$\dot{Q} = \frac{\varDelta P . \pi r^4}{8 l \eta}$$

FIG. 5.3. Diagram to illustrate Poiseuille's Law.

Poiseuille's Law is not always exactly obeyed by blood, since, unlike that of "perfect" liquids, the value of its viscosity may depend on the rate of flow and on the dimensions of the tube. Strictly, therefore, the idea of viscosity as a "constant" property of a liquid is inapplicable to blood, and the value obtained under any particular set of conditions is called the *apparent viscosity*.

In the blood vessels of a normal animal or man, the velocity is sufficiently great for the apparent viscosity to be independent of the rate of flow, and we are justified in regarding the resistance of the blood vessels as a quantity which varies only with their calibre.

(i) If blood is made to flow through a tube at a sufficiently high velocity, by applying a sufficiently high pressure, its apparent viscosity will be the same whatever actual velocity or pressure is used: it behaves as a "perfect" or "Newtonian" fluid. But if the velocity and pressure are reduced considerably, this is no longer true: the apparent viscosity becomes progressively larger as the velocity and pressure are made smaller, and the flow is now "anomalous" or "non-Newtonian". It is probable that if the rate of flow is small, the red blood cells stick together and an extra force is required to tear them apart and to allow the blood to flow; the resistance to flow, and the apparent viscosity, are thus increased. If the rate of flow is very large, they move past each other so fast that they cannot stick together, this extra force is no longer needed, and the resistance to flow, and apparent viscosity, become smaller.

Clinical measurements of the viscosity of blood, however, are sometimes made in an "Ostwald viscometer"; the movement of the blood is then so slow that the apparent viscosity is largely affected by the rate at which the blood flows through it—a matter depending on the exact design of the instrument. In a "Hess viscometer", the blood is made to flow at a velocity so great that small variations do not affect the apparent viscosity.

(ii) If the diameter of the tube through which the blood is made to flow is greater than about 0·2 mm, the apparent viscosity (in any conditions of flow) is independent of the actual value of the diameter. But if the diameter is less than about 0·2 mm, the apparent viscosity becomes smaller as the diameter is reduced still further. It is important to remember that the *resistance* to flow becomes greater as the diameter becomes smaller, whether the fluid used is "perfect" or has this anomalous property shown by blood: but the increase in resistance, for a given decrease in diameter, is smaller with blood than with a "perfect" fluid. This effect is due to the presence of a narrow layer in contact with the wall of the tube which is deficient in red cells and so has a smaller viscosity than the rest of the blood in the tube. The width of this layer (about the thickness of a red cell) is practically the same whatever the diameter of the tube. In relatively large tubes, its effect is negligible: but in small tubes, it provides a "lubricating" layer which becomes progressively more effective in allowing the blood to slip through the tube, as the diameter of the tube becomes progressively smaller.

It is with very small tubes, namely the arterioles, that we are mainly concerned as physiologists; as will be seen in Fig. 5.9 (p. 47 below), the main pressure fall between the arteries and veins occurs in the small blood vessels. In tubes of such a size (about 0·02 mm diameter) the apparent viscosity has only about one-half the value found in large tubes. Halving the apparent viscosity of the blood would be an important economy in the circulation, for it should halve the work done by the heart in maintaining a given circulation rate; for a given maximum output of work of the heart, it would about double the amount of work a man could perform in violent exercise. Moreover, in the circulation the resistance of the blood vessels is varied by changing their diameters.

Representative values of the apparent viscosity of blood are given in Table 5.1. They include about the smallest and the largest values which have been obtained on a given sample of blood, and show how greatly the viscosity may vary according to the conditions of measurement. In any conditions of flow and size of tube, the viscocity of blood increases rapidly with increase in the haematocrit value, particularly when this exceeds about 50 per cent; the figures given in Table 5.1 show, roughly, the range of physiological interest. This is the most important factor affecting the viscosity of the blood in the circulation.

TABLE 5.1

The Apparent Viscosity of Blood (relative to water) (Representative Values)

| Conditions of Measurement | Haematocrit Value (Per cent) | | | Remarks |
	30 (anaemia)	45 (normal)	60 (high-altitude acclimatization)	
Rate of flow sufficiently large				
In ordinary tubes (diameter greater than 0·2 mm)	3·0	4·5	6·5	Independent of exact conditions of measurement
In very small tubes, e.g. arterioles	2·0	2·2	3·1	Depends on size of tube
Rate of flow very small (large tubes)	15	40	130	Falls rapidly with increase in rate of flow

The *absolute* viscosity of blood, and thus the resistance to flow through a given tube, rises as the temperature falls. The effect is not large, and in ordinary conditions of life, the variation never exceeds a few per cent. At the lowest temperature compatible with life (about 23°C), the viscosity is about 40 per cent greater than in normal conditions; and at the highest temperature (about 44°C), it is about 15 per cent smaller. The effect of temperature on the viscosity of blood is nearly the same as that on the viscosity of water, so that the *relative* viscosity of blood is independent of temperature.

Streamline Flow, Turbulence

Above a certain "critical" velocity, *laminar* or streamline flow becomes turbulent and the relationship found by Poiseuille for flow in tubes between driving force and flow rate is no longer linear. Figure 5.4 illustrates this phenomenon of turbulence.

Pressure-flow Relations in Blood Vessels

We have so far considered the behaviour of Newtonian fluids in a system of rigid tubes; normally a graph of flow versus driving pressure is linear.

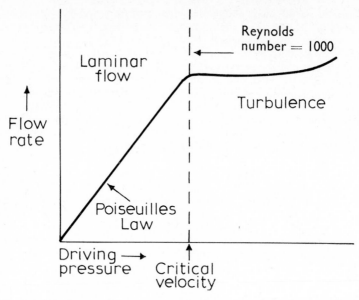

Fig. 5.4. Laminar and turbulent flow in tubes. Turbulence occurs when the Reynold's number, N_R, reaches 1000 (the critical velocity).

$$N_R = \frac{4\dot{Q}\rho}{\eta\pi D}$$

where $\dot{Q}$ is rate of flow, ρ = density, D = dia. of tube, η = viscosity of fluid.

However, when we come to measure flows and pressures in the vascular system, they are often quite non-linear. A major factor causing this discrepancy is, as one might expect, the distensible nature of the walls of all blood vessels. Blood flow is proportional to the fourth power of the radius of the vessels through which it is flowing hence anything altering vessel distension will be an important factor in determining the flow.

Laplace found that the tension, T, in the wall of a distensible vessel was proportional to the radius, r, times the transmural pressure, P. Thus

$$P = \frac{T}{r}$$

Using this formula, it is possible to calculate the tension (in dynes/cm or alternatively in gm/cm) in any blood vessel wall provided we know the radius and the pressure within it. Values actually found vary from about 250 gm/cm for a large vessel such as the aorta to 10 mg/cm for the smallest capillaries.

A thin walled and small vessel such as a capillary can safely stand quite high transmural pressures because its radius is small. As we pass to much larger veins, the tension in the wall of the vessel becomes higher again, in spite of the fact that blood pressure within the vessel may well be less. Large amounts of elastic fibres are present in the walls of large vessels for the purpose of keeping up the tension in them to counteract the distension due to the blood within.

An example to illustrate the foregoing considerations is given in Fig. 5.5. This shows the non-linear relation found between flow and driving pressure in an experiment upon a perfused rabbit's ear. The curves show the effect of increasing the vasomotor tone by electrical stimulation of sympathetic nerves at the frequencies indicated. For a Newtonian fluid in rigid tubes the curves would be straight lines through the origin, but since the vessels are distensible and can also contract when their smooth muscle is stimulated, the complex pressure-flow curves shown are found instead.

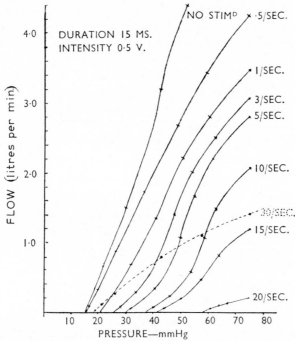

FIG. 5.5. Complex flow-pressure curves found in rabbit ear when cervical sympathetic ganglion is stimulated at various frequencies. For a "perfect" or Newtonian fluid in rigid tubes these would be straight lines going through the origin. Note the "critical closing pressure". (Burton, 1952 in *Ciba Fdn. Symp.* The Visceral Circulation. London. Churchill).

Critical Closing Pressure

The pressure within a blood vessel at which it collapses down completely and is closed to flow is termed the *critical closing pressure*. This occurs if and when the forces of muscle contraction together with the elastic forces in the wall of the vessel exceed the pressure within it. This closure occurs when the precapillary sphincters are actively contracting to control capillary flow. It is probably also an important factor during the very low arterial pressures which often occur in circulatory shock.

HAEMODYNAMICS: THE BLOOD PRESSURE

If the effects of respiration and of muscular movement on the veins are excluded, the flow of blood through the vessels is produced entirely by the pressure differences established by the heart. Although the blood pressure thus falls continuously from its highest value in the aorta to its lowest in the great veins entering the heart, it is most conveniently measured in three situations, the larger arteries, the capillaries and the great veins.

The Arterial Blood Pressure

The pressure in the arteries varies with each heart beat, and thus has a *maximum or systolic* value and a *minimum or diastolic* value; the difference between the two is termed the *pulse pressure*. In the experimental animal the arterial pressure is commonly measured by inserting into the carotid or femoral artery a glass cannula filled with a solution which prevents the blood from clotting (e.g. half-saturated Na_2SO_4), and connected through pressure tubing filled with the same solution to a mercury manometer (Fig. 5.6). Since the flow is obstructed in the vessel cannulated, the pressure recorded is that at the

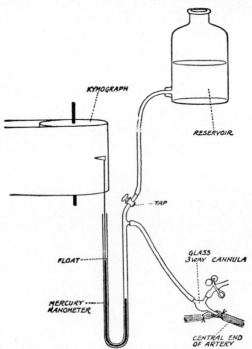

FIG. 5.6. Apparatus for Recording Blood Pressure in the Experimental Animal.

point of junction with the larger vessel that supplies it; for since there is no flow along the obstructed vessel there is also no fall of pressure. The levels to which the mercury rises in systole and diastole do not accurately represent systolic and diastolic pressures, since they are largely determined by the momentum of the heavy column of mercury. When true systolic and diastolic pressures are required the arterial cannula must be connected through a liquid system to a manometer that will respond quickly enough to record the pressure changes without lag, and in which the actual movement of the recording system is very small, so that a negligible volume of blood is withdrawn from the circulation. A "pick-up" sensitive to changes in electrical resistance ("strain-gauge manometer") or capacitance ("capacitance manometer") is used. The magnification obtained by this method is so large that the volume of blood displaced in the tubing by an extreme pressure change is less than the volume of a single red blood corpuscle. When the arterial cannula is connected to a mercury manometer of very wide bore and hence of very low frequency, the mercury column does not oscillate and records the *mean pressure* of the blood; more usually this value is recorded by using a mercury manometer of narrow bore with very high damping. The mean arterial pressure can be calculated from the systolic and diastolic values if the form of the pulse wave is also known; it approximates more closely to the diastolic than to the systolic pressure, since diastole lasts longer than systole.

Measurement of Arterial Pressure in Man

For clinical investigations, the arterial pressure in man may be measured by similar methods. Under local anaesthesia a needle is inserted into the brachial or femoral artery and connected to a capacitance manometer. For routine work an indirect method based on the following principle is used. If an artery is compressed, then the minimum pressure serving completely to stop the flow must be at least as great as the highest pressure (systolic) attained inside the vessel. As the pressure outside the artery is reduced, so blood will flow through the artery for longer and longer periods of the cardiac cycle, until finally when the compressing force is just less than diastolic pressure, blood-flow will be unimpeded, and the artery will cease to be deformed at any point of the cardiac cycle. A flat rubber bag contained in a loose but inextensible silk case is wrapped snugly around the upper arm. The interior of the bag is connected to a small hand pump through which air can be introduced or removed, and to a mercury manometer which measures the pressure of the air in the cuff. The cuff must be sufficiently wide to transmit the pressure of air it contains to the centre of the limb (12 cm for the upper arm) and sufficiently long to encircle the limb completely. The systolic and diastolic pressures are determined with this *sphygmomanometer* (Fig. 5.7) as follows.

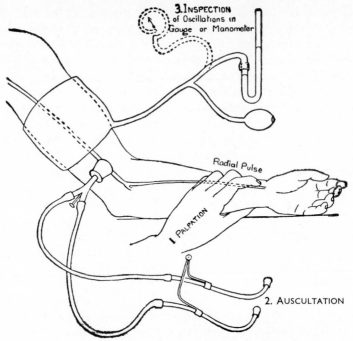

FIG. 5.7. The Measurement of the Arterial Blood Pressure in Man.
(From Harris' "Experimental Physiology".)

(1) **By Palpation.** The cuff is inflated until the pulse can no longer be felt at the wrist. Air is allowed to leak out until the pulse returns. The pressure at which the pulse beat can first be felt is taken as systolic pressure.

(2) **By Auscultation.** The bell of the stethoscope is placed over the brachial artery at the bend of the elbow, and the cuff on the upper arm inflated until all sounds disappear. Air is allowed to leak out until pulse sounds just reappear; this is the systolic pressure. As the pressure is lowered the sounds become louder and louder and then abruptly die away. The point at which the loud sounds begin abruptly to die away is taken as diastolic pressure, for below this point the pressure of the cuff has failed to deform the artery. It is to be noted that while this index is probably a reliable measure of diastolic pressure in most subjects, patients are occasionally encountered in whom the sounds continue to be heard when the pressure in the cuff is reduced to zero; in these cases this index of the diastolic pressure is clearly unreliable.

(3) **By the Oscillometer.** In some forms of the instrument the bag is connected to a high-frequency diaphragm type of pressure gauge. The oscillations of the diaphragm record the volume changes of the main artery of the limb transmitted to the air in the cuff. When the pressure in

the cuff is slowly reduced, the point at which the oscillations of the manometer first increase is taken as systolic, the point of maximum oscillation as diastolic pressure.

The auscultatory method is that most commonly used in England and the values correspond most closely with direct manometric measurements. The oscillatory method gives values for the systolic and diastolic pressures that are usually 5 to 10 mm Hg higher than those obtained by the auscultatory method. Systolic pressures obtained by palpation are, in experienced hands, in fairly close agreement with those obtained by auscultation; owing, however, to the difficulty of feeling the first weak pulse beat, the values particularly in inexperienced hands are frequently some 5 to 10 mm lower.

The Capillary Pressure

Accurate estimation of the capillary pressure in man is extremely difficult. One method is to seal on to the skin a small glass chamber open on the side next to the skin; its interior is connected to a manometer and source of air pressure. The pressure of air necessary to cause a capillary loop (observed microscopically) to disappear is taken as the capillary pressure. This method gives variable results and is less reliable than the following direct method. A finger is immobilized in a bed of plasticine and the cuticle is shaved off from the base of the nail. If a drop of glycerine is placed on the skin, the capillary loops can easily be seen with a binocular microscope and surface illumination. By means of a micromanipulator a fine glass micro-pipette containing physiological saline and sodium citrate solution is introduced into one of the capillaries, and blood allowed to enter its orifice. The pressure at which the blood neither enters nor leaves the pipette but oscillates with each heart beat is the mean capillary pressure. Owing to difficulties of fixation and of observing sufficiently large capillaries, the base of the nail is as yet the only place where the method is practicable in man.

The Venous Pressure

The veins offer little frictional resistance, and the blood flows through them with only a small fall of pressure. The venous pressure at some distance from the heart is thus very close to that in the superior vena cava. The most accurate and direct method of determining the venous pressure in man is to introduce into the median basilic vein at the elbow a wide needle connected with a manometer containing a solution of sodium citrate. The solution is allowed to flow into the vein until the meniscus shows small respiratory oscillations about a fairly constant mean value. The height of this meniscus gives the venous pressure in the vein at the point of measurement. To obtain a gauge of general venous pressure such values must be corrected for the difference in level between the vein punctured and the heart, since the pressure in the veins, as in all the vessels, is affected by gravitational forces. It is not easy to say precisely at what level the heart is in man, and so the pressures are usually referred to an easily accessible structure bearing a fairly constant relation to the heart, the junction of the manubrium with the body of the sternum (angle of Louis).

In recumbent healthy subjects when the arm lies at or below the level of the heart, the meniscus in the venous manometer comes to rest at the same level as the angle of Louis, or a centimetre or two below it. Relative to the angle of Louis the venous pressure in health is thus 0 to -2 cm H_2O.

Now the veins, being wide lax vessels, are distended when the pressure of their contained blood is greater than that of the atmosphere. When the

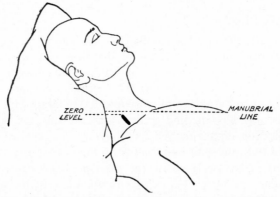

Fig. 5.8. Measurement of the Venous Pressure in Man.

The subject lies down with his head supported by pillows; the jugular vein is seen distended with blood up to a point which usually lies just below the level of the notch of the *manubrium sterni*. (Lewis.)

venous pressure is a little below that of the atmosphere the veins collapse. If therefore in the recumbent subject we trace a superficial vein, such as the external jugular, from a point well below the level of the manubrium sterni to a point above it, we see that for the lower part of its course the vein is distended, and then at some higher point it collapses and ceases to be visible (Fig. 5.8). At the junction of distended and collapsed vein, pulsations synchronous with the heart beat and respiration will be observed. From what has been said it is clear that the junction of distended and collapsed vein should give the level at which the venous pressure is equal to that of the atmosphere, and in fact it is found that when the venous pressure is measured manometrically, the meniscus lies at the same level as that to which the jugular veins are distended. The point of collapse of the jugular veins is therefore used clinically to measure the venous pressure in man. In so doing it is essential to ensure that the point at which the vein ceases to be visible is not simply the point at which it plunges deeply into the neck; this may be ascertained by noting that the vein fills to a higher level when it is obstructed below by a finger.

In resting man the venous inflow to the heart is small; the healthy heart requires but a small distending pressure to expel this inflow and maintains the venous pressure low. The failing heart, which is working at the limit of its capacity, requires a venous pressure that is several centimetres (2 to 10 cm H_2O) higher to accomplish its task; and under such circumstances the venous pressure is raised. It may be readily understood, therefore, that in the resting subject a rise of venous pressure above its normal value is the most usual and most important sign of failure of the heart. For this reason measurement of the venous pressure is of unusual importance clinically.

Normal values for the blood pressure in resting man at various parts of the vascular circuit are as follows:—

Axillary artery	systolic . .	115 mm Hg	
	diastolic . .	70	,,
	(pulse pressure .	45	,,)
Capillary of nail fold	arterial limb .	32	,,
	summit of loop .	20	,,
Superior vena cava . . .		0 to − 2	,,

Of these values the venous pressure is the most constant, rarely varying by more than 2 mm Hg (3 cm H_2O) from the mean; the capillary pressure shows slightly greater variations (5 mm Hg) and the arterial pressure

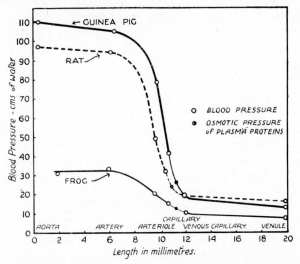

FIG. 5.9. Shows the *mean blood pressure* (circles) determined by inserting a micropipette into different parts of the mesenteric circulation of the guinea pig, rat and frog. In each curve the thin line represents the fall of pressure along the capillaries. The dots indicate determinations of the osmotic pressure of the plasma proteins in each species. (After Landis.)

considerably greater fluctuations. Thus in an individual examined at rest on several occasions, the systolic pressure may vary from 110 to 130 mm Hg and the diastolic pressure from 60 to 80 mm Hg; psychical factors are amongst the more important causes of these variations. Average values for the systolic blood pressure rise from 80 to 100 mm at the age of five, to 115 mm at the age of puberty and to 140 mm Hg at the age of sixty.

Figure 5.9 shows the blood pressure determined directly in various parts of the vascular circuit of the guinea pig, the rat and the frog, by the introduction of a micropipette into the appropriate vessel. It will be seen that there is no appreciable fall of pressure until the smaller arteries are approached, then the pressure falls rapidly until the capillaries are reached, when the gradual fall becomes more gradual. The fall of pressure as the blood traverses the veins is very small. The figure also shows that the pressure in the arterial limb of the capillary is higher, and in the venous limb lower, than the colloid osmotic pressure of the blood; fluid thus tends to pass out of the blood at one end of the capillary and to be absorbed at the other. In an active organ, as we shall see, there is considerable arterial dilatation, and increase in rate of blood-flow. The capillaries also dilate, and those previously closed, open up.

The Effect of Gravity

The above values of the blood pressure are all given for vessels lying at the same level as the heart. When the vessels lie below this level, then to the pressure which is imparted to the blood by the heart must be added the pressure due to gravity, that is the pressure exerted by a column of blood equal in height to the vertical distance of the vessels examined, from the heart. This relationship holds good for all the vessels of the perfectly flaccid limb; but in dependent limbs the venous pressure is reduced by the repeated movements which are usual during active life. Even the smallest movements empty the veins which, owing to the action of the valves, can only fill up from below. Thus in health the venous pressure in dependent limbs rarely rises very much above that of the atmosphere. This is important because if the venous pressure becomes greatly raised, then the capillary pressure is correspondingly raised and fluid tends to pass out of the capillaries and waterlog the tissue spaces. If the leg of a normal person is allowed to hang down for several hours without movement, it thus become oedematous. When the veins of the leg are distended by disease (varicose veins), the valves become incompetent, and after a day's work the feet become swollen because of the raised capillary pressure.

Chapter 6

THE ARTERIES, CAPILLARIES AND VEINS

The Arterial System

The arterial system consists of the large elastic arteries (aorta), muscular arteries, and the arterioles. The function of the arterial system is summarized as follows:—

(1) To conduct blood from the lungs and heart to the tissues.

(2) To turn the highly pulsatile output of the heart into a smooth flow of blood.

(3) To maintain a high pressure in the system so that blood will perfuse the tissues and be forced through the small vessels therein.

(4) In conjunction with (3) to regulate the flow of blood through different tissues by altering their vascular resistance.

Factors Determining the Arterial Blood Pressure

As we shall see later, the maintenance of an adequate supply of blood to the brain and to the heart is intimately dependent on the level of the general arterial pressure. This depends on the cardiac output and on the peripheral resistance; the resistance offered by the vessels being determined by their diameter and by the viscosity of the blood.

The Arterial Blood Pressure in Man

The mean pressure is generally taken as the diastolic pressure plus one-third of the pulse pressure. The relation between the cardiac output (CO), the arterial pressure (BP), and the total peripheral resistance (TPR) is defined by the relation:

$$CO = BP/TPR.$$

The fluctuation of the arterial pressure above and below the mean, that is to say the pulse pressure, depends chiefly upon how much blood is thrust into, and escapes from, the arterial tree between successive heart beats, and this depends chiefly upon the stroke volume. Increase in cardiac output by itself increases both mean pressure and stroke volume, and therefore raises systolic, diastolic and pulse pressures; increase in peripheral resistance by itself increases the mean pressure without altering the stroke volume and therefore increases the systolic and diastolic pressures without much altering the pulse pressure; increase in the pulse rate by itself does not affect the mean pressure, but reduces the stroke volume;

the pulse pressure, therefore, diminishes and the systolic and diastolic pressures approach the mean pressure. These relations, though useful as will be seen later, are only approximate; and attempts to calculate the cardiac output accurately from formulae embodying the systolic and diastolic pressures and the heart rate have not been very successful.

The Control of Arterial Vessels

From the data already given for the blood pressure in different parts of the vascular circuit it will be seen that the main fall of pressure occurs in the small arteries and arterioles. The peripheral resistance is thus chiefly constituted by these vessels and its magnitude is dependent upon the strength of contraction of their smooth muscle coats. The state of contraction, or "tone" of the arterioles, may be modified for one of two purposes: to fulfil local metabolic requirements or to safeguard the circulation to the brain.

Local Control

The arterioles are relaxed, or dilated, locally in any organ or tissue when its activity increases and there is a greater demand for oxygen. The most important of these organs are the heart, the skeletal muscles and the digestive glands. Such an adjustment of the circulation is brought about chiefly by the production in the active tissues of vaso-dilator substances which act directly on the arterioles; the blood flow is increased and a greater supply of oxygen is made available. This will be discussed again later.

Reflex Control

The arterioles in many parts of the body, on the other hand, may become constricted, or allowed to dilate, so adjusting the total peripheral resistance as to maintain the arterial pressure and thus the blood flow to the brain. A simple vaso-dilatation in any organ will lower the peripheral resistance and hence the arterial pressure. It is not surprising, therefore, that mechanisms exist which ensure that when vaso-dilatation occurs in one part of the body, this is compensated by vaso-constriction elsewhere. This control is initiated by receptors in the walls of certain arteries which are sensitive to the level of the arterial pressure and are thus called *baroreceptors*. The most important of these are situated: (*a*) in the arch of the aorta, giving rise to the "depressor reflex"; and (*b*) in the carotid sinus, the name given to the expansion at the origin of the internal carotid artery. The baroreceptors send nerve impulses to a group of nerve cells known as the "vaso-motor centre" lying in the the floor of the fourth ventricle close to the vagus nucleus. These in turn send impulses through the autonomic nerves to the blood vessels.

The Vaso-motor Centre

The maintenance of the general vaso-motor tone is intimately dependent on the integrity of this centre. Section of the hind-brain below the level of these cells leads to generalized vaso-dilatation, and the blood pressure falls from, say, 120 to 80 mm Hg. After several days, if the animal survives, the blood pressure may rise again almost to its previous level; destruction of the spinal cord reduces the blood pressure almost to zero. It thus appears that there are also vaso-motor centres in the spinal cord, but in ordinary circumstances these are mainly controlled by that of the hind-brain (medulla); when this is destroyed, then the spinal centres gradually take over control. Electrical stimulation of the vaso-motor centre, on the other hand, leads to generalized vaso-constriction and a rise of blood pressure. The normal activity of the centre in maintaining general vaso-motor tone is, as we shall see, profoundly modified by the influence of the cerebral hemispheres, as well as by afferent impulses from the baroreceptors, and by chemical stimuli, the centre being stimulated by carbon dioxide and by inadequate oxygen supply.

The rôle of carbon dioxide in determining the activity of the cells of the vaso-motor centres is well shown when the gas is excessively removed from the blood by over-ventilating the lungs. If the lungs of an anaesthetized cat are artificially over-ventilated with air, the blood pressure may fall in two minutes from 140 to 40 mm Hg. If air containing 5 per cent carbon dioxide is substituted for the ordinary air previously used, the rate of ventilation remaining the same, the blood pressure returns to its original level.

After a cerebral haemorrhage the blood pressure may rise to 150 mm Hg and the pulse is slowed. The rise of blood pressure is usually attributed to anaemia of the vaso-motor centre, arising from compression of the brain by the haemorrhage; in this way the cells of the centre would be stimulated by oxygen lack and the accumulation of metabolites.

The Vaso-motor Nerves

The nervous control of the blood vessels is chiefly effected through the sympathetic branches of the autonomic nervous system (Chapter 22). The action of the vaso-motor nerves was discovered by Claude Bernard, who found in the rabbit that when the cervical sympathetic chain was divided on one side, the ear on that side became flushed and warm, remaining so for a considerable time. Conversely, stimulation of the cervical sympathetic produces pallor and coldness of the corresponding ear. We now know that if the appropriate branches of the sympathetic nerves are stimulated under suitable conditions, then the blood vessels in all parts of the body (except perhaps the heart) constrict. The degree of constriction, however, varies in different organs. Thus stimulation of the appropriate sympathetic fibres produces

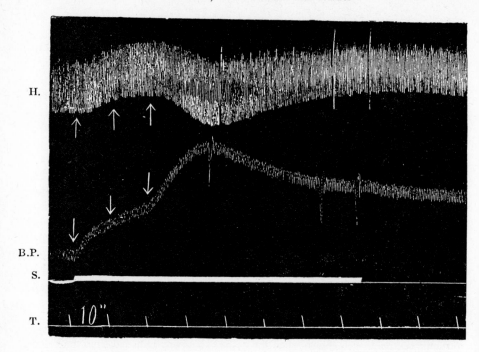

FIG. 6.1. The Effect of Stimulating the Splanchnic Nerve on the Arterial Blood
    Pressure, and on the Output and Volume of the Ventricles.

> H, heart volume (a rise in the curve indicates an increase in
> volume). B.P., arterial blood pressure. S, signal showing duration of
> stimulation of the splanchnic nerve. T, time marker, showing 10 sec
> intervals. Note that the first rise in arterial pressure is associated with
> an increase in the volume of the heart, owing to the greater power
> needed in order to expel the blood against the raised pressure, but that
> secondary rise, due to the *secretion of adrenaline*, is associated with
> a decrease in the volume, showing that the heart is beating more
> forcibly. Note also that the output is increased by the presence of
> adrenaline, as shown by the increased excursion of the cardiometer
> record (stroke volume).

intense narrowing of the vessels (vaso-constriction) of the skin and
alimentary canal (Fig. 6.1), but only slight narrowing in those of the brain
and lungs (Fig. 6.2). The vessels constricted by stimulation of the
sympathetic are particularly the arteries and arterioles, to a less extent the
capillaries and the veins. Section of the sympathetic nerves supplying an
organ leads to an increase in the blood-flow through it, and it thus appears
that normally there is a steady stream of constrictor impulses passing along
these nerves to the blood vessels. Further, since in the majority of organs
the vessels cease to participate in the vaso-motor reflexes, shortly to be
described, after their sympathetic fibres have been cut, it seems that

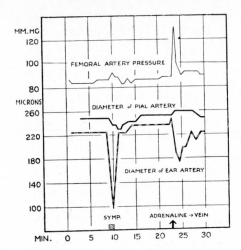

FIG. 6.2. The lower two curves record in microns the diameters of an
artery of the pia mater of the brain, and of an ear artery, observed
microscopically in a cat. The pial artery was seen through a glass
window screwed into the skull. At the signal "symp." the cervical
sympathetic trunk was stimulated and produced a pronounced
constriction of the ear artery but only a slight narrowing of the pial
artery. At the next signal 0·01 mg adrenaline injected into a vein
produced a marked constriction of the ear artery and a small
dilatation of the pial artery which is to be attributed to a passive effect
of the coincident rise of blood pressure. (Forbes, Firnley and Mason.)

changes in vascular calibre of vaso-motor origin are chiefly determined by
an increase or decrease (inhibition) of sympathetic vaso-constrictor
impulses.

Sympathectomy. Division of the sympathetic fibres supplying a limb, either
by removal of the appropriate sympathetic ganglia or section of the preganglionic
sympathetic fibres, is followed by vaso-dilatation, by loss of vascular responses to
change of body temperature, and loss of reflex sweating and pilomotor response.
The vaso-dilatation chiefly affects the skin, muscle blood-flow being little altered.
With the progress of time, the vaso-dilatation subsides and the vessels are found to
be abnormally sensitive to adrenaline, histamine and other vaso-active substances.
Complete sympathectomy, by removal in separate stages of the chain of sympathetic ganglia on both sides, has been performed in the cat and dog. The completely
sympathectomized cat is sluggish, and very susceptible to exposure to cold, to
oxygen lack, and to haemorrhage. The sympathectomized dog is normally active
and its arterial pressure at rest is little below normal. It is evident that while in the
normal animal the vaso-motor nerves are extremely important in regulating the
circulation, yet other probably chemical mechanisms can in the dog take over
much of this function.

Reciprocal Innervation and Vaso-dilator Nerves. It was thought at one time
that the blood vessels generally were supplied by both sets of autonomic nerves—
sympathetic (constrictor) and parasympathetic (dilator)—the two sets acting

reciprocally. Thus an increase in flow would be brought about by a decrease in impulse frequency in sympathetic fibres and by a concomitant increase in impulse frequency in parasympathetic fibres. Later studies showed that direct parasympathetic vaso-dilator fibres probably occur only in the nervi erigentes supplying the erectile tissue of the genital organs. The vaso-dilatation that occurs in the salivary glands during parasympathetic nerve stimulation is not brought about by true parasympathetic vaso-dilator fibres, but by the action of vaso-dilator substances formed during stimulation of the secretory cells. Skeletal muscle vessels in the cat are supplied by sympathetic vaso-dilator fibres; but these do not act reciprocally with the vaso-constrictor fibres, but quite independently.

The Depressor Reflex

The baroreceptors in the arch of the aorta send nerve fibres to the hind-brain in the trunk of the vagus (as in man) or as a separate "depressor" nerve (rabbit). Stimulation of these fibres produces a

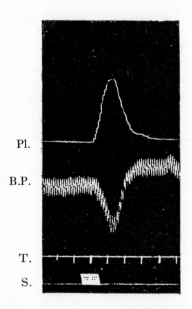

Pl.

B.P.

T.

S.

Fig 6.3. The Depressor Reflex, producing Vaso-dilatation and a Fall in Arterial Pressure.

From above downwards: volume (plethysmograph) of a loop of intestine, arterial blood pressure, time in 10 sec intervals, signal showing period of stimulation of the central end of the vagus (containing the depressor fibres). (W. M. Bayliss.)

slowing of the heart and fall of blood pressure. The slowing of the heart is largely but not entirely abolished by previous section of the vagi; it is thus due mainly to a reflex augmentation of vagal tone, and partly to a reflex inhibition of sympathetic tone. The fall of blood pressure is independent of slowing of the heart and is due to a vaso-dilatation that affects all the organs of the body except perhaps the brain (Fig. 6.3). Thus stimulation of the depressor nerve produces an increase in the volume of a limb or of a loop of intestine, and an increase in blood-flow from the submaxillary gland. The physiological stimulus exciting the depressor reflex is a rise of pressure in the arch of the aorta.

The Carotid Sinus Reflexes

It has long been known that in man pressure over the bifurcation of the common carotid artery produces a sensation of faintness accompanied by slowing of the pulse and fall of blood pressure. This effect has been shown to be due to stimulation of baroreceptors lying under the adventitia of the carotid sinus. If the sinus is compressed, or if the pressure of the blood inside is raised, or if the sensory nerve to it (a branch of the glosso-pharyngeal) is stimulated, the blood pressure falls and the heart slows-changes produced reflexly in a manner similar to those

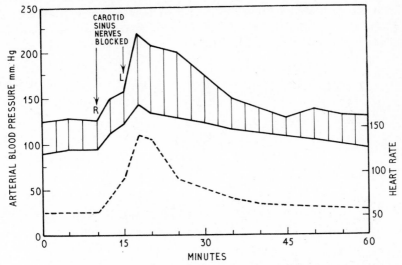

Fig. 6.4. Arterial blood pressure and heart rate in the human subject before, during, and after blocking the carotid sinus nerves with local anaesthetic. After release of the vaso-motor centre from the inhibitory impulses of these baroreceptors, the arterial pressure rose to 224/148 mm Hg (systolic/diastolic), and the heart rate increased to 140 beats per minute. (After Lampen, Kedzi and Kaufmann.)

of the depressor reflex. Conversely, if the common carotid artery is compressed so as to produce a fall of pressure within the sinus, the heart accelerates and the blood pressure rises. The paths followed by both this and the depressor reflex are very similar. The afferent impulses entering the hind-brain through the glosso-pharyngeal and vagus nerves reach the cardio-inhibitory, cardio-accelerator and vaso-motor centres lying close by in the medulla. The impulses sent out by these centres through the vagus and sympathetic nerves are thus modified in the way described.

If the carotid sinus and depressor nerves are cut, the blood pressure and pulse rate rise permanently. Blood pressure and pulse rate in man rise if the carotid sinus nerves are blocked by local anaesthesia (Fig. 6.4). In normal life, therefore, the constancy of the blood pressure and pulse rate is due largely to impulses ascending these nerves; any variation in blood pressure produces an inhibition or augmentation of these impulses, and so reflexly initiates changes which restore the blood pressure to its normal level.

When the arterial pressure falls these reflexes produce an increase in sympathetic vasoconstrictor tone, mainly in the splanchnic area, that is to say in the intestines, kidneys, liver and spleen, to a much less extent in the skeletal muscles. The cerebral vessels and pulmonary vessels are not involved. These pressor effects are reinforced by the simultaneous release of adrenaline and noradrenaline. The two reflexes are thus of extreme importance in maintaining the distribution of blood to the tissues according to their needs; at the same time they prevent undue strain on the heart by keeping the blood pressure within convenient limits.

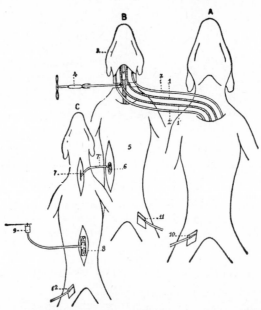

FIG. 6.5. Arrangement of Animals in a Cross-Circulation Experiment.

The head of dog B (3) is perfused from dog A by anastomosis of the carotid arteries and also of the jugular veins (1, 1′, 2, 2′), the vertebral arteries and veins being tied, the muscles of the neck divided between ligatures, and the rest of the tissues compressed round the vertebral column by the *écraseur* of Chassaignac (4). Blood from the suprarenal of B (6) is led into one of the jugular veins (7) of C, which has been adrenalectomized; the spleen of C (8) is enclosed in a plethysmograph, and contracts whenever adrenaline is secreted by the suprarenals of B. The arterial blood pressures of the three dogs are recorded from the femoral arteries 10, 11, 12. (From C. Heymans.)

Experiments on the Carotid Sinus

The methods used by Heymans and his co-workers in investigating the functions of the carotid sinus are interesting as an example of physiological technique (Fig. 6.5). One or both carotid arteries of one dog B are perfused with blood from a second dog A (cross-circulation). The head of dog B is com-

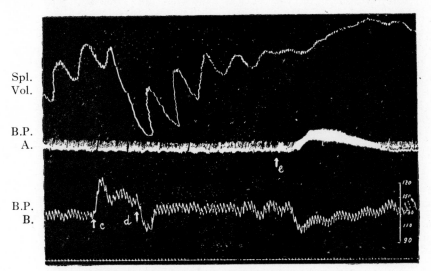

Spl.
Vol.

B.P.
A.

B.P.
B.

FIG. 6.6. The Regulation of the Arterial Blood Pressure.
(Cross-circulation experiment, see Fig. 6.5.)

From above downwards: Volume of the spleen of dog C; arterial pressure of dog A (perfusing the carotid sinus of dog B), arterial pressure of dog B.

At *c* the pressure in the carotid sinus of dog B was reduced by partially clamping the inter-connecting artery, and at *d* the pressure was returned to the initial value. A fall in pressure in the carotid sinus leads to a reflex rise in pressure in the rest of the body, and a reflex secretion of adrenaline, as shown by the contraction of the spleen of dog C; a rise in pressure in the carotid sinus has the reverse effect. At *e* 0·1 mg of adrenaline was injected into the circulation of the perfusing dog, A, raising its arterial pressure, and hence, also, the pressure in the carotid sinus of dog B. This resulted in a reflex fall in the arterial pressure of B, and an inhibition of the secretion of adrenaline, as shown by the dilatation of the spleen of dog C. (From C. Heymans.)

pletely severed from its trunk, except for the spinal cord and vagus nerves. On raising the arterial pressure in dog A and thus in the carotid sinuses of dog B, the blood pressure in the trunk of dog B falls and the heart rate diminishes; the opposite change occur when the blood pressure of dog A is lowered (Fig. 6.6). If now the suprarenal vein of dog B is anastomosed with the internal jugular vein of a third dog C (Fig. 6.5), then a fall of blood pressure in dog A produces, in addition to the effects mentioned, a contraction of the spleen of dog. C (Fig 6.6).

Thus a fall of pressure in the carotid sinus of dog B leads in this dog to an increased secretion of adrenaline, as shown by the effect of blood from its suprarenal vein on the spleen of C. The effects are abolished by denervating the carotid sinuses of dog B.

Myogenic Vascular Tone

The arterioles of the skeletal muscles are endowed with very strong *myogenic tone*. It is sometimes called basal, inherent or intrinsic tone. While the skeletal muscle is at rest some intrinsic mechanism causes the vascular plain muscle to contract spontaneously. If myogenic tone in the skeletal muscle vessels is relaxed, as in severe exercise,

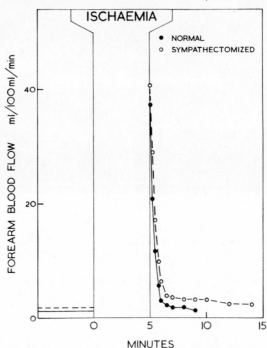

FIG. 6.7. Blood flow in the normal forearm and in the contralateral sympathectomized forearm before and after the arrest of the circulation in the arm for 5 min. (Diagram drawn from data obtained by Grant.)

vascular resistance in the skeletal muscles may fall to 1/20 of its resting value with reduction of the total peripheral resistance to 1/5 of its resting values. In exercise, loss of myogenic vascular tone is accompanied by stimulation of the rate and force of the heartbeat so that there is an increase in the cardiac output which a little more than makes up for the fall in total peripheral resistance. Arterial blood pressure, in consequence, is maintained, indeed raised a little. Loss of myogenic tone in skeletal muscle vessels takes place soon after its arterial supply is cut

The Capillaries

off (Fig. 6.7), and therefore probably soon after death. Myogenic tone in resting voluntary muscle vessels is modified by the sympathetic nervous system but not to a very great extent.

Joining the arterial and venous sides of the circulation are the capillaries, which are the thin walled vessels in tissues where the interchange of oxygen, carbon dioxide, water, ions, metabolites and hormones takes place. The ultimate function of the remainder of the circulatory system is that of bringing these substances to and from the lungs, kidneys, liver, etc. to enable the exchange in the tissues to occur. A great deal of active research work is in progress at the present time, on capillary function, work no doubt stimulated in part by the fundamental nature of capillary function and also by the fact that recent advances in electron-microscopy, micro-dissection and histochemistry make this an attractive field for investigation.

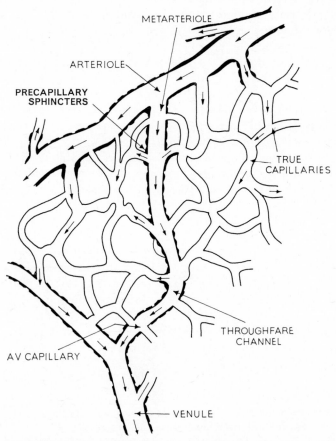

Fig. 6.8. Diagram of capillary network showing arteriole; metarterioles and capillaries. (After Chambers and Zweifach, 1947.)

Organization of the Capillary Network.

The capillary network is the distributing system for supplying blood to the tissues. The flow through it is variable in direction, rate and amount and in general is adjusted rather closely to the needs of the tissues. A theoretical diagram of the anatomy of a capillary net is shown in Fig. 6.8 which has been compiled from numerous photomicrographs and cine films taken from different body regions.

Observations of capillary function have been made using mesentery, frog's web preparations and other very thin tissues mounted under the microscope. Blood tends to flow regularly only in the so-called *throughfare channels* between arterioles and venules. Otherwise the rate and direction of flow in the *true capillaries* is unpredictable. The *precapillary sphincters*, smooth muscle thickenings at the mouths of most capillaries, contract and relax thus allowing less or more blood to pass through the capillary. The structure of the true capillaries has been the subject of hot dispute in the past—largely centred upon whether or not they are contractile. They are 8 to 10μ in diameter and up to 1 mm long, are constructed of a single layer of endothelial cells held together by connective tissue and can be shown to contract down when prodded with a fine needle. However, no muscle fibres are present according to the most recent electron microscope findings.

The surface area for exchange of substances between blood and tissues is enormous; it has been asserted that one muscle contains a capillary bed having the total area of a football field.

Venules form the collecting system; they are variable in diameter (say 10 to 100μ) and the larger ones have an outside layer of smooth muscle. The contraction of this muscle plays a part in the control of outflow from the capillary bed.

Function of Capillaries

The patency of capillary channels varies cyclically from time to time—a phasic form of activity denoted by the incongruous term, *vasomotion*. The degree of opening of the vascular bed, of course, varies with activity in the tissue concerned; in resting muscle the number of active capillaries may be only 1 to 2 per cent of the total, a proportion greatly increased in exercise.

Capillary permeability, tissue fluid formation, lymph flow and oedema are dealt with in Chapter 3.

THE VENOUS SYSTEM

The vessels collect the blood which has passed through the tissue capillary network and then lead into the larger veins. Venous pressure cannot be given a fixed value, for it depends largely upon the particular vein concerned and also on whether the subject is standing or is in the

TABLE 6.1

Venous pressure in man

| Vein | Pressure (mm Hg) | |
	mean	range
Median basilic . .	97	50–148
Femoral . . .	111	98–128
Abdominal . .	115	70–160
Dorsal metacarpal .	130	70–170
Great saphenous .	150	110–190
Dorsalis pedis . .	175	124–210

Values for an upright man; notice increase, due to hydrostatic gravitational effect, in lower limb. (*From Burch* (1950), *p.* 109.)

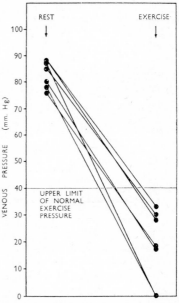

FIG. 6.9. Results showing the effect of exercise on the venous pressure in the foot. Each line shows the change in pressure for one subject.

During the exercise the subject marked time smartly, each foot being raised nine inches, sixty times per minute.

(From data of Walker and Longland)

horizontal position (Table 6.1). When standing, the pressure in the veins in the feet may rise to 100 mm Hg, if the subject is at rest or if the valves are incompetent (see Fig. 6.9). This fact accounts for the development of oedema of the feet and ankles in individuals who stand continuously, because the capillary pressure is thereby raised and re-absorption of tissue fluid is impeded.

Venous Tone

The degree to which the smooth muscle in the wall of the venous system is contracted plays a part in determining the venous return to the heart. Other things being equal, the length of time that the blood spends in the venous system will be an inverse function of venous tone. Recent studies of venous tone in the human hand and forearm and in the hind limbs of a dog have shown that it increases in exercise due to increase in sympathetic venomotor nerve impulse frequency; it decreases during sleep (Fig. 6.10). In haemorrhage also, it increases so much so that it may be impossible to get a needle into the lumen of a superficial vein.

Central Venous Pressure

This is the pressure near the openings of the venae cavae into the right auricle; it is the pressure which drives the blood into the heart. Stopping the heart causes a large rise in central venous pressure as blood accumulates in, and distends, the great veins. Other things being equal, central venous

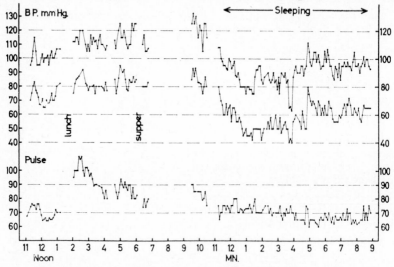

FIG. 6.10. Twenty-four hourly record of the arterial blood pressure of a normal subject. Note the fall in arterial pressure during sleep; it is accompanied by peripheral vasodilatation and by decrease in venous tone. (After Richardson, Honour, Fenton, Stott & Pickering.)

pressure is inversely related to the performance of the heart as a pump. Although cardiac output increases several fold in exercise, central venous pressure scarcely alters. The enormous increase in the venous return, of course, *tends* to raise central venous pressure; the fact that it does not rise is explained by the increase in the performance of the heart as a pump; increase in rate and the force of the heart beat enables the heart to transfer the blood more rapidly from the venous to the arterial side. As might be imagined, central venous pressure is influenced by alterations in the posture of the body and in venous tone. When blood is added to the circulation, most of it will be accommodated in the veins so that central venous pressure will increase. Heart failure is accompanied by a large increase in the pressure in the great veins.

Blood Reservoirs

The spleen is peculiar in that blood is accommodated and also concentrated by loss of plasma. In the spleen pulp there is a bypass of the circulation; in the dog the spleen can accommodate one-fifth of the total volume of blood. The other reservoirs, the liver and portal system, the subpapillary plexus of the skin, and the great veins are, unlike the spleen, part of the general circulation, but are, like the spleen, capable of considerable variations in capacity; the liver and portal system (including the spleen) at rest contain about one-quarter to one-third of the total volume of blood in the cat and dog, the skin very much less. The capacities of these structures in man are not accurately known, but it is probable that the spleen is relatively less capacious than in the cat and dog.

General Circulatory Responses

In the course of life, a man is likely to be subjected to various conditions, resulting from activity or accident, which will affect the circulatory system as a whole. The circulation will respond to these conditions in various appropriate ways, which we will now describe.

The Circulatory Adaptions to Changes in Posture

When a recumbent subject stands up, blood pools in the veins of the lower part of the body, there is less in the great veins to fill the heart and cardiac output diminishes. Arterial blood pressure tends to fall. However the carotid sinus and depressor reflexes come into play in a fraction of a minute; there is reflex stimulation of the heart and blood vessels. In the upright state arterial pressure is unchanged and cardiac output is decreased, but this is offset by increase in the total peripheral resistance. The heart beats a little more quickly.

The Valsalva Manoeuvre

This is used to test the integrity of the baroreceptor vasomotor reflex. The subject closes his glottis and attempts to expire forceably. Arterial blood pressure rises transiently and then falls because of diminution in the venous return and decrease in cardiac output (Fig. 6.11). The fall in arterial

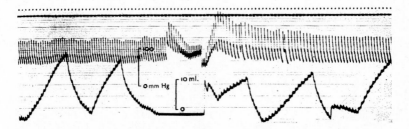

FIG. 6.11. Upper curve, arterial blood pressure in man. Lower curve forearm bloodflow. The beginning of the Valsalva manoeuvre is shown on the arterial blood pressure trace by an upward shift of about 40 mm Hg, the end by a sudden decrease in pressure 11 sec later. After the Valsalva, note the "overshoot" of the arterial pressure and vasoconstriction in the forearm. (E. P. Sharpey-Schafer, *J. Physiol.* **122**, 353.)

pressure evokes the baroreceptor reflex; heart rate increases as the record shows, and peripheral resistance increases and checks the fall in blood pressure.

After the Valsalva manoeuvre, the rush of blood through the heart in the face of a raised peripheral resistance causes an upward surge of the arterial blood pressure. Sudden stimulation of the baroreceptors causes the bradycardia now seen in the arterial tracing. The result of a Valsalva in a subject without a baroreceptor reflex is altogether different. There is no tachycardia during the Valsalva, nor any bradycardia afterwards. The arterial blood pressure fall, during the manoeuvre, proceeds unchecked by vasoconstriction and after the Valsalva there is no overshoot of the arterial pressure.

The Mess Trick and the Fainting Lark. It is possible, by combining the above procedure with a short period of hyperventilation beforehand, to produce a fall in blood pressure so marked that the brain blood supply falls to a low level and the subject loses consciousness. This effect is due to the concomitant washing out of carbon dioxide altering the oxygen dissociation curve of blood to such an extent that the lowered pressure together with decreased oxygen liberation lead to severe cerebral hypoxia.

This party piece, the "Fainting Lark", is, however, not to be indulged in for pleasure, because pleasant though the sensations accompanying the return of consciousness may be, large numbers of cortical grey cells are killed off by the hypoxia.

Circulatory Adjustments in Exercise

Higher centres of the brain can have a preparatory effect upon circulatory function, when the use of muscles is contemplated. Imminent exercise leads to subsidence of vagal inhibition of the heart, it beats more rapidly and the force of its contractions is augmented by sympathetic stimulation

TABLE 6.2

The Effect of Exercise on the Output of the Heart (after Christiansen)

Subject	Work performed Kg-metres per min	Oxygen consumption l/min	Pulse rate per min	Cardiac output l/min	Output per beat cc
Untrained female	0	0·24	77	4·6	60
	600	1·57	131	14·5	111
	720	1·79	145	17·4	120
	840	2·05	159	19·0	120
	960	2·45	168	23·8	142
Trained male	0	0·25	70	4·2	60
	720	1·93	118	16·5	140
	960	2·22	140	20·6	147
	1,200	2·83	174	23·0	132
	1,440	3·26	180	26·9	149
	1,680	3·94	179	37·3	208

and by the action of adrenaline. At the beginning of exercise, heart rate and cardiac output rise rapidly and in about three minutes will have reached levels related to the severity of the exercise. As is shown in Table 6.2 the increase in output is due partly to an increase in the frequency of the heart and partly to an increase in the amount expelled by each beat (stroke volume). X-ray pictures of the human heart show no change in the diastolic volume, and the increase in stroke volume results from the ventricles emptying more completely in systole. The diastolic volume of the ventricle of the resting untrained subject in the upright position is about 90 ml and the stroke volume 45 ml, leaving 45 ml behind—the residual volume. In very severe exercise, the ventricle empties almost completely and the stroke volume is nearly 90 ml. In trained subjects the heart hypertrophies and enlarges and in severe exercise the ventricle can discharge up to 200 ml per beat (Table 6.2).

The venous return, which in the steady state of course must equal the cardiac output, is increased proportionally to the work done. Venous pressure, measured through a catheter in the great veins near the heart or in the right auricle, remains almost constant. In a given time, a much greater volume of blood can enter the heart because the duration of the diastolic pause is increased at the expense of the systolic pause and because the ventricle relaxes more rapidly and offers less resistance to the entering blood. Owing to the increase in the force of contraction, also, the ventricle empties more rapidly and completely from a given diastolic volume.

Although in exercise the venous pressure remains constant, there is probably an increase in the "effective filling pressure". This is the difference between the pressures outside and inside the heart—that is between the pressure outside the chest, and the intra-pleural (intra-thoracic) pressure. Since the intra-pleural pressure is decreased owing to the increased respiratory movements, there is probably a corresponding increase in the effective filling pressure.

We must now consider the cause of the increase in venous return. In the resting dog, stimulation of the heart causes a fall in venous pressure and only a small increase in output of the heart. It is therefore clear that in exercise the cause of the increase in venous return is to be sought in the peripheral vascular system. If cardiac output increases six-fold, the peripheral resistance must decrease to about one-sixth of its resting value if the mean arterial pressure is to rise only slightly. The decrease in resistance is mainly in the vessels of the skeletal muscles, and to a lesser extent in those of the skin. If cardiac output increases from 5 to 30 l/min, then the flow through the muscle vessels will increase from 1 to 22 or 23 l/min, and that through the skin vessels will increase from a fraction of a litre per minute to 2 or 3 l/min. The increase in flow through the skin helps to prevent the body temperature from rising. In spite of this enormous decrease in the resistance of the vessels in the muscles and skin of the limbs, there is little or no increase in the limb volume. This is due to the action of the "muscle pump" (Fig. 6.12). When we are at rest, a good deal of blood is contained in the veins of the limbs. In exercise, muscular contraction squeezes these veins and propels the blood towards the heart, the venous valves preventing reflux from the heart. Thus the increase in the amount of blood in the dilated arterioles is more than redressed by the decrease in the amount of blood in the limb veins. Vaso-constriction occurs in the viscera, and the volume of blood within their vessels decreases, with a corresponding increase in the amount of blood in the active circulation, for which accommodation must be found. Owing to the "muscle pump" and to this redistribution of the blood, the central parts of the venous system contain more blood then they do in the resting subject. This tends

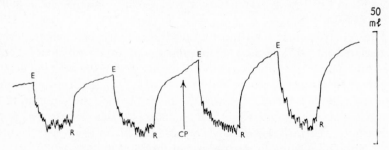

FIG. 6.12. Shrinkage of the Calf of the Leg due to the action of the "Muscle Pump".

Calf volume changes recorded with plethysmograph: downward movement of the record denotes shrinkage. E, rhythmic exercise of calf muscle for 10 sec; R, rest for 10 sec; CP, pneumatic cuff applied just above the knee and inflated to 90 mm Hg; this was maintained to the end of recording. (Barcroft and Dornhorst.)

to raise the venous pressure, and thus to increase venous return to the heart. But the stimulated heart offers less resistance to the entering stream of blood, and this will tend to lower the venous pressure. As a result, there is a large increase in the venous return without any substantial rise in pressure in the neighbourhood of the right auricle.

The following imaginary experiment may help the reader to visualize the part played by the peripheral vascular system in increasing the venous return during exercise. Suppose that the peripheral vascular system of a resting animal is being perfused by a pump. Blood is pumped from the venous side through an oxygenator into the aorta. The output of the pump is regulated by the experimenter in such a way as to keep constant the pressure in the great veins (venous pressure) at the normal resting level. Now suppose that the animal begins severe exercise. Vaso-dilatation begins in the muscles and the arterial pressure falls. The "muscle pump" and the redistribution of blood from the viscera fill up the great veins and the venous pressure rises. The operator, watching the venous pressure, adjusts the pump so as to increase its output and bring back the venous pressure to the normal resting level. Several such adjustments will be necessary, increasing the output and work of the heart, until the redistribution of blood from the viscera is complete and steady conditions are established. Finally, the venous pressure will be constant at the normal resting level, the output and work done by the pump will be increased about six-fold, the mean arterial pressure will be the same as it was initially, or slightly raised, and the peripheral resistance will have fallen to one-sixth of its initial value.

In exercise, the heart, quickened and strengthened, automatically adjusts its output so as to maintain the venous pressure constant.

The Effects of Hypoxia on the Circulation

The effects of oxygen lack (hypoxia) have been studied extensively owing to their importance in flying and space travel. When the oxygen pressure in the inspired air is reduced to one-half, the heart beats much faster (tachycardia) and the cardiac output and systolic pressure are increased. Reduction of the oxygen pressure to one-third of its normal value causes loss of consciousness; in most subjects, the "non-fainters", the circulatory changes just described are accentuated; in the others, the "fainters", vaso-vagal fainting occurs (see below).

The Effects of Haemorrhage

If blood is lost, and the volume in circulation is reduced, it is to be expected that the veins would be less well filled and that the output of the heart and the arterial pressure would fall. This does occur, particularly if the haemorrhage is severe, but the changes are smaller than might be expected owing to the existence of compensating mechanisms. Compensation is absent after section of the spinal cord in the neck and is thus effected through the central nervous system. If, in an anaesthetized dog, the blood flow through the gut, the limbs, the liver and the spleen are simultaneously measured, it is found that when, say, onetenth of the blood volume is removed, the flow through the gut and the limbs is reduced, showing that the vessels constrict in these areas. The arterial pressure does not fall, but is maintained by an increase in peripheral resistance brought about by a reduced activity of the depressor and carotid sinus reflexes. On the other hand, the outflows in the veins from the liver and spleen are found to be temporarily increased and exceed the inflows through the arteries; the blood content of these organs is largely expelled into the great veins, partly compensates for that removed, and lessens the fall in cardiac output. In the rabbit and the cat another compensatory mechanism quickly comes into action; fluid is absorbed from the interstitial spaces through the capillary walls, diluting the blood and partially restoring its volume. In the dog and man dilution of the blood is slower, and in man is not complete until 24 to 72 hr after removing 1 litre of blood. But if the quantity of blood lost is sufficient to reduce the cardiac output to 30 to 50 per cent below normal, the arterial pressure falls. After profuse haemorrhage in man, the fall may be profound enough to produce loss of consciousness through anaemia of the brain; there may be complete recovery, nevertheless.

When the circulation in the anaesthetized dog is so disturbed by bleeding that the mean arterial pressure has fallen to 30 or 40 mm Hg and remained so for six hours, a return of all the blood removed does not lead to a lasting recovery of the circulation (irreversible shock). If, after severe haemorrhage, the irreversible state is to be prevented, prompt measures must be taken to restore the depleted blood volume. This can be most effectively done by transfusing fresh or stored blood from a healthy donor of the same or a compatible blood group. In an emergency, stored plasma or serum may also be used, but in any case the amount transfused must be adequate to restore arterial pressure to normal. Saline is useless for the purpose for, having no colloid osmotic pressure, it quickly passes out into the tissue spaces. It is obviously desirable also, to know the volume of blood in circulation. In most animals, the blood normally makes up from 5 to 8 per cent of the body weight, there being about 3 to 5 litres in an average man, and 500 to 1,500 ml in an average dog of 6 to 20 kg weight.

Peripheral Circulatory Failure and Shock. A condition resembling that seen after frank haemorrhage in which the blood pressure falls, and in which the reduction in cardiac output is to be ascribed not to cardiac weakness but to changes in the vessels or circulating blood volume, is described as peripheral circulatory failure or, more loosely, shock. The following are some of the more important examples.

(1) The vaso-vagal or fainting attack is characterized by low blood pressure, slow pulse, pale cold sweating skin, and sometimes loss of consciousness. The slowing of the heart is effected through the vagus nerves and is abolished by atropine. The fall of blood pressure is due to vaso-dilatation in voluntary muscle effected through the nerves; the blood flow through the skin decreases; the cardiac output may fall. The intense pallor of the skin persists after the arterial pressure has returned to normal, and may be due to the copious secretion of the posterior pituitary which appears to occur during a fainting attack.

(2) Burns. In severe burns there is a rapid and profuse loss of plasma into the burned and adjacent tissues. The blood volume falls and the haemoglobin content of the blood rises, and in severe cases the circulation may fail. Failure is prevented by transfusion of adequate amounts of plasma.

(3) Wound Shock. Circulatory failure frequently occurs after extensive wounds, and sometimes without clear evidence of severe blood loss, in which case it has been attributed to vasodilatation from release of a histamine-like substance. Experience in the war of 1939–45 confirmed that in the war of 1914–18, in showing conclusively that wound shock is not a single entity; but the most important cause of peripheral circulatory failure after wounds is undoubtedly loss of blood, either externally, or into the tissues of the body. In fact the enormous saving of life after wounding in the second war has been due to the provision of proper supplies of

blood for early and adequate transfusion (amounts up to 7 litres have been given before and during operation) and to the use of antibacterial agents.

CHEMICAL REGULATION OF THE CIRCULATION

Adrenaline and Noradrenaline

These two substances are produced by activity of the sympathetic nervous system, are secreted by the adrenal gland, and are released at

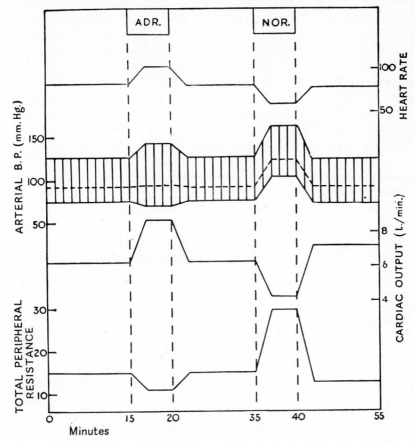

FIG. 6.13. Diagrammatic representation of the effects of intravenous infusions of adrenaline and noradrenaline on the heart rate, arterial blood pressure, cardiac output and total peripheral resistance, in man. The infusions were at the rate of 10 mg/min. (*From* Barcroft and Swan, "Sympathetic Control of Human Blood Vessels". Edward Arnold and Co.)

sympathetic nerve endings in blood vessels and the heart. In the resting human subject, minute amounts of both substances have been detected in the blood. During excitement and exercise, activity of the sympathetic nervous system increases and greater amounts of the sympathomimetic amines circulate in the blood. Their effects on the human circulation may now be briefly described.

When adrenaline is infused intravenously in man at about the rate corresponding to maximum secretion of the substance, the subject goes pale owing to constriction of the cutaneous vessels, and he soon becomes aware of his heart beats (palpitation). Figure 6.13 shows the response of the general circulation. The heart often beats a little faster owing to stimulation of the pacemaker. There is a considerable rise in the systolic pressure, the mean pressure changes little, and there is a slight fall in the diastolic pressure. Cardiac output is increased. Since the output increases relatively much more than the mean blood pressure, it follows that the peripheral resistance must decrease. That is, in physiological doses in man, adrenaline causes an overall peripheral vaso-dilatation. This is because it dilates the splanchnic, skeletal muscular, and coronary vessels more than it constricts those of the skin, kidneys and other organs.

The action of noradrenaline is rather different. The subject pales, but feels no palpitation. Both systolic and diastolic pressures are raised, but, since the cardiac output is decreased, noradrenaline must constrict the peripheral vessels strongly. It is interesting to note that the heart usually beats more slowly (bradycardia); and this is due to the large rise in arterial pressure and strong stimulation of the baroceptors in the aortic arch and carotid sinuses. Reflex vagal inhibition swamps the rather weak direct excitatory effect of noradrenaline on the pacemaker.

In some medical and surgical emergencies, vaso-constrictor tone is markedly reduced and the arterial pressure may fall dangerously. Normal tone may be temporarily, and sometimes permanently, restored by intravenous infusion of noradrenaline. If necessary, infusion can be continued for several hours. When applied in large doses locally, adrenaline causes strong vaso-constriction. For this reason it is often added to local anaesthetic solutions to localize them near the point of injection and so prolong their effect.

Acetylcholine, the transmitter liberated at parasympathetic nerve endings is so efficiently destroyed by cholinesterase that the amount in the general circulation is negligible. When injected in large doses it causes transient arteriolar vaso-dilatation. Vaso-dilator substances such as *histamine* and *adenosine triphosphate* (ATP) occur in the tissues, but only in significant amounts in the general circulation. Large quantities of *post pituitary* extracts (as compared with any likely to be released from the gland) produce in man a slight rise of blood pressure and intense pallor of the skin, due to constriction of the capillaries. There is no evidence that the posterior pituitary takes part in maintaining capillary tone in normal conditions.

Chapter 7

THE CIRCULATION IN VARIOUS ORGANS

The metabolic and functional requirements in various parts of the body are different. In consequence the general features of the haemodynamics, the blood distribution and the circulatory controlling systems differ in detail from one organ to another. For instance, the arterial pressures in the pulmonary circuit are considerably lower than in the systemic arteries because the peripheral resistance is lower and the required flow rate can be achieved with lower pressure gradients. In specialized organs, such as the kidney, other modifications to the normal vascular pattern are found. Before considering these adaptations to function in detail, it will be convenient to discuss briefly the methods available for measurement of blood flow rates through tissues.

Measurement of Blood Flow in the Experimental Animal

As in most physiological measurements, there are two important factors to be considered when assessing the accuracy of the procedure and the significance of any results obtained. First, the errors inherent in the physical measurement itself; second the interference with normal function that is introduced by the process of making the measurement. In *animal experiments*, one of several methods may be used:—

(1) A cannula is tied into the vein draining the organ; the blood is collected for a given period of time and its volume measured.

(2) An instrument for measuring the rate of the blood-flow is interposed between the cut ends of the artery or vein supplying the organ; for example, a rotameter or an electromagnetic flowmeter. The rotameter is essentially a slightly funnel-shaped vertical glass tube containing a float. The height to which the float is lifted by the blood stream is an index of the rate of flow. To express it in absolute units (say ml/min), the instrument must be calibrated. The electromagnetic flowmeter works on the principle that an electromotive force is induced in any conductor (blood for example) which is moving in a magnetic field. The blood passes through a hole in a perspex block which is pierced on each side by the poles of a powerful magnet, and above and below by a pair of electrodes. The E.M.F. developed between the two electrodes increases in direct proportion to the velocity of flow. After amplification, it is recorded by an ink-writing pen-recorder or by a cathode ray oscilloscope and camera. This instrument, also, must

be calibrated, but it has the advantage of responding accurately to very rapid changes of flow.

The bubble flow meter consists of a transparent tube, interposed in the blood stream, into which a bubble of air can be injected and its passage, along a known length of the tube, timed.

The ultrasonic flow meter, used for measurement of pulsatile flow, depends on the physical principle that sound travels faster in a moving column of fluid, when its direction is with the current. A pulse of high frequency sound is timed (electronically) in a downstream and upstream direction and the difference gives a measure of the velocity of the stream.

Two other methods, while they do not actually measure the rate of blood flow, may be used to detect changes in flow, or calibre of the blood vessels:—

(3) The organ may be placed in an airtight box for recording changes in its volume (plethysmograph). These represent changes in the volume of blood in the organ, and may be ascribed to active changes in the calibre of its vessels so long as passive changes due to alterations of the general arterial and venous pressures can be excluded.

(4) In a transparent tissue lying superficially, like the frog's web, or the conjunctiva, or in an organ that can be exposed, the vessels may be observed microscopically and their diameters measured.

Measurement of Blood Flow in Man

In experiments on human subjects, clinical investigations, or in animal experiments when it is not possible to carry out extensive operative interference, an indirect method of flow measurement must be used. These indirect methods for determining blood flow depend on two general techniques. The first is applicable to an organ which either gives off or takes up a substance present in the blood flowing through it. If the concentrations of the substance in the blood going into the organ and coming out of it can both be measured, the volume of blood passing through the organ to carry a given amount of the substance can be easily calculated. The second method is based on the injection, into the blood flowing through a vessel, of a dye which mixes with the blood but does not leave the circulation. If a known amount of the dye is introduced in a given time, the blood passing the injection point during the same time will dilute the dye and this dilution can be measured easily by withdrawing a sample of blood at a point downstream in the vascular system.

The Fick Principle

The two methods for flow rate determination outlined above are applications of the so-called *Fick principle*. The word "principle" is hallowed by text-book tradition and is clearly used because the underlying idea is very simple, being in fact, another way of stating the Law of Conservation of Mass.

If 1 gm of a dye is injected into a blood vessel, say an artery, during the course of 1 min and at some point further along the vessel (mixing having taken place), a sample withdrawn from the vessel is found to have a concentration of the dye of 1 gm/litre, then clearly 1 litre of blood must have passed along the vessel during the 1 min. This can be expressed as an equation for the flow rate, F (in say l/min).

$$F = \frac{\dot{Q}_d}{V_d}$$

Where $\dot{Q}_d$ is the amount of dye injected per minute; and V_d is the concentration of the dye found in the sample withdrawn from the vessel.

This argument can be extended to cover the state of affairs when dye is present in the arterial stream before the point of injection, simply by measuring not only the venous concentration of the dye, V_d as before but the arterio-venous difference in concentration, $(V_d - A_d)$. The Fick equation then becomes

$$F = \frac{\dot{Q}_d}{(V_d - A_d)}$$

To measure the blood flow through the lungs by this technique, a dye need not be used because ready-made substances are present in the blood in the form of oxygen or carbon dioxide. Blood can be easily analyzed for these gases and the amount of them absorbed or given off in unit time can readily be measured. The volume of oxygen added to blood per minute as it passes through the lungs can be measured with a spirometer. The difference in concentration of oxygen can be determined by measurement of samples withdrawn from the arterial side (a systemic artery will do) and from the venous side (this *must* be from the right heart or pulmonary artery). The formula used is

$$F = \frac{\dot{Q}_0}{A_0 - V_0}$$

$\dot{Q}_0$ being the oxygen consumption per minute and $(A_0 - V_0)$ the arterio-venous oxygen difference. Since the blood flow through the lungs is the same as it is through the heart, this technique is widely used in the measurement of cardiac output and we will discuss it later, in the chapter on the heart.

The practical details of the procedure are complicated by the fact that it is necessary to use a sample of *mixed venous blood* in order to arrive at a figure for the concentration of oxygen upstream of the lungs. This follows from the fact that blood samples withdrawn from the peripheral venous system vary considerably in their oxygen concentrations (depending on tissue utilization of oxygen). Mixed venous blood samples are obtained by passing a *cardiac catheter* into the right heart or pulmonary artery from a peripheral vein, commonly the antecubital vein. This is not such a drastic procedure as it sounds, provided skilled operators perform the catheterization although it must be stated that the operation, in common with all other surgery, does carry a mortality rate. The precise location of the tip of the catheter can be localized by means of viewing the patient on the X-ray screen or preferably by making use of the expected pressure changes to be found at different times in the cardiac cycle for various locations within the heart and its vessels.

The arterial sample comes from any convenient systemic artery, since blood composition does not change effectively until tissues are traversed. Oxygen consumption per minute necessitates volume measurement over quite lengthy periods, say 10 to 20 min, in order to obtain the necessary accuracy. It should be obvious from the foregoing account that flow measurements of this kind only represent the overall magnitude of blood flow (or cardiac output) during the course of a long time and must be interpreted accordingly. The *direct Fick* method, as the foregoing description is called, is the standard way of determining the cardiac output in man and is used mainly in clinical cardiological research. It is however, subject to a number of errors, particularly during severe exercise and repeated determinations or comparisons with other methods agree within about 30 per cent of the total flow.

An older and indirect method of estimating the oxygen and carbon dioxide contents of the mixed venous blood depended on the following reasoning. It is clear that if we stop breathing, the gas in the lungs will gradually tend to come into equilibrium with the venous blood, the oxygen content falling and the carbon dioxide content rising. Unfortunately, we cannot measure the composition of the venous blood as simply as this would suggest, because equilibrium takes too long to be established. If this method is to be used at all, the whole operation must be completed in a time less than that taken for any part of the blood to circulate once (about 23 sec at rest); if a longer time is taken, then the composition of the venous blood will be altered, because such blood before traversing the tissues and returning to the lungs will already have been equilibrated with an abnormal gas mixture in the lungs. The difficulty can be overcome in several different ways, the use of *intermittent rebreathing* being one of the best. In principle, the subject breathes in and out of a bag containing air, for about 10 sec or so; the bag is then closed and the subject breathes from the open air for a while, so as to get the composition of the blood back to normal again. He then rebreathes from the bag for a further short period, and so on. During each rebreathing, the composition of the air in the bag approaches that of the mixed venous blood, and eventually reaches it. In practice, the bag is made to contain about 6 per cent carbon dioxide initially, so as to reduce the time required for equilibration.

The Foreign Gas Principle

The necessity for estimating the concentration of the reference substance X in the venous blood is avoided altogether if this substance is foreign to the body, and is removed completely as the blood passes through the tissues. No such substance has yet been discovered, however (except in the special case of the kidney, as will be seen later). But if the whole sequence of procedures can be carried out in less than the circulation time—i.e. before any significant quantity of X has returned to the lungs in the venous blood—the same end is achieved. Although nitrous oxide and ethylene have been used as the foreign gas, acetylene appears to be the most suitable for this method, since it is harmless and easily estimated, diffuses readily through the lungs, and has a convenient and constant solubility in the blood. After emptying the lungs, the subject breathes quickly and deeply four times in and out of a rubber bag containing 2 litres of air and 0·5 litre of pure acetylene, a sample of the air being taken at the end of the last expiration. The lungs are thus filled with a gas mixture containing a known percentage of acetylene. Another sample of the gas is taken after two to six more breaths in and out of the bag, during which time some of the acetylene is carried away in the arterial blood. From the composition of the two samples, and from the total quantity of gases in the lungs and bag, the amount of acetylene absorbed and its average partial pressure in the alveolar air (and thus its concentration in the arterial blood) are determined.

The Hamilton Dye Dilution Method

A known amount of the dye "cardiogreen" is rapidly injected into a vein. During its passage through the pulmonary circulation, it becomes evenly distributed throughout the blood stream. Successive samples of arterial blood are collected, by means of a disc rotating at a known speed, and having attached to its circumference a large number of small tubes which in turn catch the blood flowing from an intra-arterial needle. Suppose, as an ideal simplification, that the dye first appears in the arterial blood at a time t_1 seconds after the intravenous injection, and disappears again at a time t_2 seconds. Then, if CO is the cardiac output in l/sec, the total volume of the blood in which the dye becomes distributed is

$$CO(t_1 - t_2).$$

If the arterial concentration of the dye in the interval between t_1 and t_2 is A_d and $\dot{Q}_d$ gm of dye were injected then

$$A_d = \frac{\dot{Q}_d}{CO(t_1 - t_2)}$$

or

$$CO = \frac{60 \cdot \dot{Q}_d}{A_d(t_1 - t_2)} \; l/min.$$

Actually, the calculation is more complicated than this, since the dye does not appear in the arterial blood and disappear again suddenly, nor is its concentration constant. The successive estimations of A_d must be plotted against time and the mean value of the arterial dye concentration and the best values of t_1 and t_2 determined from the curve. This method has the advantage that the subject is not required to co-operate with the experimenter in carrying out special respiratory procedures.

There are a number of variations on this theme. For instance different dyes such as Evans blue or iodocyanine green are used; or radioactive

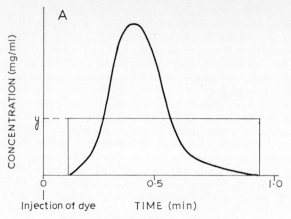

FIG. 7.1. Hamilton Dye Method.

Recording of the concentration of dye in the outflow of an organ. The amount of dye is given by the area under the curve and the time-concentration is the area as measured between two known times and shown as a rectangle. Mean concentration here, would be taken as y mg/ml. (The area under the rectangle = area under curve = $\Sigma V_d \Delta t$. Flow F, is then

$$F = \frac{\dot{Q}_d}{\int_0^\infty (A_d - V_d)\,dt} = \frac{\dot{Q}_d}{\Sigma V_d \Delta t}$$

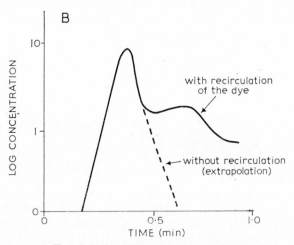

FIG. 7.2. Dye Concentration Curves.

When recirculation of dye occurs, it may do so early in the curve and the extrapolation is difficult. Experiments show that the logarithm of the downslope is linear; thus the curve can be completed, as in Fig. 7.1 and the area measured to give mean dye concentration as before.

tracers such as albumin labelled with ^{131}I, or radioactive red cells can be used. The only requirement is that the indicator is not lost from the circulation in the time required to carry out the measurements, (Fig. 7.1.)

The technical problems in applying this technique concern recirculation and inadequate mixing, of the dye. In the case of measurement of pulmonary flow or cardiac output, the blood travelling via the coronary circulation will return to the arterial side within 15 sec, so the measurements must be complete within this time or allowance must be made for recirculation in the calculation (see Fig. 7.2).

Applications of the Fick Methods of Flow Measurement

Blood from any artery can be used for the estimation of A_d; for that of V_d the blood must come from the venous outflow of the organ under consideration. This principle is used for estimating the rates of blood flow through the human hepatic, renal, cerebral and coronary circulations. If the reference substance is dissolved in the plasma only, the value of F obtained is that of the rate of *plasma* flow; the total blood-flow is obtained by dividing this by the relative volume of the plasma, which may be obtained by means of the haematocrit.

The human *hepatic blood-flow* is estimated by using the dye bromsulphthalein as reference substance; this is excreted by the liver into the bile. The value of $\dot{Q}_d$ is given by the rate of intravenous infusion; A_d is obtained from an arterial blood sample; and V_d from a sample obtained by means of an X-ray opaque non-wettable catheter introduced into an elbow vein and manipulated into the

TABLE 7.1

Approximate Distribution of a Cardiac Output of 5·0 *l/min in a Man at Rest*

	Weight kg	Blood Flow (ml/min)	
		Total	Per 100 g, Tissue
Brain	1·5	750	50
Heart	0·3	150	50
Liver	1·5	1,500	100
Kidneys (2) . . .	0·3	1,200	400
Skeletal muscles . .	25·0	750	3
Other organs . .	40·0	650	1·5

openings of one of the hepatic veins. The results, expressed in ml/min, are given in Table 7.1. Para-aminohippuric acid (PAH), or alternatively diodone, is used for estimating the human *renal blood-flow*. The value of $\dot{Q}_d$ is obtained by estimating the amount excreted in a sample of urine collected during a known time. The value of V_d may be obtained from a sample of renal venous blood obtained by means of a catheter manipulated into one of the renal veins; but this is not usually done, since it is found that if the arterial concentration is not too high, the value of V_d is so small as to be negligible. PAH and diodone are removed from the plasma flowing through the kidney almost to completion; this will be referred to again later.

Table 7.1 shows the normal rate of renal blood-flow. To estimate the *rate of the cerebral circulation,* the subject is made to breathe air containing a small proportion (about 15 per cent) of nitrous oxide. The nitrous oxide accumulates in the brain tissues, and after about ten minutes a state of equilibrium is reached. The total quantity of nitrous oxide taken up by unit mass of brain is then given by the product of the solubility coefficient (discovered in separate, *in vitro,* experiments, or on experimental animals), and the partial pressure of nitrous oxide in the venous blood at the end of, say, the tenth minute. This quantity is equal to $10 \times \dot{Q}/W$, if the determination has lasted exactly ten minutes, where W is the weight of the brain (not, of course, accurately known). The determinations of the arterio-venous concentration difference $(A_{N_2O} - V_{N_2O})$ is more complicated, since initially, when

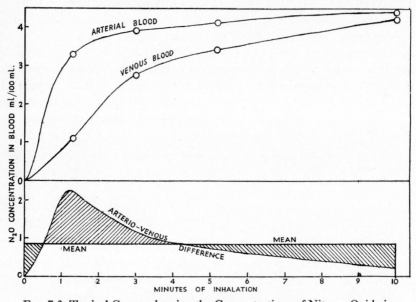

Fig. 7.3. Typical Curves showing the Concentrations of Nitrous Oxide in the Arterial and Jugular Venous Bloods of a man during a ten-minute period of inhalation of 15 per cent nitrous oxide. From curves such as these, the mean value of the arterio-venous concentration difference can be calculated, as is indicated in the lower part of the diagram. (After Kety and Schmidt.)

there is no nitrous oxide in the blood, it is zero, and finally, when equilibrium has been reached, with the tissues, it is again zero. It is necessary, therefore, to find the effective average value during the intervening period. This is best done by plotting the values of $(A_{N_2O}$ and V_{N_2O}, determined every few minutes, against time, as in Fig. 7.3. Any number of values of $(A_{N_2O} - V_{N_2O})$ may be read from the smoothed curves drawn through these points and the arithmetic mean calculated; but in practice, it is sufficient to take the values at the end of each minute. We can now apply the equation of the Fick Principle, but since we can only discover $\dot{Q}/W$, and not $\dot{Q}$, we can only measure F/W—i.e. the rate of blood-flow through unit weight (usually 100 g) of brain tissue. The cerebral venous samples are obtained from a needle placed in the jugular bulb just below the exit of the internal jugular vein from the skull. The insertion of the needle is done under local anaesthesia, and is safe in expert hands. Table 7.1 shows the normal result. The nitrous oxide method has been used occasionally to estimate the human *coronary flow*. The venous blood samples are obtained from a catheter in the coronary sinus.

The Venous Occlusion Plethysmograph

Part of an extremity is enclosed in a plethysmograph (Fig. 7.4) which is a rigid watertight case. Any change in the volume of blood in the part enclosed is transmitted to a sensitive volume recorder. The blood-flow is measured by recording the rate of increase of volume during temporary occlusion of the venous drainage. This is done by throwing a pressure of about 60 mm Hg into a pneumatic cuff surrounding the limb just above the plethysmograph.

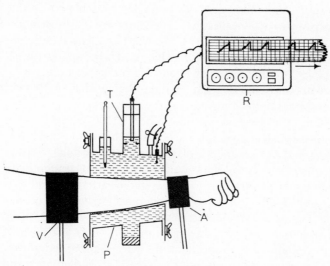

FIG. 7.4. Determination of the Rate of Blood-flow in the Human Forearm by Venous Occlusion Plethysmography.

The plethysmograph (P) is filled with water maintained at a temperature of 34–35°C. To record the blood-flow, a pressure of 200 mm Hg is thrown into the lower cuff (A) to arrest the circulation in the hand. A minute later a pressure of 60 mm Hg is thrown into the venous occlusion cuff (V). The arterial inflow is recorded on moving paper. After the experiment, the pen-recorder (R) is calibrated, the speed of the paper is ascertained, and the forearm volume found by water displacement. From the slope of the inflow tracing, the rate of the blood-flow is calculated and expressed in ml per minute for each 100 ml of forearm.

The volume is recorded as a change in the electrical resistance between the water in the plethysmograph and a carbon rod partly immersed in the side-arm. The output of this transducer system (T) is amplified and recorded by a hot wire writing on heat sensitive paper.

Measurement of Changes in Blood Flow by Calorimetry

The finger or hand or foot may be placed in stirred water in a calorimeter; the rate of heat elimination is proportional to the rate of blood flow.

THE PULMONARY CIRCULATION

The whole output of the right ventricle is delivered into the pulmonary artery at a pressure of 15 to 20 mm Hg. The blood-flow through the lungs is the same as the outflow through the aorta, i.e. at rest about 4 l/min; in exercise it may rise to 30 l/min or more. The resistance offered by the pulmonary vessels appears to be low. Since there is no alternative route for the blood between the right and left sides of the heart, it is not surprising that the vaso-motor supply is unimportant.

The chief factor modifying the pulmonary circulation is the pressure change accompanying respiration. The lungs are elastic structures which are kept open by the chest wall; if the chest is opened the lungs collapse. In consequence of this pull of the lungs, if a needle is thrust into the pleural cavity of man and connected to a manometer, this will normally register a pressure about 4 cm of water below that of the atmosphere. During inspiration the lungs are further stretched and the intrapleural pressure falls by as much as 20 cm of water. These negative pressures affect all intra-thoracic structures but particularly the pulmonary capillaries, the great veins and the chambers of the heart in diastole, whose walls are yielding; the effect on the thick-walled arteries is of less consequence.

The effects of respiration on the systemic arterial blood pressure are complex and variable. In man during quiet respiration of the thoracic type (i.e. mainly by the intercostal muscles) the blood pressure falls during inspiration and rises during expiration. This effect which is usual in man is probably due to mechanical changes in the pulmonary vessels; when the lungs expand the pulmonary vessels are pulled open and fill with blood, and diversion of this extra blood from its onward movement leads to a reduced flow into, and output from, the left ventricle. Occasionally in man when the breathing is abdominal in type (i.e. mainly by the diaphragm), the blood pressure rises during inspiration and falls during expiration.

During inspiration blood is aspirated into the great veins and heart from extra-thoracic structures, and the rise of intra-abdominal pressure produced by descent of the diaphragm forces blood from the abdomen into the chest; in this way the filling and output of the heart would be increased during inspiration. X-ray photography, after intravenous injection of an opaque substance, shows that during inspiration the flow through the superior vena cava is increased, but in the dog, cat and rabbit the inferior vena cava is constricted by contraction of the diaphragm; in these animals at least it is unlikely, therefore, that the flow through the inferior vena cava is increased during inspiration.

The pulse is accelerated during inspiration and slowed during expiration—a reflex effect which is abolished by section of the vagi.

Regulation of Pulmonary Circulation

The pulmonary arterial pressure does not vary a great deal in spite of the large changes in blood flow through the lungs, a fact indicating that the pulmonary vascular resistance decreases in inverse proportion to the blood flow. This change in the vascular bed consists of a passive dilatation of the arterioles and capillaries.

It should be noted that the regulation of the pulmonary vascular resistance is very largely passive in character and the sympathetic innervation plays only a small part.

Pulmonary vascular resistance is increased by breathing gas mixtures which stimulate respiration (e.g. low oxygen or high carbon dioxide contents)—an effect said to be separable from the increase in cardiac output and arterial pressure which also results. Local effects of this nature occur in the lung's circulation and one may look upon it as a compensatory mechanism which controls gas exchange in different parts of the lung. An underventilated alveolus, having in consequence a low Po_2 and a high Pco_2 will have in its local circulation a high peripheral resistance. Hence, the local blood flow will be small and gas exchange across the pulmonary capillary membrane will proceed at a slow rate. It can be seen that this is a self-regulating homeostatic mechanism, to ensure even gas exchange throughout the lung. It is of considerable importance in pathological conditions affecting alveolar membranes, or giving rise to arterio-venous shunts in the lung.

The pulmonary venous pressure is about 5 mm Hg. It depends almost entirely upon the left atrial pressure and in failure of the left side of the heart the venous pressure is raised, and in turn, with it, the capillary pressure. This leads to fluid exudation and pulmonary oedema.

Pulmonary capillary pressure is of extreme importance in normal lung function. In the systemic circulation, capillary pressure is around a mean of 30 mm Hg and as we have already seen, the arterial end having a slightly higher value than this acts as a site of formation of tissue fluid. In the lung the formation of tissue fluid must be prevented. In fact, the low capillary pressure 10 to 7 mm Hg is well below the colloid osmotic pressure of 25 to 30 mm Hg in the plasma, so tissue fluid formation is minimal. Until the capillary pressure rises to several times its normal level, pulmonary oedema will not occur.

THE CEREBRAL CIRCULATION

While the cerebral vessels are to some extent influenced by vaso-dilator metabolites during cerebral activity, they are little affected by vaso-motor impulses; persistent inquiry failed to reveal any vaso-motor supply, until it was shown that stimulation of the cat's cervical sympathetic produced a slight narrowing of the pial arteries observed through a glass window screwed into the skull. The cerebral blood-flow is thus determined in the main by the height of the arterial blood pressure, and it is rather surprising that this should be regulated exclusively by receptors lying outside the brain, in the corotid sinus and arch of the aorta. For if these receptors are excluded, then alterations in blood-flow to the brain lead to no reflex changes altering the height of the arterial pressure, unless the cerebral blood-flow is so reduced that it produces asphyxia of the vaso-motor centre. Table 7.1 gives some data about the cerebral circulation in man.

The importance and significance of the reflexes controlling blood pressure is now evident, for the brain is the master organ of the body and is extremely sensitive to reduction of its blood supply; if the blood-flow to the brain ceases for five seconds consciousness is lost and after twenty seconds epileptic twitching begins. By means of the carotid sinus and depressor reflexes the arterial blood pressure, and thus the cerebral blood-flow are maintained by appropriate regulation of the rate and force of the heart-beat and of the blood-flow through organs other than the brain.

The normal cerebral flow is about 50 ml/100 gm of brain tissue per minute; this represents about 750 ml/min or about one fifth of the cardiac output.

Control of Cerebral Blood Flow

If the Pco_2 of carotid blood rises the brain undergoes vasodilatation (e.g. doubling the Pco_2 doubles the flow rate). A similar but less marked effect occurs when the Po_2 falls. This is another local autoregulation system as we have described in the blood vessels of the lung previously. The physiological value of a system such as this is fairly obvious; at high values of Pco_2, cortical neurones (and indeed all brain nerve-cells), become relatively inexcitable. A high local blood flow will wash out excess carbon dioxide.

The overall metabolic rate of the brain alters little; deep sleep, intense mental activity or the motor output occurring during exercise, do not give rise to measurable changes in metabolism or blood flow in any part of the brain. On the other hand the flow in localized areas of brain alters very rapidly and concomitant with local neuronal activity. The experimental evidence for this is that the surface blood flow in vessels on the pia mater can be observed directly under the microscope and correlated, say, with siezure activity in the cells beneath. Also, measurements can be made electrometrically using gold, or gold-plated wires inserted into the brain substance, in order to find the oxygen tension. At the same time, local neuronal firing can be recorded and it has been demonstrated that a period of intense local activity can raise the blood flow in the neighbourhood by as much as 50 per cent. Gold wires used in this type of experiment have been inserted into human patients for the determination of oxygen tensions in the brain in various forms of mental disease and it has been found that the oxygen tension tends to show a cyclic variation about a mean level with a period of about $\frac{1}{2}$–1 sec.

It must be emphasized, however, that the *mean* cerebral blood flow is remarkably constant in spite of local changes. In the face of an alteration in the carotid systolic pressure of from 50 to 200 mm Hg cerebral blood flow does not alter. Pressures have to fall below about 50 mm Hg before the brain becomes relatively ischaemic.

Two types of *cerebral vascular accident* occur, particularly in patients having raised arterial pressure. About three-quarters of these are haemorrhages, which destroy the surrounding brain tissue; the remainder are arterial occlusions (cerebral thromboses). In either case paralysis, blindness and dementia may occur, the nature of the illness depending upon the site of the lesion.

THE CORONARY CIRCULATION

The heart muscle in mammals is supplied with blood from two coronary arteries arising from the aorta just beyond the semilunar (aortic) valves. The blood is returned to the right auricle by a number of openings of which by far the largest is the coronary sinus. The rate of the coronary blood-flow in an experimental animal may be measured by inserting a cannula into the coronary sinus; the blood issuing represents, in the dog, three-fifths of the total flow through the whole coronary system.

The rate of flow in the coronary circulation has been measured in the human subject at rest and is about 150 ml/min. It is not possible to measure it during severe exercise; but to supply the heart with enough oxygen to produce the energy needed for a cardiac output of 30 l/min, the coronary flow would have to be nearly 1 l/min. Since the arterial blood pressure in severe exercise increases from 120/70 only to, say, 180/70, the six-fold increase in coronary flow cannot be due to an increased perfusion pressure. It is probably due to the vaso-dilator action of metabolites produced by the heart muscle during a condition of lowered oxygen pressure. The effect of lowered oxygen partial pressure is illustrated in Fig. 7.5. When, in the heart-lung preparation, the lungs were ventilated for a short time with nitrogen, the coronary blood-flow increased about 10 times. The condition is not quite the same in exercise because the arterial blood is almost fully saturated with oxygen. Nevertheless the enormous increase in rate of oxygen usage by the heart must, at least temporarily, lower the oxygen saturation of the venous blood and the oxygen pressure of the tissue fluid bathing the plain muscle of the arterioles. This may relax them directly; or they may be relaxed by vaso-dilator metabolites diffusing in from the heart muscle.

The autonomic nervous control of the coronary vessels is probably weak and its action easily swamped by the effects of local deficiency of oxygen. Stimulation of the sympathetic causes vaso-dilatation, and stimulation of the vagus causes vaso-constriction; but these effects may be due to concomitant alterations in heart metabolism. In the fibrillating heart, which no longer beats, the opposite effects are obtained during nerve stimulation. Probably, therefore, the sympathetic has a constrictor action, and the vagus a dilator one.

For a short time at the beginning of systole, contraction of the heart muscle arrests the coronary circulation. Studies of the rate of inflow into

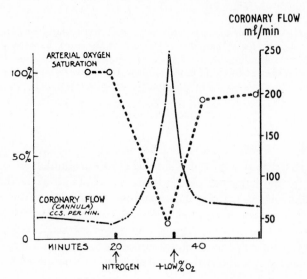

Fig. 7.5. The Relation between Coronary Blood Flow and Oxygen Saturation of the Arterial Blood.

Observations on a heart-lung preparation. Between the first and second arrows the lungs were ventilated with pure nitrogen, and from the second arrow onwards with nitrogen to which a little air had been added. The coronary flow varies inversely with the oxygen saturation of the blood. (Hilton and Eichholtz.)

one of the coronary arteries show that the flow is intermittent—most rapid in diastole, and stopped during the isometric contraction phase of the cardiac cycle, the coronary branches being compressed and occluded between the tightly contracting muscle strands. In this respect, cardiac muscle resembles skeletal muscle, in which, too, the flow is arrested during strong contraction.

Certain hormones influence coronary blood flow. Adrenaline (and nor-adrenaline with weaker action) dilate the coronaries. Acetylcholine also dilates the coronary vessels. 5-hydroxytryptamine is a powerful vaso-dilator of the coronary vessels.

A number of drugs are used to increase coronary flow in coronary heart disease.

Commonly employed is nitroglycerin which acts both on the coronaries to dilate them, thus improving the blood supply to the heart muscle and on the peripheral circulation as well by lowering peripheral resistance and hence the work load of cardiac muscle.

Coronary Occlusion and Angina Pectoris

The function of the heart, like that of every organ, is intimately dependent on its blood supply and the arrangements that we have discussed are such that in health, increased work of the heart is accompanied by increased blood-flow. If a coronary artery is suddenly blocked by a clot, then the patient may die at once from ventricular fibrillation or after some hours from congestive heart failure; in a large number of cases, particularly if the area deprived of its blood supply is small, the remaining healthy heart muscle is adequate to maintain the circulation at rest, the bloodless area is slowly converted into fibrous tissue and the patient recovers. Such small coronary occlusions are accompanied by intense substernal pain, probably due to the stimulation of sensory nerves in the heart itself by chemical substances released locally from the ischaemic muscle. If the coronary arteries are thickened and narrowed by disease, they are incapable of dilatation, and the circulation becomes inadequate to the demands of muscular work. In this condition substernal pain (angina pectoris) is produced on exercise, probably again by the release of metabolites from the inadequately oxygenated heart muscle. A somewhat similar pain known as intermittent claudication is experienced in the muscles of the legs on walking, when the arteries are narrowed or blocked by disease. The student may reproduce this pain by working the muscles of his forearm, after the circulation has been arrested by inflating a cuff on the upper arm to above systolic pressure. He may ascertain that the rate at which pain develops depends on the frequency and the force of the muscular contractions. On stopping work the pain remains present until the circulation is restored, when it quickly disappears. The pain thus seems to be due to stimulation of the nerve endings in the muscles by a substance released during muscular contraction, and normally removed by the circulating blood.

THE CIRCULATION IN SKELETAL MUSCLES

The Effect of Exercise

The changes in muscle blood-flow during exercise are of particular interest and are the outcome of two opposing factors—vaso-dilatation and mechanical compression of the vessels. In weak sustained contractions, the blood-flow increases; but when the contraction is strong, as is that of the human gastrocnemius and soleus muscles, for example, when a person is standing tiptoe on one leg, the circulation in the muscle is almost arrested by the pressure of the taut tissue. It is not surprising that such contractions can only be kept up for three or four minutes. In rhythmic exercise, the muscle vessels dilate, but the pattern of flow depends upon the kind of movement. Blood-flow is continuous if the contractions are weak, but intermittent if they are strong.

During exercise, muscle blood-flow may rise ten-fold (Fig. 7.6). The multilayered arterioles, the site of the main resistance, are widely dilated and the number of open capillaries increases many times, as do their diameters. Capillary surface area in the human gastrocnemius and soleus muscles may increase from the size of a handkerchief to that of a sheet.

As Fig. 7.6 shows, this vaso-dilatation occurs in sympathectomized subjects, and is due to a local factor. In exercise, it is probable that the greatly increased rate of oxygen usage leads to a reduction in the oxygen pressure in the neighbourhood of the arterioles. Like the coronary vessels,

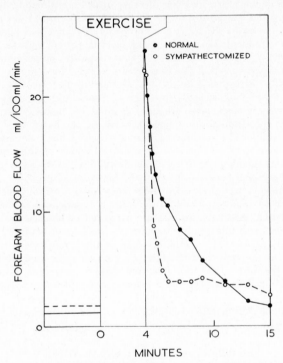

FIG. 7.6. Results showing that exercise causes vasodilatation in human muscles; the vasodilatation occurs in sympathectomized muscle and is due to the action of vasodilator metabolites. Venous occlusion plethysmography. The exercise was gripping a bar tightly in each hand for forty seconds.

the muscle vessels will be relaxed, either directly by the lack of oxygen or by vaso-dilator metabolites from the muscle fibres, perhaps for example, by adenosine triphosphate (ATP) or adenosine diphosphate (ADP). It is unlikely that alteration in the local acidity (pH), or in the local carbon dioxide or lactate concentration, is adequate to account for the vaso-dilatation. Thus the dominant feature of the control of the vessels supplying skeletal muscles, like that of the vessels supplying the heart, is a local control of the circulation in accordance with metabolic requirements.

Myogenic Tone

The vaso-motor centre and sympathetic vaso-constrictor nerves maintain in resting skeletal muscle a small amount of constrictor tone. A change from the recumbent to the upright position brings reflexes into play to prevent fall in arterial blood pressure, and the vaso-motor centre constricts the vessels in skeletal muscles. Reflex vaso-constriction also occurs during haemorrhage. In the common faint (vaso-vagal syndrome) the fall in arterial blood pressure is due to vaso-dilatation in the skeletal muscles, mediated by the sympathetic, and unaccompanied by compensating vaso-constriction elsewhere. In exercise, the effect of the vaso-motor centre on skeletal muscle vessels is of little significance and easily swamped by the local vaso-dilator mechanism.

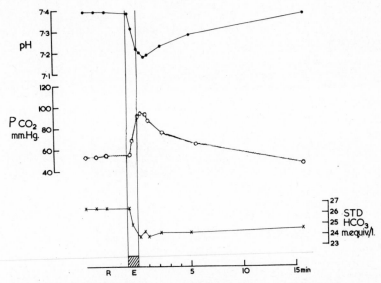

FIG. 7.7. pH, P_{CO_2} and standard bicarbonate in the venous blood draining the forearm muscles, before, R, during and after 1 min strong hand grip, E. (Barcroft, Greenwood and Rutt.)

Observations on a policeman, aged 23, on whom bilateral lumbar sympathectomy was performed in order to prevent excessive sweating of the feet also proved that relaxation of myogenic tone in the skeletal muscles is predominently due to the action of metabolites released by the active muscle. On the day before the operation he ran 380 yd in 65 and 61 sec respectively; on the 99th day after the operation, he again ran the same distance twice in 60 and $62\frac{1}{2}$ sec. His time was not affected by sympathetic denervation of his leg muscles.

When the amount of adrenaline in the general circulation increases, the muscle vessels dilate; but they constrict when adrenaline is applied to them

directly. That is to say, intravenous and intra-arterial infusions of adrenaline in man have opposite effects on the muscle circulation. The reason is
not yet known.

Although there is decrease in pH, and an increase in Pco_2 and lactate in
the venous effluent from active muscle (Fig. 7.7) it is unlikely that any or
all of these bring about the loss of mygenic tone.

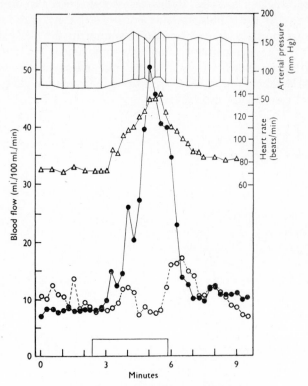

FIG. 7.8. Emotion and Muscle Blood flow.

The effect of severe emotional stress (at time of rectangle) is to
produce a fivefold increase in forearm blood flow (●). There is little
change in hand flow (○). The effects on arterial pressure and heart
rate are also shown. (Blair, Glover, Greenfield and Roddie.)

Occlusion of the blood flow to a muscle is followed by reactive hyperaemia (vaso-dilatation). The degree of hyperaemia depends directly on the
duration and also whether it has been induced by arterial occlusion or
venous occlusion. In the latter case the reactive hyperaemia is much less.
This is thought to be due to the fact that myogenic relaxation occurs only
when the arterial inflow is restricted and the tension of the smooth muscle
fibres in the vessel walls is reduced thereby. In venous occlusion, on the
other hand, the pressure in the vessels is higher than usual and the smooth

muscle reacts by contracting—an effect which tends to counteract the dilator response to low Po_2 and accumulated metabolites.

Emotional Factors and Muscle Blood Flow

Sympathetic vaso-constriction also occurs in exercise in muscles that are not active. In fright, excitement and emotional stress muscle blood flow is increased in all skeletal muscles. Forearm blood flow is increased (Fig. 7.8); there is no change in the arterio-venous oxygen difference in blood taken from a superficial vein draining the skin, nor in blood taken from a deep vein draining the forearm muscles. However, A.V. oxygen difference is greatly diminished, signifying increase in muscle blood flow. This is mediated by sympathetic cholinergic vasodilator fibres and by an increase in the amount of circulating adrenaline. In the common faint (vaso-vagal syndrome) the fall in arterial pressure is due to vaso-dilatation in the skeletal muscles, mediated by the sympathetic, unaccompanied by compensatory increase in cardiac output or vaso-constriction elsewhere.

Control of Muscle Blood Flow

The blood flow through resting muscle varies from 1 to 10 ml/100 gm/min. The hyperaemia of exercise together with the increase in cardiac output may raise this figure to 50 ml/100 gm/min.

Control of muscle blood flow, as already outlined in the previous two sections, is brought about by chemical, hormonal and nervous mechanisms.

Chemical factors are mainly the accumulation of metabolites and lowered Po_2, which dilates muscle vessels and increases flow. Hormones involved are adrenaline and nor-adrenaline (Table 7.2) while nervous control is mediated via the sympathetic innervation.

TABLE 7.2

The Control of Blood Vessels in Muscle

	Vasoconstriction	*Vasodilatation*
Local factors		Metabolites
		(? vasodilator specific substance)
		A.T.P. A.D.P.
Nervous	Sympathetic constrictor fibres	Sympathetic vasodilator fibres
Hormonal	Nor-adrenaline	Adrenaline
		Acetyl-choline

Many influences control muscle blood vessels. Observe that the sympathetic nervous innervation can be either constrictor or dilator.

Figure 7.9 shows the effect of an infusion of adrenaline on the forearm blood flow. There is an initial transient fivefold increase followed by a return to about double the resting value for the duration of the infusion. These changes are to a very large extent in the skeletal muscles. First stimulation of the β-receptors relaxes the muscle vessels and this is very soon followed by stimulation of the α-receptors and contraction, enough to reduce the flow to double its resting value. The blood vessels of the hand have no β-receptors, adrenaline causes simple constriction.

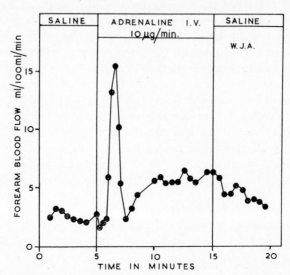

Fig. 7.9. The effect of an intravenous infusion of adrenaline on forearm blood flow. The changes are for the most part in the muscle vessels. The result of stimulation of the β-receptors, marked vaso-dilatation, is soon reversed by vasoconstriction due to stimulation of the α-receptors.

The Circulation in Other Regions

The Salivary Glands

Stimulation of the parasympathetic nerve to the submandibular gland causes secretion and marked vaso-dilatation. Activity of the salivary secreting cells is accompanied by the release from them of a proteolytic enzyme, and in the presence of this enzyme, tissue fluid protein is hydro-lyzed, forming a polypeptide known as *bradykinin*. This substance is a potent vaso-dilator, and its action on the neighbouring vessels increases submandibular blood flow in accordance with the metabolic requirement. It is probable that local vasodilator mechanisms are brought into action during the secretion of all other digestive glands, but this is not known for certain.

The Liver and Portal System

The blood-flow through the liver is very large; about half the blood-flow through the inferior vena cava comes from this source. After leaving the intestinal capillaries the blood gathered into the portal vein traverses a second set of capillaries in the liver. Since the portal pressure in the dog is only about 8 cm water the resistance offered by the liver vessels must be very small. The liver is also supplied by the hepatic artery, which contributes about a quarter of the blood and 40 per cent of the oxygen supplied to the organ. The liver, the portal vein and the territory it drains ordinarily accommodate about one-third, or more, of the total blood volume. Experiment suggests that a large proportion of this is expelled in the early stages of haemorrhage. After the injection of adrenaline or stimulation of the sympathetic nerves the outflow from the liver exceeds its inflow, a large part of its blood being thus discharged into the great veins. It is likely, therefore, that the liver and portal system constitute a variable reservoir, whence blood is discharged to augment the inflow and output of the heart in conditions such as haemorrhage, emotion and exercise.

A piece of dog's colon, transferred to the outer abdominal wall with its nerve and blood supply intact, blanches at the beginning of exercise, though, as exercise is continued, it slowly fills again with blood. This presumably illustrates what happens to the vessels of the whole gut in exercise.

The Spleen

The branches of the splenic artery open into venous sinuses, which unite to form the splenic vein. Along the course of the artery and vein are perforations communicating with the spleen pulp, which contains red and white blood corpuscles in its network. In the dog the spleen has been brought to the exterior through an incision on the abdominal wall and left there for many months. Its size at rest indicates that it may hold one-fifth of the total blood volume. During haemorrhage, emotion, asphyxia and muscular exercise the muscular capsule of the spleen contracts, and its blood content, which is exceptionally rich in red cells, is expelled into the general circulation. The reservoir function of the spleen appears to be less important in man.

The Skin

Heat is lost from the skin by conduction, radiation and evaporation. The rate of heat loss is regulated by the temperature regulating centre acting through the sympathetic nerves to the cutaneous blood vessels and sweat glands. According to the manner of this regulation, the skin of the body can be divided into two areas. Thus the skin of the hands, feet, nose, lips and ears has to be considered separately from that of the forehead, trunk and limbs as far as the wrists and ankles.

When the room temperature is below about 20°C (68°F), the vessels in the hands, feet, lips and ears of an ordinarily clothed man are constricted—strongly so if the temperature is below about 16°C (about 60°F). The effect of a rise of environmental temperature on the blood-flow through the skin of the hand is shown in Fig. 7.10. This flushing of the hand is chiefly due to a release of the vaso-constrictor tone brought about by sympathetic nerves, because blocking the nerve supply by local anaesthesia causes a similar increase in flow. The chief factor in the regulation of the skin blood-flow in accordance with changes in the environmental temperature is a central mechanism which responds to a rise in blood temperature by reduction of sympathetic tone, and *vice versa*. In this connection an important part is played by the arterio-venous communications, short wide connections between the arterioles and venules, which

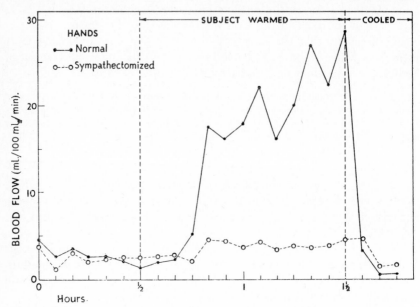

FIG. 7.10. Results showing that warming the body causes vasodilatation in the hand; this does not occur in the sympathectomized hand. It is mainly, if not entirely, due to the release from sympathetic constrictor tone. Venous occlusion plethysmography. The body was warmed by covering the subject with blankets and immersing the feet in water at 44°C; and cooled by removing the blankets and immersing the feet in water at 17°C. (Barcroft.)

are very abundant in man in the nail beds, the skin covering the volar surfaces of the fingers and palm of the hand and in the corresponding sites of the foot. The changes in blood-flow through the fingers which may occur in response to changes in body temperature are very large, ranging from 1 ml/min through each 100 ml of finger when the body is cool, to 100 ml/min when the body is hot.

The skin of the forehead, trunk and proximal parts of the limbs has very little, if any, sympathetic vaso-motor innervation. Nevertheless, in a very warm subject marked vaso-dilatation occurs, though without much flushing because the vessels lie too deeply. This vaso-dilatation accompanies sweating. It is due to the vaso-dilator action of bradykinin, formed during sweat gland activity. It will be recalled that the vaso-dilatation which accompanies salivary secretion is also due to the formation of bradykinin.

The colour and temperature of the hand and face are closely related to the state of the skin circulation. The hot pale hand, common in summer, is one in which blood flows rapidly through the deeply situated invisible arterio-venous anastomoses in the fingers and palms. The superficial capillaries whose contents give colour to the skin are narrow and poorly filled. The cold red hand seen in winter is one in which the arterio-venous anastomoses and arterioles are narrow and the capillaries dilated. The blood remains red, since little oxygen is removed by the cold tissues. The cold blue hand is one in which the arterial vessels are still further constricted, and the flow becomes so slow that an appreciable fraction of the oxygen content of the blood is removed even by the slowly metabolizing tissues.

Although the vaso-motor and temperature regulating centres predominate in the regulation of the skin circulation—directly through vaso-motor nerves or indirectly through local vaso-dilator substances—there are some other responses which must be briefly described.

(1) *Reactive Hyperaemia*. This important response was first seen in the arm and leg. If the circulation to a warm limb is arrested for a few minutes and then released, a bright flush, reactive hyperaemia, at once suffuses the skin and then slowly fades. After circulatory arrest lasting ten minutes the blood-flow to the forearm may be increased to ten or twenty times the normal; both muscle and skin vessels share in this vaso-dilatation. The intensity and duration of reactive hyperaemia depend on the duration of circulatory arrest and on the temperature of the limb. The flush represents a dilatation of the minute vessels; it is independent of any central or local nervous mechanism and is due to the action of vaso-dilator substances formed locally and normally removed by the circulating blood. When, as is constantly happening, areas of skin and of subcutaneous tissue are rendered bloodless by supporting the weight of the body, they may be said to accumulate a blood-flow debt; reactive hyperaemia ensures the discharge of this debt as soon as blood is free to enter the tissues again.

(2) *The White Reaction*. This is chiefly of interest as the basis of an experiment performed by Lewis to show that human capillaries can contract actively. If the skin of the forearm or back is lightly stroked with the end of a ruler, the line of the stroke becomes marked by pallor. This is due to narrowing of the minute vessels (capillaries and venules), for these are the only vessels which come near enough to the surface of the skin for blood within them to be visible. Narrowing of the capillaries in this white reaction might be due to (*a*) constriction of the deeper arterioles and passive collapse of the more distal capillaries; or to (*b*) active contraction of the capillary walls. Lewis showed that the white reaction can be induced

in the forearm skin after the circulation in the arm has been arrested. In this case, the pallor cannot be due to constriction of the underlying arterioles, for this would, if anything, tend to increase capillary pressure; therefore the capillary walls themselves must contract.

(3) *Triple Response.* If the skin is injured by scratching, by lightly burning, by freezing or by pricking in injurious substances such as hydrochloric acid or caustic soda, the point of injury is marked by reddening of the skin, which later gives place to whealing as fluid passes out of the capillaries and distends the tissue spaces of the skin. Around the local reddening is a diffuse red mottled flush or "flare", which is due to the

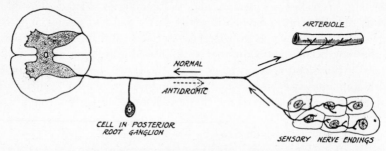

FIG. 7.11. Diagram of the Nervous Connections concerned in the Axon Reflex.

opening of the surrounding arterioles. The local redness due to widening of the minute vessels (capillaries and venules), the wheal due to their increased permeability, and the flare are the components of the triple response of the vessels to injury. The whole response is independent of the central nervous system, being unchanged immediately after section of all nerves to the skin. After all the nerves have degenerated, however, the flare is absent; if the sympathetic supply alone has degenerated the flare is unimpaired. The flare is an example of a local axon reflex through the sensory fibres. The fibres entering the posterior roots of the cord divide at their periphery into branches to the blood vessels and to the tissues. Injury to the skin stimulates the sensory branches, and the stimulus passes proximally to the point of bifurcation and back down the other branch to the arterioles (see Fig. 7.11). The whole of the triple response has been shown to be due to the release of a chemical substance from the injured skin, and this, from its resemblance to histamine, has been termed "H substance". The triple response is, in the skin, the vascular basis of the phenomenon of inflammation.

Section 3
THE HEART

Chapter 8

THE MECHANICAL AND ELECTRICAL EVENTS IN CARDIAC ACTION

Structure of the Heart

The heart is divided longitudinally into the right and left hearts, each consisting of two communicating chambers, the atrium (or auricle) and ventricle. The capacity of each ventricle when fully relaxed is about 140 to 200 ml in man. The heart wall consists essentially of muscle (the myocardium), which has an inner covering (the endocardium), lined by endothelium, and an outer covering (the epicardium or visceral layer of the pericardium). Covering the heart is a fibrous sac, the pericardium, which at its attachment to the great vessels is reflected over the outer surface of the heart, thus leaving between its outer or parietal layer and its inner or visceral layer a potential space, the pericardial cavity. The pericardium is attached to the surrounding structures, and thus partially fixes the heart while it allows it such freedom of movement as is essential for its contraction.

The heart muscle consists of quadrilateral cells, which are joined longitudinally to form fibres and anastomose with neighbouring cells by short bridges. It is an arrangement in which the cells communicate with one another and is termed a syncytium. The properties which these muscle cells possess in common with other contractile tissues will be dealt with in the chapter on Muscle. Over the auricles the muscular wall is relatively thin, over the ventricles relatively thick; the wall of the left ventricle is four times as thick as that of the right. The thickness of the muscular wall of each chamber thus corresponds to the tension developed during its contraction. The muscle fibres of the right auricle are continuous with those of the left, those of the right ventricle are continuous with those of the left ventricle. The muscle fibres of the auricles, however, are separated from those of the ventricles by a fibro-tendinous ring, the auriculo-ventricular ring. The heart muscle is modified to form two important structures. (Fig. 8.1). The first or *sino-auricular node* lies close to the junction of the superior vena cava with the right auricle and is about 2 cm long and 2 mm wide in man. It consists of a plexus of fine muscle fibres embedded in fibrous tissue. The second is the *auriculo-ventricular connection*, which forms the only functional junction between the muscular tissues of the auricles and the ventricles. This begins at the base of the inter-auricular septum close to the mouth of the coronary sinus as the auriculo-ventricular node, composed of slender interlacing muscle fibres. Continuous with the auriculo-ven-

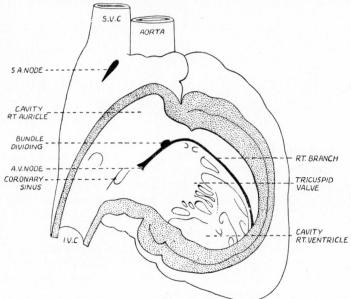

FIG. 8.1. A diagram of the human heart to show the Sino-auricular Node (S.A. node), the Auriculo-ventricular Node (A.V. node) and Bundle of His. The walls of the inferior vena cava, right auricle and right ventricle have been partially removed to expose the septa. The cut surfaces are stippled.

tricular node is the auriculo-ventricular bundle (of His), which runs across the fibrous ring between auricles and ventricles and enters the inter-ventricular septum, where it divides into right and left branches distributed to the appropriate ventricles. Each branch is continuous with a network of large, poorly striated cells, rich in glycogen, the Purkinje tissue, which forms a plexus under the endocardium of each ventricle.

The cavity of each auricle is separated from that of the corresponding ventricle by an auriculo-ventricular valve, a fibrous membrane covered with endocardium and arising from the auriculo-ventricular ring. On the right side the valve is divided into three flaps (tricuspid), on the left into two (mitral). To the ventricular aspects of the margins of these valves are attached tendinous chords (chordae tendineae), which terminate in nipple-like projections of the ventricular muscle (papillary muscles). These valves are so arranged that when blood flows from auricle to ventricle the valves lie flat against the ventricular wall. When the ventricular pressure rises above the auricular pressure the valves are floated out by eddies and seal the auriculo-ventricular openings; the chordae tendineae, aided by the contraction of the papillary muscles, prevent the valves from being thrust out into the auricular cavity. The openings of the right ventricle into the pulmonary artery and of the left ventricle into the aorta are each guarded by semilunar valves, consisting of three semi-circular pockets whose cavities face away from the ventricles. The openings of the caval veins into the right, and of the pulmonary veins into the left auricle are unguarded; they are, however, sealed at the beginning of auricular systole by the contraction of the auricular muscle fibres surrounding them.

THE CARDIAC CYCLE

The series of mechanical events, pressure changes, valve actions and electrical potentials which occur during one complete heart beat are collectively termed the *cardiac cycle*. It should be emphasized that the cardiac cycle is merely a convenient and logical descriptive system devised for the study of the heart's action.

The contraction of the heart can be seen in man by means of X-rays, and in experimental animals directly by opening the chest. The cardiac cycle begins with a simultaneous contraction of both auricles (*auricular systole*), which are seen to become paler and smaller in size. After a short pause both ventricles contract (*ventricular systole*), at first becoming paler and more rounded, then smaller in size. As the ventricles empty, the aorta and pulmonary artery fill. After contraction, each chamber relaxes (*diastole*) and then gradually fills, to empty again at its next beat. The hardening and change in shape which constitute the first phase of ventricular contraction are accompanied by a thrusting of the apical region of the ventricles against the chest wall. This thrust commonly moves the overlying intercostal space, and the movement, known as the cardiac impulse ("*apex beat*"), indicates the point at which the region of the apex of the heart lies. The position of the impulse has great importance clinically in indicating the size and position of the heart. In physiological terminology the terms "systole" and "diastole" are applied to each chamber of the heart.

The Contraction of Heart Muscle

The whole of the musculature of the auricles contracts at the same time, and is soon followed by contraction of the whole of the muscle of the ventricles. This property of simultaneous activation of all the muscle fibres comprising a chamber of the heart is of course necessary if the auricles and ventricles are to act as a pumping mechanism. Indeed, as we shall see later, when the synchronization does not occur, as in fibrillation of the ventricle, the output of the heart falls to zero. Skeletal muscle, which is composed of large numbers of separate fibres (grouped into motor units) could be induced to contract synchronously and rhythmically as does the heart, by means of synchronous bursts of action potentials travelling in the nerves supplying it. This mechanism, however, does not account for the cardiac contractions, for cardiac muscle is a so-called *functional syncytium* which means that the whole muscle behaves as if it were composed of a single cell. This syncytium also has the property of *rhythmicity*, i.e. it is able to generate its own rhythm of contraction without an input from the nervous system.

In common with other types of muscle, the contraction in cardiac muscle results from a membrane depolarization due to the propagation of action potentials, both in the muscle fibres themselves and in muscle fibres specialized for the purpose. We will discuss the electrical events connected with the heart in more detail in the last part of this chapter; it is sufficient for the moment to state that the spread of activity over the wall of the atrium is two-dimensional, rather like waves on a pond produced by a stone dropped into it. In the thick-walled ventricle spread is three-dimensional.

The Origin and Spread of the Heart Beat

A suprathreshold stimulus (electrical pulse of some kind), applied at any point on the heart will give rise to electrical and mechanical activity which spreads throughout the muscle. However, in the normal body it can be shown that although all the heart is potentially capable of initiating the rhythm of contraction, only one region does in fact do so.

If a mammalian heart is excised, it will continue to beat for hours, provided that an adequate supply of warm oxygenated fluid of suitable composition is supplied to the muscle through the coronary vessels from the aorta. It is clear, then, that the origin of the heart-beat is independent of any connection with the rest of the body. Now the heart contains nerve ganglia, chiefly derived from the vagus, but even if these are dissected out in the cold-blooded heart, the beat continues; strips of auricular and ventricular mammalian muscle devoid of ganglia may contract rhythmically if placed in warm oxygenated Ringer-Locke solution. Further, in the chick embryo the heart begins to beat before it has received any nerves. Thus we may conclude that the beat originates in the heart muscle itself.

Although heart muscle is thus endowed with the property of contracting rhythmically, different parts of the heart behave differently in this respect. This is most easily shown in the classical experiments of Stannius on the heart of the frog (Fig. 8.2). If a ligature is tied tightly around the junction of the sinus venosus with the auricles, the auricles and ventricle stop beating while the sinus continues at the same rate as before. After five to thirty minutes the detached part of the heart begins to beat, but a slower rate than that of the sinus; the auricle contracts before the ventricle. If now a ligature is tied tightly between auricles and ventricle (second Stannius ligature), the auricles continue to beat as before, while the ventricle stops, after making a few rapid beats due to the stimulus of the ligature. The ventricle begins to beat again after about an hour, at a very slow rate. Thus although each chamber of the heart is able of itself to contract rhythmically, the frequency of contraction varies from the sinus venosus at one end to the ventricle at the other; in the intact heart the rate of beating

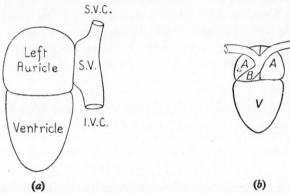

FIG. 8.2. Diagram of the frog's heart (*a*) from the side, and (*b*) from the ventral aspect. The first Stannius ligature is tied tightly round the junction of the sinus venosus and right auricle (lying behind the left in the figure), the second between auricles and ventricle. S.V. = sinus venosus; S.V.C. = superior vena cava and I.V.C. = inferior vena cava; *B* = bulbus arteriosus.

is that of the fastest chamber—the sinus venosus. This experiment thus suggests that in the frog the heart-beat begins in the sinus region and spreads over the chambers successively; the same is true of the mammalian heart.

Instead of recording mechanical movements of the heart, the spread of activity over the walls of the auricles and ventricles can be just as easily demonstrated by recording the cardiac action potentials. The technique of electrical recording, of course, has one big advantage, namely that the time-relations of the process can be measured with accuracy. The first experiments of this kind were carried out by Sir Thomas Lewis using a string galvanometer; nowadays amplifiers and cathode ray oscilloscopes are employed.

Recording from various parts of the heart's surface, the electrical changes associated with the excitation of these parts can be observed and accurately timed. In this way, it was shown by Lewis that the electrical change which accompanies contraction of the mammalian heart begins in the sino-auricular node which lies in that part of the heart corresponding with the sinus venosus of the frog. From here the wave of electrical disturbance radiates in all directions over the auricular muscle, because heart muscle cells are a syncytium, and for a short distance up the great veins. When the wave arrives at the auriculo-ventricular node it passes thence along the auriculo-ventricular bundle through the Purkinje tissue and into the ventricular muscle. The rate of conduction through the Purkinje tissue is very rapid (500 cm/sec) as compared with its rate through the ventricular muscle (50 cm/sec). Thus in spite of their size all parts of the ventricles contract almost simultaneously. That the normal heart-beat actually originates in the sino-auricular node (the pace-maker) is confirmed by the fact that when this structure alone is warmed or cooled, the heart-beat quickens or slows respectively; when other parts of the heart are similarly warmed or cooled the frequency of the heart-beat is unaltered.

The Mechanical Properties of Cardiac Muscle

(a) *Development of Tension*

Within limits, the force of contraction of a heart muscle fibre is proportional to the initial (i.e. resting) length of the fibre. As we shall see in the Section about muscle, this relationship is a fundamental property of contractile systems. In the heart, it can be applied to the whole of the organ because the force of contraction determines cardiac output, while the initial length of the fibres is dependent upon the pressure in the

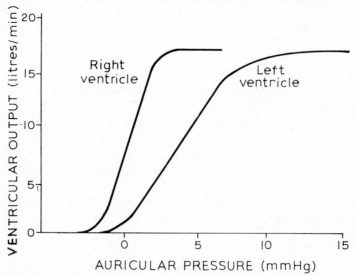

FIG. 8.3. Relation between cardiac output and auricular pressures in a normal human subject.

chambers of the heart. Thus we can re-state the relationship in the form that cardiac output is directly proportional to the right auricular pressure (within limits). This is shown in Fig. 8.3.

(b) Duration of the Contraction

In *cardiac muscle* the action potential lasts very much longer than it does in skeletal muscle, and the membrane does not recover until the contraction is almost completed. Correspondingly, the refractory period lasts almost as long as the whole period of contraction and relaxation. If two

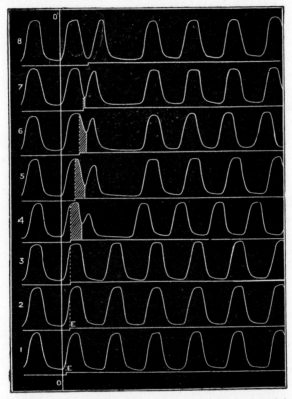

FIG. 8.4. Tracings of spontaneous contractions of frog's ventricle, to show refractory period and compensatory pause. (Marey.) An electrical stimulus is given at the step in the base-line (see text).

stimuli are applied in succession, the second stimulus produces no effect at all unless it is applied so long after the first that the responses of the two are independent contractions occurring one after the other. *No summation* of contractions and *no tetanus* can be produced under normal conditions in heart muscle. If the second stimulus occurs during the relative refractory period, the contraction produced is usually smaller than a normal one, owing to imperfect recovery of the contractile process, as may be seen in Fig. 8.4.

Let us observe a spontaneously beating heart, and interrupt its rhythm by interpolating an electric shock applied to the ventricle. Fig. 8.4 shows the ventricular contraction during such an experiment, in which a series of shocks was applied, each at a slightly later phase of the normal contraction. In the lower three records, the stimulus fell in the absolute refractory period and produced no effect. In the upper ones it fell later and produced a smaller or greater contraction according as it occurred sooner or later. This contraction took place, abnormally, before its time, and was accompanied by its own refractory period. It was followed by a pause known as the *compensatory pause*, before the next (normal) contraction, because one of the regular stimuli transmitted from the pacemaker found the ventricle in a refractory state and so produced no effect. Comparable effects are sometimes produced in the human heart by abnormal contractions (premature contraction or extra-systole) originating at some irritable focus independently of the normal rhythm.

If the frequency of the stimuli initiated by the pacemaker (or applied artificially) is progressively increased, a time will come when the interval between successive stimuli is so short that it is less than the refractory period of, say, the ventricular muscle; the muscle will then suddenly respond only to alternate stimuli. If the frequency be further increased so that of three stimuli, the second and third fall within the refractory period accompanying the response to the first, the muscle will respond only to every third stimulus. Analogous events are observed in certain cases of "heart-block" in human disease as discussed later, in which the ventricle responds to only a fraction of an abnormally rapid sequence of stimuli coming from the auricle. If the frequency of stimulation be constant, and the duration of the refractory period be sufficiently increased, a similar omission of the response to alternate stimuli may be observed.

If the rate of stimulation be increased gradually, the refractory period will itself become gradually shorter and so enable the heart to beat faster than it could have done had the rate of stimulation been suddenly increased. This may explain the fact that in certain conditions the human heart can attain a rate of 200 beats per minute; such a rate would be impossible without an actual shortening of the normal refractory period.

(c) *The "All or None" Properties of the Heart Muscle*

Since the muscle is a syncytium, when excited *all* the muscle contracts. If the stimulus strength is below threshold, the fibres do not contract— there is no half-way state; gradation of contraction is not possible. At first sight this *"all or none"* law appears to be contravened by the statement in paragraph (a) about fibre-length. Many factors will alter the force of contraction including fibre-length but provided these factors are kept constant, the stimulation of heart muscle will produce either contractions of given strength or none at all.

Pressure Changes in the Heart During the Cardiac Cycle

Before embarking on a detailed description of the pressure changes in the auricles and ventricles, it is of interest to see what methods are available for making the measurements of these pressures.

Recording Techniques (see Fig. 8.5 for details)

The same methods are used in recording intracardiac pressures in experimental animals and in human subjects. They involve the introduction of catheters (sterile for human patients!) into a vein and thence into the various chambers of the heart. This of course confines observations to the right side of the heart in humans.

The requirements for an acceptable recording system are that it shall have a uniform response characteristic up to about 50 c/sec. Hence U-tube manometers and simple tambours cannot be used. Sensitivity should be such that pressures between 2 to 200 mm Hg can be accurately reproduced as a tracing.

Various types of optical manometer have been used, consisting of a metal or glass diaphragm to which is cemented a small mirror. As the membrane is pressed inwards and outwards by pressure variations in the cannula attached to it, the mirror reflects a beam of light onto photographic recording paper.

Recently, pressure transducers have been constructed which convert the pressure changes into an electrical output which is then amplified and displayed either on the cathode ray tube or recorded permanently on heat-sensitive paper with a hot-wire pen. These transducers usually work on the strain gauge principle, variable capacitance measurement or on the variable reluctance of a coil into which is introduced a core.

An example of the latter type can now be constructed of dimensions so small that it fits into the tip of a catheter—doing away with one of the problems inherent in the usual technique, namely the distortions introduced by recording at the end of a long and somewhat narrow tube.

The Pressure Changes accompanying the Cardiac Cycle

Although the heart consists of two pumps, the right and left hearts, these work simultaneously and in the same way, and it will be convenient to describe the pressure changes only of the left auricle and ventricle; those of the right auricle and ventricle are similar and simultaneous though of less magnitude. Of the various events of the cardiac cycle whose time relations are shown in Fig. 8.6 the jugular pulse and electrocardiogram have been considered already; the pressure changes in heart and aorta and the change in ventricular volume will now be described. The pressure changes have been recorded by electrical or optical manometers connected by means of rigid tubes filled with fluid to cannulae thrust into chambers of the heart.

The Intra-auricular Pressure Curve

This shows waves of rise of pressure (positive waves) corresponding to auricular systole (first positive wave) and the sudden closure of the

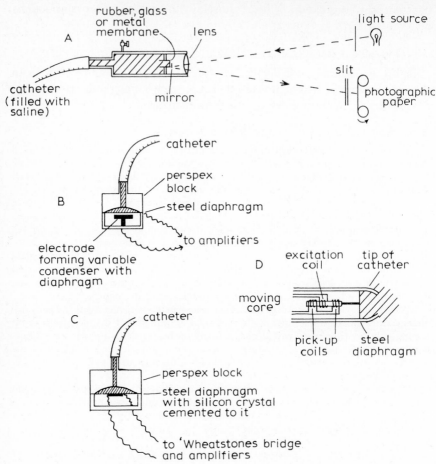

FIG. 8.5. Methods for Measuring Pressures

A. Optical manometer.

B. Capacitance manometer. The pressure variations bend the steel diaphragm and change the capacity between it and the static electrode. A frequency-modulation phase-discriminator (!) is used to detect and record the changes.

C. Strain-gauge transducer. Here the bending of the diaphragm is transmitted to a crystal of silicon cemented to it which forms one arm of a Wheatstone's bridge. The out-of-balance current is amplified and put onto a pen-recorder.

D. Variable reluctance transducer.

A little transformer is wound on a core which moves as the pressure changes bend the diaphragm. The centre coil is supplied with alternating current. As the core moves the voltage in the two pick-up coils will vary with its actual displacement. After rectification and amplification the output is displayed on the oscilloscope or pen-recorder. This device is very small and fits into the tip of a cardiac catheter.

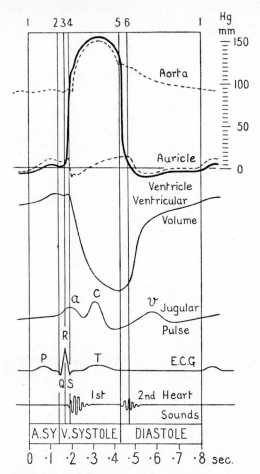

FIG. 8.6. The Sequence of Events in the Cardiac Cycle.

The upper four curves have been taken from actual records obtained from the dog's heart (Wiggers); they represent the pressure changes in aorta (broken line), left ventricle (continuous line), and left auricle (broken line), and the curve of ventricular volume. The lower three curves, representing the jugular pulse, the electrocardiogram, and the heart sounds, have been reconstructed from data obtained on human subjects (Lewis). The vertical lines represent the following events: 1 = auricular excitation (P wave of electrocardiogram), 2 = ventricular excitation (Q wave of electrocardiogram), 3 = auriculo-ventricular valves close, 4 = aortic valve opens, 5 = aortic valve closes, 6 = auriculo-ventricular valves open. A.SY represents the duration of auricular systole. (More usual times for the duration of auricular systole in man would be 0·10 sec, of ventricular systole 0·24 sec, and of diastole 0·46 sec.)

auriculo-ventricular valves (second positive wave). The pressure then abruptly falls as the relatively emptied auricle relaxes. Blood flows into the auricles from the great veins, producing a gradual rise of pressure (third positive wave), which is interrupted when the auriculo-ventricular valves open and put the relaxed and relatively emptied ventricle into connection with the auricle. It will be noted that during diastole both intra-auricular and intra-ventricular pressures are below atmospheric pressure, which is represented as 0 mm in Fig. 8.6. This is not due to any sucking action of the heart, but to the transmission of the sub-atmospheric pressure in the thorax through the slack heart wall.

Ventricular and Aortic Pressure

While the ventricles are quiescent, blood is flowing into them from the auricles, and the intra-ventricular pressure is slightly lower than, and closely follows, the intra-auricular pressure. With the onset of ventricular contraction the intra-ventricular pressure rises abruptly until it exceeds the aortic pressure, the aortic valves now open, blood is forced into the aorta, and the two pressures mount together. As ventricular ejection begins to decline the ventricular and the aortic pressures begin to fall, at first slowly, then rapidly, as the ventricle passes into diastole. The aortic valves now close; the aortic pressure falls slowly as blood flows out at the periphery and the ventricular pressure falls abruptly. The ventricular pressure now falls below auricular pressure, which has been rising owing to the venous inflow, the auriculo-ventricular valves open and blood flows into the ventricle, gradually raising its pressure until the next cardiac cycle begins.

The Ventricular Volume Changes

The volume of the ventricles is slightly increased during auricular systole. The onset of ventricular contraction is associated with no diminution of volume, for the ventricle is now a closed cavity separated from the auricle by the auriculo-ventricular valves and from the aorta by the aortic valves. The first period of ventricular systole is thus a period in which the muscular contraction is isometric (associated with no change in length). With the opening of the aortic valves the ejection phase begins and the ventricular volume rapidly diminishes. The rate of ejection gradually lessens as the ventricle empties and ceases as the aortic valves close, and the ventricle passes into diastole. With the opening of the auriculo-ventricular valves blood enters the ventricles, whose volume increases rapidly.

The Arterial Pulse

The sudden ejection of blood into the aorta that occurs with each beat of the ventricles produces a wave of increased pressure that is propagated along the arteries towards the periphery; this is known as the pulse wave, and it may be felt and recorded in any of the superficial arteries of the body as the pulse beat. The velocity at which this pressure wave is propagated may be determined by recording the times of its arrival at two different points such as the subclavian and radial arteries, and dividing the time differences by the distance between the two points at which measurements are taken. The pulse wave velocity varies in different subjects chiefly with the thickness and elasticity of the arterial wall, and since the arteries tend to become more rigid with advancing years (arteriosclerosis), the velocity increases from an average rate of 5·2 m/sec at the age of five to an average of 8·6 m/sec at the age of eighty. It is important not to confuse the pulse wave, which is simply a wave of increased pressure, with the movement of the blood itself; the velocity of blood-flow is nowhere greater than 0·5 m/sec at rest and is considerably less in the smaller vessels.

The Form of the Pulse

The changes in pressure and their spacing in time that occur in a superficial artery such as the radial may be recorded by the *sphygmograph*, an instrument in which the pulsations of the artery are transmitted to a lever

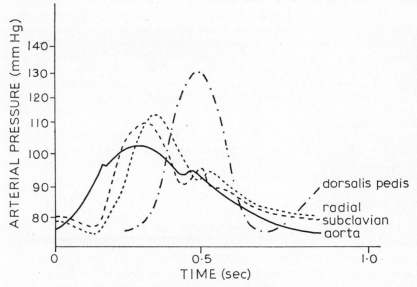

FIG. 8.7. Arterial Pulses.

The form of the arterial pulse varies with the distance from the heart.

(a) There is a progressive delay the greater the distance.

(b) Pressure at the peak of the wave increases with distance.

(c) The slope of the pressure-front becomes steeper.

writing on a piece of smoked paper moving at a suitable speed. With practice the main features exhibited by such a record can usually be ascertained with the finger. The main deflection in the pulse record, the primary wave (Fig. 8.7), is the result of the sudden distension of the aorta during ventricular systole. Following the primary wave are a number of secondary waves, which arise in several ways. The most constant and conspicuous secondary wave results from closure of the aortic (semi-lunar) valves. At the end of ventricular systole the pressure in the ventricle falls rapidly, and blood begins to flow back from the aorta, but is suddenly checked by closure of the aortic valves. This sudden check causes a rise of pressure in the aorta, and this wave travels down the arterial tree with the same velocity as the primary wave which it follows. This secondary wave is known as the dicrotic wave and is preceded by a notch, the dicrotic notch. From what has been said it will be realized that the upstrokes of the primary and of the dicrotic waves are separated by the same interval of time as the opening and closure of the aortic valves. In addition to those two waves there are a number of inconstant and small waves arising from the reflection of the primary wave by obstacles such as the birfurcations of the arteries.

Modifications of Form of Pulse Wave

The form of the pulse wave is modified by such conditions as affect the discharge of the blood from the heart and its escape through the arteries. Thus, when the aortic valves are narrowed by disease (aortic stenosis) the distension of the aorta during systole is very slow and the pressure in the peripheral arteries rises slowly to its maximum; this slow-rising pulse is termed anacrotic. When, on the other hand, the aortic valves do not close properly (aortic regurgitation), the pressure in the aorta falls very quickly during diastole and is suddenly and greatly raised during systole; in this condition the upstroke of the primary wave is unusually sudden and its downstroke rapid; from the sudden thrust on the finger feeling the artery this pulse is described as "water hammer". In conditions of low pressure and rapid blood-flow, as may occur in children and in fevers, the dicrotic wave may be so pronounced as to be easily felt at the wrist; the frequency of the heart may thus be mistaken for twice its true value.

The Venous Pulse

The polygraph records simultaneously on a strip of moving paper pulsations of the jugular vein and of the radial artery or heart's impulse. Chief interest in the records so obtained (Fig. 8.8) attaches to those of the venous pulse. In normal subjects this consists of three waves in each cycle, a, c and v. The a wave is due to auricular contraction and is caused by the arrest of venous inflow to the heart by constriction of the mouths of the great veins. The c wave indicates ventricular systole and is largely trans-mitted from the carotid artery. The v wave is of less importance and is largely due to slowing of the venous flow consequent on the filling of the heart in diastole. The object of the radial pulse tracing is to time ventricular systole and thus to identify the *c* wave of the jugular pulse; the *c* wave of the jugular pulse occurs about 0·1 sec before the radial pulse, the difference in time corresponding to the difference in their distances from the heart. The most important feature of the jugular pulse is the *a* wave. In the early stages of heart block where conduction through the

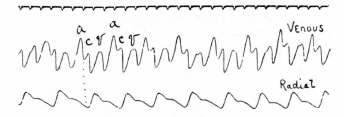

FIG. 8.8. A simultaneous record of the jugular and radial pulses obtained by the polygraph; the time marker records ⅕ sec. In the radial pulse curve the main upstroke is the primary wave; the small hump following it is the dicrotic wave.

bundle of His is impaired, the interval between auricular and ventricular contractions and that between the *a* and *c* waves is prolonged. In the later stages, the ventricle ceases to respond to each auricular systole, and the *a* waves are not always followed by *c* waves. Lastly, in auricular fibrillation, where co-ordinated contraction of the auricles has ceased, the *a* wave is absent.

The Action of Valves in the Cardiac Cycle

We have seen how the pressure varies during the cardiac cycle in the four chambers of the heart. For flow of blood to take place in one direction only, as a result of these pressure changes, valves must be present between the auricles and ventricles, and between the ventricles and the arterial tree.

The aortic and pulmonary valves prevent blood flowing back from the arterial tree during diastole. They have three tough cusps making a triangular opening. The A–V valves (mitral and tricuspid) have two large cusps and prevent reflux of blood in ventricular systole. The cusps of these valves are held back by the chordae tendinae which act like the cords of a parachute to prevent the valves from everting under the strain of full ventricular pressure. The details are shown in Fig. 8.9.

The valves open and shut entirely passively according to the pressure differences across them. When regurgitation of blood begins the flaps close; also various rather complex eddies are set up in the vicinity of the cusps which tend to close them slightly before any actual reflux of blood has taken place. These eddies are in part responsible for the heart sounds.

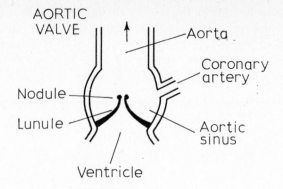

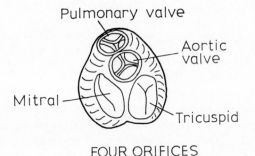

FOUR ORIFICES
IN THE HEART

Fig. 8.9. The Heart Valves.

The Normal Heart Sounds

The sounds associated with cardiac contraction may be heard by placing the ear on the chest wall over the heart; they are usually detected by placing over the heart a hollow metal or vulcanite cone connected through rubber tubing to ear-pieces (the stethoscope). Each contraction of the normal heart is associated with two sounds, the first prolonged and of low pitch, the second abrupt and of higher pitch. They are usually somewhat crudely imitated by the sounds "lubb", "dup". The first sound is produced in part by muscular contraction and in part by eddies set up by closure of the auriculo-ventricular valves, the second is produced by closure of the aortic valves. Occasionally a third heart sound is heard, and is said to be due to the floating up of the auriculo-ventricular valves as the ventricle fills with blood in the early part of a long diastole.

Murmurs. When the valves of the heart are diseased, the heart sounds are usually accompanied or followed by abnormal sounds termed murmurs. Murmurs occurring with the first sound or between it and the second are associated with ventricular systole and are termed systolic. Systolic murmurs are not infrequent in normal subjects when the action of the heart is augmented, as after exercise. Murmurs occurring after the second sound and between it and the next first sound are associated with ventricular diastole and are termed diastolic; they are purely pathological and are of first importance in detecting valvular disease of the heart. These murmurs are probably produced by the vibrations set up in the neighbourhood of diseased valves by the rapid stream of blood passing over them.

Valvular disease of the heart consists of narrowing of the orifice of the valve, *stenosis* or an interference with proper water-tight closure, *incompetence*. Both conditions lead to turbulent flow (since there is in each case a relatively narrow orifice for blood to pass and the critical velocity for laminar flow is exceeded). Sometimes a cusp is ruptured which then vibrates producing an adventitious sound which is musical in character.

Clinical examination of cardiac function includes the detection of abnormal heart sounds. The valve responsible can be determined by timing the murmur in relation to systole and diastole and the kind of sound heard differentiates between stenosis and incompetence.

ELECTRICAL EVENTS IN THE CARDIAC CYCLE

Action Potentials in Cardiac Muscle

If the auricle of a heart which is at rest is stimulated at any point, and the stimulus is above threshold, the whole sheet of cardiac muscle contracts, and change in the strength of the stimulus does not produce any change in the strength of the contraction. If electrodes are placed on the auricle, diphasic action potentials will be recorded, which are of the same size whatever the strength of the stimulus (above threshold) and wherever the electrodes are placed. This experiment may equally well be done on the ventricle. The whole ventricle will contract, and action potentials, all of the same size, will be picked up from any point. The excitation is normally conducted to the ventricles from the auricles by means of the auriculo-ventricular bundle and the Purkinje tissue which spreads out over the interior surface of the ventricle. These consist of cardiac muscle cells, of rather a specialized kind, but not essentially different from those in the rest of the heart. Both the excitatory disturbance and the wave of contraction are thus conducted from one muscle cell to another in all directions over the whole heart. This functional continuity of cardiac muscle is a reflection of the protoplasmic continuity of the cells of which it is composed. If any part of the heart contracts, it all contracts (except in abnormal conditions); there is no gradation of the contraction with gradation of the excitation, as different fibres are successively brought into action, as there is in skeletal muscle.

The response of the whole heart is thus "all-or-none", and this type of response was first noticed in heart muscle (by Bowditch in 1871). But it must again be emphasized that many other factors, such as stretching and drugs, can produce changes in the degree of contraction of cardiac muscle, and that variation in intensity of stimulus, with which the all-or-none type of response is alone concerned, may never occur except under experimental conditions.

The spontaneous rhythmic contraction of cardiac muscle is, as we have shown, an intrinsic property of the muscle and not due to external stimulation. The property is shown in different degree by different portions of the heart, as is demonstrated by the experiments with the Stannius' ligatures. The excitable membrane of cardiac cells differs from that of skeletal muscle fibres in that it is not stable in the resting (polarized) condition, but undergoes a relatively slow "spontaneous" depolarization. When this depolarization has reached a critical value, there is an "explosive" self-

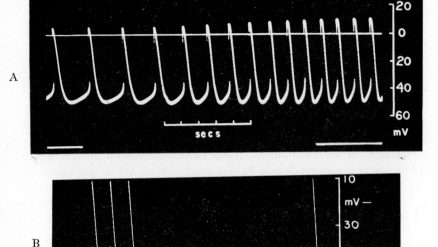

FIG. 8.10 Membrane Potentials of Frog's Heart.

Intracellular recording from a "pacemaker" fibre in a spontaneously beating sinus venosus. (The upstrokes of the action potentials, being very rapid, have been lost in the reproduction.)

A. During the break in the lowest reference line, the vago-sympathetic trunk was stimulated at 20/sec, the action of the vagus fibres being inhibited by atropine $1:10^6$. Note the increase in slope of the slow "pacemaker potential" from which the action potential arises, and the increased overshoot of the action potential.

B. During the four breaks in the reference line the vagus nerve was stimulated at 20/sec. (The tops of the action potentials have been cut off in the recording.) Note the hyperpolarization, reduction in slope of the pacemaker potential and the rapid repolarization, as shown particularly in the "escaped beat" at the beginning of the 4th stimulation period. (Hutter and Trautwein, 1956.)

accentuating increase in permeability to sodium ions and potassium ions, successively, just as there is in a nerve fibre or skeletal muscle fibre, and a propagated disturbance is set up. The spontaneous depolarization in the resting state occurs more rapidly in those cells which constitute the "pacemaker" and in consequence these cells drive the rest of the heart.

Application of adrenaline, or stimulation of the sympathetic nerve fibres supplying the heart, increases the instability; the depolarization occurs more rapidly and an action potential is initiated after a smaller delay, as is indicated in Fig. 8.10A; the frequency of the beat is thus increased. Application of acetylcholine or stimulation of the vagus nerve, on the other hand, increases the stability, accelerates the repolarization of the membrane, shortens the action potential and increases the delay before the next beat is initiated, as indicated in Fig. 8.10B. The resting potential, also, may be increased, so that a larger change in membrane potential is needed before the critical value for excitation is reached.

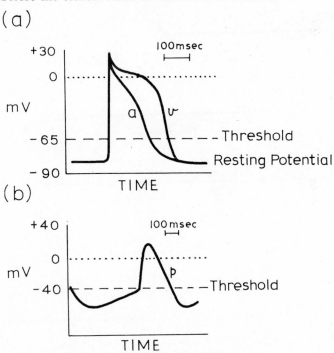

Fig. 8.11. Cardiac Action Potentials.

(a) Intracellular recording of membrane potentials in an atrial fibre, a, and ventricular fibre, v. The depolarization is rapid but is succeeded by a plateau in the depolarized state, longer in the case of ventricular muscle.

(b) Similar recording from pacemaker fibre, p. Note the gradual spontaneous depolarization occurring during diastole; when threshold is reached, a spontaneous action potential is generated.

Administration of acetylcholine, or stimulation of the vagus nerve has been shown to increase the permeability of the excitable membrane to potassium ions. In consequence, the membrane potential is more firmly "locked" in a state of maximum polarization and large depolarizing currents are needed before the critical state of depolarization is reached, at which the "explosive" increase in permeability to sodium ions occurs. Repolarization of the membrane, after excitation, which results from the delayed increase in permeability to potassium ions, also occurs more rapidly, as may be seen in Fig. 8.10B.

The shape and duration of the cardiac action potential differs between pacemaker fibres, auricular fibres and ventricular fibres (see Fig. 8.11).

The Electrocardiogram, ECG

Conduction of the impulse is by depolarization spreading from one part of the heart to another in the same manner as in nerve or skeletal muscle.

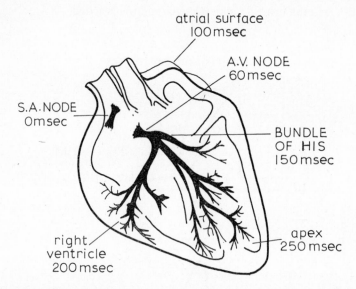

FIG 8.12. Conduction rates and the pathways concerned. Figures, in msec are times after firing of the pacemaker that the depolarization occurs at a point.

Reference to Fig. 8.12 shows that there is no specialized conduction system between the pacemaker (SA Node) and the AV node; excitation spreads over the auricular muscle. In the human heart excitation spreads at about 1 m/sec. The AV node contains fibres with an even slower conduction velocity, about 0·1 m/sec (probably due to their small diameter, small fibres having a slower conduction velocity than large ones). The conduction in the Purkinje system is faster, about 5 m/sec, a fact which tends to make all the ventricular muscle contract more or less simultaneously.

Generation of the ECG

The cardiac action potentials are large enough to be recorded from the body surface in humans and animals. In a volume conductor, which animal tissue is, the potential recorded at the surface of it does not resemble the generating waveform closely. Consideration of Fig. 8.13 will make this clear.

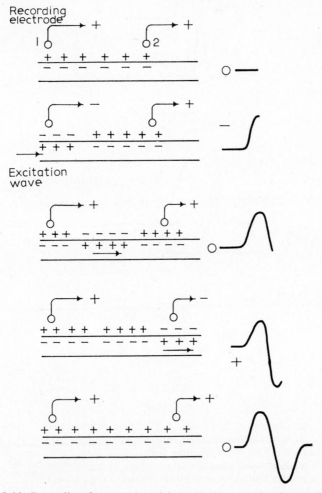

FIG. 8.13. Recording from a potential source in a conducting medium. The wave of depolarization travels from left to right and in doing so passes under each recording electrode in turn. This gives a "*diphasic*" record, quite unlike the actual variation with time, of the potential at the membrane's surface. The shape obtained depends among other things on the velocity of propagation of the impulse, its duration at any point on the membrane and the geometrical arrangement of the pick-up points with respect to the membrane.

After this, it will not be surprising to learn that the electrocardiogram (ECG), as recorded between two points on the body surface has a rather complex form; it may be considered as an esoteric example of a diphasic (or rather, multiphasic) action potential.

The actual shape is shown in Fig. 8.14. The P-wave, occurring first is due to auricular systole. After an iso-electric interval of about 200 msec

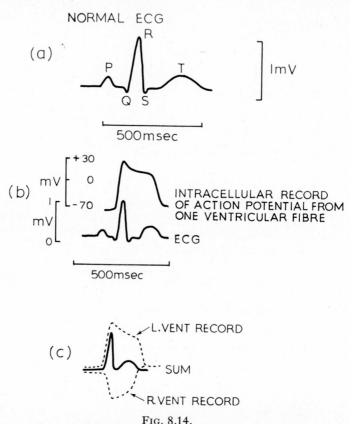

FIG. 8.14.

(a) Normal ECG as recorded between R arm and L leg (lead II).

(b) The same compared with the membrane changes in a single muscle cell on the same time scale.

(c) Algebraic summation of action potentials due to R and L ventricles leading to a waveform similar to the normal ECG.

due to the conduction delay in the AV node and the bundle of His, the QRS complex follows. The QRS complex together with the T-wave are due to depolarization in the muscle fibres of both ventricles. Fig. 8.14 also shows how action potentials in the two ventricles tend to be of opposite polarity when recorded from the surface of the body since they travel in opposite directions in the muscle of each. Algebraic summation, taking into account the fact that the left ventricular action potential is larger than that of the right, gives a good approximation to the actual waveform of the QRST waves.

Clinical Use of the ECG

(1) The Rhythm

It is possible to measure heart rate and observe whether the heart rate is regular or not. The origin of irregularities can be detected. Auricular fibrillation and flutter have a characteristic appearance in the ECG.

(2) The Electrical Axis of the Heart

Comparison of the voltage and polarity of the QRS complex in leads from arm to arm and arm to leg shows whether the heart is anatomically displaced or if the electrical output is greater from one of the ventricles, than normal.

(3) Heart Block

Delay in the P–R interval indicates interference with conduction. Dissociation of P-waves and QRS complexes occurs in block, giving 2 :1, 3 :1 or 4 :1 etc. block. Bundle branch block gives bizarre QRS waves usually spiky and having abnormally long duration.

(4) Cardiac Infarction

Coronary thrombosis leads to death (*infarction*) of muscle, since coronary arteries are *end arteries*, i.e. they have no possibility of forming functional anastomoses. This gives a characteristic abnormality of the ECG and empirically from the recording it is possible to tell the location of the infarct. The picture alters with time and an old infarct can be detected in many instances.

CHAPTER 9

THE CONTROL OF CARDIAC OUTPUT

By far the most important aspect of the physiology of the heart and its control is the manner in which its output is adjusted to suit the demand for blood by the various organs and tissues. This may be studied conveniently when the heart is isolated, many observations on the mammalian heart having been made with Starling's heart-lung preparation.

The Heart-Lung Preparation. In studying the behaviour of the isolated heart it is of great advantage to leave the lungs in full functional connection with the heart, because the blood can be aerated and the necessary oxygen supplied to the heart by ventilating the lungs, and because the lungs remove vasoconstrictor substances which develop in shed blood and make perfusion of isolated mammalian preparations difficult.

The preparation is shown diagrammatically in Fig. 9.1, and is made briefly as follows. The venous reservoir having been filled with warm defibrinated dog's blood, a dog's chest is opened under artificial respiration; cannulae are tied into the brachiocephalic artery and superior vena cava and all the other systemic vessels (inferior vena cava, azygos vein, subclavian artery and aorta) are tied. The blood entering the heart from the venous reservoir must now pass from the aorta through the arterial cannula and artificial circulation. In the artificial circulation the two important features are (a) the air cushion (B, Fig. 9.1) consisting of an inverted bottle containing suitably compressed air which simulates the elastic reservoir provide by the aorta and larger arteries, and (b) the resistance R consisting of a thin rubber sleeve inside a glass tube containing air under the known pressure of a large reservoir with which it is connected; blood will only flow through the sleeve at a pressure higher than that of the air outside it, and thus the arterial pressure may be kept constant and independent of output. By these two devices the blood pressure in the aorta is prevented from falling too far during diastole and so the coronary circulation to the heart is well maintained.

In this preparation the nerves to the heart are severed and the heart beats at a constant rate, which may, however, be varied by altering the temperature of the blood (action on the sino-auricular node).

By using the heart-lung preparation, it is possible to vary independently the venous input to the heart, and the arterial pressure developed; the first by adjusting the height of the venous reservoir, or better by opening and closing a screw-clip on the tube between the reservoir and the vena cava, the second by adjusting the air pressure outside the rubber sleeve in the "arterial resistance". By varying the rate of venous inflow, the output of the heart can be varied smoothly over a very wide range; in this, it is totally unlike a rigid mechanical pump in which the output is fixed by the cross section of the cylinder, the throw of the crank and the

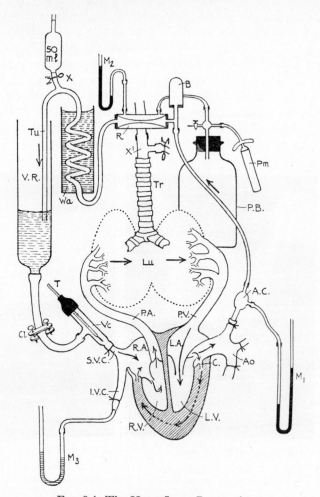

FIG. 9.1. The Heart-Lung Preparation.

The direction of the flow of blood is shown by arrows. V.R., venous reservoir; Cl, clamp for adjusting the rate of inflow to the heart; Vc, venous cannula, with thermometer, T; S.V.C., superior vena cava; I.V.C., inferior vena cava, connected to the manometer M_3 for measuring the venous pressure; R.A., right auricle; R.V., right ventricle; P.A., pulmonary artery; Lu, lungs; Tr, trachea, with cannula X^1; P.V., pulmonary vein; L.A., left auricle; L.V., left ventricle; C, coronary artery; Ao, aorta, ligatured; A.C., arterial cannula in brachiocephalic artery, connected to the manometer M_1 for measuring the arterial pressure; B, elastic cushion; R, arterial resistance; pressure is applied to the outside of the sleeve by the pump Pm, is stabilized by the pressure bottle P.B., and measured by the manometer M_2; Wa, warming coil in hot water; X, clamp for admitting blood to the graduated vessel when it is desired to measure the output of the heart; Tu is then temporarily clamped.

number of strokes per minute. Variation of the arterial pressure, on the other hand, has no action on the output of the heart, within an upper limit set by the capability of the heart to do the necessary work, and a lower limit below which the heart is inadequately nourished through the coronary circulation. In this respect, it is quite similar to the rigid mechanical pump. The heart, in fact, acts very effectively in propelling the blood available in the venous system against any normal value of the arterial pressure; neither allowing the veins to become engorged by propelling too little, nor sucking them empty by propelling too much.

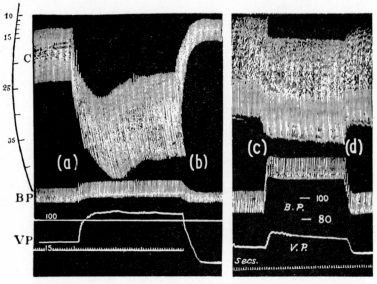

(1) Venous inflow changed.   (2) Arterial pressure changed.

FIG. 9.2. Effect of changing: (1) the Venous Inflow, and (2) the Arterial Pressure on the Volume of the Heart.

C, cardiometer curve, the curved line at the side indicating the value of the cardiometer excursions, i.e. of alterations of ventricular volume, in millilitres; movement downwards indicates *increase* in volume; B.P., arterial pressure; V.P., venous pressure (water manometer) in the inferior vena cava. (Patterson, Piper and Starling.)

Intrinsic Heterometric Autoregulation—Starling's Law. Any variation in the output of the heart (at a constant frequency) must be accompanied by a parallel variation in the amplitude of the beat—i.e. in the change in length of the muscle fibres on contraction. Similarly, any variation in the arterial pressure must be accompanied by a parallel change in the force which the muscle must exert in order to expel the blood. The way in which these adjustments are made may be demonstrated by recording the volume changes of the ventricle by means of a *cardiometer*.

In its simplest, and original, form this consists of a glass cup the shape of a wine glass, the stem of which is hollow and connected to a volume recorder; the open end of the cup is fitted with a rubber membrane in which a suitably sized hole has been burned. The ventricles are slipped through this hole, the edge of which grips lightly but securely the auriculo-ventricular groove.

Fig. 9.2 shows the results of experiments on a heart-lung preparation: a movement downward in the cardiometer tracing, C, indicates an increase in the size of the heart; the volume at the end of diastole is thus given by the lower limit of each movement, and the volume at the end of systole by the upper limit; the total excursion gives the output of the heart per beat (stroke volume). When at (a) (left-hand record) the venous inflow is increased from 516 ml/min to 840 ml/min, the venous pressure rises from 95 mm H_2O to 145 mm H_2O, and the ventricles distend, at first putting out less blood than they receive. The diastolic volume of the ventricles thus gradually increases, and this is associated with a gradual rise in the output per beat, until finally the output equals the inflow and the heart ceases to dilate. The arterial pressure remains practically constant, rising from 124 mm Hg to 130 mm Hg only, since the arterial "resistance" is specially designed for this purpose. The heart remains at the new size until at (b) the venous inflow is suddenly reduced to 198 ml/min; the heart puts out more per beat than it receives, and the diastolic volume gradually falls. Finally, at a new and smaller diastolic volume the heart again puts out precisely what it receives, the venous pressure having fallen to 55 mm H_2O.

In the right-hand record of Fig. 9.2, the venous inflow is kept constant at 924 ml/min. When at (c) the arterial "resistance" is altered, so that the arterial pressure is raised from 98 to 128 mm Hg, the ventricles at first fail to put out as much blood as they receive and so increase in size. The increase in diastolic volume is associated with a progressive recovery in the output per beat until the heart, at an increased diastolic volume, is again ejecting all that it receives. When the arterial pressure is again reduced, at (d), the ventricles at first expel more than they receive and so decrease in size.

Now the output per beat—which, in a steady state must be equal to the inflow per beat—and the arterial pressure are the two factors which determine the work done by the heart on each beat; variations in either, as we have just seen, are accompanied by variations in the diastolic volume. It is found experimentally, moreover, that similar increases in the rate of work, whether produced by augmented output or by raised aortic pressure, are accompanied in a given heart by similar expansions of diastolic volume. The energy set free by skeletal muscle during contraction varies with the initial length of its fibres, and so it seems to be with the heart. When the diastolic volume of the heart is increased, the muscle fibres are stretched, the energy set free in systole is increased and the heart is able to perform more work. This relationship between the energy of contraction of the heart and its diastolic volume was formulated by Starling as "The Law of the Heart".

The Effect of Metabolites

The effect of accumulated metabolites during heterometric autoregulation has, under certain conditions, a further effect in increasing force of contraction. This may sometimes be large enough to allow the venous pressure to fall. In Fig. 9.2

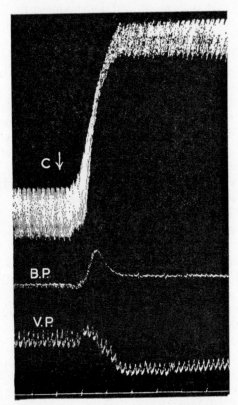

FIG. 9.3. Effect of Adrenaline on the Volume of the Heart.

C, cardiometer curve; a rise indicates reduction in volume of the heart; V.P., pressure in the inferior vena cava.

At the arrow, 0·1 mg adrenaline was added to the blood in the venous reservoir.

The resistance to the venous inflow was not altered. The changes in arterial blood pressure reflect the large transient increase in output while the volume of the heart was falling; and a smaller permanent increase in output owing to the increased inflow produced by the rise in level of the blood in the venous reservoir and the fall in venous pressure. (Patterson.)

the rise of the cardiometer tracing from its lowest point is due to homeometric autoregulation. The mechanism of this effect is thought to be that the increased work done by the heart muscle gives rise to leakage of potassium ions through the cell membranes and accumulating in the tissue fluid. Another theory implicates intracellular calcium ions.

Extrinsic Regulation. The Sympathetic Nervous System. Stimulation of the sympathetic nerve supply to the heart, or the administration of adrenaline, increase the force of contraction of heart muscle *from a given length*. This will be seen from the results of a heart-lung preparation experiment shown in Fig. 9.3. Following the addition of adrenaline to the blood in the venous reservoir, the cardiometer tracing shows that the heart volume decreased. The heart performed the same amount of work from a smaller diastolic volume. It did so not only because, owing to the action of adrenaline, it beat faster, and the output per beat was therefore less, but also and chiefly because the amount of energy liberated from a given length was increased.

In Fig. 9.4 have been plotted diagrammatically the relationships between cardiac output and venous pressure for a number of doses of adrenaline. It will be seen from such a "family of curves" (after Sarnoff): (*a*) that increase in venous pressure increases cardiac output; and (*b*) that for any given venous pressure the cardiac output is greater during the action of adrenaline.

As previously stated, the inflow into the heart in the conventional heart-lung preparation is determined almost wholly by the resistance to the passage of blood past the screw-clip placed on the tubing between the venous reservoir and the heart (Fig. 9.1, Cl), this resistance being large compared with that opposed to the entry of blood into the heart itself. Accordingly changes in frequency and strength of the beat can have little effect on the inflow and thus on the output of the heart. An altogether different situation arises, however, if the screw-clip is removed and the venous reservoir quickly lowered until the level of the blood in the reservoir is the same as that in the venous manometer. In these circumstances, owing to the capacity of the reservoir, the level of blood and the venous pressure must remain nearly constant. The main resistance to the flow of blood into the heart is now that of the heart itself. In this preparation adrenaline causes a large increase in output, and this is not surprising as the heart fills much more readily (Fig. 9.4).

Changes in the Performance of the Heart Mediated Intrinsically by the Starling Mechanism. When a standing subject lies down blood is transferred from the swollen veins in the legs to the veins of the abdomen and chest. Central venous pressure, venous inflow and diastolic volume increase. Cardiac output increases (heterometric autoregulation). However, a rise in arterial blood pressure is prevented by the baroreceptors. These bring about reflex peripheral vasodilatation accompanied by some slowing of the heart and weakening of the force of contraction (extrinsic regulation of the force of ventricular contraction), causing a further

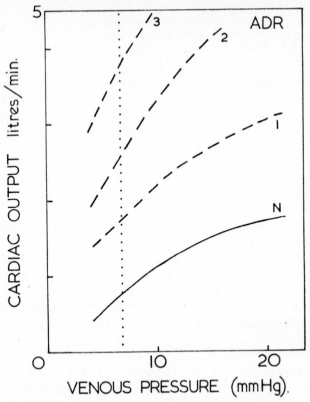

FIG. 9.4. Diagram Showing Relations between *Venous* Pressure
and *Cardiac* Output in the Heart Lung Preparation.

N before adrenaline, 1, 2, 3, after the addition of successively
greater amounts of adrenaline to the circulating blood, causing
increase in rate and force of the heart beat. For a venous pressure
of 8 cm of water the cardiac outputs were 800, 1,300, 2,500 and
3,500 ml/min respectively.

Venous pressure in the healthy human heart is maintained at a
much lower pressure.

rise in central venous pressure. In a few seconds all is in order, central venous
pressure is raised, diastolic volume is increased, heart rate is slowed, cardiac output
is increased, arterial blood pressure is constant, total peripheral resistance has
fallen.

Starling's law plays an important rôle in everyday life in maintaining
the balance between the pumping of the right and left ventricles. This
balance must be exact. Only a delicate adjustment of strength of contraction to the degree of filling can explain their maintained balance of output.

Sometimes a normal heartbeat is followed early in diastole by an extrasystole,
there is then a compensatory pause or dropped beat and normal rhythm is resumed.

The extrasystole may be heard over the apex of the heart but not felt as a pulse at the wrist; the heartbeat after the compensatory pause is often so powerful as to be felt by the subject. The duration of diastole before the extrasystole is unusually short, the diastolic volume of the heart is small, the force of contraction is not enough to open the aortic valves. After the compensatory pause the diastolic volume is so large, and the beat so powerful, as to be felt as a "thump".

Changes in the Performance of the Heart Mediated Extrinsically in the Animal by the Sympathetic Nervous System. Severe exercise is accompanied by an enormous decrease in vascular resistance in the skeletal muscles, by activity of the pumping action of the muscles on the blood in the veins, by veno-constriction and other factors which increase venous return four-fold or more. At the same time, or even before, the sympathetic nervous system quickens and strengthens the heart beat remarkably, so that the subject is aware of his beating heart (palpitation), the corresponding increase in the performance of the heart as a pump explains why there may be no increase in venous pressures or in end diastolic volume of the heart (X-ray). Heterometric autoregulation which many regard as synonymous with "Starling's Law" is often not manifested in exercise.

Work done by the Heart

The external work done by each ventricle during a single contraction is the sum of the potential and kinetic energy imparted to the expelled blood. In symbols, work done per minute $= (P.V. + \frac{1}{2}\rho Vv^2)\,N$, where P represents the mean aortic pressure, V the stroke volume or output per beat, v the velocity of blood in the aorta, ρ the density of the blood and N the number of beats per minute.

Assuming that the pressure developed in the right ventricle is one-sixth that of the left, the external work done by the whole heart per minute becomes: $V(\frac{7}{6}P + \rho v^2)\,N$.

The oxygen consumption of the heart beating at constant rate is found to be proportional to the external work done and thus to the diastolic volume of the heart. If the heart rate is varied, then it is found that the oxygen consumed per unit of work done is greater at a high rate of beat than at a low. Since the oxygen consumption is a measure of the total energy liberated, we may say that the efficiency of the heart, $\dfrac{\text{external work done}}{\text{energy set free}}$, is greater at low rates than at high. The efficiency of the isolated heart is usually about 0·2 (20 per cent).

The Cardiac Output in Man

The output of the heart is remarkably constant for each individual under conditions of complete physical and mental rest, that is after the subject has been lying down and fasting for ten or more hours (basal conditions).

In different individuals the output is closely related to the surface area of the body; it varies from 4 to 5 l/min (2·5 l/min for each square metre of body surface), as estimated by the acetylene and dye injection methods, though rather higher values have been obtained by the method of cardiac catheterization.

The cardiac output is reduced by a change from the recumbent to the standing position, which produces a fall in right auricular pressure. Small increases are produced by excitement (about 1 l/min), and by the ingestion of food and drink (up to 2 l/min); but it is in muscular exercise that the greatest increases are found. Even such slight exercise as flexing the thigh once every second doubles the cardiac output. With more severe exercise, such as cycling, running, or swimming, the cardiac output increases proportionately to the rate of work, commonly reaching 20 l/min, and in trained individuals, values of over 30 l/min have been attained.

THE AUTONOMIC CONTROL OF CARDIAC FUNCTION

The Innervation of the Heart

The heart receives two sets of nerve fibres from the autonomic system, parasympathetic fibres from the vagus and sympathetic fibres. The vagal fibres terminate in ganglion cells in the heart, from which fibres pass to the sino-auricular and auriculo-ventricular nodes and the auricular muscle. Stimulation of the vagus slows the heart by action on the pace-maker, and also depresses the conduction from the auricle to the ventricle by action on the auriculo-ventricular node; it may also reduce the force of the auricular contractions, but in the mammal has little action on the ventricles themselves. The sympathetic fibres arise from cell stations in the middle and inferior cervical ganglia and terminate around the sino-auricular and auriculo-ventricular nodes and in the heart muscle. Stimulation of the sympathetic fibres quickens the heart by action on the pacemaker, facilitates conduction from auricle to ventricle, and augments the force of the auricular and ventricular contractions. It may thus be seen that the action of the vagus on the heart is almost the converse of that of the sympathetic (reciprocal innervation). Normally, impulses are passing to the heart along each set of nerves, for section of the vagus quickens the heart and section of the sympathetic slows it.

The Control of the Frequency of the Heart Beat

The rhythm of the pace-maker is affected by impulses in the vagal and sympathetic nerves, by the concentration in the blood of adrenaline and thyroxine, and to some extent by the temperature of the blood. The nervous impulses come from the cardiac parts of the vaso-motor centre. The activity of this centre depends upon local conditions and upon reflexes from the cardio-pulmonary system and from receptors (*baroreceptors*) in the walls of the aorta and carotid artery which respond to a rise in arterial pressure. In the normal resting subject, the natural rhythm of the pace-maker is made slower by vagal impulses from the centre: if the vagal nerve endings are paralysed by atropine (belladonna), the heart rate increases from about 70 to about 180 beats per minute. This is due largely to the fact that the baroreceptors are normally in a state of moderate excitation, one of their actions being to bring about a reflex slowing of the heart.

The heart rate is *increased* in the following circumstances:

(*a*) In a warm environment, and by fevers.

(*b*) By haemorrhage, and when a recumbent subject stands upright. There is a reduction in venous return, owing to an actual reduction in blood volume, or to blood pooling in the lower part of the body; the cardiac output decreases and the arterial pressure tends to fall. The baroreceptors— and thus the cardiac centre—are less excited, there is a reduction in vagal inhibition and an increase in heart rate.

(*c*) By excitement, fright, exercise and lack of oxygen. This is due, at least initially, to an action of the higher centres of the brain on the vaso-motor centres, reducing or abolishing the normal vagal inhibition of the heart. Later, in exercise, reflexes from the cardio-pulmonary system, the increase in the amount of circulating adrenaline, and the increase in the temperature of the blood accentuate and prolong the increase in heart rate. Reflex action through the vasomotor centres contributes, also, to the effects produced by breathing air deficient in oxygen; but the site of the receptors has not yet been discovered. The arterial pressure rises both in exercise and during lack of oxygen; reflexes from the baroreceptors will thus tend to slow the heart, but their effect is swamped by the predominant accelerating action of the other factors.

The heart rate is *decreased* greatly during a fainting attack, and in some subjects when consciousness is lost as a result of severe lack of oxygen.

Increase in the intracranial pressure, as, for example, by a cerebral tumour, often slows the heart; and this is believed to be due to restriction of cerebral flow and to the effect of lack of oxygen on the vagal centre. Adrenaline injections in pregnant rabbits slow the foetal heart; this is because constriction of the uterine vessels causes oxygen lack in the foetus; the mechanism for accelerating the heart does not function, and so the effect of the oxygen lack on the pace-maker becomes manifest.

CARDIAC DYSFUNCTION

Cardiac Failure

The function of the heart is to propel blood through the vessels at a rate fast enough to meet the metabolic requirements of the tissues; failure to do so may result either from a lesion of the heart itself or because the supply of blood to the heart from the great veins is inadequate (peripheral circula-tory failure). Heart failure in man is frequently accompanied by a condition of stenosis (narrowing) or incompetence (leakiness) of one or more valves, the heart is then working at a mechanical disadvantage; yet it will readily be appreciated that the origin of heart failure is usually to be sought in disease of the heart muscle itself. The earliest symptom of heart failure is undue breathlessness on exertion. In advanced heart failure the patient is breathless at rest and more so in the recumbent than the sitting posture; venous pressure in the cervical veins is increased, the liver is enlarged and extensive accumulations of fluid occur, in the tissues (oedema) of the legs and in the peritoneal (ascites) and pleural cavities. In such an advanced case the cardiac output may be reduced to half the normal. This reduction is not the chief cause of the symptoms since a similar or greater reduction of cardiac output in peripheral circulatory failure is associated with an entirely different clinical picture. The chief factor in producing the symptoms in cardiac failure is the rise in venous pressure which, on the left side of the heart, produces engorgement of pulmonary veins and capillaries, and by thus increasing the rigidity of the lungs leads to breathlessness and may lead to oedema of the lungs; on the right side of the heart the raised venous pressure distends the hepatic veins and thus enlarges the liver, and by raising capillary pressure favours the passage of fluid out of the capillaries into the tissues.

The most instructive example of cardiac failure in man is that seen in paroxysmal tachycardia in which the heart suddenly begins to beat at a rate of 180 to 200 beats/min. As we have seen, for a given output and arterial pressure, the rate of oxygen consumption by the heart rises as the frequency of the beat becomes greater. The flow of blood in the coronary vessels, moreover, occurs chiefly during diastole; if the duration of diastole is reduced excessively, the rate of supply of oxygen will fall, and may well become inadequate. At very high frequencies, then, even previously healthy hearts may after some hours display the phenomena of cardiac failure. With the onset of the paroxysm the patient gradually becomes breathless, the neck veins swell, the liver enlarges, and the cardiac impulse moves outwards for perhaps 2 in. This movement of the impulse is due to the enlargement of the diastolic size (cardiac dilatation) consequent on the increased venous pressure. Even with such a cardiac dilatation the output of the heart is found to be reduced. With the end of the paroxysm, the neck veins collapse, the liver decreases in size and the heart's impulse returns to its normal position; the relationship between cardiac output, diastolic size and venous pressure once more becomes normal.

Usually both sides of the heart go into failure. However, in many patients, early failure occurs predominantly in the left side of the heart only. In rare cases right-sided failure occurs alone, particularly in congenital abnormalities of the heart.

A lowered cardiac output is by no means always present in cardiac failure. Failure quite often occurs in patients who have outputs well above normal levels. They are in failure because the auricular pressures are very high. This happens, usually as a result of peripheral circulatory maladjustment leading to a greatly increased venous return. Such conditions include (1) *arterio-venous shunts,* in which blood passes directly between the arteries and veins (by-passing the main peripheral resistance), (2) *beri-beri* in which the avitaminosis leads to generalized systemic vasodilatation, although usually myocardial weakness is superadded to the peripheral factors mentioned, so that the signs of congestion are even worse than they would otherwise be.

Heart Block

This occurs clinically in cases in which the bundle of His is affected by some pathological process. The block may be either partial or complete. In partial heart block, most but not all of the auricular contractions excite ventricular ones. Often every third or fourth auricular beat fails to do so; the radial pulse is then "regularly irregular". In complete heart block the auricles beat normally and the ventricles contract quite independently and much more slowly, thirty to forty times a minute. If complete heart block occurs suddenly, the ventricle may stop entirely for several seconds before taking up its independent rate of beat. During the period of complete ventricular quiescence, consciousness is lost, and an epileptiform seizure may occur, due to cessation of the circulation to the brain (Adams-Stokes attack).

Extra Systoles

These may occur in normal subjects and usually arise outside the pacemaker (ectopically).

Auricular Flutter and Fibrillation

These two forms of disordered heart action in man are characterized by extremely rapid auricular beats as judged by the waves of the electrocardiogram. In auricular fibrillation the auricular waves occur irregularly at the rate of about 400 to 500/min; in flutter the waves are regular at 250 to 300/min. The bundle of His is incapable of conducting impulses at such rates and a variable degree of heart block is always present, the ventricle usually beating at about 100 to 150, perhaps regularly in flutter, always irregularly in fibrillation.

Conditions analogous to flutter and fibrillation can be produced experimentally by stimulating the auricle with rapid rhythmic electric shocks, or by touching it with a brush dipped in aconitine. At first sight, the fibrillating auricle appears to have stopped beating. However, on close inspection the whole surface is seen to be writhing and shimmering. Numerous small waves replace the P-wave of the electrocardiogram.

According to Lewis, in flutter and fibrillation the excitation wave circulates continuously through the auricular muscle around the mouths of the caval veins. But results obtained more recently by means of the high-speed camera and by the cathode ray oscillograph, have thrown some doubt on this classical explanation of flutter and fibrillation; the movements are not circus in character, but radiate from some fixed point in the auricle. This finding is supported by experiments on auricles made to fibrillate by applying aconitine. Cooling the spot to which the aconitine was applied abolished the fibrillation and restored the normal rhythm.

Ventricular Fibrillation

This occurs in man after blockage of the coronary vessels and during electrocution. Owing to the cessation of ventricular contractions, it is rapidly fatal. It can be induced experimentally by faradic stimulation of the ventricles.

The immediate cause of death in *fresh-water drowning* is usually ventricular fibrillation, which in this case is due to a rapid, large rise in the serum-potassium levels. Water is inhaled into the lung in the terminal struggling and, passing through the alveolar-capillary membrane, gives rise to dilution of the pulmonary blood. The consequent fall in osmotic pressure causes a massive haemolysis, with the liberation of potassium ions (among other things!) in sufficient amounts to increase the excitability of cardiac muscle to the level needed to initiate fibrillation. Note that salt-water drowning does not end in this sudden manner because the sea contains about 3·5 per cent of dissolved salts and in fact haemoconcentration occurs.

Defibrillation

Since fibrillating heart muscle will not act as a pump (since no volume changes are occurring) it is clear that a method for restoring the normal beat would be a life-saving measure. A strong current passed briefly through two electrodes, one on each ventricle, will defibrillate the heart. It excites all the muscle fibres in both ventricles simultaneously and they subsequently become refractory. The heart is then quiescent for two or three seconds, whereupon it commences beating again, the pacemaker taking over the initiation of the beat (sometimes another irritable focus in the conducting system or in the ventricular muscle becomes the pacemaker). In the case of ventricular fibrillation occurring during open chest surgery, this method of restoring the beat is useful. Often, however, the cause of the original initiation of fibrillation is still present and after a variable interval, fibrillation sets in once more. Using electrodes placed on the heart, 50 V at 50 c/s usually gives a current flow of about 1 A and this is customarily employed in the operating theatre.

Electrical defibrillation can also be used through the chest wall but the number of instances where the outcome has been successful is small. This is because there is less than two minutes available in which to apply the current, otherwise lack of coronary blood renders the heart too feeble to respond when the normal rhythm is restored and lack of blood supply to the brain for this length of time is fatal. With electrodes above and below the heart, on the anterior chest wall, about 500 V at 50 c/s is required. This gives a current flow of about 5 A (the resistance of the skin and rib cage is higher than cardiac muscle alone).

Cardiac Massage

By alternately compressing and releasing the ventricles in the hand, the surgeon can maintain a cardiac output sufficient to keep a fibrillating patient alive. (This has been done for up to two hours.) Defibrillation may be successful at the end of this time. It is also possible to carry out cardiac massage in the intact subject by compressing the anterior chest wall with the hand, at regular intervals. The ventricles are squeezed, as a result, between the sternum and the vertebral column. A detailed account of cardiac arrest and resuscitation will be found on pages 237–242.

Section 4
THE TRANSPORT OF
GAS BY THE BLOOD

CHAPTER 10

THE CARRIAGE OF OXYGEN

THE blood, in its circulation, brings to the tissues the foodstuffs and oxygen necessary for their metabolism, and carries away the carbon dioxide and other waste products. The blood, however, is no mere indifferent circulating fluid, but has remarkable "buffering" properties; these enable it to change its composition with respect to the most important substances—oxygen and carbon dioxide—without at the same time bringing about an equally large change in the composition of the fluids surrounding the tissue cells. It can transport much larger quantities of these substances, for example, than could a simple saline solution circulating at the same rate. This property, which is clearly of great importance to the "efficiency" of the blood as a carrier of oxygen and carbon dioxide, is due to the presence of the red "respiratory pigment" **haemoglobin.** Indeed, in the absence of a substance which has the remarkable physical, chemical and physiological properties of haemoglobin, the only animals which could exist would be small and sluggish, living in well-aerated water. One other substance, only, is known which has these properties, and that is *haemocyanin*, the blue "respiratory pigment" of the molluscs and some arthropods.

The Red Blood Corpuscles

When observed under the microscope, blood is seen to consist of an enormous number of pale yellow discs, which are the red blood corpuscles (also called *erythrocytes*, or *red cells*), floating in the clear colourless plasma. (When seen in bulk, in much thicker layers, the plasma is yellow, and the erythrocytes red.) The cells are biconcave discs, thicker near the edge than in the middle, their average diameter in human blood is about 8.6μ and their thickness is about 2.6μ. Their specific gravity is greater than that of the plasma (about 1.10 against about 1.03), which accounts for the fact that they settle out when blood is allowed to stand, or is spun in a centrifuge. The haemoglobin, which is responsible for the red colour of blood, is thus contained entirely within the red blood corpuscles. This does not appreciably affect its properties as an efficient carrier of oxygen and carbon dioxide; but if it were in simple (colloidal) solution, it would be lost from the blood through the kidneys. In some circumstances, the viscosity of a suspension of red cells is smaller than that of a solution containing the same quantity of haemoglobin in unit volume, so that less power is needed to drive it round the circulation at the required rate.

The Red Cell Count

The estimation of the number of red cells per cubic millimetre of blood (the *Red Cell Count*) is important for both clinical and research purposes. The apparatus used for this purpose is called a *haemocytometer* (from the Greek for "blood-cell measurer").

The blood is first diluted 200-fold in a special pipette with "Hayem's fluid" which "fixes" the corpuscles (in the histological sense). A special microscope slide is then used, in the middle of which is a polished surface lying exactly 0.1 mm below the general level of the slide. A drop of the diluted blood is placed on the surface, and a cover slip lowered over it, so that it spreads and forms a film exactly 0.1 mm thick. On the floor of the slide are engraved two sets of fine lines, 0.05 mm apart, crossing at right angles to form a large number of squares. When the red cells have settled down, they are counted under the microscope, those in each square having previously been suspended in $0.05 \times 0.05 \times 0.1 = 0.00025$ mm^3 of fluid. To obtain the average number of cells per cubic millimetre, in the original blood, about 500 cells are counted; the count is first divided by the number of squares that the cells occupy, then by the volume of fluid above each square (0.00025 mm^3), and is finally multiplied by the dilution factor (200).

The red cell count in healthy men varies from 4.5 to 6 million per mm^3, the average being about 5.5 million. In women the count is even more variable, but on an average about 10 per cent lower than in men. The uncertainty in the method of obtaining a blood count, as ordinarily performed, is likely to be at least ± 5 per cent.

The red blood corpuscles normally occupy 40 to 45 per cent of the volume of the blood in man. This important ratio can be measured by means of the *haematocrit* (from the Greek for "blood-separator"). This is a graduated capillary tube of uniform bore, which is filled with blood and centrifuged at high speed until the column of sedimented red cells shows no further shrinkage; the volume of the tightly packed cells can then be read off and compared with that of the whole blood.

The microscopic examination of the blood cells is conveniently carried out on dried and stained smears of blood. On drying, the red cells shrink, so that their diameters are diminished by 8 to 16 per cent. In such dried preparations of normal human blood the average diameter of the red cells is only $7.4 \pm 0.3\mu$. The shrinkage and distortion of the cells so prepared are of no great consequence in the clinical examination of the blood, because the characteristic changes in blood associated with different diseases are commonly described in terms of the changes which appear in the dried smears.

Red blood corpuscles have no nuclei, but are, nevertheless, living cells; they have quite active metabolic processes, and require energy for their existence, which they obtain, chiefly, by means of the anaerobic breakdown of glucose. But they have a relatively short life-time, and old ones are continually being destroyed and replaced by new ones formed, in post-natal life, in the blood spaces of the bone marrow. In normal individuals, the rate of production is adjusted so as to be equal to the rate of destruction when the number of red cells in the circulating blood is such that the red cell count has its normal value of about 5 million per mm^3; but, following an abnormally large loss of blood, for example after a haemorrhage, the rate of production is greatly increased until the loss is made good. The primary stimulus for this is the reduction in the rate of supply of oxygen to the tissue cells generally; with less haemoglobin in each litre of blood, less oxygen can be carried round from the lungs. The production of red cells is accelerated, also, when the supply of oxygen to the tissues is deficient by virtue of an inadequate supply of oxygen to the lungs, as at high altitudes. The bone marrow itself does not respond directly to the deficient supply of oxygen, but, apparently, to some substances in the circulating blood, produced elsewhere and not yet identified.

Life-time of Red Cells

Many different methods have been used to estimate the average life-time of a red blood cell and widely different values have been obtained. In principle, a certain proportion of the circulating red cells is "labelled" in some way, and the rate of their disappearance measured. (1) Cells may be injected intravenously which contain a different type of agglutinogen from that of the cells normally present care being taken, of course, that the cells injected are not such as to be affected by agglutinins in the plasma of the recipient. (2) Cells which have been removed from the subject under investigation may be allowed to take up in vitro the radioactive isotope of phosphorus ^{31}P (as phosphate), or that of chromium ^{55}Cr (as chromate), and then returned to the circulation. (3) The haemoglobin incorporated in the cells formed in the ordinary way in the bone marrow may be "labelled" by injecting intravenously, over a suitable period of time, either (a) salts of the radioactive isotope of iron ^{59}Fe, or (b) the amino-acid glycine in which the ordinary carbon or nitrogen atoms, ^{12}C and ^{11}N, have been replaced by those of the isotopes ^{14}C and ^{15}N, as the case may be; the rate at which these cells appear may be measured as well as, or instead of, the rate at which they disappear. None of the various methods used is without its difficulties, and various corrections must be made to the results obtained. The most reliable measurements indicate an average life-time in man of some 100 to 130 days.

Formation of Red Cells

In certain abnormal conditions, the rate of production of the red cells may be unduly small, or the rate of destruction unduly large. In either event, in the steady state when the two rates are equal, the red cell count will be less than the normal value, producing *anaemia*.

(1) Study of the disease pernicious anaemia (and certain other related kinds of anaemia) has shown that for the normal development of the red cells two specific *vitamins* are necessary: these are known as *vitamin B_{12}* (which contains the rather uncommon element cobalt, and is also known as cobalamin) and *folic acid* (or pteroyl-glutamic acid). Both vitamins are present in adequate quantities in normal protein foods of animal origin, and particularly in liver; folic acid is present also in fresh green vegetables, and vitamin B_{12} is synthesized by many kinds of micro-organism, including some of those in the alimentary tracts of mammals. Anaemia may result from malnutrition but more usually, owing to some diseased condition of the alimentary tract, the vitamins are not properly absorbed and anaemia results even though the diet is fully adequate.

When given as a subcutaneous injection, vitamin B_{12} is highly active in improving the condition of a patient with pernicious anaemia but when given by mouth it is far less active. It would appear that it is not well absorbed from the alimentary canal unless first acted upon by a constituent of the gastric juice, known as the *intrinsic factor*, vitamin B_{12} being the *extrinsic factor*. This intrinsic factor is absent from persons suffering from pernicious anaemia.

(2) The cells of the bone marrow, like other actively dividing cells, are very susceptible to the action of *ionizing radiations* and particles—X-rays and the γ-rays, α-particles, electrons and neutrons emitted during radioactive disintegration of unstable atomic nuclei. After excessive exposure to such radiations, cell division in the bone marrow ceases, or becomes disordered, the rate of production of normal red cells is greatly reduced, and abnormal kinds of cell may appear in the circulation.

(3) Iron is needed for the synthesis of the haemoglobin within the red cells; the iron released from destroyed cells is used again in the production of new ones, and ordinary diets contain sufficient to make up for any deficiency. Small amounts of copper are essential for the proper utilization of the iron. Anaemia, however, may occur in infants during the suckling period, owing to an almost complete lack of iron in the milk; it can be cured by administration of salts of iron.

(4) The rate of destruction of the red cells may be abnormally great owing to a congenital defect in their structure or metabolic processes, which shortens their life-time; or to the presence in the plasma, as a result of disease, of a specific "anti-body" which destroys them.

Development of Red Cells

In the earlier stages of their development, red cells possess nuclei. Two stages in the development of nucleated red cells from the mesenchymal parent cell are distinguished; they are known successively as *erythroblasts* and *normoblasts*. The normoblast becomes an adult red cell when it loses its nucleus. For the first few days of its adult life, spots and threads of basophilic material can be demonstrated in the red cell by vital staining with cresyl blue. In this stage it is known as a *reticulocyte* or reticulated red cell. After the first week of life reticulocytes form only about 1 per cent of the circulating red cells, but they form a larger proportion of the red cells found in bone marrow. The proportion of them in circulating blood rises considerably whenever the new formation of red cells is increased, as after a haemorrhage, or after the successful treatment of pernicious anaemia.

The haemoglobin in the fragments of the old red cells is converted by the reticulo-endothelial cells into inorganic iron and the pigment *bilirubin*. These travel in the plasma to the liver, and the bilirubin, after a slight change, is secreted into the bile. In the bowel bilirubin is changed into *stercobilinogen* and *stercobilin*, which gives the faeces their dark colour. Not all the bile pigment is excreted. Some is reabsorbed into the portal blood stream in the form of a colourless compound called *urobilinogen*, which is picked up by the liver, perhaps to be used in the production of new haemoglobin. When large quantities of bilirubin are formed (as in haemolytic jaundice), and consequently large amounts of urobilinogen absorbed, appreciable amount of urobilinogen are excreted in the urine. This is to be distinguished from the excretion of bilirubin in the urine which occurs when the bile passages are obstructed, for example, by a gall-stone (obstructive jaundice). Urobilinogen is also found in the urine when the liver function is impaired, and thus unable to deal with the normal quantities carried to it in the portal blood stream.

HAEMOGLOBIN

Chemically, haemoglobin consists of an iron-porphyrin complex, known as reduced haematin, or *haem*, united with a protein, *globin*. Haem is closely related chemically to the prosthetic groups of many enzymes concerned in the oxidation of the foodstuffs, notably the cytochromes, and peroxidase. Haem can unite with a number of nitrogen-containing substances, forming *haemochromogens;* haemoglobin is a special case of a haemochromogen.

Haem and the haemochromogens contain iron in the *ferrous* (divalent) state. If treated with a suitable oxidizing agent, the iron is oxidized to the *ferric* (trivalent) state, with the formation of *haematin* from haem, and *methaemoglobin* from from haemoglobin.

Haematin unites with hydrochloric acid to form the hydrochloride *haemin*; this substance crystallizes readily from solution, and the character of the crystals is sufficiently distinct to be used as a chemical test for blood pigments. Haemoglobin itself only crystallizes easily when derived from certain species, e.g. the horse, rat or guinea-pig. The shape of the haemoglobin crystals varies with the species of blood used. For further information as to the chemical relations of haemoglobin, reference should be made to a text-book of biochemistry. All the compounds concerned have characteristic absorption spectra, which are invaluable for their identification.

Haemoglobin combines with oxygen to form a scarlet compound, *oxyhaemoglobin;* this contains 1 gram-molecule of oxygen for each gram-atom of iron in the haemoglobin. The oxygen can be removed again, just as if it were in simple solution, by shaking the haemoglobin solution repeatedly in a vacuum, or with gas containing no oxygen, such as hydrogen or nitrogen. The colour of the solution changes to purple when the oxygen is removed, and the haemoglobin is then said to be reduced. Haemoglobin, oxygen and oxyhaemoglobin are thus components of a reversible chemical reaction:

$$Hb + O_2 \rightleftharpoons HbO_2$$

(Hb being the symbol generally used for haemoglobin). In this reaction, the oxygen is attached to the haem part of the haemoglobin molecule, but the iron atom remains in the bivalent state; the reaction, therefore, is not one of oxidation, in which the iron would become trivalent, but is referred to as *oxygenation*. Reactions of this kind, in which the oxygen combined with the haem can be removed merely by removing the oxygen dissolved in the solution, occur only when the haem is united to the particular protein, globin; other haemochromogens may be oxidized, but not oxygenated, by oxygen in solution. It is the existence of this easily reversible reaction with oxygen that enables haemoglobin to act as a carrier of oxygen. In the carriage of carbon dioxide, easily reversible reactions are again involved, but with the globin part of the molecule, rather than the haem part; they are not accompanied by colour changes, and so are less conspicuous. But it is one of the outstanding features in the properties of haemoglobin that the haem and the globin parts interact with one another. The globin not only allows the haem to react reversibly with oxygen but small changes in its precise chemical composition, or state of ionization, may affect considerably the affinity of the whole molecule for oxygen, as will be discussed later. Conversely, the state of oxygenation of the haem affects the ionization of the globin, and its affinity for carbon dioxide.

Oxygen Capacity of Blood

For an adequate rate of transport of oxygen and carbon dioxide to and from the tissues and the lungs, it is essential that there should be an adequate concentration of haemoglobin in the blood and that the haemoglobin should be able to take up, and lose, oxygen and carbon dioxide. A man may become unduly distressed by going upstairs or running for a bus, not only because his heart or lungs are inadequate, but also because there is not enough haemoglobin in his blood to carry the oxygen and carbon dioxide, or to prevent his tissues from becoming too acid. A blood count, of course, will indicate whether he has the normal number of red cells, but these may not contain the normal amount of haemoglobin. The concentration of haemoglobin in the blood may be measured in terms of the maximum quantity of oxygen with which unit volume (usually 100 ml) will combine—i.e. the *oxygen capacity* of the blood, as described below or, more simply, in terms of its colour, since haemoglobin has so strong a red colour.

Haemoglobin Estimation

The colorimetric (or more strictly absorptiometric) estimation is usually made with the haemoglobin in combination with carbon monoxide (carboxyhaemoglobin); acid haematin and reduced haemoglobin can also be used; all three substances are more stable than oxyhaemoglobin. In the *Haldane Haemoglobinometer*, the appropriate volume of the blood under test (20 mm³) is treated with coal gas, so as to convert the haemoglobin to carboxyhaemoglobin, and is then diluted in a special tube, of the proper size, until it has the same depth of colour as has an arbitrary standard; this may either be a solution of carboxyhaemoglobin in a sealed tube, or better, a solid rod of suitably coloured glass. The final volume of the diluted unknown blood is then read on special graduations on the tube, which give the haemoglobin concentration as a percentage of that of the standard. This value, sometimes known as the "haemoglobin concentration", does *not* give the actual haemoglobin concentration of the blood, but only the relation to the standard. This latter is conventionally adjusted to contain 15·6 g Hb per 100 ml blood, which is equivalent to an oxygen capacity of 19·8 ml O_2 per 100 ml blood. These figures, therefore, will also apply to any blood which has "100 per cent haemoglobin".

Alternatively, and more accurately, the haemoglobin concentration may be measured directly in terms of the transmittance of the solution—i.e. the fraction of the incident light which is transmitted through unit depth of solution; the intensities of the incident and transmitted lights being measured by means of a photo-electric cell. It is best to use light of such a colour that it is strongly absorbed by haemoglobin. Solutions of oxyhaemoglobin absorb light in the whole of the blue-violet region of the spectrum (this is why they have a red colour) and in the extreme red end. There are also two well-defined absorption bands, one in the yellow and the other in the green, which are valuable for purposes of identification. Solutions of reduced haemoglobin absorb light more strongly in the extreme red end of the spectrum than do solutions of oxyhaemoglobin, and less strongly in the blue-violet region, and there is only one band in the yellow-green region; this is broad and dim. By the use of suitably coloured filters, transmitting light of certain wave-lengths only, and photo-electric cells for measuring the transmittance of the blood or haemoglobin solution at these wave-lengths, it is possible to measure, independently, the concentration of oxyhaemoglobin and the concentration of reduced haemoglobin. The complete apparatus for doing this is known as an *oximeter:* it can be made small enough to be attached to the lobe of a man's ear, for example, and will give a continuous record of the degree of oxygenation of his blood.

The haemoglobin content of the average red blood cell is expressed in terms of the *Colour Index.* The haemoglobin concentration of the blood, as per cent of the standard value, is divided by the red cell count, also as a percentage of the standard value (taken as 5 million per mm³, so that the per cent red cell count is the actual red cell count multiplied by 20). The colour index is thus ordinarily about unity in healthy persons, but is decreased considerably in secondary anaemia (e.g. after repeated haemorrhage), in which the haemoglobin concentration may fall to 50 per cent of the standard value, and it is often increased in pernicious anaemia, in which the red cell count may fall to one million or less.

COMBINATION OF OXYGEN WITH HAEMOGLOBIN

The amount of oxygen actually combined with the haemoglobin in unit volume of some particular sample of blood—the *oxygen content*—is often expressed as a percentage of the amount that would be combined if it were fully saturated—i.e. as the *percentage saturation*. It is often convenient, also, to refer to the degree of *unsaturation* of a sample of blood; this is a measure of the extent to which the actual oxygen content falls below the oxygen capacity. Thus if, for example, the oxygen content were found to be, say, 10 ml/100 ml blood, and the oxygen capacity of the same, or of an exactly similar, sample of blood were found to be, say, 15 ml/100 ml blood, the percentage saturation would be 66·7: the sample would have an unsaturation of 5 ml/100 ml and the percentage unsaturation would be 33·3.

If haemoglobin takes part in a reversible chemical reaction with oxygen, to form oxyhaemoglobin, it is to be expected that in any particular sample of blood, the percentage saturation would depend on the concentration of oxygen in solution in the blood (provided, of course, that the haemoglobin is not fully saturated with oxygen). The concentration of oxygen in solution—the amount which is physically dissolved in unit volume—is directly proportional to the partial pressure of oxygen in the gas with which the blood is brought into equilibrium.

The partial pressure of a gas in a mixture of several gases is that fraction of the total pressure which can be considered as being contributed by that gas. This is considered in more detail in the next chapter, where examples are given of the partial pressures of the gases in gas mixtures under various conditions.

Oxygen Dissociation Curves

It is usual to relate the quantity of oxygen combined with haemoglobin to the partial pressure of oxygen in the gas with which the blood is equilibrated. This relation is shown in Fig. 10·1. Curves such as these are known as *dissociation curves* (or, more properly, *equilibrium curves*). The points through which they are drawn are determined by shaking a sample of blood gently with a suitable mixture of oxygen, nitrogen and, if desired, carbon dioxide, until equilibrium is reached (thirty to forty-five minutes), then measuring the oxygen content of the blood and, by analysing the gas mixture, the partial pressure of oxygen. At the partial pressure at which the haemoglobin is sensibly fully saturated (100 mm Hg), the amount of oxygen dissolved in the blood is about 1/70 of the amount combined with the haemoglobin.

Gas Analysis

The type of *gas analysis apparatus* used in establishing the facts given in this chapter was that devised by Haldane. A sample of the gas to be analysed is drawn into a water-jacketed burette, previously completely filled with mercury, and its volume measured. Carbon dioxide is then absorbed by transferring the gas into a vessel from which it displaces a strong solution of caustic potash; it is then brought back into the burette and its volume measured again. Oxygen is absorbed by transferring it in a similar manner into a vessel previously filled with an alkaline solution of pyrogallol, and the residual volume measured once more. Absorption of the carbon dioxide and oxygen is hastened by passing the gas to and from the appropriate absorbing vessels and the burette by raising and lowering the reservoir of mercury connected with the lower end of the burette. Various modifications have been made to the original design in attempts to make its use quicker and simpler. The Scholander apparatus, for example, is specially designed so as to need only 0·5 ml of gas for analysis (the Haldane apparatus needs about 10 ml). It has some advantages over the Haldane apparatus even when plenty of gas is available for analysis; some find it easier to use and keep in proper order.

Modern instrumentation includes the "oxygen meter" which gives a direct reading of O_2 per cent on a scale. The principle of its operation is that oxygen has para-magnetic properties and a little soft-iron dumbell, suspended in a magnetic field, is deflected by this field in varying degrees depending on the amount of oxygen present. The infra-red CO_2 meter is also a direct reading instrument and works on the principle that infra-red waves are absorbed by CO_2. A source and a detector are separated by a tube through which the sample to be analysed is passed and the absorption (proportional to CO_2 concentration) is measured directly on a meter.

The *amount of oxygen combined with haemoglobin* is estimated by driving off the oxygen from the blood, either: (1) by boiling *in vacuo*; or (2) by adding ferricyanide; or (3) by both together.

(1) The first was the method used by the earliest workers, who evacuated a large vessel by means of a mercury pump, for example, a Töpler pump, and ran a known volume of blood, previously warmed to 40°, into it. The gas liberated was then pumped off and delivered to a gas analysis apparatus, where its total volume and composition were determined.

(2) If oxy-haemoglobin is treated with ferricyanide, the reduced haemoglobin which is always present in small quantities is converted into methaemoglobin, so that the equilibrium between oxy-haemoglobin and reduced haemoglobin is upset; in an attempt to restore equilibrium oxyhaemoglobin gives up its oxygen, and more reduced haemoglobin is formed; this is again removed by the ferricyanide, and more oxyhaemoglobin decomposes, and so on. In this way, the whole of the oxygen in reversible combination can be driven off under suitable conditions, and its volume measured. When this reaction was discovered, it seemed that it would be a much easier way of determining the oxygen combined with haemoglobin than the vacuum pump methods previously used. Haldane, indeed, at once adopted the principle in his blood gas apparatus. In this, oxyhaemoglobin is mixed with *alkaline* ferricyanide (the alkalinity prevents the escape from the solution of any carbon dioxide gas) and the only gas evolved is oxygen, which is measured directly in a burette over water. The same principle is also used in the Barcroft differential apparatus. Much work has been done by these two methods, but doubt has been cast on their general applicability by the finding that the evolved oxygen is some-times in part reabsorbed owing to a secondary reaction with the blood in presence of ferricyanide. This can be overcome by taking adequate precautions.

(3) This error is avoided by combination of vacuum extraction and addition of ferricyanide. This principle has been developed by van Slyke to a high pitch of perfection, and his apparatus has been applied to numerous other estimations besides that of oxygen and carbon dioxide in blood. An acid ferricyanide solution and a known volume of the blood under examination, are run into an evacuated vessel; the gases given off are extracted by shaking, and the residual solution is discharged by means of a two-way tap at the bottom of the extraction vessel. The volume of the extracted gases is determined either by transferring them to a burette,

over mercury, and measuring the volume occupied at atmospheric pressure (constant pressure apparatus), or by compressing them to a known volume over mercury and measuring the pressure exerted, with a mercury manometer (constant volume apparatus). This is the more accurate method, since the scale on which the measurements are made is a great deal longer, and no errors can arise from faulty adjustment of the pressure of the gas in the burette. Carbon dioxide is absorbed from the extracted gases by adding a caustic soda solution, and oxygen by adding a solution of pyrogallol or sodium hyposulphite; the contraction in volume (or reduction in pressure) is measured at each stage, and represents the volume of the respective gas present in the extracted mixture.

When plotted in terms of the oxygen content of the blood, the equilibrium curve rises, at large values of the oxygen pressure, to the value of the oxygen capacity. This depends on the haemoglobin concentration of the blood, as measured, for example, by the haemoglobinometer. When plotted in terms of the percentage saturation, the equilibrium curves of all samples of blood rise, of course, to the same maximum value. But such curves may be steeper or flatter, may be compressed or spread out along the axis of oxygen pressure, as the temperature and the acidity of the blood are decreased or increased; and according to the kind of animal, or even particular individual, from which the blood was obtained. Increase of acidity, in particular, decreases the percentage saturation at a given oxygen pressure, i.e. decreases the affinity of the haemoglobin for oxygen, and thus makes the curve flatter—an effect, as already remarked, which results from the interaction between the haem and the globin. Increased carbon dioxide pressure increases the acidity and hence has the same effect, as is shown by the family of curves at different carbon dioxide pressures given in Fig. 10·1. (It is possible that carbon dioxide also exerts a specific effect due to its combining directly with haemoglobin to a slight extent. Lastly, the shape of the curve, as indicated by the size of the inflection at low pressures of oxygen, may depend on the electrolyte composition of the blood.

The dissociation curve of whole mammalian blood is always found to be S-shaped, as in Fig. 10.1. This shape is of distinct physiological service, since it enables a large amount of oxygen to dissociate from the haemoglobin without too severe a drop in the oxygen pressure with which it is in equilibrium. This is an important point as regards supply of oxygen to the tissues, for it is the partial pressure of oxygen in the blood, and not the amount of combined oxygen, that determines the rate of diffusion of oxygen from the blood to the tissues. A curve of the rectangular hyperbola type (v. broken curve in Fig. 10.1) would, from this point of view, be obviously unserviceable.

Shape of Dissociation Curve

The shape of the dissociation curve can be explained by applying the Law of Mass Action to the equilibrium between oxygen and haemoglobin; but the reaction is somewhat complicated and is not accurately represented by the simple equation

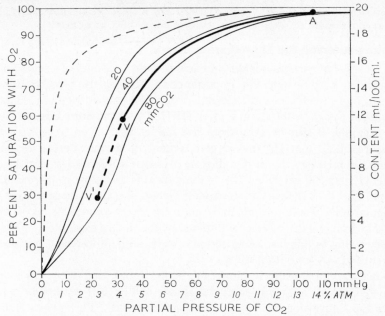

F<small>IG</small>. 10.1. Oxygen Equilibrium (Dissociation) Curves of Blood at various
Partial Pressures of Carbon Dioxide.

The scale of oxygen content on the right of the diagram may be used
with reasonable accuracy for normal human blood. If the haemoglobin
concentration of the blood considered differs from the normal value,
an appropriately different scale must be used.

AVV' is the "physiological oxygen dissociation curve", A being
the arterial point, V the venous point at rest, and V' the venous point
during exercise. Compare Fig. 10.3.

The broken curve is a rectangular hyperbola; note how little
oxygen is given off until the partial pressure of oxygen is reduced
to very low values. Such a curve is given by *myoglobin*, which will
thus readily withdraw oxygen from haemoglobin in the conditions of
venous blood. (After Bock, Field and Adair, and R. Hill.)

given above. Chemical analysis shows that the weight of haemoglobin which
contains 1 atomic weight of iron, i.e. 56 g, is 16,700 g. Direct determinations
of the molecular weight of haemoglobin from mammalian blood, by osmotic
pressure determinations, or by the ultracentrifuge, give a value of 67,000. Thus
each molecule of haemoglobin contains 4 atoms of iron, and will combine with
4 molecules of oxygen. These can combine with the Hb_4 molecule one by one,
forming the intermediate compounds Hb_4O_2, Hb_4O_4, Hb_4O_6, and finally Hb_4O_8.
The S-shape of the dissociation curve is due to the fact that the affinity of each of
the 4 haem groups for oxygen depends on whether any or all of the other 3 have
already combined with oxygen or not; in Hb_4O_6, in particular, the remaining
unoccupied haem must be presumed to have a much greater affinity for oxygen
than it had when all 4 of the haems were unoccupied. The 4 haem groups must
thus interact with each other, presumably through the globin part of the molecule.
Since the magnitudes of all these interactions are not yet known, the Mass Action

equation must contain 4 arbitrary constants. But if these are suitably chosen, the rather complicated equation fits the observed curves very accurately.

Factors Altering the Dissociation Curve

The effect of carbon dioxide (and acidity) on the affinity of haemoglobin for oxygen is of considerable importance in enabling the blood to unload oxygen more readily into the tissues. It was first studied by Bohr, Hasselbalch and Krogh in 1904, and is often referred to as the **Bohr Effect.** Thus, for example, it can be seen from the curves that at an oxygen partial pressure of 32 mm Hg the oxygen content of normal human blood is 13 ml/100 ml when the carbon dioxide pressure is 40 mm Hg, and a little under 12 ml/100 ml when the carbon dioxide pressure is increased to 50 mm Hg. Now the partial pressure of carbon dioxide is about 40 mm Hg in the arterial blood, and about 50 mm Hg in the venous blood, so that roughly 1 ml of extra oxygen is obtained by the tissues from each 100 ml of blood, owing to this displacing action of acid, without lowering the partial pressure of oxygen within them.

Since carbon dioxide is blown off in the lungs, and taken up in the tissues, none of the family of curves shown in Fig. 10.1 accurately represents the "physiological oxygen dissociation curve". This passes from a point A, corresponding to the conditions met with in the lungs, i.e. 98 per cent saturation with oxygen at a partial pressure of 108 mm of oxygen and 40 mm of carbon dioxide, to a point V, corresponding to the conditions met with in the tissues, i.e. 58 per cent saturation with oxygen at a partial pressure of 32 mm Hg of oxygen and 50 mm Hg of carbon dioxide.

It will be observed that the whole of the oxygen is never removed from the blood. This is due, first, to the fact that a small, but definite partial pressure of oxygen must exist in the tissue cells, and secondly, to the fact that oxygen must diffuse from the blood capillaries to the tissue cells, sometimes over quite a long distance. A considerable head of pressure is thus needed to drive the oxygen across at the requisite rate.

Exercise

In exercise, the rate at which oxygen is needed by the muscles is greatly increased, and the amount of oxygen taken from each millilitre of blood is also increased, with the result that the partial pressure of oxygen in the venous blood is decreased (point V' in Fig. 10.1). There is thus a smaller head of pressure available for an increased rate of diffusion. This apparent contradiction is resolved by the observation that the number of capillaries carrying blood, per unit volume of muscle, is enormously increased when the muscle becomes active—possibly becoming 100 times greater. Consequently, not only is the distance decreased over which the oxygen must diffuse, but also the surface is increased over which oxygen can leave the blood.

The Foetal Blood

The haemoglobin in the blood of the foetus has a greater affinity for oxygen than has that in the maternal blood. Its dissociation curve, even at relatively high partial pressures of carbon dioxide, would lie to the left, in Fig. 10.1, even of that drawn for 20 mm of carbon dioxide. When the maternal blood, therefore, is, say, 50 per cent saturated with oxygen, the foetal blood will be, perhaps, 80 per cent saturated. Oxygen will consequently pass readily from the mother to the foetus in the placenta. There is, of course, a corresponding disadvantage, in that the partial pressure of oxygen in the foetal tissues must be small before the foetal haemoglobin will part with its oxygen.

Myoglobin

Most mammalian muscles contain a pigment which is closely related chemically to haemoglobin, and is known as *myo-haemogoblin*, or *myoglobin*. It differs from haemoglobin in having an oxygen dissociation curve which is a rectangular hyperbola (broken curve in Fig. 10.1). Myoglobin will become nearly fully saturated with oxygen at partial pressures normally found in the tissues, and at which haemoglobin has parted with most of its oxygen. It is known, also, that the tissue oxidation enzymes will function at oxygen pressures down to 5 mm Hg or a little less, and at these pressures myoglobin will part with about 40 per cent of its oxygen. Myoglobin, therefore, can act as an effective reservoir of oxygen in the muscles.

Speed of Reactions

Under physiological conditions the combination of oxygen with haemoglobin, and the dissociation of oxyhaemoglobin only take about 1/100 sec, and are thus too rapid to limit the rate of exchange of oxygen between the circulating blood in the capillaries (which each corpuscle takes about a second to traverse) and the lungs or tissues. Diffusion through the tissue cells and into the interior of the red blood cells seems to be the main factors which limit the rapidity of oxygen exchange in the animal.

Such very rapid chemical reactions cannot be timed by the ordinary methods—they require the special methods of Hartridge and Roughton for measurement of their rates. To determine the speed of combination, for instance, a solution of reduced haemoglobin and a solution of oxygen in water are driven through separate leads into a small chamber where they mix in less than 1/1,000 sec and travel thence into an observation tube. The percentage oxyhaemoglobin in the streaming fluid at various positions along the observation tube is measured spectroscopically, the fluid being kept in motion whilst the readings are taken. From the rate of flow of the liquid and the distance of the point of observation from the mixing chamber, the time taken by the reaction to reach the oxyhaemoglobin percentage recorded by the spectroscope is simply calculated, and hence the velocity of the reaction can be determined.

The Combination of Haemoglobin with Carbon Monoxide

Carbon monoxide also combines reversibly with haemoglobin, forming a compound usually known as *carboxyhaemoglobin*, and often written COHb. If a solution of haemoglobin is equilibrated with a mixture of oxygen and carbon monoxide, the partial pressures, Po_2 and Pco being so large that no reduced haemoglobin is present, the ratio of carboxy-haemoglobin to oxyhaemoglobin is defined by the equation:

$$\frac{COHb}{O_2Hb} = M.\frac{Pco}{Po_2} \text{ where M is about 250.}$$

Thus, if the pressure of carbon monoxide is about 1/250 of that of oxygen, one-half of the haemoglobin will be combined with carbon monoxide, and one-half with oxygen; haemoglobin has about 250 times as great an affinity for carbon monoxide as it has for oxygen. This great affinity is due to the fact that carboxyhaemoglobin dissociates at least 1,000 times more slowly than does oxyhaemoglobin. In other respects, the reaction between carbon monoxide and haemoglobin is very like that between oxygen and haemoglobin—the volume of carbon monoxide combined at maximum saturation is the same as that of oxygen; the dissociation curve (in the absence of oxygen) is also S-shaped and similarly affected by acidity and temperature.

Carbon Monoxide Poisoning

The great affinity between carbon monoxide and haemoglobin accounts for the danger attending the inhalation of small amounts of carbon monoxide or a mixture of gases containing it, e.g. coal gas. Blood can be completely saturated with carbon monoxide at a partial pressure of only 0·5 per cent of an atmosphere at 37°C, whereas it requires at least 15 per cent of oxygen before even approximate saturation is reached. If the whole of the available haemoglobin becomes saturated with carbon monoxide, no oxygen can be carried, and the animal will be asphyxiated.

No marked symptoms are detectable until about 30 per cent of all the haemo-globin in the body is saturated with carbon monoxide. Vision, hearing and intelli-gence become impaired when the carbon monoxide saturation reaches 50 per cent, and death has been known to occur at 60 per cent saturation; 80 per cent saturation is almost invariably fatal. The average dissociation curve of carboxyhaemoglobin shows that with most people the first symptoms would be observed when the air they were breathing contained about 0·03 per cent (1 part in 3,000) of carbon monoxide, while 0·4 per cent (1 part in 250) would be fatal; different people, however, have somewhat different susceptibility.

If an ordinary gas leak occurs in an ordinary room (a gas fire is turned on and not lighted, for example), it is very unlikely that there will ever be more than 0·25 per cent of gas in the room, owing to leakage up the chimney and through the cracks of the window and diffusion through the walls and the ceiling to adjacent rooms (this would probably not apply to the case of a large gas cooker in a small kitchenette). Ordinary coal gas contains, as a rule, about 10 per cent of carbon monoxide; water gas, however, is now usually added, and the gas as supplied may contain 20 per cent, or more, of carbon monoxide. There might thus be as much as 0·5 per cent of carbon monoxide in the room, so that an ordinary leak in an ordinary room might have fatal consequences, and would almost certainly produce serious symptoms. Coal gas, it must be remembered, is lighter than air, and hence rises to the ceiling; a tall man may thus notice symptoms of anoxaemia before a short man. Natural gas, on the other hand, may contain up to 80 per cent methane, and is much safer.

Tobacco smoke contains appreciable quantities of carbon monoxide, and some of the deleterious effects of over-smoking have been attributed to a chronic anoxaemia produced by the continuous presence of carboxyhaemoglobin in the blood;* it is, indeed, quite easy to detect the presence of this compound in the blood of a heavy smoker. The exhaust gas of motor cars also contains considerable amounts of carbon monoxide.

The treatment in all cases of carbon monoxide poisoning should be the administration of oxygen. The high pressure of oxygen not only facilitates the eventual dissociation of the carboxyhaemoglobin, but also enables an appreciable amount of oxygen to be carried in simple solution in the blood.

Carboxyhaemoglobin is cherry pink in colour rather than scarlet, like oxyhaemoglobin. Its absorption spectrum shows two bands in the visible spectrum, one in the yellow, the other in the green. These resemble the corresponding bands of oxyhaemoglobin, except that they are not quite so distinct and are nearer to the blue end of the spectrum. Unlike oxyhaemoglobin, carboxyhaemoglobin is very readily dissociated by exposure to strong light.

The estimation of carbon monoxide in blood is of importance both from the medico-legal and from the physiological points of view (cf. estimation of blood volume); a variety of methods have been used:—

(1) *Optical*. (*a*) Depending on the difference in colour between carboxyhaemoglobin and oxyhaemoglobin (cf. Haldane's carmine titration method).

(*b*) Depending on the difference in position between the absorption bands of carboxyhaemoglobin and of oxyhaemoglobin (cf. Hartridge's reversion spectroscope).

(2) *Chemical*. Depending on the colour of the precipitate formed by COHb with tannic acid.

(3) *Gasometric*. Depending on an adaptation of van Slyke's methods for oxygen and carbon dioxide estimation in blood.

Where sufficient blood is available, the gasometric method is the most accurate and reliable.

The Regulation of the Hydrogen Ion Concentration

When oxygen is shaken with water, it merely goes into physical solution, and does not form any chemical compound, unless there be added to the water some substance like haemoglobin, which is specially capable of combining with the oxygen. Carbon dioxide, on the other hand, not only dissolves readily in water (or any watery fluid), but also reacts chemically with the water to form carbonic acid, H_2CO_3; this being a weak acid, splits up to some extent into hydrogen ions and bicarbonate ions. Bicarbonate ions are also capable of splitting up further into hydrogen ions and

* This poisonous effect of tobacco smoking is additional to its proven association with the induction of carcinoma of the lung. Smokers beware!

carbonate ions, but this second ionization only occurs appreciably at more alkaline reactions than those found in the body fluids.

The first ionization, viz, the formation of H^+ and HCO_3^- ions, is, however, very marked under the conditions in the body and hence the blood would go markedly acid when it takes up carbon dioxide in the tissues, were there not present some chemical mechanism to counteract such changes, namely, the buffer mechanism explained later. The presence of the latter is hardly to be wondered at, for many processes in living organisms, such as the velocity of enzyme actions, and the stability of proteins, are greatly affected by changes in acidity and to *different extents;* hence any marked change in acidity would tend to throw the whole organism out of gear.

Carbon dioxide transport and maintenance of neutrality are both important, and both closely interconnected; for a clear understanding of them some knowledge of the general physical chemistry of buffer systems and of ionic equilibria in solution is needed. The reader is recommended to consult a suitable text-book of biochemistry or physical chemistry.

Buffer Action

If we titrate a weak acid, such as carbonic acid, with a strong base, such as sodium hydroxide, and plot the pH of the solution against the number of gram-molecules of base added, we get a curve such as that shown in Fig. 10.2. Clearly, the steeper is the titration curve, the more base (or, of course, acid) must be added in order to produce a given change in pH, and the more strongly is the solution said to be *buffered*. The salt of the weak acid is very nearly completely ionized, while the free acid is almost completely un-ionized; we can thus regard the variation with pH of the amount of base added, as equivalent to the variation with pH of the degree of ionization of the acid. The maximum slope, and the strongest buffer action, occurs when the weak acid is exactly half titrated, i.e. when the hydrogen ion concentration is equal to the apparent dissociation constant of the weak acid. In practice, the region of hydrogen ion concentration over which the buffering power is reasonably large is taken to be ten times greater to ten times less than the value of the dissociation constant. Alternatively, we can say that the pH must be within one unit on either side of the value of pK'.* The buffering power of a given solution is also, of course, directly proportional to the concentration of those buffer substances whose pK' is within one unit of the pH of the solution. Exactly similar arguments can be used in connection with weak bases, when titrated with strong acids; they also act as buffers, but are not met with in any appreciable concentration in solutions of physiological interest.

* pK is the negative logarithm of the dissociation constant. It is comparable in origin with pH, the negative logarithm of the hydrogen ion concentration.

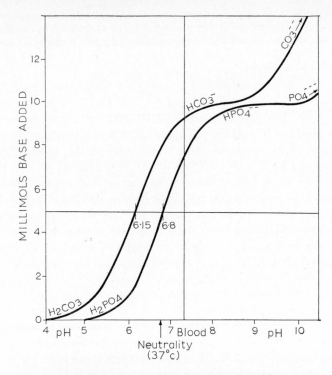

FIG. 10.2. Titration Curves of Weak Acids.

H_2CO_3 and NaH_2PO_4 in 10 mM solution are titrated with NaOH. The value of pK' is given by the pH at which the acid is half titrated. This value varies with the nature and concentration of the other ions in the solution; the curves are drawn approximately for the conditions in plasma. The vertical line is drawn at the pH of blood. (After L. J. Henderson.)

The reader may perhaps be reminded that the pH is a convenient measure of the hydrogen ion concentration, which is usually extremely small. The pH is defined as the negative logarithm of the hydrogen ion concentration; so that a hydrogen ion concentration of, say, 5×10^{-8}, or $10^{-7.3}$ g ions per litre corresponds to a pH of 7·3.

The shape of the titration curves may be deduced from the Law of Mass Action. If we have a weak acid HA which dissociates into H^+ and A^-, the following reaction will be in equilibrium.

$$HA \rightleftharpoons H^+ + A^-$$

whence

$$[H^+] = K_a \cdot \frac{[HA]}{[A^-]}$$

or

$$pH = pK_a + \log \frac{[A^-]}{[HA]}$$

square brackets denoting concentrations. These equations indicate that so long as the H^+ ion concentration is of the same order of magnitude as the dissociation constant K_a, the greater is the H^+ concentration, the less is the acid ionized.

The Buffers in Blood

The buffer substances present in blood are (a) bicarbonate, (b) haemoglobin, (c) the plasma proteins, and (d) phosphates. From Fig. 10.2 we see that the bicarbonate system is not, by itself, a very effective buffer at the normal pH of blood—its pK value is 1·2 units from the pH of blood. It is present, however, in relatively high concentration, so that its effect is quite appreciable. The $Na_2HPO_4 - NaH_2PO_4$ system, on the contrary, is effective as far as buffer power is concerned, but the concentration of phosphates is so low that they play little part in buffering the blood. In the urine, phosphates provide the greater part of the buffering in normal circumstances. The most important buffering substance in the blood is undoubtedly haemoglobin; this, in the corpuscles, exists as a mixture of the potassium salt KHb, which may be regarded as ionized into K^+ and Hb^-, and the free acid HHb, which is un-ionized. Haemoglobin is a complex polybasic acid, and its titration curve consists of a large number of the S-shaped curves of Fig. 10.1 on top of one another, and overlapping. The general conception of buffer action is nevertheless still applicable. The plasma proteins behave in a similar way, but are present in much smaller concentration. If, then, we add a small quantity of an acid to some blood, the hydrogen ion concentration will be increased. This, however, will lead to a reduction in the ionization of both haemoglobin and carbonic acid, and many of the extra hydrogen ions will be absorbed and tucked away in the undissociated acids. Conversely, if an alkali be added, the extra hydroxyl ions will combine with hydrogen ions to form water, and the effect will be exactly the opposite of that which occurs when acid is added. Haemoglobin and carbonic acid will dissociate more completely, and provide extra hydrogen ions to replace those which were removed by the alkali. All this is, of course, but a verbal description of the fact illustrated in the titration curves, that in a buffered system the pH changes only slowly with the addition of acid or alkali.

The efficiency of the buffering process in the blood is indicated by the following calculation. If we take blood at a pH 7·4 and add acid until it has a pH 7·2, the increase in free hydrogen ion concentration is

$$10^{-7 \cdot 2} - 10^{-7 \cdot 4} \text{ or } 2 \cdot 3 \times 10^{-8} \text{ g-ions per litre.}$$

During the course of this change in pH, however, the haemoglobin absorbs, by buffer action, no less than $660,000 \times 10^{-8}$ g-ions per litre, while the carbonic acid absorbs $70,000 \times 10^{-8}$ g-ions per litre. The total amount of hydrogen ions which must be added to produce this change in pH is thus $730,000 \times 10^{-8}$ per litre of blood, of which only $2 \cdot 3 \times 10^{-8}$ remain free. If we remove hydrogen ions from normal blood (or add hydroxyl ions) until the pH is 7·6, the decrease in free hydrogen ion concentration is $1·5 \times 10^{-8}$ g-ions per litre, while haemoglobin releases again $660,000 \times 10^{-8}$ g-ions per litre and carbonic acid releases $44,000 \times 10^{-8}$ g-ions per litre. These figures indicate the relative importance of carbonic acid and haemoglobin in buffering the blood. Roughly, 90 per cent of the hydrogen ions added or removed are absorbed or released by haemoglobin, and 10 per cent by the carbonic acid-bicarbonate system.

The above calculations are based on the following equations: (1) The buffering power of haemoglobin is represented by the empirical equation

$$[HbO_2^-] = 0·22 \, [HbO_2] \, (pH - 6·60)$$

$[HbO_2^-]$ is expressed in milli-equivalents per litre and $[HbO_2]$ in grams per litre.

(2) The buffering power of the carbonic acid-bicarbonate system is represented by the well-known Henderson-Hasselbalch equation

$$pH = 6·12 + \log [HCO_3^-] - \log [H_2CO_3]$$

The values taken are:

[HbO_2] 150 g/litre.
Total $CO_2 = [H_2CO_3] + [HCO_3^-] = 24·8$ millimoles/litre.
Total base $= [HCO_3^-] + [HbO_2^-]$ at pH 7·4 $= 50$ millimoles/litre.

In this example, we have imagined that no carbon dioxide is lost or gained by the blood when the pH is changed. This approximates to the conditions in the capillaries when some acid product of metabolism is formed in the tissues and diffuses into the blood stream. If we consider the body as a whole, however, the conditions are different, since carbon dioxide can be blown off in the lungs and acid or base can be excreted by the kidneys. As we shall see in later chapters, the respiratory centre and the kidneys adjust the ventilation rate and pH of the urine, respectively, in such a way as to keep the pH of the blood constant. The buffering is thus perfect. Confining ourselves for the moment to the actions of the respiratory centre, we see that the buffering results, in the end, entirely from the increased loss, or retention, of carbon dioxide in the lungs. The extra hydrogen ions are entirely absorbed, or released, by the bicarbonate system, and haemoglobin in the long run plays no part. There are thus three lines of defence against changes in hydrogen ion concentration: (1) direct buffering in the blood, mainly by haemoglobin; (2) indirect buffering by the action of the respiratory centre in controlling the free carbon dioxide concentration in the blood; and (3) indirect buffering by the kidneys, which more slowly excrete the excess acid or base, as the case may be.

Chapter 11

THE CARRIAGE OF CARBON DIOXIDE

Blood loses oxygen and gains carbon dioxide in its passage through the tissues and undergoes the reverse changes during its passage through the lungs. In the tissues and lungs the changes are roughly equal and opposite, so that it will only be necessary to describe one of them. For convenience, we shall consider the uptake of carbon dioxide by the blood in the tissues. The partial pressure of carbon dioxide in arterial blood is usually about 40 mm Hg, and the total carbon dioxide content (as estimated by vacuum extraction with acid) is about 50 ml (at N.T.P.) per 100 ml. The partial pressure of carbon dioxide in the tissues is higher than that in the arterial blood, hence carbon dioxide diffuses from the tissues into the blood capillaries. The amount of carbon dioxide taken up by the blood is some twenty times greater than the amount taken up by the water under like conditions of carbon dioxide pressure, hence only about 5 per cent of the carbon dioxide uptake by the blood is by simple solution, the remaining 95 per cent being through chemical combination.

The problem then, as in the case of oxygen, is to discover the means whereby each unit volume of blood takes up in the tissues, and gives out in the lungs, so much more carbon dioxide than would water in similar circumstances. We now know that there are two chief means by which this is done; one resulting from the combination of carbon dioxide with water, to form carbonic acid, which is buffered just as is any other acid; and the other resulting from a direct combination of carbon dioxide with haemoglobin.

In forming our ideas as to the transport of carbon dioxide, we must distinguish between the results of experiments in which blood is shaken outside the body with various gas mixtures, and the behaviour of the blood in the circulation. The former usually takes about fifteen minutes or longer; in the latter, the blood is often only in contact with the tissues (where it takes up carbon dioxide) and with the lungs (where it gives up carbon dioxide) for times of the order of one second. Attention must therefore be paid to the speed of the various processes, and this has revealed the presence of important factors which would otherwise have been missed.

Carbon Dioxide as an Acid

We have already discussed, in the previous section, how carbon dioxide combines with the water in which it is dissolved, to form carbonic acid; and how the buffer substances in the blood (chiefly haemoglobin) prevent the acidity from changing to any serious extent. The reactions involved may be written:

$$CO_2 + H_2O \rightleftharpoons H_2CO_3$$
$$H_2CO_3 \rightleftharpoons H^+ + HCO_3^-$$
$$H^+ + Hb^- \rightleftharpoons HHb$$

These reactions can be combined into the one equation:

$$CO_2 + H_2O + Hb^- \rightleftharpoons HCO_3^- + HHb$$

The net result of the series of reactions therefore is that almost all the extra carbon dioxide is carried in the blood in the form of HCO_3^- ions, the negative charges being supplied by the Hb^- ions. By this means the amount of carbon dioxide that can be carried in a given volume of blood is increased enormously over that which would be carried at the same partial pressure, in simple solution.

This does not, strictly, express the whole story. There must be some increase in hydrogen ion concentration, otherwise there would be no reason why the ionization of the haemoglobin should be depressed. This rise in hydrogen ion concentration has the effect of preventing some of the added carbon dioxide from being converted into bicarbonate ions. A little, therefore, remains as carbonic acid (the partial pressure of the carbon dioxide in venous blood is greater than that of arterial blood); the majority forms hydrogen and bicarbonate ions, and most of the hydrogen ions are absorbed by the haemoglobin.

The reaction of carbon dioxide with the plasma proteins may be expressed in a similar way, viz:

$$H_2CO_3 + Pr^- \rightleftharpoons HCO_3^- + HPr$$

and with phosphates by the equation:

$$H_2CO_3 + HPO_4^{2-} \rightleftharpoons HCO_3^- + H_2PO_4^-$$

The plasma proteins contribute only about 7 per cent, and the phosphates less than 3 per cent of the total buffering and carbon dioxide carrying power of the blood. They are, therefore, of minor importance as compared with haemoglobin.

Oxyhaemoglobin and Reduced Haemoglobin as Acids

This superior efficiency of haemoglobin over the plasma proteins is in part due to its higher concentration and its greater ionization in the physiological pH range; but it is, in the main, due to a much more important factor which has not yet been considered. In the living animal, when blood takes up carbon dioxide it also loses oxygen from combination with haemoglobin, so that the latter is left in the reduced form. Now it has been definitely shown that reduced haemoglobin is a *weaker acid* than oxyhaemoglobin, i.e. at a given pH, reduced haemoglobin is less ionized than oxyhaemoglobin. This means that the reaction

$$H_2CO_3 + Hb^- \rightleftharpoons HCO_3^- + HHb$$

must proceed further to the right at a given partial pressure of carbon dioxide, than does the reaction

$$H_2CO_3 + HbO_2^- \rightleftharpoons HCO_3^- + HHbO_2$$

i.e. the reduced haemoglobin ions do not hold on to their negative charges so firmly as do the oxyhaemoglobin ions, and so transfer them more readily to the bicarbonate ions. Reduced blood, therefore, takes up carbon dioxide in the tissues more readily than does oxygenated blood. Conversely, in the lungs when oxyhaemoglobin is re-formed from reduced haemoglobin the carbon dioxide will be liberated from the blood more readily.

These relationships are well shown by a comparison of the CO_2 dissociation curves of oxygenated and reduced blood. In curves of this kind the total concentration of carbon dioxide (chemically combined and

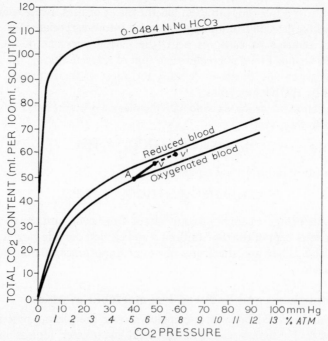

FIG. 11.1. Carbon Dioxide Equilibrium (Dissociation) Curves of Oxygenated and Reduced Blood, and of a Solution of Sodium Bicarbonate of the same concentration of Total Available Base as the Blood.

AVV' is the "physiological carbon dioxide dissociation curve", A being the arterial point, V the venous point at rest, and V' the venous point during exercise. (After Parsons.)

dissolved) is plotted against the partial pressure of carbon dioxide in the gas phase when equilibrium has been reached with the blood. In Fig. 11.1 the point A represents the average condition of the arterial blood, V the average condition of the mixed venous blood at rest, V' the condition of the venous blood in exercise. V and V' are both situated between the oxygenated and reduced blood curves, since in the circulation the venous blood is only partially reduced. It will be seen that the line AV is about twice as steep as the carbon dioxide dissociation curve of oxygenated or reduced blood. The change from the fully oxygenated to the partially reduced state enables the blood to take up about twice as much carbon dioxide for a given increase of CO_2 pressure as it would if there were no change in the strength of the haemoglobin as an acid. This phenomenon, first studied by Christiansen, Douglas and Haldane in 1913, is sometimes known as the **Haldane Effect.**

The whole difference in CO_2 carrying power of oxygenated and reduced blood must not be attributed to the difference in acid strengths of oxy- and reduced haemoglobin. The formation of carbamino compounds is also partly responsible.

The explanation of how reduced haemoglobin comes to be a weaker acid than oxyhaemoglobin is probably that one of the $-NH_2$ groups in the molecule, which takes up H^+ ions, is close to the haematin nucleus and that when O_2 combines with the latter, it reduces the ease of binding of the H^+ ion at this neighbouring $-NH_2$ group. Oxyhaemoglobin, being thus less able to bind H ions, behaves as a stronger acid.

The fact that loss of oxygen from the blood, as it passes through the tissues, renders it *ipso facto* more competent to take up carbon dioxide, just where such extra power is needed, and conversely, the fact that the uptake of carbon dioxide *ipso facto* drives off oxygen into the tissues, are beautiful examples of the way in which divers chemical phenomena are co-ordinated into a harmonious physiological process.

The "Chloride Shift"*

When carbon dioxide enters the blood from the tissues, some stays in the plasma, and the rest passes into the corpuscles. In both media the carbon dioxide combines with water to form carbonic acid, which dissociates into hydrogen ions and bicarbonate ions. Owing to the far greater buffering power of the corpuscle contents, this dissociation will proceed much more extensively in the corpuscle than in the plasma. Consequently, there will be a concentration gradient propelling carbon dioxide (undissociated) from plasma to corpuscle, and another gradient propelling bicarbonate ions from corpuscles to plasma. The membranes of the corpuscles, although permeable to anions such as chloride or bicarbonate, behave as if they were impermeable to cations such as sodium or potassium.

* Or also termed Hamburger interchange after Dutch physiologist of that name.

Bicarbonate ions will begin to diffuse out under the influence of the concentration gradient, but since they cannot be accompanied by ions of the opposite charge, the corpuscle will immediately develop a net positive charge. The positively charged corpuscle will then draw in negative ions of all kinds from the plasma. Chloride ions, being the most readily available, will predominate, and the process will continue until finally an equilibrium is reached at which

$$\frac{[HCO_3^-] \text{ in corpuscle}}{[HCO_3^-] \text{ in plasma}} = \frac{[Cl^-] \text{ in corpuscle}}{[Cl^-] \text{ in plasma}}$$

this being a case in which the physico-chemical principle known as the Donnan membrane equilibrium applies. The net result is that when the carbon dioxide content of the blood is increased, there is a migration of bicarbonate ions out of the corpuscles into the plasma, and a migration in exchange of chloride ions from the plasma into the corpuscles. When the carbon dioxide content is reduced, chloride ions come out of the corpuscles into the plasma, and bicarbonate ions enter instead. The carbon dioxide carrying power of the plasma is thus brought up to the level of, or even beyond that, of the corpuscles. Since the plasma hydrogen ion concentration is determined by the ratio of the carbon dioxide pressure to the concentration of bicarbonate ions, the transfer of bicarbonate ions from the corpuscles will assist in preventing the hydrogen ion concentration of the plasma from rising. The superior buffering power of the corpuscles is thus shared out with the inferior buffering power of the plasma—a process often spoken of as "secondary buffering" of the plasma: it is accompanied by the chloride shift only because the red cell membrane is sensibly impermeable to sodium and potassium ions.

If the plasma is replaced by isotonic NaCl solution, the chloride shift again occurs when the blood corpuscle suspension in NaCl is shaken with carbon dioxide, and for the same reasons as above. If, however, isotonic sugar solution is used, there is now no ion in the outside fluid to exchange with HCO_3^- from the corpuscle, so that when the corpuscle suspension is shaken with carbon dioxide the outside sugar solution cannot be secondarily buffered, and, since it contains no intrinsic buffer, it therefore goes very acid.

Separated Plasma and True Plasma

The chloride shift is mainly responsible for the difference between the carbon dioxide dissociation curve of "separated plasma" and that of "true plasma". The curve for *separated plasma* is obtained by centrifuging the blood, removing the supernatant fluid, shaking the latter with various pressures of carbon dioxide and then estimating the total CO_2 content at each CO_2 pressure. Over the physiological range of carbon dioxide pressure the curve is almost as flat as the CO_2 dissociation curve of a solution of sodium bicarbonate (Fig. 11.1): such a curve would be of little physiological service, since the extra amount of carbon dioxide which would be taken up when its pressure is raised from 40 to 50 mm Hg would be so small. The dissociation curve of "*true plasma*" is obtained by equilibrating the *whole* blood with various pressures of carbon dioxide, and then transferring the blood to a centrifuge cup (the escape of carbon dioxide into the air is prevented by a layer of liquid paraffin); the supernatant fluid, separated by centrifuging, is estimated for total CO_2, and the latter plotted against CO_2 pressure. Each sample of plasma thus is in equilibrium, not only with each different pressure of CO_2, but also with the corpuscles —whereas all the samples of separated plasma were in equilibrium with the corpuscles at one particular CO_2 pressure, namely, that which happened to obtain in the blood at the time when the plasma was centrifuged off. The true plasma dissociation curve is clearly quite different from the separated plasma curve; it is, indeed, of the same type as that of whole blood, and like the latter is of a serviceable shape as regards carbon dioxide transport.

As a result of all these mechanisms, the hydrogen ion concentration of the plasma is kept remarkably constant in the neighbourhood of pH 7·4 when the body is at rest. The difference in pH between arterial and venous blood at rest is only about 0·03, but in work it is rather greater, viz, about 0·08.

The Speed of the Processes involved in Carbon Dioxide Transport

Most of the individual chemical reactions we have described as occurring in the uptake or output of carbon dioxide are of an ionic type, e.g.

$$H_2CO_3 \rightleftharpoons H^+ + HCO_3^-,$$
$$H_2PO_4^- \rightleftharpoons H^+ + HPO_4^{--},$$
$$\text{HPr (protein molecule)} \rightleftharpoons H^+ + Pr^-.$$

Simple ionic reactions of this type have been generally supposed to be very rapid—experiments have, indeed, shown that all these reactions reach to within 1 per cent of equilibrium within 1/1,000 sec (from whichever side of it they start); they must therefore be too fast to limit the rate of output or uptake of carbon dioxide by the blood. The final chemical reaction, which, on the bicarbonate hypothesis, comes just before the evolution of carbon dioxide into the expired air is, however, a non-ionic one, viz, the formation of CO_2 from H_2CO_3.

The value of the velocity constant of this reaction has been measured by several physical chemists; it can thence be calculated that at body pH and temperature, and with the usual concentration of bicarbonate ions in the blood, carbon dioxide could only be evolved in the lungs at about 1/200th the rate at which it actually escapes into the expired air. Either, then, there must be something in the blood which speeds up the reversible reaction between carbon dioxide and water; or else there must be some other reaction, besides the bicarbonate one, which takes part in the transport of carbon dioxide. There are, in fact, both.

Carbonic Anhydrase

It can be shown, by quite simple experiments, that the red blood corpuscles contain a substance which catalyses strongly the reaction

$$H_2CO_3 \rightleftharpoons CO_2 + H_2O.$$

This substance has been isolated, was found to have all the properties of an enzyme, and was thus given the name "carbonic anhydrase". It is not present in the plasma, but the amount in the corpuscles, if it is as efficient there as in solution, is enough to accelerate the formation of CO_2 from H_2CO_3 about 600 times under body conditions. Presumably during the short time the circulating blood is in the capillaries, the change from CO_2 to bicarbonate and *vice versa* must occur chiefly in the red corpuscles.

Carbhaemoglobin

Blood can still react *rapidly* with a small amount of carbon dioxide even when carbonic anhydrase is absent or incapacitated by addition of some enzyme poison, e.g. KCN; this residual rapid reaction cannot be bicarbonate formation or the reverse (since both these processes, in the absence of carbonic anhydrase, only proceed slowly). There is chemical evidence that it is due to a direct reaction of CO_2 with the $-NH_2$ groups of haemoglobin to form compounds of a carbamino type, e.g.

$$Hb(NH_2) + CO_2 \rightarrow Hb(NHCOO^-) + H^+$$

This type of reaction is well known in the case of simpler $-NH_2$ containing compounds, such as ammonia and glycine, and is a very rapid one even in the absence of special catalysts.

Carbamino bound carbon dioxide plays an appreciable *rôle* in carbon dioxide transport, even though the absolute amounts of such compounds under physiological conditions form only a small fraction of the total amount of carbon dioxide present in the blood (in the neighbourhood of 5 per cent). Reduced haemoglobin takes up carbon dioxide in the carbamino form more readily than does oxyhaemoglobin. Of the total quantity of carbon dioxide carried from the tissues to the lungs—i.e. of the difference between the carbon dioxide contents of venous and arterial blood—it is estimated that about one-quarter is in the carbamino form.

Other evidence, of a more physico-chemical type, suggests that some carbon dioxide combines directly with haemoglobin, not only in the carbamino form, but possibly in some other form.

SUMMARY

The uptake of carbon dioxide by the blood in the tissues is believed to occur as follows:—

(1) CO_2 diffuses from the tissues into the blood plasma.

(2) Some of the CO_2 hydrates slowly in the plasma to form H_2CO_3; the latter then yields its H^+ ions to the plasma proteins and phosphates and forms bicarbonate ions.

(3) Most of the CO_2, however, passes into the red corpuscles:

    (*a*) Some combines directly with haemoglobin to form compounds of a carbamino type—this combination is increased as the haemoglobin loses oxygen in the blood capillary.

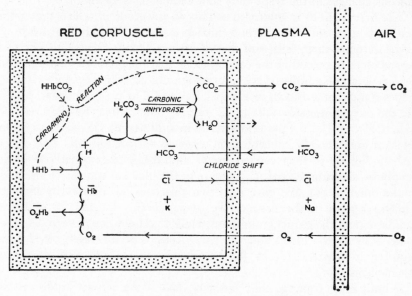

FIG. 11.2. Scheme showing the Most Important Changes involved in the Liberation of Carbon Dioxide from Blood into Air. (Roughton.)

    (*b*) By far the greater part changes over rapidly into H_2CO_3 under the influence of the enzyme carbonic anhydrase; the H_2CO_3 then yields its H^+ ions to the haemoglobin, forming bicarbonate ions. The latter process is much increased as the haemoglobin changes from the oxy- to the reduced form, since reduced haemoglobin, being a weaker acid than oxyhaemoglobin, absorbs H^+ ions more readily and thereby allows H_2CO_3 to become more completely ionized.

(4) Bicarbonate ions begin to diffuse out from the corpuscles into the plasma; this sets up an electric field which draws Cl^- ions into the corpuscles from the plasma in place of the HCO_3^- ions, which have diffused out (the chloride shift). The twin process goes on until an equilibrium is reached. The CO_2 carrying power and buffer efficiency of the plasma are thereby brought up to the level of the red corpuscles.

In the lung carbon dioxide is formed and evolved by a reversal of all these processes, as indicated in Fig. 11.2.

THE EFFECTS OF EXERCISE

The changes that take place in the blood as a result of exercise, or of increased activity of any kind, are quantitative rather than qualitative, and their magnitude depends largely upon the magnitude of the simultaneous changes in the respiratory and circulatory systems.

The first result of an increased activity in any group of cells is that more oxygen is used and more carbon dioxide evolved; the partial pressure of oxygen around them falls, and that of carbon dioxide rises. This effect is passed on to the blood in the capillaries, so that the quantities defining the venous points on our dissociation curves are altered, taking up, for example, values somewhat as shown in Figs. 11.1 and 11.2 by the points marked V', i.e. the oxygen pressure falls to 22 mm Hg, the carbon dioxide pressure rises to 58 mm Hg, the per cent saturation with oxygen falls to 30, and the total carbon dioxide concentration rises to 60 ml/100 ml. The extra carbon dioxide is thus carried away, and the extra oxygen provided, simply by allowing the partial pressure in the blood of the one to rise and of the other to fall. We have seen that this does not necessarily involve similar changes in the tissue cells, owing to the opening up of extra capillaries and the reduction in the distance that has to be traversed by the gases between the blood and the tissue cells. The increased blood-flow required is provided for by the vasomotor reflexes and local chemical mechanisms.

A limit must come to this, however, and if the activity continues to become greater, the oxygen pressure in the tissue cells begins to fall, and the oxygen supply to be deficient. The cells go into "oxygen debt", and, if this is severe enough, begin to liberate lactic acid. This addition of extra hydrogen ions drives the equilibrium reaction,

$$H_2CO_3 \rightleftharpoons H^+ + HCO_3^-$$

from right to left. The carbonic acid so formed is converted to carbon dioxide and blown off in the lungs (the respiratory centre adjusts the rate of ventilation so as to ensure this). The buffering power of the tissues is reduced, nevertheless, since the buffer salt, bicarbonate, is replaced by the fully ionized lactate, which has no buffer action; the hydrogen ion concentration of the tissues rises. If the exercise continues, there may be so much lactic acid produced that the hydrogen ion concentration of the arterial blood is affected to a significant extent. We shall see in the next section that the carbon dioxide pressure in the lungs may rise also, and these two effects may so alter the oxygen dissociation curve that the per cent saturation of the arterial blood falls. The oxygen and carbon dioxide transport system has now got into a vicious circle, and the exercise must stop. It is, indeed, sometimes terminated by unconsciousness.

It should be remarked that the whole of the body is affected by the changes that result in the blood from one group of muscles going into oxygen debt; the lactic acid, indeed, diffuses into all the wet tissues of the body, and may be oxidized in them—and particularly in the liver and heart—as well as in the muscles in which it was formed. The blood buffers play somewhat the part of a bank which allows one of its clients to overdraw his account at the expense of the rest, but if the overdraft is allowed to increase until it is comparable in size with the whole of the negotiable securities of the bank—and this in spite of the activities of the other clients to redeem it—the bank's failure is inevitable.

Section 5
RESPIRATION

CHAPTER 12

MECHANICS OF BREATHING

CONTINUED vital activity of tissues demands the appropriate interchange of the gases, oxygen and carbon dioxide, between the tissues and the atmosphere. In its more usual sense, respiration means the operation of the special apparatus concerned with the absorption of oxygen by, and the removal of carbon dioxide from, the body as a whole; this is termed external respiration. Internal, or tissue respiration, on the other hand, is the local process of utilization of oxygen and production of carbon dioxide by the tissue cells, and will be considered in a later chapter on Metabolism. In the present chapter we are mainly concerned with the process of external respiration.

The Structure of the Trachea-bronchial Tree

Air enters and leaves the lungs by traversing, first the nasal passages (and also the buccal cavity when the mouth is open), where the vascular mucous membrane warms and moistens the incoming air; next the pharynx, the larynx, and lastly the trachea into the main bronchi. The main bronchi then subdivide into airways of diminishing diameter, the bronchioles and respiratory bronchioles (Fig. 12.1). The final branching network of the bronchial tree opens into the terminal air sacs with their alveolar saccules, or alveoli (Fig. 12.1). It is in the alveoli that the respiratory gases, oxygen and carbon dioxide, are able to make close contact with the blood in the capillaries.

The tubes of the trachea and bronchi are kept permanently open by a series of cartilaginous rings embedded in their walls. These are partly made up of a dense fibro-elastic membrane. The whole of the bronchial tree is richly supplied with elastic fibres, mainly disposed in a longitudinal direction. These fibres, along with the elastic tissues in the lungs,

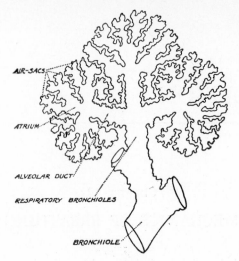

FIG. 12.1. Sectional diagram of a Structural Unit of the Lungs.
(After Miller.)

account for the recoil of the lungs and the bronchial tree which takes place during expiration (Fig. 12.2).

The respiratory passages are lined with ciliated and with mucus-secreting cells. The cilia produce a constant wave-like motion in the direction of the nasal and buccal cavities and are very efficient in expelling any foreign material that may come to rest on their surfaces.

The pharynx is a common pathway for air and food. In order to prevent the food going down the "wrong way," the aperture of the larynx is guarded by the epiglottis. During the process of swallowing, the arytenoid cartilages are closely approximated and pulled forwards towards the

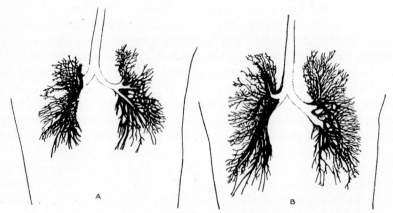

FIG. 12.2. X-ray photographs (retouched) of the Bronchial Tree of a young woman: (A) in full expiration, (B) in full inspiration. (Macklin.)

epiglottis, and at the same time breathing is inhibited (deglutition apnoea).

The lungs are so constructed that an almost instantaneous exchange of gases can take place between the air within them and the pulmonary blood passing through them. The pulmonary capillaries, although individually only about 8 μ in length and 8 μ in diameter, may altogether expose a surface area to the alveolar gases of approximately 70 m²; the blood in passing through these capillaries is exposed for no more than half a second (Fig. 12.3). Interposed between the blood and the air in the alveoli are two delicate membranes each of one cell thickness, namely, the

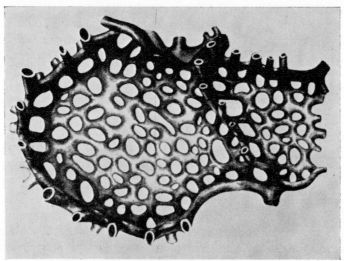

Fig. 12.3. The network of capillaries in the walls of the alveolar sacs (× 375). (From Miller, S. W. (1947). *The Lung*. C. C Thomas, Springfield.)

epithelium forming the alveolar wall and the endothelium of the capillary. The respiratory gases can readily diffuse across these membranes.

The Bronchial Muscles

The walls of the bronchi and bronchioles contain strips of plain muscle which run spirally round them forming a "geodesic" network.* Contraction of this muscle, therefore, narrows the bore and increases the resistance to the passage of air in and out of the lungs. Difficulty in breathing occurs when the contraction is excessive.

Blood Supply. The whole of the bronchial tree, as far as the respiratory bronchioles, is supplied by the bronchial arteries which are branches of the aorta. The blood is collected by bronchial veins and eventually drains into the right atrium; part of the blood is returned to the left atrium via the pulmonary veins.

* A "geodetic" line is the shortest distance between two points on a curved surface. A method of aircraft construction employed geodetic ribs since these give great strength to a fuselage, combined with light weight.

Nerve Supply. The *efferent* nerve supply is derived entirely from the autonomic nervous system. The vagus nerves are constrictor to the bronchioles whereas stimulation of the sympathetic nerves dilates them. The bronchioles also respond to the action of autonomic drugs; para-sympathomimetic ones, such as acetylcholine or pilocarpine, constrict, and sympathomimetic drugs, adrenaline and isoprenaline, dilate them. There is also some evidence that the calibre of the bronchi and bronchioles increases during inspiration and diminishes again on expiration, thereby assisting the diaphragm and the intercostal muscles in renewing the air in the lungs. The mechanism for this is largely passive.

The *afferent* nerve supply to the laryngeal mucosa is the superior laryn-geal nerve. Stimulation of its nerve endings, by the presence of a foreign body or as a result of disease, reflexly causes coughing. From pulmonary stretch receptors in the bronchial tree, afferent fibres run up in the vagus nerves; the chief function of these receptors is to indicate to the respiratory centre the degree of expansion of the lungs. This will be referred to later.

Asthma. Under certain conditions the muscles in the bronchioles are stimulated by irritation in various parts of the body, especially the nose and the air passages themselves, and undergo spasmodic contraction. This results in the condition known as asthma, in which great difficulty is experienced in breathing, particularly in expiration, since this is normally a passive movement. Bronchial asthma is associated also with hyper-sensitivity to certain proteins, notably those in the pollens of some grasses. This is analogous to the sensitivity of an anaphylactic type responsible for urticaria and hay fever. Anaphylaxis in general appears to be associated with the production of a histamine-like substance and it may be significant in this connection that histamine has a powerful constricting action on the bronchioles in some animals. Relief is rapidly obtained on administra-tion of adrenaline, isoprenaline and sometimes of anti-histamines, when they bring about relaxation of the bronchial muscles.

Respiratory Movements

A constant renewal of air in the lungs is brought about by movements of the diaphragm and thorax, and this constitutes normal breathing. With inspiration the cavity of the thorax is enlarged, and the lungs enlarge as well to fill the increased space. As a result the capacity of the air passages of the lungs is increased, and air is drawn in through the trachea. Inspiration is immediately followed by expiration, which causes a diminu-tion of the capacity of the thorax and expulsion of the air. During quiet breathing, expiration lasts 1·3 to 1·4 times as long as inspiration. Respira-tory movements are to some extent under the control of the will, and one can, for instance, cease breathing for a time. It is impossible, however, to prolong this respiratory standstill for much more than a minute, for the urge to breathe becomes excessive and against our will we are forced to breathe.

Inspiration. Inspiration is achieved, first, by descent of the diaphragm which enlarges the thorax from above downwards. The diaphragm, which is innervated by the phrenic nerves, is the most important muscle of respiration although its exact contribution in normal quiet breathing varies widely in different subjects. During deep breathing it may be responsible for as much as 65 per cent of the total volume of air inspired. Secondly, the thorax is enlarged by elevation of the ribs, mainly the second to the tenth. Since each pair of corresponding ribs forms a ring directed obliquely from behind downwards and forwards, this movement of the anterior end causes elevation of the sternum and an increase in the antero-posterior diameter of the thorax. At the same time there is an outward or lateral movement of each rib which increases the transverse diameter of the thorax.

The action of the intercostal muscles is at present uncertain but it would appear that in man at least, they are responsible for elevation of the ribs. When surface electrodes are placed over the intercostal muscles in the lower rib spaces, bursts of impulses occur only during inspiration in normal quiet breathing.

Expiration. The muscles of inspiration relax. The thoracic cage through its own elasticity diminishes in size and the walls of the chest are brought closer together assisted by the recoil of the bronchial tree and the lung tissues (see Fig. 12.2). In quiet breathing, expiration is probably entirely passive.

If a subject is observed in the supine position, it will be noticed that the abdominal wall rises and falls in each respiratory cycle. This due to the movements of the diaphragm displacing the abdominal contents, and is sometimes referred to as "abdominal respiration."

The *abdominal muscles* form a group of muscles having two important mechanical actions: first, raising the intra-abdominal pressure which results in the abdominal contents being pressed against the diaphragm and forcing it to ascend; and, secondly, drawing the lower ribs downwards and medially. These muscles show no electrical activity during quiet breathing. Activity appears, however, during the expiratory phase of respiration when breathing is increased, and in other circumstances involving voluntary expiratory manoeuvres, e.g. coughing, defaecation.

The *accessory muscles of respiration* comprise the scalene and sternomastoid muscles, the pectorals and serratus anterior, the rhomboids, trapezius and latissimus dorsi. For the ribs to be raised effectively during inspiration by the intercostal muscles, the thoracic inlet, i.e. the first rib, must be fixed. This is done by contraction of the scalene muscles which show electrical activity only during inspiration. Of the other accessory muscles of respiration, the sternomastoid muscles are probably the most important and show activity during voluntary inspiratory efforts and in patients with *dyspnoea*, that is, difficulty in breathing.

The Pleura and the Pleural Cavities

The lungs are enveloped in a closed membranous sac. The outer wall of the sac lines the chest wall and is called the *parietal* pleura. This is reflected at the root of the lungs, where it is continuous with the visceral layer which covers the lungs. The potential space between the layers is spoken of as the pleural cavity. It contains a small amount of fluid which acts as a lubricant. When the thorax alters in volume during the phases of respiration, the parietal and the visceral layers of the pleura normally maintain contact with each other. Even at the end of normal expiration the healthy adult lungs are in a stretched condition and this may be shown by the fact that if an opening is made in the pleural cavity, air rushes into the opening and the lungs collapse. The condition where air is present in the pleural cavity is called a *pneumothorax*. Since the lungs are always tending to collapse due to their elasticity, it is evident that they must exert a pull on the thoracic wall. The pressure in the pleural cavity is called the *intrapleural pressure*. It may be measured either by injecting a very small volume of air between the two layers of pleura and inserting a needle, connected to a suitable manometer, into this pocket of air or, more conveniently, by measuring the intra-oesophageal pressure, a tube being passed through the mouth for this purpose. The walls of the oseophagus are lax and so the pressure in its lumen is practically the same as the intrapleural pressure.

Owing to the pull of the lungs, the intrapleural pressure is below the pressure of the surrounding atmosphere and is called a "negative pressure" in consequence. In the expiratory position, it is 3–5 mm Hg below atmospheric pressure; in normal inspiration it becomes 5–10 mm Hg below atmospheric. If the lungs are more fully distended by a deep inspiration, the elastic forces are brought more into play, and the negative intrapleural pressure may amount to 30 mm Hg.

In forced expiration with the glottis closed (Valsalva's manoeuvre) and in other circumstances involving expiratory efforts such as straining, coughing and defaecation, enormous increases in intrapleural pressure occur. The maximum pressure that can be maintained voluntarily for 1–2 seconds is about 110 mm Hg. Transient intrapleural pressures of 300 mm Hg may occur during severe coughing.

The lungs may be thought of as a pair of bellows with an elastic recoil provided by a spring (Fig. 12.4). In order to expand the bellows, we must pull on the handles with a force which is sufficient: (1) to extend the spring; (2) to deform the material out of which the bellows are made; and (3) to overcome the resistance to airflow through the nozzle. The first part of the force depends on the amount to which the spring is stretched—

i.e. on the volume of air in the bellows. The two other parts depend on the *rate* at which the bellows are being expanded—i.e. on the rate at which air is being drawn in. Similarly, when the lungs are expanded during inspiration, the respiratory muscles must overcome both an *elastic resistance*, analogous to that exerted by the spring, and a *non-elastic* or *"viscous" resistance*, exerted by the lung tissue and by the flow of air through the bronchial tree.

If the lungs were perfectly elastic, and the viscous resistance negligible, the change in intrapleural pressure (analogous to the force pulling on the handle of the bellows) would depend only on the change in the volume of the lungs; the pressure–volume relation would be the same whether the lungs were being expanded or allowed to collapse. Furthermore, during respiration, the greatest negative pressure would coincide with the maximum volume at the end of inspiration, and the least negative pressure

FIG. 12.4. A simple model of the lungs represented by a pair of bellows and a spring. (From J. L. D'Silva, after R. V. Christie.)

with the minimum volume at the end of expiration; the cyclic changes in intrapleural pressure and in tidal air volume would be in phase with each other and the relationship between the two parameters would be linear (interrupted line in Fig. 12.6). Examination of the records in Fig. 12.5, however, shows that the two curves are not in phase; the changes in intrapleural pressure precede the changes in tidal air volume. This is because of the viscous resistance of the lungs. At the beginning of inspiration, the intrapleural pressure falls more rapidly than would be expected, since not only has it overcome the elastic resistance of the lungs, but also the viscous resistance, which increases as the rate of expansion of the lungs increases. In the same way, an additional force has to be exerted on the handle of the bellows to deform the material and draw air in through the nozzle. Conversely, when the rate of expansion becomes smaller, towards the end of inspiration, this additional fall of intrapleural pressure also becomes smaller until, at the end of inspiration (and again at the end of expiration), the lungs are momentarily at rest and the "viscous" forces vanish. During expiration, the rate of change of volume is reversed (the volume is decreasing, instead of increasing), the additional

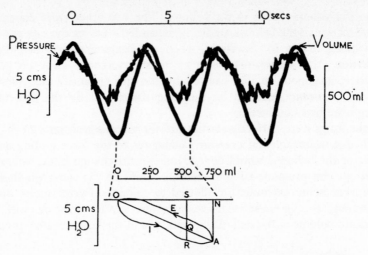

FIG. 12.5. Simultaneous records of intra-oesophageal pressure (representing intrathoracic pressure) and tidal air volume in a normal subject at rest. (McIlroy, Marshall & Christie.)

pressure necessary to overcome the viscous resistance is also reversed, and is subtracted from the pressure necessary to overcome the elastic resistance, instead of added to it; the pressure–volume relation is a closed loop, as shown in Fig. 12.6.

The existence of viscous, as well as elastic, resistance has two consequences of some importance. First, it contributes to the work which must

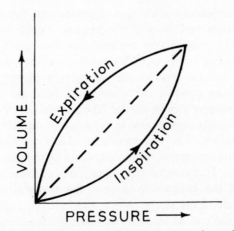

FIG. 12.6. Diagram showing the relationship between intrapleural pressure and tidal volume. The interrupted line shows the relationship were the lungs to comprise only an elastic resistance. The continuous line shows the relationship during inspiration and expiration with the viscous component added.

be done and to the oxygen consumed by the respiratory muscles to ventilate the lungs; this oxygen consumption is added to that needed for more "useful" work and of itself necessitates an increase in the volume of air inspired. The work done in overcoming the viscous resistance is about 40 per cent of the total, which increases disproportionately as the respiratory minute volume increases. Normal values are 0·5 ml oxygen per litre of ventilation, or 0·5 kg-m/min at rest; when a subject breathes maximally (about 180 litres/min) the work of breathing amounts to 250 kg-m/min. Secondly, the ratio of the viscous resistance to the elastic resistance determines the speed at which the lungs collapse. If, for some reason, the viscous resistance increases without a corresponding increase in the elastic resistance (the strength of the spring in Fig. 12.3), the lungs may not return to the initial expiratory state before the next inspiration begins. The volume of air in the lungs will become progressively greater (the spring will be increasingly stretched) until a new steady state is reached and the work needed to maintain the respiration will be greatly increased. This may occur during an attack of asthma.

Foetal Respiration and Expansion of the Lungs at Birth

The lungs of the foetus are airless and unexpanded; they contain a small amount of amniotic fluid. Only about 20 per cent of the right ventricular output passes through the pulmonary circulation, the greater part of the blood flow being short-circuited by an anastomotic channel between the pulmonary artery and aorta, the ductus arteriosus. It is probable that small but ineffective respiratory movements are made *in utero*. In animals these movements become accentuated when the mother is given a gas mixture containing little oxygen to breathe, and sometimes when the carbon dioxide content is increased. Increased respiratory movements also occur when the placental circulation is obstructed.

At birth, respiration is brought about by contraction of the diaphragm and intercostal muscles. At the same time, the pulmonary circulation is established although it is some hours before the ductus arteriosus closes completely. There are probably many factors coming into play in promoting the first breath. Of major importance in this connexion are the impulses emanating from the skin and from proprioceptors in the muscles, tendons and joints after birth of the foetus into the atmospheric air. Not only is the foetus exposed to the cold air and to contact with surrounding objects, but its transfer from its aqueous environment subjects it to the strains put upon it by its own weight. Another factor which may be important in bringing about the first breath is the chemical change in the blood when the umbilical cord is tied or the placental circulation fails; the oxygen supply to the foetus is cut off and carbon dioxide produced by the body accumulates. Consequently a state of asphyxia results in which the arterial blood oxygen partial pressure (Po_2) falls and carbon dioxide partial pressure (P_{CO_2}) rises. But how these changes affect respiration in the foetus is not fully understood.

The pressure necessary to inflate the foetal lungs for the first time is much greater than for subsequent breaths. This is due to the fact that in the foetal lung, two resistances have to be overcome: (1) that due to the cohering bronchiolar and alveolar surfaces which have to be separated by the residual volume of air, and (2) the resistance offered by the elastic tissue and smooth muscle of the lung parenchyma. The first of these is considerable and as a result pressures of up to − 35 mm Hg must be applied to the outside of the foetal lungs to inflate them.

Surfactant. We have spoken of the elastic recoil of the lungs as being due to the presence of elastic tissue. Another important factor is the presence of a special surface film lining the alveoli, called surfactant, which contributes to the elastic force of the lungs. All the alveoli have a liquid-air interface, and quite irrespective of the presence of elastic fibres in the lungs, will tend to collapse just as a bubble does due to surface tension.

Surface Tension. An atom or molecule in the centre of a solid or liquid is held on all sides by cohesive forces which may be of different kinds such as a chemical link between atoms or a metallic bond where positive ions of the metal are held in a sea of electrons. Near the surface of a medium, however, the force is not balanced because the surface particle is not completely surrounded by neighbours. As a result there is an attraction perpendicular to the surface tending to draw the particles inwards so that they will be at a higher potential energy than those in the bulk of the medium. The result of this imbalance of intermolecular forces is that the surface shrinks to its smallest possible area. The inward force upon atoms or molecules at a surface is mathematically equivalent to a tension in the surface, and the term *surface tension* has arisen to describe the phenomena associated with the high potential energy of such a region. Tension operates in the same plane as the surface, so that in a sphere the tension in the wall tends to make the sphere smaller. To prevent this happening there must be an equal and opposite force opposing it created by the pressure within the sphere. In a bubble, for instance, the tension in the wall contracting it is equal to that exerted by the pressure within the bubble. Then $P = \dfrac{2T}{r}$, where r is the radius of the sphere (Law of Laplace). If the surface tension in a bubble remains the same, irrespective of its radius, the pressure required to inflate it diminishes as the radius increases and vice versa. This explains why, when two different sized bubbles are put in communication with each other, the small one empties into the large one.

If the lung is considered to be made up of millions of bubbles of varying size representing the alveoli, it is inherently an unstable system, for the air in the smaller alveoli would empty into the larger ones with the result that all the alveoli would either be collapsed or hyperinflated. The presence of surfactant lining the alveoli prevents this from happening. The surface lining, however, must do more than simply alter the surface tension by the same amount in all alveoli. Alveoli vary in size throughout the lungs, some having a radius 3–4 times that of others, so that if all air spaces are to be kept inflated, the pressure would also have to vary 3–4 times. In alveoli which freely communicate with each other, this clearly cannot happen. The explanation lies in the fact that the surface tension of the alveolar lining decreases as the area of the surface film diminishes, and this property ensures that all alveoli, irrespective of their size, are stable.

The alveolar surface lining in contact with the alveolar gas is an insoluble lipoprotein layer about 50 Å thick. Between this layer and the alveolar epithelium is a layer of saline—dispersible lipoprotein 300–2,000 Å thick. This is the "living complex" or "alveolar surfactant" which acts as a reserve from which the insoluble "lining film" is formed. There is still some doubt about the identity of the alveolar cells responsible for forming surfactant. It appears in human foetal lungs between the 21st and 24th week intra-uterine life.

Respiratory Distress Syndrome of the New-born. This condition occurs in a minority of new-born babies, more commonly prematures. They rapidly develop difficulty in breathing with an indrawing of the thoracic cage with each inspiration, and impairment of the oxygenation of the blood. The mortality rate is about 50 per cent. Examination of the lungs of such cases post-mortem shows that they are collapsed and, significantly, there is an absence of the lung lining complex. It would appear, therefore, that the lungs instead of remaining inflated after the first breath, collapse due to the increased alveolar surface tension consequent upon the deficiency of surfactant.

Sounds Associated with the Movements of the Lungs

There are two distinct sounds associated with the movement of air into and out of the normal lungs, both of which may be heard by placing the ear on the chest or, better, by using a stethoscope. The first of these is a fine rustling noise, occurring during inspiration and the beginning of expiration, known as *vesicular breathing*; the second, heard only when the stethoscope is placed over one of the larger air passages, is louder and rougher, like a whispered "hah," and is known as *bronchial breathing*.

CHAPTER 13

LUNG VOLUMES, VENTILATION AND DIFFUSION

The Primary Subdivisions of the Lung Volume

The diagrammatic representation of a tracing of respiratory movements shown in Fig. 12.6 was taken from a subject who, after a few normal quiet respirations, took the deepest inspiration that he could and then expired to the limits of his ability. The upward stroke represents inspiratory and

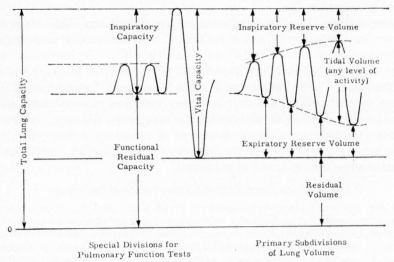

FIG. 13.1. Diagram showing lung volumes and capacities.

the downward stroke expiratory movements. The lung volumes may be divided into two main divisions, the "volumes" which can be breathed by the subjects, these being dynamic volumes, and the "capacities," each of which includes two or more of the primary volumes.

Values for the volumes are obtained by breathing in and out of a *spirometer* such as that shown in Fig. 13.2. This is a volume recorder on the lines of a gasometer; a cylindrical bell, closed at the upper end, is immersed in a tank of water, and counterbalanced. Air blown through a pipe passing through the water-seal raises the bell and the distance the bell travels is recorded by a writing-point on a moving paper. The spirometer is calibrated by injecting into it known volumes of air.

The volume that is inspired and expired during quiet breathing is referred to as the tidal volume and varies from 350 to 600 ml in different subjects. The tidal volume multiplied by the frequency of the respirations

174

per minute gives the total volume of air breathed per minute; this is known as the respiratory minute volume. At rest this is usually 4–8 l/min. The volume of the deepest inhalation that can be taken at the end of a normal inspiration is called the inspiratory reserve volume and is about 2,500 ml. The deepest exhalation possible at the end of a normal expiration is called the expiratory reserve volume and is about 1,500 ml.

Vital Capacity. When a subject, after the deepest inspiration, expires the largest volume that he can into a spirometer, the volume of air that

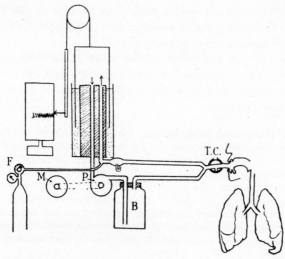

FIG. 13.2. Spirometer arranged in a closed circuit respiratory system to determine lung volumes. T.C., tap; B, bottle with absorbent for CO_2 (soda-lime or caustic potash solution); P, air-circulating pump driven by motor, M; volume of the system maintained constant by running in O_2 from cylinder F at the same rate as usage. (Redrawn from Herrald and McMichael.)

he expires is termed his *vital capacity*. Reference to the diagram in Fig. 13.1 shows that this volume is the sum of his tidal, inspiratory and expiratory reserve volumes and amounts to 4–5 litres. This amount is not an expression of the total volume of air in his lungs, since when he has completed his forced expiration there still remain about 1,500 ml of the *residual volume* which could only be expelled by opening the chest wall and allowing the lungs to collapse. To determine the total capacity of the lungs this residual volume must be estimated and added to the vital capacity. Even in the collapsed lung a small volume of the air is trapped; it is this which gives the collapsed lungs their buoyancy in water and is used in medico-legal investigations to ascertain whether the lungs have ever expanded and so determine whether a child breathed after birth.

The vital capacity is affected by the volume of blood in the pulmonary circulation. It is smaller when the subject is supine than it is when he is standing, the larger volume of blood in the pulmonary vessels presumably encroaching on the air capacity of the lungs. In certain forms of heart failure, also, particularly in left ventricular failure where the pulmonary vessels are congested, there is a reduction in vital capacity. These conditions are often accompanied by respiratory distress or difficulty in breathing (dyspnœa), but the mechanism by which it is brought about is still uncertain.

The *inspiratory capacity* is the maximum volume of gas that can be inspired from the resting expiratory level and is the sum of the inspiratory reserve volume and the tidal volume (Fig. 13.1).

The volume of gas remaining in the lungs at the resting expiratory level is known as the *functional residual capacity*. Reference to Fig. 12.6 will show that this is the sum of the residual volume of the lungs and the expiratory reserve volume.

Methods of Recording Respiration. Ideally, the record of the respiratory movements should allow us to discover (a) the frequency of respiration, (b) the depth of respiration and (c) the degree of expansion of the lungs at any moment, even if respiratory movements have stopped. There are only two ways in which this can be done. The first, which is shown in Fig. 13.2, is to connect the mouth of the subject (or the tracheal cannula of an anaesthetized animal) with a spirometer, to remove continuously the carbon dioxide from the expired air, and to add oxygen to make up for that used in the metabolism—to make use, in fact, of exactly the same apparatus as is used for determining the metabolic rate, as will be described later.

The simpler forms of apparatus for recording the respiration in man do not give accurate measurements of the total ventilation, but are useful, nevertheless, for many purposes. The *stethograph*, as now commonly used, consists of a piece of large diameter rubber tubing stoppered at both ends and connected with a tambour by a side tube at the centre; this is tied round the chest or abdomen, the movements of which distort it, and drive air into or out of the tambour. Many other devices for recording the movements of the chest or abdomen have also been described.

Pulmonary Function Tests

These tests "should now be performed on every patient with known or suspected cardio-pulmonary disease, just as haemoglobin determination, blood pressure measurement and urine analysis are performed routinely . . ." (Comroe). They provide an understanding of the functional changes in the lungs and assist in the detection of impairment of lung function but do not of course tell us where the lesion is or what it is if one is present. The results of such tests must be considered in relation to others, e.g. the history and clinical examination of the patient, X-ray evidence etc., and then they enable a more complete assessment of the clinical condition of the patient. In effect these tests must be considered analagous to those carried out to determine, for instance, renal function.

To carry out pulmonary function tests, the only equipment needed is a spirometer and recorder.

(1) **Lung Volumes and Capacities.** These are determined as discussed above. In certain patients it is also valuable to obtain values for arterialb lood P_{O_2}, P_{CO_2} and pH as an indication of the function of the lungs.

(2) **Forced Vital Capacity** (FVC). This is the gas volume expired after a maximal inspiration, with expiration being as rapid and complete as possible. Normal values are equivalent to those of the vital capacity, 4·5–5·5 l.

(3) **Maximal Voluntary Ventilation** (MVV). This was formerly called the maximal breathing capacity (MBC). The patient breathes as deeply and as quickly as possible for a period of 15 sec and the expired volume is measured and converted to l/min. Normal values vary from 125–170 l/min, but what is more important and significant in any one patient is a gradual change in the value one way or the other. The maximum voluntary ventilation is a test of function of motor neurones, respiratory muscles, lung volume and tissue, and airway resistance.

(4) **Forced Expiratory Volume** (FEV). In this test the patient inspires fully and then breathes out forcibly and maximally. The volume is recorded on a rapidly moving kymograph. The volumes expired at the end of 1, 2 and 3 seconds are determined from the record and expressed as a percentage of the total volume expired. The forced expiratory volume is designated $FEV_{1.0}$, $FEV_{2.0}$ to indicate the value determined after 1 and 2 seconds respectively. Normal values are: $FEV_{1.0}$ 83 per cent, $FEV_{2.0}$ 94 per cent, $FEV_{3.0}$ 97 per cent.

(5) **Forced Expiratory Flow** (FEF). This is the average rate of air flow for a specified volume segment of a record of a forced expiratory volume. Usually the volume measured is between 200 ml and 1,200 ml and the flow rate is expressed in l/min. The normal $FEF_{200-1200}$ is 400 l/min. The normal forced inspiratory flow ($FIF_{200-1200}$) is also 400 ml/min.

Composition of the Respired Air

Expired Air. The tissues of the body use oxygen for the oxidation of various materials and in consequence produce carbon dioxide. A man weighing 70 kg consumes about 250 ml oxygen/min and produces about 200 ml carbon dioxide/min. The blood reaching the lungs contains more carbon dioxide and less oxygen than arterial blood and in passing through the lungs therefore gives off carbon dioxide and takes up oxygen through an interchange with the air in the alveoli. This air is continually renewed by breathing, and hence expired air contains less oxygen and more carbon dioxide that than which is inspired. The composition of expired air, however, is not constant.

A sample of expired air is obtained by making the subject breathe through valves so arranged that he breathes in from the atmosphere and out into an airtight bag, known as a *Douglas* bag, from the name of its first user. Samples of air for analysis are drawn off from the bag and the volume of air collected in the bag in a given time is measured by pressing out its contents through a gas meter.

The expired air of a normal resting subject at sea-level contains 3·0–4·5 per cent of carbon dioxide and 16·0–17·5 per cent of oxygen. A comparison of the composition of inspired (atmospheric) and expired air is shown in Table 13.1.

TABLE 13.1

Composition of inspired and expired air

	Inspired air (per cent)	Expired air (per cent)
Oxygen	20·95	16·4
Carbon dioxide	0·04	4·1
Nitrogen (including argon).	79·01	79·5

As mentioned above, the volume of oxygen used up per minute is larger than the volume of carbon dioxide added to the expired air. The total *volume* of nitrogen leaving the lungs is, however, the same as that taken in. In the above analyses, the nitrogen percentage is seen to be higher in the expired air. This is because the volume at N.T.P. of air expired is less than that inspired, owing to the disappearance of a certain amount of oxygen without the production of a corresponding amount of carbon dioxide, so that the relative amount of nitrogen is slightly increased.

Alveolar Air.

This is defined as the gas in the alveoli which participates in gas exchange. Of the 500 ml of air drawn into the lungs during an average breath, only about 350 ml reach the alveoli. The other 150 ml are contained in the conducting air-way from the nose down to the respiratory bronchioles. This volume is known as the *respiratory dead space* and does not participate in gas exchange in the lungs. Hence alveolar air must contain more carbon dioxide and less oxygen than mixed expired air which consists of alveolar plus unchanged dead space air.

At the end of an expiration the dead space has been swept out by, and remains filled with, alveolar air. Based on this fact, a sample of alveolar air may be obtained for analysis in the following way. A piece of rubber or plastic tubing, 25 mm diameter and 1·5 m long, is fitted with a mouth-piece, near to which is connected a gas-sampling tube which is provided with a tap at each end. Before an experiment, the sampling tube is evacuated. The subject of the experiment applies a nose-clip and after breathing normally a few times, puts his mouth to the tube at the end of a normal inspiration, expires quickly and deeply and closes the mouth-piece with his tongue. The tap of the sampling-tube is then turned, and the air near the mouth-piece, which is that last expelled from the lungs, rushes into it. The tap of the tube is then turned off, and the gas sample removed for analysis. A similar sample is then taken, in which the subject expires deeply at the end of a normal expiration. This sample will contain slightly more CO_2 and less O_2 than that obtained at the end of inspiration. The mean of the two samples is taken as the average composition of the subject's alveolar air.

The significance of the composition of alveolar air will be better under-stood by reference to Fig. 13.3. This is a diagrammatic representation of what happens to the partial pressure or tension of the carbon dioxide and oxygen in the alveolar air and in the blood as it circulates through the lungs. (The partial pressure or tension of a gas is denoted by the symbol P followed by the suffix, thus, P_{CO_2}, P_{CO_2}, P_{N_2}). Let us suppose that a sample of the venous blood entering the lungs by the pulmonary artery contains carbon dioxide at a pressure of 46 mm Hg. As this sample circulates through the pulmonary capillaries some of the carbon dioxide will diffuse out into the air in the alveoli and will continue to diffuse until there is no further pressure difference between blood and alveoli. If the pressure of carbon dioxide in the alveolar air is 40 mm Hg, the pressure of carbon

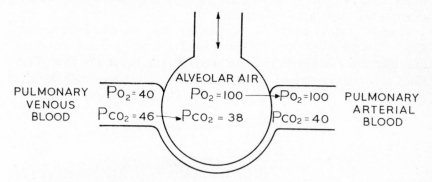

FIG. 13.3. Diagrammatic representation of alveolar air (see text).

dioxide in the blood in the distal end of the pulmonary capillary will also reach this value. This means that the carbon dioxide pressure in the alveolar air is almost the same as that of the arterial blood leaving the lungs.

The average composition in volumes per cent of alveolar air for adult men at rest, at 760 mm Hg pressure, is shown in Table 13·2, together with the partial pressures exerted by the constituent gases. It is better to express the data regarding respiratory gases in terms of partial pressures, as in the last column of this table, than in terms of percentage composition, as this is more meaningful since diffusion is dependent among other factors on the difference in the partial pressure of a gas on the two sides of the alveolar membrane and not on the difference in the content of the gases. From Dalton's law we know that the total pressure exerted by a mixture of gases is equal to the sum of the separate pressures which each gas would exert if it alone occupied the whole volume. Alveolar air is in contact with wet tissues and is saturated with aqueous vapour; its partial pressure, depending only on the temperature (47 mm Hg at 37°C), must

TABLE 13.2

Composition of alveolar air

	Volumes (per cent) (dry)	Partial Pressures (mm Hg) (wet)
Carbon dioxide	5·6	40
Oxygen	13·8	99
Nitrogen	80·6	574
Water vapour	0·0	47
	100·0	760

be included as a part of the total (i.e. barometric) pressure. The following example will explain the calculation.

Suppose that a sample of alveolar air had the composition (dry), $CO_2 = 5·6$ per cent; $O_2 = 13·7$ per cent; $N_2 = 80·7$ per cent by volume, and that the barometric pressure was 755 mm Hg at the time. Then, since the aqueous vapour pressure $= 47$ mm Hg, the remaining gases together contribute $(755 - 47) = 708$ mm Hg, and of this

$$P_{CO_2} = \frac{5·6}{100} \times 708 = 40 \text{ mm Hg}$$

$$P_{O_2} = \frac{13·7}{100} \times 708 = 97 \text{ mm Hg}$$

$$P_{N_2} = \frac{80·7}{100} \times 708 = 571 \text{ mm Hg}$$

These are the pressures exerted by each gas on any boundary surface.

Dead Space. As has already been mentioned, this refers to those parts of the respiratory tract—the nose, pharynx, trachea, bronchi and bronchioles—which act as a conduit for the passage of gases to the alveoli and in which there is no gas exchange. This is known as the *anatomical dead space*. The *physiological dead space* includes the anatomical dead space and two additional volumes: (1) the volume of inspired gas which ventilates alveoli which receive no pulmonary capillary blood flow, and (2) the volume of inspired gas which ventilates alveoli in excess of that volume required to arterialize the blood in pulmonary capillaries. In the normal subject, these two additional volumes are negligible and so the anatomical and physiological dead spaces are equal.

The volume of dead space cannot be measured directly, but can be calculated using Bohr's equation. This states simply that the gas expired from the lungs is a mixture of gas from the dead space and from the alveoli; if two of these (the expired air and alveolar air) are known, the third (the dead space air) can be calculated. From Tables 13.1 and 13.2, we can take the following representative figures: (1) CO_2 in alveolar air: 5·6 per cent; (2) CO_2 in expired air: 4·1 per cent. We will take the volume of tidal air as 600 ml (all measured dry and at room temperature). Then the total quantity of carbon dioxide expired in each breath is $\dfrac{600 \times 4\cdot1}{100} = 24\cdot6$ ml. But this quantity of carbon dioxide is contained in $24\cdot6 \times \dfrac{100}{5\cdot6} = 440$ ml of alveolar air; so that the 600 ml of expired air has the same composition as 440 ml of alveolar air mixed with 160 ml of inspired air, containing no carbon dioxide. The dead space consequently would have a volume of 160 ml. It must be remembered that this is the volume of the gas in the dead space measured dry and at a lower temperature than that at which it was when in the body. But since we wish to measure the volume of a cavity within the body, we must correct this gas volume to body temperature (37°C) and saturate with water vapour (47 mm Hg). (For details see textbooks of practical human physiology.)

The volume of the dead space varies, not only in different individuals, but even in the same individual according to posture and other factors. The most reliable measurements indicate that normally the dead space volume varies between 100 and 250 ml.

In disease, the physiological dead space may greatly exceed the anatomical dead space when ventilation in parts of the lungs is greater than that required to arterialize the blood.

Alveolar Ventilation. We have seen how the product of the tidal volume and frequency of breathing gives a value for the respiratory minute volume, or the turn-over of air as measured at the mouth. It must be realized, however, that part of the inspired air at each breath never reaches the alveoli, but remains in the dead space and is in consequence expired again without undergoing any change. The respiratory minute volume therefore gives little indication of the turn-over of air in the *alveoli*, which is of vital importance when considering how effectively oxygen is supplied to the alveoli and carbon dioxide is got rid of during breathing. The turn-over of air in the alveoli is known as the *alveolar ventilation* and is the product of the (tidal volume—dead space) and frequency of breathing. To illustrate how changes in breathing may affect the respiratory minute volume and alveolar ventilation differently we may consider the following example. A subject has a tidal volume of 500 ml, respiratory frequency 16/min and dead space 150 ml. His respiratory minute volume $= 500 \times 16 = 8,000$ ml/min. On the other hand, his alveolar ventilation $= (500 - 150) \times 16 = 350 \times 16 = 5,600$ ml/min. Now, if the subject doubled his tidal volume (to 1,000 ml) and halved his frequency (to 8/min), his respiratory minute volume would remain unchanged. His alveolar ventilation, however, would increase to 6,800 ml/min. This emphasizes the importance of the measurement of the volume of inspired air entering the alveoli rather than that entering the upper respiratory tract as a measure of the turnover of air in those parts of the lungs concerned with gas exchange.

The Mechanism of Gaseous Exchange between the Lungs and the Blood

In the lungs, carbon dioxide leaves the blood stream and enters the air in the lung alveoli, and oxygen leaves the alveoli and enters the blood. Since in doing so the gases have to pass through two membranes, the walls of the alveoli and the walls of the capillaries, the question arises as to whether the interchange of gases between the alveolar air and the blood in the pulmonary capillaries can occur by the purely physical process of diffusion. To answer this question we must study the tensions of oxygen and of carbon dioxide in the alveolar air, in venous blood coming to the lungs and in the arterial blood leaving the lungs. If the process is one of diffusion, the partial pressures and hence the flow of oxygen must be, in descending order: alveolar air, arterial blood, venous blood; and those of carbon dioxide in the reverse order.

The results of determinations made on man under normal conditions are summarized in Fig. 13.3 and show that the partial pressure of oxygen in the arterial blood is very close to that in the alveolar air. The pressure of oxygen in the alveoli is about 100 mmHg, and the venous blood, there-fore, with an oxygen pressure of 40 mmHg, brought to the alveoli will rapidly take up oxygen from them and approach the point of saturation.

The pressure of carbon dioxide in venous blood is about 46 mm Hg and that of the alveolar air is about 40 mm Hg. This pressure gradient will tend to cause a flow of carbon dioxide from the blood into the alveoli.

It is now generally agreed that the respiratory gas exchange is accom-plished by a process of simple diffusion, the direction and extent of which depends almost entirely upon the difference in tension or pressure on the two sides of the alveolar membrane, that is, the molecules of oxygen pass from a region of high partial pressure to one of lower partial pressure.

Diffusion. In the lungs of man, about 3 litres of alveolar air, corres-ponding to the functional residual capacity (see Fig. 13.1), surround about 100 ml blood contained in the capillary network of the pulmonary vascular bed. The pulmonary capillaries provide an effective area of about 40 m², and a freely permeable membrane less than $1.5\,\mu$ thick, separating the blood from the alveolar air. This area however is not the total alveolar area nor the total pulmonary capillary area, but represents that of functioning alveoli which are in contact with pulmonary capillaries in which blood is flowing. Nor is the area constant in any individual. It increases, for instance, in exercise.

The various structures comprising the alveolar membrane are shown in Fig. 13.4 from which it may be seen that an oxygen molecule entering a

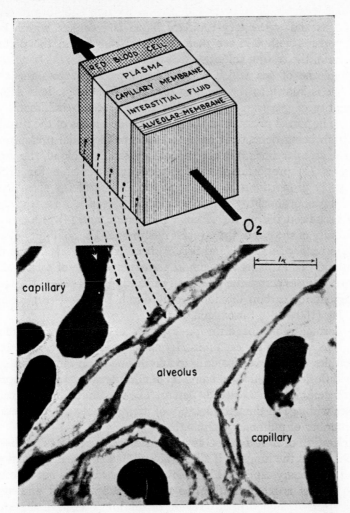

FIG. 13.4. Electron-micrograph of rat lung showing the tissues through which oxygen must pass from the gas phase in the alveolus until it combines with haemoglobin within the red cell blood ($\times$ 20,000). No attempt has been made in the diagram to portray the relative thickness of the different structures. (From Comroe *et al*.1955, after Low, 1958).

red blood corpuscle from the alveolus must pass through the layer of surfactant, alveolar epithelial lining, capillary endothelium, plasma and the red cell membrane. Diffusion of gases across the alveolar membrane will be impaired if there is any thickening due to disease or if there is an excess of fluid in the alveoli (pulmonary oedema).

The diffusion of gases across the alveolar membrane is very rapid, and at normal tensions of oxygen and carbon dioxide equilibrium between alveolar gas and pulmonary capillary blood is complete within 0·3 sec. This compares with 0·75 sec that the blood remains in the pulmonary capillaries in the resting subject.

The volume of gas which is capable of passing across the alveolar membrane is known as the *diffusing capacity of the lungs*. It is defined as the quantity of gas transferred each minute for each millimetre of Hg difference in partial pressure of the gas on the two sides of the membrane. Apart from being dependent on the difference in partial pressure of the gas in the alveolar air and in the pulmonary capillary blood, the diffusing capacity is (1) proportional to the total area available for diffusion, (2) inversely proportional to the average thickness of the alveolar membrane, (3) proportional to the ease with which the gas diffuses through the type of tissue comprising the alveolar membrane, and (4) proportional to the solubility of the gas in the alveolar membrane. The solubility of carbon dioxide in watery solutions (and tissues) is very much greater than that of oxygen, and this explains why almost the same volume of carbon dioxide as oxygen diffuses across the pulmonary membrane in spite of the fact that the gradient for carbon dioxide is only 6 mm Hg (46 — 40), as against 60 mm Hg (100 — 40) for oxygen.

The normal value for diffusing capacity of normal young adults is 20–30 ml oxygen/min for each mm Hg partial pressure difference. It more than doubles during exercise on a treadmill due to an increase in surface area for diffusion caused by opening up of additional pulmonary capillaries and to dilatation of others already patent. The maximum diffusing capacity decreases with age in the later decades of life, probably due to a reduction in the number of pulmonary capillaries.

Distribution of Blood and Gas in the Lungs. We have so far discussed gas exchange in the lungs as if all the alveoli had an equal ventilation and an equal pulmonary capillary blood flow. This, however, is not strictly true because neither is really uniform so that the supply of air and blood is never perfectly matched in any region of the lungs, even in the lungs of normal healthy man. In this connection the important factor is the *relation* between alveolar ventilation to capillary blood flow in different regions of the lungs, for as we shall see this has a bearing on the degree of oxygenation of the arterial blood.

The distribution of inspired gas in upright man is not equal in all parts of the lungs. Expressed in terms of ventilation per unit volume of the lung it is greatest at the bases of the lungs and diminishes up the lung so that it is smallest at the apices. This has been demonstrated by administering a single breath of radioactive carbon dioxide (Fig. 13.5). The rise in counting rate, measured by scintillation counters over different parts of the chest, is determined by the ventilation of the lung in the counting field and its volume. During the subsequent 15 second breath-holding period, radio-

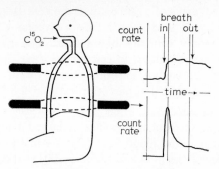

FIG. 13.5. Method of measuring regional ventilation and blood flow in the lung with radioactive carbon dioxide. Each pair of scintillation counters over the chest is connected to a recorder. The subject takes a single breath of labelled gas and holds his breath for about 15 seconds. The counting rate at the end of inspiration is proportional to the ventilation of the lung in the counting field and its volume, while the slope of the tracing during breath-holding (clearance rate) measures the regional blood flow (West, 1963).

active gas can only be removed by the pulmonary capillary blood flow. The slope of the counting rate tracing (clearance rate) is a measure of regional blood flow. This technique has shown that not only does the ventilation decrease up the lung, but the blood flow as well. A comparison of the two is shown in Fig. 13.6 from which it may be seen that the reduction in blood flow up the lungs is greater than that of the ventilation. This is also evident from a consideration of the relationship between ventilation and pulmonary capillary blood flow in different parts of the lungs, which

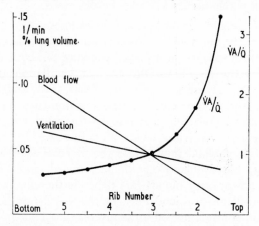

FIG. 13.6. The distribution of ventilation, blood flow, and ventilation-perfusion ($\dot{V}A/\dot{Q}$) ratio in different parts of the upright human lung. Note that because the blood flow falls more rapidly than ventilation with distance up the lung, the ventilation-perfusion ratio rises, at first slowly, then more rapidly. (West, 1965).

may be expressed in terms of a ratio, called the ventilation-perfusion ratio. The symbol $\dot{V}A$ is used to denote the mean alveolar ventilation/min and $\dot{Q}$ the mean pulmonary capillary blood flow. The ratio is then $\dot{V}A/\dot{Q}$. The normal alveolar ventilation in resting man may be taken as 4 l/min and the pulmonary blood flow 5 l/min. Then by dividing one by the other a value for the ventilation-perfusion ratio of 0·8 is obtained.

Returning now to Fig. 13.6, when the ratio is calculated for different parts of the lungs, different values are obtained because of the local variations of ventilation and blood flow. The ventilation-perfusion ratio is low (0·6) at the base of the lung and high ($> 3·0$) at the apex. This means that the alveoli at the base of the lung are slightly over-perfused in relation to their ventilation, whereas alveoli at the apex are under-perfused in relation to their ventilation.

What is the significance of this ratio?

When considered for the lungs as a whole (ventilation 4 l/min; blood flow 5 l/min; $\dot{V}A/\dot{Q}$ 0·8) the calculated value may give a false impression as to what is happening in individual parts of the lungs and therefore to pulmonary function. An extreme example of this is as follows. If the alveolar ventilation and pulmonary blood flow are normal ($\dot{V}A/\dot{Q}$ 0·8), but all the ventilation goes to the left lung with no blood flow, and all the blood flow goes to the right lung with no alveolar ventilation, the patient would quickly die of asphyxia! What is important therefore is not so much the absolute value for the ventilation-perfusion ratio for the whole of the lungs, but whether the normal ratio exists in all parts of the lungs. When it does not, then pulmonary function may be impaired and lead to arterial hypoxaemia. How this occurs will now be discussed.

The value of the alveolar, and hence the pulmonary end-capillary, Po_2 is about 100 mm Hg, and this level is determined by a balance between the rate at which fresh oxygen (at a partial pressure of about 150 mm Hg in room air) enters the alveoli via the alveolar ventilation and the rate it disappears from the alveoli via the blood. Thus, if the alveolar ventilation decreases while the oxygen consumption remains constant, the alveolar (and end-capillary blood) Po_2 will fall. In the same way, if the rate at which oxygen is removed from the alveoli is increased by augmenting the pulmonary capillary blood flow, while the alveolar ventilation is maintained constant, the alveolar Po_2 will be reduced, and vice versa. The alveolar (and end-capillary blood) Po_2 depends therefore on the *ratio* of the alveolar ventilation to blood flow, or the ventilation-perfusion ratio. In fact this ratio controls not only the alveolar Po_2, but in a similar way the Pco_2 as well.

The presence of some underventilated alveoli in relation to their blood flow, even in normal lungs, has important implications in so far as the degree of oxygenation of arterial blood is concerned, because blood leaving these areas will not be fully saturated with oxygen. Relative hyperventilation of other areas cannot raise the Po_2 of mixed arterial blood enough to compensate for this. The reason is that the dissociation curve of oxyhaemoglobin is almost horizontal between values of Po_2 of 95 and 125 mm Hg, and so blood leaving relatively hyperventilated areas at a Po_2 of, say, 125 mm Hg contains hardly any more oxygen than blood leaving alveoli with a normal ventilation-perfusion ratio. The result is that the partly unsaturated blood from relatively underventilated alveoli lowers slightly the Po_2 and saturation of the mixed blood from all parts of the lungs. This largely accounts for the fact that the normal arterial haemoglobin saturation is only 97 per cent and not 100 per cent. Gross unevenness of ventilation in relation to blood flow is the commonest cause of arterial hypoxaemia seen in patients in hospital wards.

With regard to carbon dioxide, the dissociation curve, unlike that for oxygen has no horizontal portion in the physiological range (Fig. 11.1). The CO_2 content of blood leaving relatively underventilated alveoli will be compensated by the lower CO_2 content of blood leaving relatively over-ventilated alveoli. The mixture of blood from all parts of the lungs, that is arterial blood, may therefore have a normal carbon dioxide content and Pco_2.

Alveolar-arterial Po_2 and Pco_2 Gradient. The unevenness of alveolar ventilation in relation to blood flow means that although complete equilibrium is reached between blood and gas in each alveolus, the arterial blood Po_2 is slightly lower than the alveolar Po_2. This is known as the alveolar-arterial blood Po_2 gradient and in man is 5–15 mm Hg. The gradient for carbon dioxide is considerably less, about 0·5 mm Hg.

CHAPTER 14

THE REGULATION OF BREATHING

EVERY movement of inspiration involves co-ordinated contraction of a number of muscles as a result of a discharge of impulses along their motor nerves. The extent to which these muscles contract determines the volume of air taken into the lungs. During expiration these impulses diminish or cease altogether and the inspiratory muscles relax. The elastic recoil of the lungs and chest wall is therefore largely responsible for expulsion of the air from the lungs, but active expiration may take place under certain circumstances and then a number of expiratory muscles contract. The respiratory rhythm and the extent of contraction of the two groups of muscles are regulated by the central nervous system, from which the impulses to the muscles of respiration are derived, in such a way as to keep the composition of the gases in the alveoli and arterial blood practically constant. To a large extent this is due to afferent impulses from chemically sensitive receptors reaching the specialized areas of the brain controlling respiration, so that any deviation in the Po_2 or Pco_2 is immediately compensated by alterations in breathing.

In this chapter we discuss first the rhythmic control of breathing by the central nervous system, and then the ways in which respiration is modified by nervous and chemical factors.

Discharge in Efferent Nerves. The regulation of breathing is brought about by alterations of the activity of the groups of motoneurones in the spinal cord which control the respiratory muscles. These motoneurones are in turn controlled by groups of nerve cells in the brain which are collectively known as the respiratory centres. The activity of these centres is determined by agents acting directly on them via the blood and also reflexly through the arrival of afferent impulses.

The main muscles of respiration are the diaphragm, innervated by the phrenic nerves which originate from the spinal roots C_2, C_3 and C_4, and the intercostal muscles which receive their innervation via the intercostal nerves, T_1–T_6. Each act of inspiration involves a discharge along these and a number of other nerves, e.g. the facial to the muscles moving the alae nasi and the vagus to the muscles of the larynx. Thus many segmental levels are involved in the innervation of the muscles of respiration, and the respiratory act is integrated not only in the brain stem but also in the spinal cord.

Studies of the activity of motor units in the diaphragm and inter-costal muscles have shown that there is activity throughout the whole phase of respiration, but that it is greater in inspiration than in expiration. During expiration the rate of firing is slow and is responsible for the thorax being maintained in a state of partial inspiration. The periodic increases and decreases in volume of the thorax are therefore superimposed on an underlying postural tone. The expiratory muscles also exhibit tonic activity. The act of inspiration begins, therefore, on a background of tonic activity in both the inspiratory and expiratory muscles, but whereas the activity of those fibres supplying inspiratory muscles which are in tonic contraction increase their rate of firing, that of expiratory neurones is reciprocally inhibited. Furthermore, as inspiration proceeds, new motor units come into action, or are "recruited," as shown in Fig. 14.1, so that the inspiratory act gains force as it proceeds. Then, when inspiration

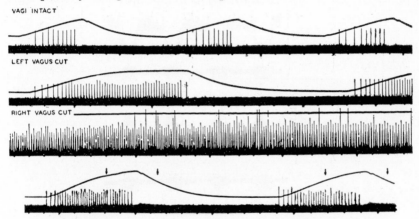

Fig. 14.1. The effect of cutting the vagus nerves on respiratory activity in a cat after section of the brain stem immediately below the pneumo-taxic centre. The lowest record shows the production of apneusis.

Each record shows, from above downwards: respiratory movements (upstroke = inspiration); nerve impulses in two phrenic motoneurones; time in 0·2 second. (Pitts, 1942.)

reaches a peak, it is abruptly terminated by various factors which control the depth of respiration. As expiration occurs, the units which maintain inspiratory tone revert to their former steady rate of firing, whereas the tonic discharge in expiratory units returns.

The control of respiration is integrated at two levels in the central nervous system; firstly, in the pons and medulla by the respiratory centres, and secondly, at a spinal level. The respiratory centres are considered below, but in the spinal cord it is the respiratory motoneurones that have the integrative function. These are large cells in the anterior horn of the grey matter, and in the cervical region they innervate the diaphragm; in the thoracic region they innervate internal and external intercostal muscles. Cells in both regions innervate accessory muscles of respiration.

Studies with micro-electrodes have demonstrated that their membrane potential is about 60 mV. Each cell has a number of afferent endings on its surface and some of these afferents when activated cause depolarization of the membrane with the result that the cell fires off and the impulses cause contraction of some respiratory muscle fibres. On the other hand, other afferent fibres when activated cause hyperpolarization of the cell membrane and then the cell is inhibited and stops firing. These fluctuations in potential of the cell membrane can be observed during normal respiration and are called "central respiratory drive potentials" (Fig. 14.2). Since the potentials continue after cutting the dorsal roots of adjacent segments of the spinal cord, they must be largely central in origin. These respiratory motoneurones are therefore the site of convergence of a large number of

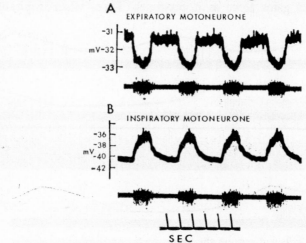

FIG. 14.2. The "central respiratory drive potentials". Upper traces in *A* and *B*, intracellular d.c. recordings from thoracic respiratory motoneurones; lower traces, diaphragm electromyogram (EMG). *B*, recorded approximately 15 min. after *A*. The records have been aligned above each other according to the diaphragm EMG. (Sears, 1964).

excitatory and inhibitory pathways of central and reflex mechanisms which affect the size and timing of the central respiratory drive potentials. Of importance in the control of breathing, therefore, are not only the impulses reaching the respiratory motoneurones from the respiratory centres, but those from the periphery, such as evoked by stretch receptors, which give rise to *segmental reflexes*.

RESPIRATORY CENTRES

Section of the brain stem above the level of the pons in the dog and cat does not affect breathing, but respiratory activity ceases altogether when all but the lower third of the medulla is removed. This indicates that the centres controlling respiration lie in the pons and upper part of the medulla.

Several methods have been used to locate these centres. The first is one already mentioned, namely, to transect the brain stem at different levels and observe the effects on respiration. Another is to stimulate electrically various parts of the brain through a fine electrode placed in position by a mechanically operated device. The actual position of the tip of the electrode is checked histologically after the experiment and correlated with the respiratory response observed by stimulation of that area. A third method is to analyse the electrical activity of neurones in specific

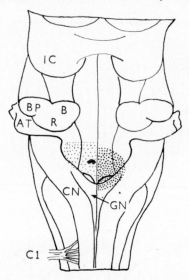

FIG. 14.3. Dorsal view of the brain stem (cat) with cerebellum removed, showing the projection of the medullary respiratory centres on the floor of the fourth ventricle. To avoid overlapping, the *expiratory* centre is shown only on the left, and the *inspiratory* centre only on the right. IC, inferior colliculus; BP, brachium pontis (middle cerebellar peduncle); B, brachium conjunctivum (superior peduncle); R, restiform body (inferior peduncle); AT, acoustic tubercle; CN, cuneate nucleus; GN, gracile nucleus; C1, first cervical root. (Pitts, Magoun & Ranson, 1939.)

parts of the brain stem. And fourthly, localized injections of carbon dioxide-bicarbonate buffer solutions have been made to indicate the areas of the brain stem giving rise to respiratory responses.

Our present knowledge of the location of the respiratory centres is based largely on investigations of this sort. These so-called "centres" are nerve cells arranged not in descrete groups as the term would imply, but diffusely in certain areas of the reticular formation of the pons and medulla. It is believed that there are four such centres, and these have been called: the *inspiratory* and *expiratory* centres in the medulla, and the *apneustic* and *pneumotaxic* centres in the pons.

Medullary Centres. The *inspiratory centre* is in the ventral reticular formation immediately over the cephalic four-fifths of the inferior olive at the level of the entrance of the vagus nerve (Fig. 14.3). Electrical stimulation of this region causes deep inspiration involving both the thorax and diaphragm.

The *expiratory centre* consists of neurones which intermingle with those of the inspiratory centre but extend slightly higher up in the medulla and lie more dorsally and laterally in the reticular formation (Fig. 14.3).

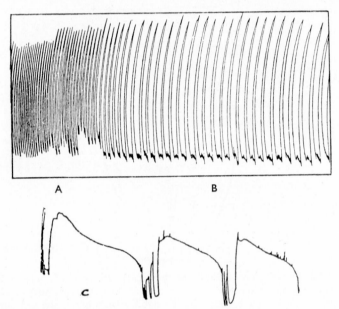

Fig. 14.4. Respiratory movements of a cat, showing the Different Types of Respiration.

A. Normal respiratory movements (inspiration upwards).
B. The same after Section of the Vagi.
C. The Apneustic type, with prolonged inspiratory tonus.

Electrical stimulation of the expiratory centre causes cessation of respiration in the expiratory position and contraction of the expiratory muscles.

Pontine Centres. *Apneustic centre.* If the vagus nerves are cut to exclude impulses from pulmonary stretch receptors initiating the Hering-Breuer reflex and the brain-stem sectioned in the lower pontine region, rhythmic breathing ceases and is replaced by prolonged inspiratory spasms. This type of breathing is called *apneusis* (Figs. 14.1 and 14.4). On the other hand, if further transections of the brain stem are made more caudally so as to involve the upper part of the medulla, rhythmic respiration returns. Transection below a level 2 mm caudal to the border between the pons and medulla results in abolition of all respiratory movements, as already stated.

The origin of the apneustic type of breathing has been a matter of controversy for many years, but it now appears to be due to uninhibited activity of an apneustic centre situated in the middle and caudal regions of the pons. This centre dominates the inspiratory centre in the medulla, but can be inhibited experimentally by electrical stimulation of the central (rostral) end of the cut vagus nerve.

A further point which emerges from these observations is that when the medullary centres are cut off from all afferent impulses, rhythmic respiration continues. This is interpreted as indicating that these centres are inherently rhythmical. But it must be mentioned that the rhythmic respiration seen under these conditions (transection of the brain at a level of the upper part of the medulla combined with division of the vagus nerves) is not normal breathing; it is of the gasping type in which each inspiration is maximal and involves all inspiratory muscles.

The *pneumotaxic centre* lies in the upper part of the pons and has been localized accurately by electrical stimulation to the locus caeruleus and the neighbouring dorsolateral reticular formation of the isthmus of the rostral pons. The neurones fire predominantly during inspiration but are not inherently rhythmical. The activity is dependent on impulses from the inspiratory centre.

Functional organization of the respiratory centres. The neurones of the medullary respiratory centres are closely related synaptically and excitation of a small part of one may lead, through the synaptic interconnexions, to activity of the whole of that centre. It is assumed that the normal respiratory rhythm originates within this medullary neuronal network through a self-re-exciting mechanism. The apneustic centre, however, overrides the medullary centres and under certain circumstances discharges tonically to maintain an inspiratory spasm without interruption and is clearly so powerful as to be able to obliterate the normal rhythmicity of the medullary centres.

In normal breathing the apneustic centre is rhythmically inhibited by two mechanisms, firstly, by impulses from pulmonary stretch receptors which are excited during inspiration, and secondly, by impulses from the pneumotaxic centre.

The present concept of the organization of the respiratory centres is shown diagrammatically in Fig. 14.5, and the sequence of events is briefly as follows: (1) the activity of the inspiratory centre, dominated by the apneustic centre, brings about inspiration. (2) Impulses from the inspiratory centre excite the pneumotaxic centre, and at the same time the frequency of impulses from pulmonary stretch receptors increases as the lungs inflate. (3) At the height of inspiration impulses from the pneumotaxic centre and from the pulmonary stretch receptors cause inhibition of

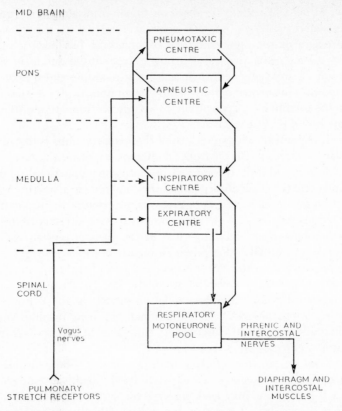

FIG. 14.5. Diagrammatic representation of the organization of the respiratory centres in the brain stem of the cat. For explanation, see text. (After Wang).

the inspiratory centre through an action largely on the apneustic centre. (4) Expiration is thereby brought about passively. Then as the inhibitory effects of the activity of the pneumotaxic centre and pulmonary stretch receptors wane, the cycle of events starts all over again.

PROPRIOCEPTIVE CONTROL OF RESPIRATORY MUSCLES

We have so far discussed the control of respiratory movements as if they depended entirely on the activity of the respiratory centres sending impulses via the descending tracts to the spinal motoneurones of the principal respiratory muscles. These muscles are, of course, skeletal muscles which in the limbs are known to be affected not only by the direct pyramidal tracts, but also by the stretch reflex. It is now evident that this reflex can also be elicited from the intercostal muscles and that it plays an important part in the control of respiratory movements.

The stretch reflex is elicited in a limb muscle by a sudden pull on the muscle, and this causes an immediate contraction of the same muscle. The response is reflex in nature, being abolished by cutting the corresponding dorsal or ventral root. The sensing element in muscle is the muscle spindle and its stretch receptor, the annulospiral ending, fires impulses which pass by nerves to the anterior horn cells in the spinal cord to form a mono-synaptic reflex. The impulses then pass down the motor nerves to the same muscle, and the resulting contraction and shortening of the muscle causes the muscle spindle to shorten as well, thereby releasing the stretch on its receptor. The afferent impulses then cease. Histologically these muscle spindles have been shown to be present in the intercostal muscles and also, though in fewer numbers, in the diaphragm. Their physiological characteristics are similar to those in limb muscles.

The muscle spindle is not a simple stretch receptor, however, and its physiology is more complicated than is indicated in the paragraph above. It will suffice to give a brief résumé here of its dominant features.

The spindles in limb muscles are arranged in parallel with the skeletal (extrafusal) muscle fibres and have a low mechanical threshold to stretch. Their primary afferent (1A) fibres are connected at a spinal level so as to excite the α-motoneurones of the same muscle via the monosynaptic pathway. This is a "feedback" servo-loop Within the connective tissue capsule of the muscle spindle lie spindle (intrafusal) muscle fibres innervated by the small motor or gamma fibres which leave the spinal cord by way of the ventral roots. The motor outflow from the spinal cord consists therefore of two effectively distinct motor systems: (1) the α-motor fibres innervating extrafusal skeletal muscle fibres and constituting Sherrington's "final common path" and (2) the γ-efferent or fusimotor fibres innervating exclusively the intrafusal muscle fibres of the muscle spindles.

The muscle spindle, lying parallel to the skeletal muscle fibres, acts as a detector of changes in length of the extrafusal muscle fibres of the parent muscle, and through reflex pathways brings about contraction (or relaxation of an already con-tracted muscle) to oppose any further lengthening (or shortening) of the muscle. The sensitivity to any change in length of the muscle spindle may be altered by means of the activity of the fusimotor fibres changing the length of the intrafusal muscle fibres. For instance, if increased activity is evoked in the intrafusal fibres through their γ-efferent innervation, the sensory element will generate more im-pulses and reflexly increase the rate of discharge in the α-motor fibres causing contraction of the extrafusal muscle fibres. As the muscle shortens, the stretch on the muscle spindle diminishes and its afferent discharge diminishes. In fact the sensory element is all the time signalling a difference in length or a misalignment between the muscle spindle and the main skeletal muscle fibres.

During spontaneous breathing it has been found that there is an increased discharge of impulses not only in α-motor fibres to the inter-costal muscles, but also in the fusimotor fibres. On this evidence, it could be postulated that the increased α-motoneurone activity responsible for inspiration is the result of an increased discharge from muscle spindles consequent upon the augmented activity in fusimotor fibres. Alternatively, the α-motoneurones may be "driven" by impulses from the respiratory centres during inspiration in spite of a decreasing excitatory input from the muscle spindles, the increased discharge in the fusimotor fibres being insufficient to prevent a reduction in the discharge from the muscle spindle as a result of shortening of the extrafusal fibres. Studies of the impulse activity in afferent fibres from intercostal muscle spindles show clearly that during contraction of the external intercostal muscles in the phase of inspiration, the muscle spindle increases its rate of firing. This means that intrafusal contractions through fusimotor fibre activity dominate over extrafusal contractions. Selective block of the fusimotor fibres results in a pronounced reduction in the discharge from muscle spindles during inspiration. There is still little information about the central mechanisms whereby the increased activity in the fusimotor fibres is brought about during inspiration.

It has been suggested that another rôle of the muscle spindles in the control of respiratory movements is to adjust automatically the force of contraction of muscle in such a way that any "demand" for a certain tidal volume is achieved in spite of variations in load. For instance if the load on an intercostal muscle is increased by imposing an inspiratory resistance, the muscle will not shorten so much as against a smaller load, and the passive shortening (unloading) of the muscle spindles will be less with the result that their discharge will be greater. This is similar in effect to imposing a stretch on the muscle spindles and the extra depolarization of the α-motoneurones so evoked would summate with the concurrent "central respiratory drive potentials" to increase the discharge frequency of the active motoneurones and to recruit others into activity. This is spoken of as a "load compensating reflex".

Further information about the rôle of the muscle spindles in the control of breathing has been obtained from observations on human patients in whom certain cervical or thoracic sensory roots were cut on one side to relieve pain caused by cancer. Division of the posterior roots of the cervical segment from which the phrenic nerve arises or of the 4th–7th thoracic nerves led to a temporary paralysis of the diaphragm or temporary decreased activity of the intercostal muscles respectively. These observations provide further evidence that the sensory input from muscles to the spinal cord is an important factor exciting the anterior horn cells either directly or by facilitating impulses descending from higher parts of the central nervous system.

Another mechanism by which the force of muscular contraction can be modified reflexly is through the Hering-Breuer reflex operating by way of alterations in intercostal muscle spindle activity. The sequence of events is as follows. If the trachea of an anaesthetized rabbit is temporarily occluded at the height of inspiration there is prolongation of the subsequent expiratory pause and powerful contraction of the expiratory muscles. The impulse discharge increases not only in α motor fibres to expiratory muscles, as would be expected, but also in expiratory fusimotor fibres as well. All these effects do not occur if the vagus nerves have been cut. More specifically, however, it is found that the increased activity in α-motor fibres is reduced or abolished after cutting the dorsal roots indicating that it is the afferent discharge from muscle spindles which is exciting or facilitating monosynaptically the motoneurones.

An important point which emerges from all this is that so far as the control of muscle spindle activity is concerned, the "load compensating reflex" and the vagal reflex behave as complementary systems.

THE CHEMICAL AND REFLEX CONTROL OF BREATHING

One factor in the control of breathing is the sensitivity of chemo-receptors in the medulla to changes in the carbon dioxide pressure. This is known as the *chemical* control. Normal breathing in the resting subject continues its even tenor so long as the carbon dioxide pressure in the alveolar air, and so in the arterial blood leaving the lungs, remains constant at about 40 mm Hg. If the P_{CO_2} falls below this, level breathing is inhibited, until carbon dioxide accumulation once more restores it to the normal value. On the other hand, a rise in the alveolar P_{CO_2} acts as a respiratory stimulant and the pulmonary ventilation is increased in an effort to maintain the alveolar P_{CO_2} at the normal value, or nearly so. The part played by oxygen in the chemical control of breathing is, at sea-level, a relatively minor one.

In addition, the activity of the respiratory centres is affected by reflex mechanisms. The afferent pathways for these are:

(1) The carotid sinus nerves and the aortic (depressor) nerves carrying impulses from peripheral arterial chemoreceptors, the carotid body and aortic bodies, situated in the bifurcation of the common carotid artery, and in the arch of the aorta, respectively.

(2) The vagus nerves carrying impulses from stretch receptors in the lungs.

(3) Afferent fibres from proprioceptors in the limbs.

(4) Afferent fibres from receptors of various kinds in the skin and the mucous membranes of the respiratory tract.

Chemical Control

Central Chemoreceptors. The increase in pulmonary ventilation brought about by inhalation of a carbon dioxide-enriched atmosphere is due to stimulation of cells within the central nervous system. For a long time it was thought that these cells were the same medullary neurones that constitute the medullary respiratory centres. There is now good evidence however, that they are anatomically quite separate from the centres co-ordinating respiration and since they serve a specific function, have been called *chemoreceptors*, being sensitive to carbon dioxide and to hydrogen ions. To distinguish them from the peripheral arterial chemoreceptors in the carotid bodies and aortic bodies, they are usually referred to as the central or medullary chemoreceptors.

The chemosensitive cells or their sensory nerve endings are located on the lateral surfaces of the upper part of the medulla, near the exit of the 9th and 10th cranial nerves (Fig. 14.6). Their localization is based on

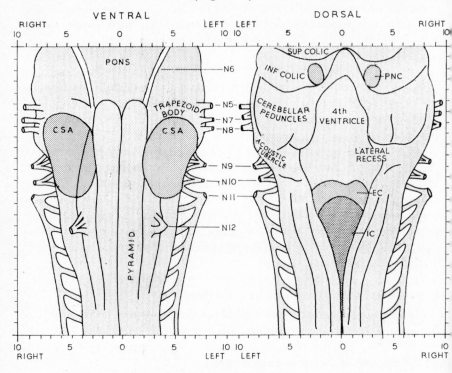

FIG. 14.6. Dorsal and ventral views of the medulla and pons of the cat. Stippled areas (CSA) represent the regions of respiratory chemo-sensitivity to high P_{CO_2} and H^+, nicotine or acetycholine. Areas PNC, pneumotaxic centre in region of locus ceruleus; areas IC and EC, inspiratory and expiratory centres in reticular formation; region AP, area postrema located superficially in fourth ventricle. *Abscissa* and *ordinate*, stereotaxic co-ordinates (mm). (Mitchell, 1966).

experiments in which solutions, to which have been added carbon dioxide, hydrogen ions or drugs such as acetylcholine or nicotine, have been applied locally to various parts of the surface of the medulla. Hyperventilation occurs when application is made to the lateral surfaces. The chemo-receptors have not yet been studied histologically but they send afferent impulses to the medullary respiratory centres. In contrast to the peripheral arterial chemoreceptors, they do not appear to be stimulated by decreased P_{O_2} (hypoxia).

The central chemoreceptors lying superficially on the brain surface, can be influenced more by changes in the composition of the cerebrospinal fluid, especially [H$^+$], than by that of the blood. When carbon dioxide is inhaled, the arterial blood P_{CO_2} increases, and CO_2 being freely diffusible, passes rapidly across the blood-brain and blood-cerebrospinal fluid barriers with the result that within a few minutes the cerebrospinal fluid P_{CO_2} rises. But whereas the increase in arterial blood [H$^+$] is small, that in the cerebrospinal fluid is far greater. This is because cerebrospinal

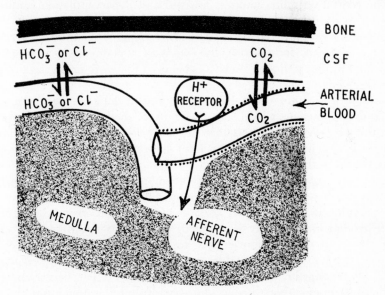

Fig. 14.7. Diagram of a central chemoreceptor or H$^+$ receptor near the surface of the medulla. It is influenced by the P_{CO_2} and [H$^+$] of the cerebrospinal fluid (CSF) and by the arterial P_{CO_2}. There is a ready diffusion of CO_2 molecules across the walls of the capillaries, but not of other molecules due to the blood-CSF barrier (represented by the interrupted lines). An active exchange of HCO_2^- and Cl$^-$ occurs across some capillaries.

fluid lacks a protein buffer, such as haemoglobin in blood, to accept H$^+$ ions. When a rise in arterial blood P_{CO_2} occurs, therefore, it takes time for changes in the P_{CO_2} and [H$^+$] of the cerebrospinal fluid bathing the central chemoreceptors to take place, and this accounts for the delay in the respiratory response reaching its maximum.

A diagrammatic representation of the central H$^+$ receptor is shown in Fig. 14.7. It will be noted the diffusion of HCO_3^- and Cl$^-$ ions between blood and cerebrospinal fluid is also depicted. This is an active transport mechanism which comes into operation when prolonged changes in arterial blood and cerebrospinal fluid P_{CO_2} take place. This is considered in more detail on p. 226 but an example may be cited briefly. In chronic hypoxia the hyperventilation due to the low oxygen pressure reduces the arterial blood and hence the cerebrospinal fluid $P\text{CO}_2$. As the cerebrospinal fluid is unbuffered the H^+ ion concentration is reduced and this depresses the central chemoreceptors to carbon dioxide, a state of affairs which would be detrimental to the organism in the face of a poor oxygen supply. However, bicarbonate ions diffuse out of the cerebrospinal fluid to restore the $HCO_3^-/P\text{CO}_2$ ratio and hence the H^+ ion concentration. The threshold of the central chemoreceptors is lowered and hyperventilation continues in spite of the lowered arterial blood $P\text{CO}_2$.

Rôle of central chemoreceptors in normal breathing. When the arterial blood $P\text{CO}_2$ is reduced, for instance by voluntary over-breathing, respiration ceases for a short period of time. It is believed therefore that a certain level of carbon dioxide in the blood is necessary for normal rhythmic respiration. Cessation of breathing may also be produced in the anaesthetized animal by applying procaine, a local anaesthetic, to the medullary chemoreceptors and this observation suggests that the normal activity of the respiratory centres is dependent on a certain level of continuous discharge of nerve impulses from the chemoreceptors.

The way in which the medullary chemoreceptors respond to carbon dioxide can be demonstrated by a number of simple experiments.

(1) **Asphyxia.** The proper aeration of the blood may be interfered with by allowing a subject to re-breathe repeatedly in and out of a small bag. If his respiratory movements are recorded, they will be seen to increase gradually in depth and frequency. This is known as *hyperpnoea*.

(2) **Hypercapnia.** In asphyxia, two factors are present, first an increase in the amount of carbon dioxide, and secondly a diminution in the amount of oxygen in the blood. Each factor has certain effects on breathing and it is important, therefore, to distinguish *oxygen deficiency (hypoxia)*, and excess of carbon dioxide or *hypercapnia*. These two states can be separated in a simple experiment. If a subject is made to re-breathe from a bag containing room air, respiration becomes noticeably increased when the concentration of carbon dioxide in the bag reaches about 3 per cent and that of the oxygen falls to about 17 per cent. If the experiment is repeated, but this time with a soda lime tower situated between the subject's mouth and the bag to absorb the carbon dioxide and prevent it accumulating in the bag, there is no appreciable increase in respiration until the oxygen concentration in the bag falls to about 14 per cent. The carbon dioxide concentration in the bag remains, of course, zero. Finally, if the subject is made to breathe 100 per cent oxygen and the carbon dioxide is again allowed to accumulate, the hyperpnoea becomes intolerable when the carbon dioxide concentration reaches 8–9 per cent, despite the fact that the oxygen concentration is abnormally high. These experiments demonstrate two things: first, that the hyperpnoea of re-breathing is due

largely to accumulation of carbon dioxide, and secondly, that a reduction in the concentration of oxygen in the inspired air stimulates breathing.

(3) Another experiment demonstrating the way in which the medullary chemoreceptors respond to carbon dioxide and maintain a constant alveolar PCO_2 is to add small quantities of carbon dioxide to the inspired air. The typical effect is shown in Fig. 14.8. The smallest effective concentration of carbon dioxide in the inspired air is about 1 per cent (7·6 mm Hg) and this causes a measurable increase in respiratory minute

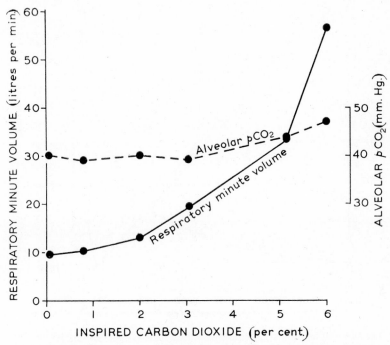

FIG. 14.8. The effect of increasing the concentration of carbon dioxide in the inspired air on the respiratory minute volume (continuous line) and alveolar PCO_2 (interrupted line) of a man.

volume, although the subject is unaware of it. As the carbon dioxide concentration of the *inspired air* is increased the respiratory response also increases until at about 3 per cent his respiratory minute volume is double the normal value when he is breathing room air. It will be noted in Fig. 14.8, however, that breathing this concentration of carbon dioxide failed to cause a measurable increase in the alveolar PCO_2. As the inspired carbon dioxide concentration is raised still further, larger increases in respiratory minute volume occur and a rise in alveolar PCO_2 is also evident. But the point to be emphasised here is that the alveolar PCO_2 when breathing 6 per cent carbon dioxide is very much less than the value would have been, had no increase in pulmonary ventilation occurred. In this connexion, J. S. Haldane found that changing his own inspired gas from room air to 3·8 per cent carbon dioxide increased his pulmonary ventilation by 258 per cent, but the alveolar carbon dioxide concentration rose only from 5·62 to 5·97 per cent, equivalent to an increase in alveolar P_{CO_2} from 40 to

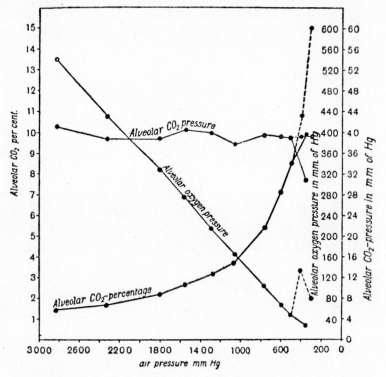

FIG. 14.9. The effect of alterations in the barometric pressure on the pressure of carbon dioxide, the percentage of carbon dioxide, and the pressure of oxygen in the alveolar air of a man.

The dotted lines show the results obtained when oxygen was added to the air breathed. Note the constancy of the carbon dioxide pressure until the barometric pressure was reduced to values less than 500 mmHg (corresponding to a height of about 10,000 ft), and the respiration was stimulated by oxygen lack. (Boycott and Haldane.)

42·5 mm Hg. Without such an increase in pulmonary ventilation, his alveolar CO_2 concentration would have risen to about 9 per cent which is equivalent to an alveolar P_{CO_2} of about 64 mm Hg.

This experiment demonstrates that the central medullary chemoreceptors are very sensitive to carbon dioxide, an increase of only 1·6 mm Hg in alveolar P_{CO_2} being sufficient to double the respiratory minute volume. It should be emphasized, however, that the normal carbon dioxide content of the atmospheric air (0·04 per cent) is too small to have any measurable effect on respiration and is in no way responsible for the maintenance of normal respiration.

The importance of the *partial pressure* of carbon dioxide rather than its percentage can be seen by examination of Fig. 14.9. Here can be seen the effect of alterations in the barometric pressure, both above and below the normal value, on the alveolar partial pressure and percentage of carbon dioxide, and on the alveolar pressure of oxygen. It will be observed that while the alveolar Po_2 falls steadily as the atmospheric pressure falls, as might be expected, the percentage of carbon dioxide rises steadily and in such a way as to maintain the alveolar Pco_2 constant. This relation breaks down when the atmospheric pressure falls below 500 mm Hg (corresponding to an altitude of about 10,000 ft and an oxygen pressure of 14 per cent of an atmosphere), owing to the stimulating action of oxygen deficiency.

Sensitivity to Carbon Dioxide. Sensitivity is determined by measuring the respiratory minute volume and the arterial blood or alveolar Pco_2 simultaneously under steady state conditions and is calculated as the

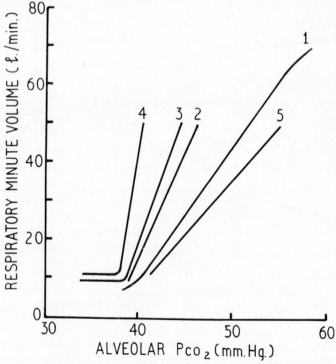

Fig. 14.10. The main factors altering the slope of the curve relating the respiratory minute volume to alveolar Pco_2. *1*, control; *2*, noradrenaline; *3*, hyperthermia; *4*, hypoxia; *5*, hyperoxia (oxygen breathing). (After Perkins, 1963).

change in minute volume per mm Hg change in arterial blood or alveolar Pco_2. Above about 42 mm Hg alveolar Pco_2, the relationship is a linear one and the average value for healthy men is 2·5 l/min/mm Hg change in alveolar Pco_2. The sensitivity, however, is not a constant one; it is depressed by drugs such as morphine and barbiturates, and increased by a rise in body temperature and also by a fall in arterial blood Po_2. Figure 14.10 shows the effect of increasing hypoxia (deficiency in oxygen) on the relationship between respiration minute volume and alveolar Pco_2 in man. It will be noted that there is a gradual increase in sensitivity to carbon dioxide as the alveolar Po_2 falls.

The Effect on Breathing of a Reduction in Alveolar Pco_2. A fall in the alveolar Pco_2 can be brought about by forced breathing. If the subject is suitable a tracing of his subsequent respiratory movements will follow a pattern similar to that in Fig. 14.11. In this figure there are three

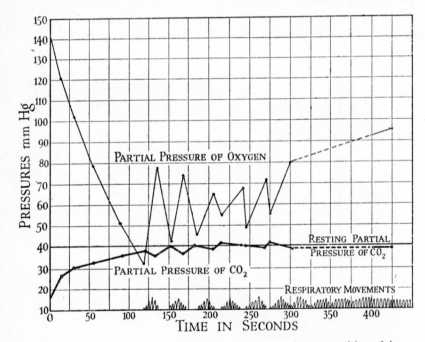

FIG. 14.11. The effect of Voluntary Hyperpnoea on the composition of the alveolar air and on the frequency and depth of respiration.
    Voluntary hyperpnoea was carried out for two minutes before the beginning of the record. Note that the first group of respirations begins at a moment when the alveolar carbon dioxide pressure is definitely less than the normal value, due to the low value of the alveolar oxygen pressure. Similarly, respirations cease before the alveolar oxygen pressure has reached the normal value, due to the low alveolar carbon dioxide pressure, the result being the production of periodic (Cheyne-Stokes) respiration. (Douglas and Haldane.)

graphs. The lowest is a tracing of the respiratory movements; the upper and middle curves represent the alveolar Po_2 and Pco_2. It can be seen from examination of the respiratory tracing that the period of forced breathing was followed by cessation of breathing (apnoea). Then followed a period during which a few breaths were taken, and then a second apnoeic period. This "periodic breathing" continued with shortening periods of apnoea until normal breathing was resumed. Amongst the interesting questions which we have to answer are:

Why are respiratory movements inhibited after forced breathing?

Why is there a waxing and waning rhythm or periodicity?

The period of respiratory inhibition or apnoea which followed the period of forced breathing was due to the inhibitory effect of the low alveolar Pco_2 for the following reasons.

(1) During the forced breathing, the carbon dioxide was washed out of the lungs and its pressure was lowered. Examination of the curve in Fig. 14.11, representing the changes in the alveolar Pco_2, demonstrates that in this subject after the period of forced breathing, the carbon dioxide pressure fell to 15 mm Hg—well below his normal pressure of 40 mm Hg —and thus exerted an inhibitory effect on breathing.

(2) If such a subject repeats the forced breathing with a gas mixture containing carbon dioxide (approximately 4·5 per cent), apnoea will not develop since the alveolar Pco_2 remains at approximately the resting value.

(3) It can be shown that the rise in alveolar Po_2 is not to blame, since gas mixtures containing a high percentage of oxygen have no inhibitory effect on breathing.

The explanation of the "periodic breathing" is as follows. During the first period of apnoea, the blood Po_2 fell to a level where it acted as a respiratory stimulus, despite the fact that the carbon dioxide pressure was still below normal, and would thus have exerted an inhibitory influence. It was to satisfy this oxygen deficiency that the subject began to breathe again. A few breaths sufficed to satisfy the oxygen requirements, so that once again the low alveolar Pco_2 could exert its inhibitory influence, and thus a second apnoeic period followed. This periodicity continued until the alveolar Po_2 and Pco_2 returned to normal.

Reflexes from Peripheral Chemoreceptors. Peripheral arterial chemoreceptors are situated in two locations: in the carotid body at the bifurcation of the common carotid artery and in the aortic bodies in the region of the arch of the aorta. They are supplied by the carotid sinus nerve, a branch of the glossopharyngeal, and by the aortic nerve, a branch of the vagus, respectively. These receptors are not to be confused anatomically with the pressoreceptors (baroreceptors) in the carotid sinus and arch of the aorta.

The carotid and aortic bodies consist of epithelial cells which are surrounded by a rich network of sinusoidal blood vessels (Fig. 14.12). For its size, the carotid body has a greater supply of blood than any other organ of the body, equivalent to 2,000 ml/min/100 g tissue, or about four times that of the thyroid gland and 40 times that of the brain.

The chemoreceptors, as their name implies, are sensitive to changes in the chemical composition of the arterial blood. They are stimulated by:

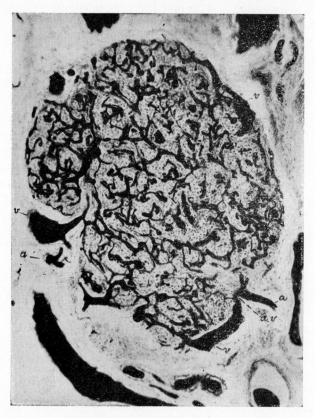

Fig. 14.12. Carotid body of the adult cat injected with gelatine-carmine showing enormous blood supply, arteries (*a*), veins (*v*) and arterio-venous anastomoses (*a.v.*). (De Castro, 1940.)

(1) *Hypoxic (arterial) hypoxia.* This is a reduction in the Po_2 of the arterial blood.

(2) *Stagnant hypoxia.* If the arterial blood pressure falls the chemo-receptors are stimulated even although the Po_2 and the Pco_2 of the arterial blood does not change. This is due to the fact that the fall in blood pressure reduces the blood flow through the chemoreceptors and causes local *stagnant hypoxia* whereby there is greater extraction of oxygen from the blood resulting in a reduction in tissue Po_2. Such a mechanism comes

into operation during severe haemorrhage. Other factors causing a reduction in carotid body blood flow, such as stimulation of the sympathetic vasoconstrictor supply to the organ, or noradrenaline, also stimulates chemo-receptors.

(3) *Histotoxic hypoxia*. Chemicals, such as cyanide, which poison the respiratory enzyme systems, also stimulate chemoreceptors.

(4) *Increased arterial* P_{CO_2}. In the presence of a normal arterial P_{O_2}, carbon dioxide is a relatively weak stimulant of the chemoreceptors.

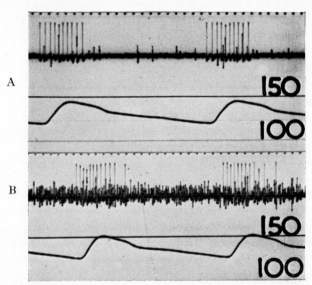

FIG. 14.13. Afferent impulses in a few fibres of the carotid sinus nerve. The large action potentials are from a single baroreceptor fibre firing synchronously with the anacrotic wave in the blood pressure record; the small potentials are those from chemoreceptor fibres. Cat spontaneously breathing air in A, and 10 per cent O_2 in N_2 in B. Note the increase in chemoreceptor activity during hypoxia. Blood pressure calibration in mm Hg. Time trace, 50 cycles per second. (Heymans & Neil, 1958.)

(5) *Decreased arterial pH*. Again, a weak stimulant of chemoreceptors in the presence of a normal arterial blood P_{O_2}.

Interaction of O_2 and CO_2. The action on the chemoreceptors of a low arterial P_{O_2} and of a high P_{CO_2} interact so that their combined effects are the algebraic sum of their separate effects. This means that when the arterial P_{O_2} is lowered to a certain value, the chemoreceptor response will be greater if the P_{CO_2} is elevated at the same time compared to the response at constant P_{CO_2}. If the P_{CO_2} falls, on the other hand, the response to the lowered P_{O_2} will be less. Likewise, the chemoreceptor response to increasing the P_{CO_2} depends on the P_{O_2}. If the P_{O_2} remains normal

(100 mm Hg), the response will be minimal, but if the Po_2 falls at the same time that the Pco_2 is increased, then an enhanced effect of the Pco_2 response occurs.

The activity of the chemoreceptors may be studied by recording the electrical activity in fibres of the carotid sinus or aortic nerve. Such studies indicate that, in anaesthetised animals breathing room air, the chemoreceptors are only very slightly active (Fig. 14.13A). If the arterial Po_2 is normal, then lowering the arterial blood Pco_2, by hyperventilating the animal, from its normal value of 40 mm Hg to 30–35 mm Hg, will abolish this normal chemoreceptor activity. If, however, the animal is made to breathe a gas mixture low in oxygen content, a marked increase in chemoreceptor discharge occurs (Fig. 14.13B).

Reflexes from the carotid bodies may be studied by isolating the chemoreceptors from the circulation and perfusing them with arterial blood from a donor animal. Changing the gaseous composition of the blood in the donor, and hence in the recipient animal's carotid bodies, evokes changes in respiratory minute volume in the recipient. Lowering the blood Po_2 and to a lesser extent increasing the blood Pco_2 or H^+ ion concentration, causes an increase in the rate and depth of breathing. Denervation of the chemoreceptors by cutting the carotid sinus nerves abolishes the response, indicating that it is reflex in nature.

Alternatively, if in an intact animal the arterial blood Po_2 is lowered by administering a gas mixture with reduced oxygen content, an increase in respiratory minute volume results. This hypernoea is due entirely to a *reflex* stimulation via the chemoreceptors, for inhalation of the same gas mixture after cutting the afferent nerves supplying these receptors causes only depression of respiration (Fig. 14.14). This latter effect is due to an action on the medullary chemoreceptors. The effects of "denervation" of the carotid and aortic bodies on the ventilatory response to hypoxia are similar in man. It will be noted in Fig. 14.15 that after blocking transmission in the 9th and 10th cranial nerves with a local anaesthetic in a normal conscious human subject the hyperpnoea due to inhalation of 8 per cent O_2 in N_2 was completely abolished.

On the other hand, inhalation of gas mixtures containing small quantities of carbon dioxide, say 5 per cent, also causes hyperpnoea, but this response is unaffected by section of the carotid sinus nerves, as indicated in Fig. 14.14. The reflex mechanism, therefore, appears to play only a small part in the control of respiration by changes in arterial blood Pco_2, the main action being a direct one of carbon dioxide on the central medullary chemoreceptors.

The mechanism of the effect of carbon dioxide on respiration requires a little more explanation in the light of studies of action potentials in chemoreceptor fibres, which have shown that a small increase in impulse discharge occurs as the arterial blood Pco_2 is raised. How is it, therefore, that interruption of these impulses does not modify the *respiratory response* to hypercapnia. The position may be summarized by saying: (1) the chemoreceptor discharge produced by raising the arterial blood Pco_2 is relatively small compared to that caused by lowering the arterial blood Po_2 by inhalation of 7–10 per cent oxygen in nitrogen; (2) the main effect of carbon dioxide is on the medullary chemoreceptors, and this overshadows the reflex component; and (3) increasing the arterial blood Pco_2 of itself tends to diminish the effects of reflexes by an action on central synapses. Thus the small discharge of impulses from chemo-

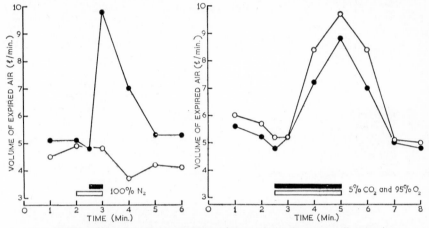

Fig. 14.14. The effect of denervation of the carotid sinuses on the respiratory response of an unanaesthetised dog to inhalation of nitrogen and of carbon dioxide. Both experiments were made on the same animal: ●, normal, O denervated. (Gemmill and Reeves.)

receptors evoked by inhalation of carbon dioxide become blocked, and therefore ineffective, somewhere along the reflex nervous pathway.

Rôle of the Chemoreceptors in Respiratory Depression. Certain drugs, such as morphine and the barbiturates, depress the respiratory centres and the respiration becomes very much slower. There is an increase in depth, but this does not fully compensate for the decrease in frequency, and the respiratory minute volume is diminished. In consequence, there is a rise in the alveolar Pco_2 and in the arterial blood Pco_2, and a fall in the alveolar and blood Po_2. The sensitivity of the medullary chemoreceptors to carbon dioxide is reduced and it can be shown experimentally that if a subject is given morphine, his respiratory response to an increase in the carbon dioxide concentration in the inspired air becomes smaller than it was before.

In large doses, the sensitivity of respiration to carbon dioxide may be so depressed that breathing is maintained only by the chemoreceptor reflex mechanism stimulated by the reduction in arterial blood Po_2. In these circumstances, administration of oxygen may have the unexpected, and undesirable, effect of stopping respiration altogether, due to withdrawal of this reflex drive to the respiratory centres.

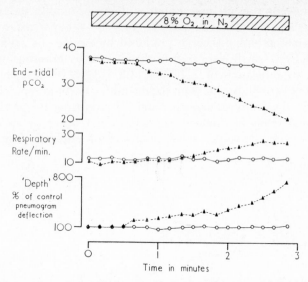

FIG. 14.15. The effects of "denervation" of the carotid and aortid bodies by bilateral block of the IX and X cranial nerves on the response to hypoxia in a healthy conscious human subject. Closed triangles (▲), control observations; open circles (○), during "denervation". (Guz et al. 1966).

The Part Played by Afferent Impulses from the Lungs in the Control of Breathing. Nerve endings are present in the bronchi and bronchioles which are sensitive to distension of the lungs, but are insensitive to changes in the partial pressures of oxygen and carbon dioxide. Their afferent fibres run in the vagus nerves.

In 1868 Hering and Breuer showed that interruption of breathing by blocking the respiratory passages during inspiration and expiration had marked effects upon the pattern of breathing, but that when the vagus nerves were cut these effects were completely absent. A few years later, in 1889, Head again demonstrated this reflex (now known as the Hering-Breuer reflex), by observing the effect of inflation of the lungs on the movements of the diaphragm in the rabbit. The rabbit is unique in that its diaphragm is so arranged that it is possible to separate that part which is attached to the ensiform cartilage from the remainder, without damaging the blood supply or nervous connections. The active movements of this strip follow exactly those of the remainder of the diaphragm, and can easily be recorded without interference from movements of the chest or diaphragm as a whole, whether active or passive. The essence of Head's results is shown in the accompanying Fig. 14.16.

In the first tracing (A) a positive inflating pressure has been applied to the trachea, and it can be seen that while the pressure is applied the activity of the diaphragm is inhibited. In the lower figure (B) suction applied for a very short period causes an immediate contraction of the strip of the diaphragm. These effects were abolished when the vagus nerves were cut.

In 1933 Adrian observed in the cat that action potentials were set up in the vagus nerve by inflating the lungs, and that the rate of discharge of the impulses was roughly proportional to the degree of inflation (see Fig. 14.17). When he recorded the impulses in a single vagal fibre from a cat during normal breathing, he observed that the frequency waxed and waned in rhythm with the inspiratory and expiratory phases of breathing. The impulses from the lungs fell to zero at the completion of expiration. He also observed that no impulses were recorded when the lungs were

A

POSITIVE PRESSURE

B

SUCTION OR NEGATIVE PRESSURE

FIG. 14.16. Recordings of contractions of a slip from the diaphragm of a rabbit. (Upward trend of lever represents contraction of the slip.)

A. Between the arrows a positive pressure was applied to the lungs. The contractions of the slip, and inspiratory movements, were inhibited.

B. A "momentary" diminution in the volume of the lungs (suction) was produced during normal respiration, as indicated. An increased contraction of the slip, i.e. an increased inspiratory effort, resulted. (After Head.)

deflated (except when such a deflation was far greater than could occur during any normal respiratory movements).

The function of these afferent impulses in the vagus nerve in normal breathing is to signal the depth of inspiration to the respiratory centres and allow expiration to take place, after an adequate tidal volume has ventilated the lungs. Double vagotomy in an otherwise intact animal removes this signal and thus the inspiratory phase is prolonged, and breathing becomes slower and deeper (see Figs. 14.1 and 14.4); a normal respiratory minute volume, however, is maintained. Thus when the medullary inspiratory centre transmits its impulses to the inspiratory muscles, it is subjected, via the apneustic centre, to an afferent discharge from the lungs which progressively increases in intensity until it inhibits the inspiratory activity and initiates the expiratory phase, allowing the chest wall to relax in a passive manner. Consequently a cycle of (a) inspiratory activity and (b) progressive inspiratory inhibition takes place during normal quiet breathing. It has already been pointed out that when the brain stem is transected between the pneumotaxic and apneustic centres combined with division of both vagus nerves, rhythmic respiration ceases and apneustic type of breathing occurs. If such a brain-stem section is made when the vagus nerves are intact, rhythmic breathing will continue, due to the part the vagus nerve plays in the cycle of events just described.

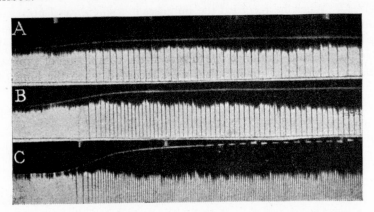

FIG. 14.17. Oscillograph record of the Action Potentials in the Vagus Nerve of a Spinal Cat.

The nerve was cut high up in the neck, and subdivided with fine needles, after removal of the sheath, until only one active fibre remained.

At the top of the record are marks made by a time-signal every quarter second; below this is a white line indicating the position of the lungs, a rise denoting inspiration; at the bottom is the oscillograph record of the action potentials.

The lungs were inflated by a pump, and the frequency of the discharge of the sense organ increases as the inflation increases.

A. Inflation   65 ml. Maximum frequency of discharge   80 per sec.
B.   ,,   115 ml.   ,,   ,,   ,,   120 ,, ,,
C.   ,,   230 ml   ,,   ,,   ,,   250 ,, ,,

(Adrian.)

To summarize: In *quiet breathing*, the respiratory centres initiate inspiratory activity. Afferent impulses in the vagus nerve signal the degree of expansion of the lungs. This afferent vagal discharge (which increases as inspiration progresses), inhibits the general inspiratory activity and thus the respiratory muscles relax and expiration takes place.

Cortical Control. Breathing is under voluntary control, but this control is limited to the extent that if voluntary changes in respiration are brought about which alter the chemical composition of the blood, then the latter exerts its effects on breathing which overcome those produced voluntarily. For instance, one can hold one's breath voluntarily but only for a maximum period of about 1 minute. Then one is forced to breathe due to the rise in arterial blood Pco_2 and fall in arterial blood Po_2.

Reflexes from Muscle and Joint Receptors. In experimental animals and in human subjects, passive movements of a limb result in an increase in pulmonary ventilation even when the circulation is cut off by a pressure cuff to prevent metabolic products from the muscles entering the circulation and hence reaching the respiratory centres. In man, it was found that passive movement of one leg at the knee 100 times per minute with the circulation occluded increased the respiratory minute volume by 40 per cent. Stimulation of such receptors may play an important part in the increased respiration occurring in muscular exercise.

Protective Reflexes. Stimulation of cutaneous afferent nerves produces an increase in both rate and depth of respiration. Presumably, the afferent fibres which mediate the sensation of pain and temperature are mainly responsible for this increased breathing. Most of us have observed how a cold shower "takes our breath away."

Reflexes arising from stimulation of receptors in the respiratory tract are concerned with the protection of the tract itself. During *swallowing*, respiration is reflexly inhibited by impulses running in the glosso-pharyngeal nerve from the post-pharyngeal wall. Inhibition of breathing also occurs as a result of stimulation of mucous membranes of the nasal passages by irritant gases. The sensory nerve endings of the trigeminal nerve are involved. In other instances, stimulation of these endings causes *sneezing*, a modified respiratory act. *Coughing* follows similar irritation of the mucous membranes of the pharynx, larynx, trachea and bronchi. The afferent pathway is in the glossopharyngeal nerve from the pharynx, and in the vagus nerve from the larynx, trachea and bronchi. The explosive quality of the act of coughing is the result of the initial closure of the glottis, which only opens after the beginning of the expiratory phase.

The Influence of Changes in Blood Pressure.

A rise or fall in arterial blood pressure causes a diminution and an increase in respiratory minute volume respectively. By employing suitable experimental techniques, these changes in respiration have been shown to be due largely to reflexes from baroreceptors in the carotid sinus and arch of the aorta. Such reflexes probably play a minor *rôle* in the nervous control of breathing in the normal animal; they must not be confused, however, with the very important part played by the baroreceptors in the reflex regulation of the blood pressure.

Catecholamines. Adrenaline or noradrenaline infused intravenously in conscious man or anaesthetized animals in doses giving blood concentrations within the normal physiological range cause an increase in respiratory minute volume. Such doses have little or no effect on arterial blood pressure. The hyperventilation is due predominantly to a constrictor action of these amines on the carotid body blood vessels, diminishing carotid body blood flow thereby stimulating the chemoreceptors by stagnant hypoxia.

Large doses (outside the normal physiological range) of adrenaline and noradrenaline cause apnoea in anaesthetized animals. This is largely reflex in nature due to stimulation, by the profound rise in arterial pressure, of the carotid sinus and aortic arch baroreceptors.

Other Factors Modifying Breathing. There are many circumstances in which the normal pattern of breathing is modified and yet are quite

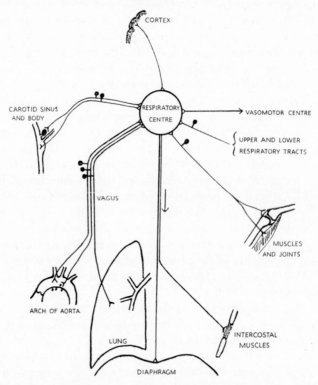

FIG. 14.18. Diagrammatic representation of the Nervous Control of Breathing.

unrelated to the need for an adequate alveolar ventilation. Some examples, viz., swallowing, sneezing and coughing, have already been discussed.

Speaking, singing or whistling all involve changes in breathing which interrupt the normal rhythmic pattern. The act of singing or speaking can only be carried out while air is being expelled from the lungs so that at intervals it is necessary to take in air during which time there is no phonation.

Another procedure modifying breathing is Valsalva's manoeuvre. Experimentally this consists of voluntarily closing the glottis and then attempting to expel the air from the lungs by contraction of the abdominal and thoracic expiratory muscles. The intrathoracic and intra-abdominal pressures rise, sometimes to values exceeding 100 mm Hg. In effect a similar manoeuvre is carried out during defaecation. These high intra-thoracic pressures do not place any added stress on the airways or alveoli. The reason for this is that during the Valsalva manoeuvre the pressures in the airways and alveoli and the intrapleural pressure are all equal, so that the difference in pressure across the walls of these structures (the trans-mural pressure) remains the same. There are, however, profound effects on the circulatory system. The high intrathoracic pressure reduces the venous return to the right side of the heart which in turn causes a fall in cardiac output and arterial blood pressure. This reduction in blood pressure is partly compensated by reflex peripheral vasoconstriction. On cessation of the Valsalva manoeuvre, there is a sudden rise in cardiac output against the increased peripheral vascular resistance so that the blood pressure temporarily "overshoots" above the control until it is restored by the baroreceptor mechanisms.

The various factors concerned in the nervous control of breathing are summarized diagrammatically in Fig. 14.18.

CHAPTER 15

EXAMPLES OF RESPIRATORY ADJUSTMENTS

Hyperventilation

In hyperventilation, one form of which involves a subject voluntarily over-breathing, large volumes of air are moved in and out of the lungs with the result that carbon dioxide is washed out thereby reducing the alveolar CO_2 concentration and P_{CO_2}. The fall in the alveolar P_{CO_2} increases the diffusion of carbon dioxide from blood to the lungs and so the arterial blood CO_2 content and P_{CO_2} fall as well.

The relationship between alveolar ventilation and alveolar P_{CO_2} (which is the same as the blood P_{CO_2}) is shown in Fig. 15.1. It will be noted that at a normal alveolar P_{CO_2} of 40 mm Hg the alveolar ventilation is 4·5 l/min. By doubling ventilation, the alveolar P_{CO_2} falls to half this value (20 mm Hg). It will also be seen that changes in alveolar P_{O_2} occur as well. Doubling alveolar ventilation increases the turn-over in the alveoli of fresh oxygen and consequently the P_{O_2} rises to a value closer to that of oxygen in atmospheric air (about 150 mm Hg). Referring again to Fig. 15.1, the alveolar P_{O_2} increases from 105 to 125 mm Hg. The blood P_{O_2} will of course rise to a similar level, but in spite of this the arterial blood will carry very little extra oxygen. The oxygen saturation remains about the same (Fig. 15.1) and this is because in this range of P_{O_2}, the oxyhaemoglobin dissociation curve is almost flat.

As a result of the lowering of the arterial blood P_{CO_2}, the blood becomes more alkaline with a rise in pH (Fig. 15.1).

The above changes in alveolar and blood P_{O_2} and P_{CO_2} will occur during hyperventilation when unaccompanied by any change in the body's metabolism. We must distinguish this from hyperventilation which takes place during muscular exercise, and here respiratory adjustments are such that the increase in alveolar ventilation balances the metabolic need for oxygen. The increased volumes of oxygen and carbon dioxide diffusing across the alveolar walls results therefore in there being little or no change in the alveolar and blood P_{O_2} and P_{CO_2}.

Hypoventilation

Fig. 15.1 also shows what happens to the alveolar and blood P_{O_2} and P_{CO_2} during hypoventilation. This can be induced voluntarily for a limited period of time or may result from depression of the respiratory centres,

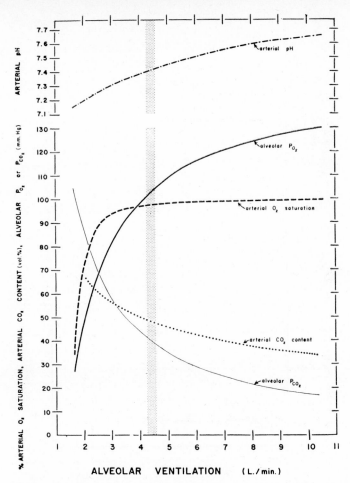

Fig. 15.1. The relationship between alveolar ventilation and alveolar gas and arterial blood O_2, CO_2 and pH. (Comroe *et al.*, 1962).

e.g. by drugs. There is an increase in alveolar and blood P_{CO_2} and a reduction in P_{O_2}.

The Hyperpnoea of Muscular Exercise

The respiratory minute volume increases with the demand for oxygen; in fact, there is a linear relationship between oxygen consumption and the volume of air breathed under steady-state conditions when the work is moderate in amount (Fig. 15.2). For any given amount of work, there are two phases in the response of respiration. There is an initial rapid increase in breathing which occurs before any metabolites could reach the respiratory centres and is probably due to irradiation of nerve impulses from

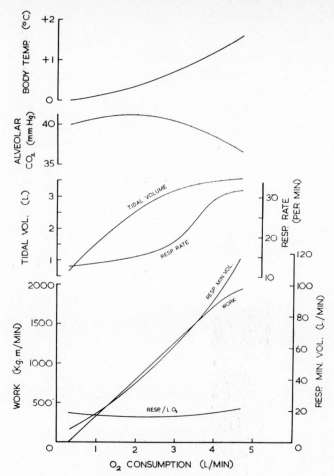

FIG. 15.2. The respiratory responses to exercise on a bicycle ergometer.
All the data was obtained from the same experiment on six physically
fit young men. (Data from Chistensen, 1932).

higher centres (Fig. 15.3). This is followed by a slow rise in respiration to
its final value which depends on the severity of the exercise. Maximum
values for the respiratory minute volume are of the order of 80 to 120
l/min.

This second phase is difficult to explain. Ever since Haldane stressed
the importance of the chemical control of respiration by carbon dioxide,
much attention has been given to its possible *rôle* in the production of
the hyperpnoea of muscular exercise. The increase in ventilation has
been attributed to the rise in P_{CO_2} and reduction in pH of the arterial
blood due to the increased oxidation and to the accumulation of lactic
acid. Such a view is untenable, however, because the hyperpnoea some-

times occurs without any demonstrable alteration in the arterial blood Po_2 or Pco_2. Furthermore, the maximum ventilatory response to increasing the inspired carbon dioxide concentration in the resting subject is considerably smaller than that produced by severe exercise.

The possible mechanisms responsible for the hyperpnoea of muscular exercise may be classified under two headings:

(1) **Neural Component.** The immediate increase in ventilation and the rapid fall on cessation of exercise (Fig. 15.3) are almost certainly of

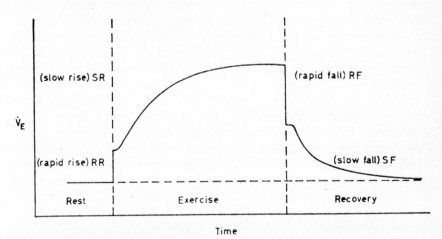

FIG. 15.3. Components of the ventilatory response to exercise (after Dejours, 1963). $\dot{V}E$ is the respiratory minute volume, and RR and RF represent the neural components of the drive to respiration at the beginning and end of exercise. SF is due to the humoral component continuing to act during the period of recovery whilst SR is the result of interaction between the neural and humoral components. (Cotes, 1966).

neural origin as they occur too quickly to be accounted for by a blood-borne agent.

Mechanoreceptors in muscles and points. Passive movements of a limb in man may increase pulmonary ventilation by 40 per cent due to stimulation of receptors in the limb. This could therefore be a contributory mechanism increasing respiration in exercise.

Central irradiation. Impulses arising from higher centres to the respiratory centres has been suggested as a cause for the hyperpnoea. In subjects exercising after hypnosis and suggestion that it was going to be pleasant and effortless, it was found that they ventilated less compared with the control value before hypnosis. The alveolar Pco_2 was about 8 mm Hg higher indicating that the lower ventilation was not due to a reduction in the level of metabolism.

(2) **Humoral Component.** *Carbon dioxide.* It might appear because the alveolar P_{CO_2} does not alter during exercise that carbon dioxide is not concerned in the hyperpnoea. But recent evidence suggests that the respiratory response to inhalation of small quantities of carbon dioxide is greater immediately after a period of exercise than at rest. The threshold of the central chemoreceptors for carbon dioxide may in some way be reduced during exercise with the result that at the normal level of arterial blood P_{CO_2}, the respiratory minute volume is elevated.

Low oxygen. Blood returning from exercising limbs is much more venous than normal so that the mixed venous blood in the right atrium and pulmonary artery has a lower P_{O_2} than normal and a higher P_{CO_2}. The possibility that there might be chemoreceptors in the veins or pulmonary circulation responding to a low P_{O_2} or high P_{CO_2} has been considered but the evidence for this is still controversial.

Considering now the P_{O_2} in *arterial* blood: there is general agreement that this does not alter appreciably, at least during mild and moderate exercise, and certainly the changes, as small as they are, are not sufficient to stimulate the arterial chemoreceptors in the carotid and aortic bodies. The possibility exists, however, that during exercise, the arterial chemoreceptor blood flow may be reduced by sympathetic vasoconstriction resulting in local stagnant hypoxia. This is known to be a stimulus to the carotid bodies. Further experimental evidence is required, however, to substantiate this view.

Taking the evidence as a whole, there is still very little to indicate that in exercise a lowering of the P_{O_2}, which is confined to venous blood, is a cause of the hyperpnoea. Yet it must be borne in mind in this connexion that the respiratory minute volume is very closely related to oxygen consumption and moreover, when during exercise oxygen is substituted for atmospheric air, there is a reduction in breathing. The possibility that low oxygen is in some way a stimulus to breathing in muscular exercise cannot yet be dismissed too lightly.

Hydrogen ion concentration. There is now good evidence that there is a small increase in hydrogen ion concentration of arterial blood during exercise. Since this is not associated with any appreciable change in arterial P_{CO_2}, it must represent a change in the amount of fixed acid in the blood (metabolic acidosis). It has been calculated that the observed changes in arterial pH may account for up to 60 per cent of the exercise hyperventilation, the site of action being probably the central and peripheral chemoreceptors.

Body temperature. When the temperature of the body at rest is raised artificially pulmonary ventilation is increased. The body temperature also increases during exercise. Experimentally it has been shown that a steady raised body temperature increases the sensitivity of respiration to carbon dioxide and lowers the threshold. (Fig. 14.10). The hyperpnoea of muscular exercise may therefore be due, at least in part, to an effect of the rise in body temperature causing a lowering of the threshold to carbon dioxide.

Other humoral agents. Evidence has been obtained for the release of a humoral agent from exercising muscle, which on gaining access to the carotid circulation causes stimulation of breathing. The nature of this agent is not known.

Catecholamines (adrenaline and noradrenaline) released from the supra-renal medulla may also be involved as they are known to stimulate breathing in physiological doses through an action on the carotid bodies (see Fig. 14.10.

Pulmonary ventilation is adjusted closely to the metabolic needs of the body so as to maintain a perfect, or near perfect, homeostasis. In all probability, this is brought about not by any one single factor, but by a combination of several contributory causes.

HYPOXIA

Whenever for any reason the cells of the body do not have, or are unable to utilize, sufficient oxygen to carry on normal function, they are said to be suffering from an oxygen deficiency or hypoxia. Hypoxia may be classified into four types: hypoxic, anaemic, stagnant and histotoxic.

(1) *Hypoxic hypoxia* occurs when there is defective oxygenation of the blood in the lungs causing a reduction in the arterial oxygen pressure. This may result from two causes: (*a*) reduction in the partial pressure of oxygen in the inspired air such as occurs from the addition of an inert gas such as nitrogen or to a fall in the total atmospheric pressure associated with ascents to high altitude. (*b*) Reduction in respiratory minute volume through depression of the respiratory centres by various drugs including anaesthetics, or paralysis of the respiratory muscles.

Under normal conditions, as shown in Fig. 15.4, the blood leaves the lungs about 97 per cent saturated with oxygen and reaches the tissues containing about 19·5 volumes per cent of oxygen (at a pressure of 80 mm Hg). Here about 5 volumes per cent are abstracted during rest, so that mixed blood contains about 14 volumes per cent of oxygen (around 70 per cent saturated and at a pressure of 35 mm Hg). The gradient between arterial and capillary oxygen pressure under normal conditions is therefore about 45 mm Hg (80 minus 35). During hypoxia when the arterial oxygen saturation is, say, 75 per cent (oxygen pressure 40 mm Hg), there is still about 15 volumes per cent of oxygen available to the tissues. Since the latter require 5 volumes per cent, the remaining 10 volumes in venous blood is held at a relatively low partial pressure of about 25 mm Hg. This results in an arterial-capillary oxygen pressure gradient of only 15 mm Hg and a lowering of the oxygen pressure at which the cells have to metabolize.

(2) *Anaemic Hypoxia.* This type is caused by haemorrhage or anaemia.

As will be seen in Fig. 15.4, the arterial oxygen pressure is normal and the haemoglobin is 97 per cent saturated. But because the amount of haemoglobin per unit volume of blood is considerably reduced, the oxygen content of the blood is diminished by a similar proportion. A large part of the oxygen supply to the tissues must therefore be delivered at a lower pressure than normal unless the rate of the blood-flow is increased.

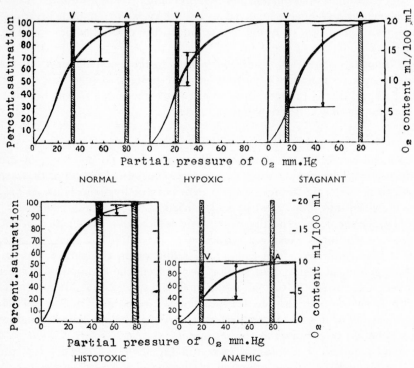

Fig. 15.4. Diagram illustrating the oxygen dissociation curves in various types of hypoxia. The vertical columns, representing the arterial (A) and venous (V) blood, indicate the amount of oxygenated haemoglobin (shaded portion) and reduced haemoglobin (black portion). The perpendicular arrows denote the volume of oxygen per unit volume of blood delivered to the tissues. (See also text.)

(3) *Stagnant Hypoxia* occurs in conditions in which the circulation rate through the tissues is slowed. Although the oxygen content, haemoglobin saturation and oxygen pressure of the arterial blood are normal (Fig. 15.4), the venous blood is considerably more reduced than usual resulting in a low tissue oxygen pressure. This is simply due to the blood spending longer time in the capillaries and, in consequence, a larger volume of oxygen per unit volume of blood is extracted.

(4) *Histotoxic Hypoxia* occurs when the respiratory enzyme systems in the tissues are poisoned, e.g. by cyanide. The cells are, therefore, unable

to utilize the oxygen carried to them and, as a result, the venous blood
has a high oxygen content (Fig. 15.4).

Acute hypoxia

We have seen that when the inspired oxygen concentration is lowered,
hyperventilation results, though little change in breathing occurs until
the inspired concentration falls to about 14 per cent (equivalent to 100
mm Hg) and this corresponds to an alveolar Po_2 of about 60 mm Hg. When
the alveolar Po_2 falls below 60 mm Hg, the respiratory minute volume
increases and this is due entirely to a reflex drive from the carotid and
aortic chemoreceptors. However, the chemoreceptors are much more
sensitive to a decrease in arterial blood Po_2 than is indicated by the change
in respiratory activity disclosed by measurement of the respiratory minute
volume. Whereas the respiratory response to inhalation of gas mixtures
of lower oxygen content does not begin until the arterial blood Po_2 falls
to 60 mm Hg (arterial oxygen saturation of 90 per cent), the electrical
activity in chemoreceptor fibres increases with arterial oxygen tensions
below 100 mm Hg. This is due to the fact that the respiratory response
evoked by the chemoreceptor drive is antagonized by three opposing
factors: (1) a direct depressant effect of hypoxia on the respiration by a
central mechanism; (2) depression of the central chemoreceptors due to a
lowering of the arterial blood Pco_2 by washing out of carbon dioxide through
the reflex hyperpnoea; and (3) alkalosis resulting from an increased
amount of reduced haemoglobin. Partially reduced haemoglobin is able
to mop up more hydrogen ions than is oxyhaemoglobin and the effect of
the slight alkalotic change in the blood antagonizes the chemoreceptor
drive. Thus, the respiratory response to hypoxia would be much greater
if these three antagonistic mechanisms could be prevented. We can
illustrate the effect of maintaining the alveolar Pco_2 constant during
hypoxia by taking the following example. A human subject breathing
room air has a resting ventilation of 9 l/min and an alveolar Pco_2 of
36 mm Hg (see lower part of curve A in Fig. 15.5). He is then made
hypoxic by lowering his alveolar Po_2 to about 47 mm Hg and as a result
his respiratory minute volume increased to 13 l/min and his alveolar
Pco_2 fell to about 27 mm Hg (see lower part of curve B). His alveolar
Pco_2 was then raised by adding carbon dioxide to his inspired air, the
alveolar Po_2 being maintained at the same level as before. It was found
that his breathing was unaffected until the alveolar Pco_2 was artificially
raised to 30–33 mm Hg, then with further increases in alveolar Pco_2, the
respiratory minute volume increased linearly (curve B). When the alveolar
Pco_2 had reached its control level of 36 mm Hg the respiratory minute
volume was 36 l/min. This experiment demonstrates that the ventilatory
response to hypoxia is much greater if the concomitant reduction in
alveolar Pco_2 is prevented by administering carbon dioxide.

Figure 15.5 shows one other interesting phenomenon. Curves A, B and C represent the relationship between respiratory minute volume and the alveolar P_{CO_2} at three different levels of alveolar P_{O_2}, 169 and 110, 47 and 37 mm Hg, respectively. It will be noted that the slopes of curves B and C, in acute hypoxia, are greater than that of curve A, in normal conditions of air breathing. This means that the sensitivity of the respiratory mechanism to carbon dioxide is greater during acute hypoxia than during air breathing.

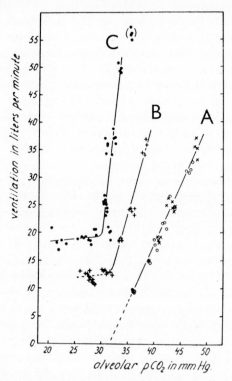

FIG. 15.5. The relationship between pulmonary ventilation and alveolar P_{CO_2} (37°C; prevailing barometric pressure saturated). Alveolar P_{O_2}: (Curve A), ✗, 168·7 ± 2·1 mm Hg. ○, 110·3 ± 1·9 mm Hg. (Curve B), +, 47·2 ± 1·5 mm Hg. (Curve C), ●, 36·9 ± 1·3 mm Hg. (Nielsen and Smith, 1952.)

In other words, the effects of oxygen and carbon dioxide excess are not simply additive, but there is a positive interaction between them, and this is of some physiological importance in asphyxia when hypoxia and hypercapnia occur together.

Chronic Hypoxia

At high altitudes, the percentage of oxygen in the atmosphere is the same as at sea-level, but since the barometric pressure is reduced, the partial pressure of oxygen is diminished to a comparable degree. The effects on man of oxygen deficiency depend not only on the altitude to which he ascends, but also on the rate of ascent.

The Mountain Climber.

The first signs and symptoms of oxygen lack occur when the healthy mountaineer ascends slowly to about 12,000 ft (3,700 m) above sea-level, corresponding to a pressure of 480 mm Hg. They are headache, nausea, vomiting and a feeling of lassitude and are regarded as characteristic of "mountain sickness." Mental features such as a feeling of well-being, exhilaration, talkativeness and sometimes emotional outbursts of laughing or crying, and development of fixed ideas may be evident. These effects wear off as the climber becomes "acclimatized" after a few days. The altitude to which man may climb varies with the individual, but without the additional use of oxygen is in the region of 28,000 ft (8,600 m) (close to the summit of Mount Everest). The limit is determined by the pressure of oxygen in his alveoli.

It is found that with increasing altitude, the pulmonary ventilation increases and there is a reduction in both the alveolar Po_2 and Pco_2 (Fig. 15.6). The augmented pulmonary ventilation is the result of stimulation of the peripheral arterial chemoreceptors by the lowered arterial blood Po_2, and not of the diminished barometric pressure *per se*. The hyperpnoea in turn causes the observed fall in alveolar Pco_2, the increased elimination of carbon dioxide leading at first to an increase in alkalinity of the blood and to the excretion of an alkaline urine.

Acclimatization to Hypoxia.

After a period of time at high altitude, processes of adaptation come into operation which improve the delivery of oxygen to the tissues and enable the mountaineer to withstand the effects of hypoxia better than would otherwise be the case. The term acclimatization is given to these processes of adaptation. This is well illustrated by the fact that climbers can attain heights of about 29,000 ft (8,900 m); in a relatively fast ascent, such as that made in 1875 by Tissandier and his two colleagues in a balloon to the same height, two of the party succumbed.

During acclimatization several changes occur:

(1) *There is an increase in the number of red blood cells and haemoglobin* due to a stimulant action of hypoxia on the blood forming organs. After several weeks' duration at high altitude, values up to 8 million red cells/ mm³ and 21 g haemoglobin/100 ml blood have been recorded. The increased amount of haemoglobin raises the oxygen capacity of the blood so that at any given Po_2 the arterial blood will contain more oxygen. The main advantage of this to the organism is that more oxygen is given up to

the tissues for a given fall in oxygen saturation and Po_2. This means that the tissue Po_2 will be higher than would otherwise be the case.

(2) *The increase in respiratory minute volume* is maintained in spite of the persistent low Pco_2. The pH of the blood however is partially or wholly restored by the renal excretion of bicarbonate. The question arises as to how the increased ventilation is maintained because administration of oxygen to an acclimatized subject at altitude causes only a slight reduction in breathing and increase in alveolar Pco_2, the latter still remaining well below the sea-level value of about 40 mm Hg. This is in contrast to the effect of giving oxygen in *acute* hypoxia, when the respiratory minute volume is restored to normal. It is apparent therefore that when the hypoxic stimulus is removed in the acclimatized subject by giving 100 per cent oxygen, respiration remains "driven" by an alveolar, and hence arterial blood Pco_2 which is considerably lower than normal under sea-level conditions. It is also of interest, in this connexion, that if an acclimatized subject is quickly brought down to sea-level, his respiratory minute volume is higher than his control value observed before exposure to chronic hypoxia.

These findings suggest that the chemical threshold of the central chemoreceptors becomes altered during acclimatization. It is believed that at altitude the hypoxia at first excites the peripheral arterial chemoreceptors which, by stimulating breathing reflexly, reduces the arterial blood Pco_2. Carbon dioxide being readily diffusible, the cerebrospinal fluid Pco_2 is quickly reduced to a similar extent. But the cerebrospinal fluid contains no buffers and so its pH rises. However, the active transport of bicarbonate out of the cerebrospinal fluid restores a normal HCO_3^-/Pco_2 ratio. From the point of view of the central chemoreceptors (or H^+ receptors) this reduction in cerebrospinal fluid HCO_3^- permits ventilation to increase and the Pco_2 to fall during the sojourn at altitude more than during administration of gases of comparable inspired oxygen tension acutely at sea-level. The threshold of the central chemoreceptors to carbon dioxide is lowered therefore during the process of acclimatization; the sensitivity to carbon dioxide, however, is unchanged.

These adjustments in the pH of the cerebrospinal fluid occur more quickly than those in the pH of arterial blood through renal compensation.

(3) *The increases in heart rate and cardiac output* associated with acute hypoxia are well maintained during acclimatization. The increased blood-flow in tissues is another important adaptive mechanism helping to compensate for the reduction in tissue Po_2 consequent upon the fall in arterial Po_2. Redistribution of circulating blood also takes place, so that the more vital tissues will receive a priority of supply.

The above mechanisms are involved in helping to maintain the internal environment of the tissue cells as close as possible to that at sea-level. In this connexion it is of interest that at high altitude there is a marked reduction in the gradient between the Po_2 of the ambient air and the Po_2 of the arterial blood. At sea-level, the gradient is $159 - 100 = 59$ mm Hg: at 20,000 ft (6100 m), for instance, it is $74 - 40 = 34$ mm Hg. There is a corresponding reduction in the gradient between the ambient air Po_2 and the mean capillary blood Po_2.

Hypoxia in Flying.

It has already been pointed out that the climber who ascends slowly and has time in which to become acclimatized has been able to reach heights of 28,000 ft (8600 m). When an aircraft pilot climbs rapidly, there is no time for these processes to take place and it is, therefore, impossible for him to reach such altitudes without the use of oxygen. Should he expose himself to the atmosphere at 25,000 ft (7600 m) for as long as ten minutes he is likely to die.

The effects of oxygen deficiency first show themselves at about 5,000 ft (1500 m), by increased breathing. Above 12,000 ft (3700 m), mental and physical functions are impaired and over-confidence develops. At 18,000 ft (5500 m), circulatory changes occur, producing an increase in pulse rate and blood pressure. The senses of touch, pain, vision and hearing are impaired. At these altitudes the flyer may observe how much brighter the day appears and how much louder the engines sound when he breathes from his oxygen mask. Between the heights of 18,000 and 30,000 ft (5500 and 9200 m), unconsciousness—which is sudden in onset and without warning—followed by paralysis and death may occur.

The effects of oxygen deficiency are affected by bodily activity. During quiet walking oxygen consumption may be three times that of the resting individual, and the pilot should, therefore, reduce his movements to a minimum.

The changes that occur in the pressures of the lung gases in the high altitude flyer can be seen in Fig. 15.6. The alveolar air pressures shown were taken at heights up to 25,000 ft (7600 m), under conditions where oxygen was not inhaled; 25,000 ft (7600 m) is the highest altitude to which a subject can fly without the use of oxygen. The top curve represents the Po_2 in the atmosphere; the next curve represents the oxygen saturation of the blood in the lungs; and the third curve represents the alveolar Po_2. This last curve does not follow a course parallel to that of the atmospheric Po_2 because of the hyperventilation caused by the low oxygen pressure; for the same reason the alveolar Po_2 (bottom curve) falls, instead of remaining constant. The horizontal broken line represents the water vapour pressure in the lungs which remains constant at 47 mm Hg.

If the effects of hypoxia are to be avoided, it is essential that pilots breathe 100 per cent oxygen above about 10,000 ft (3,000 m). This will maintain an adequate alveolar and arterial Po_2 up to altitudes of about 40,000 ft (12,200 m). At this height the barometric pressure is 140 mm Hg, the aqueous vapour pressure is 47 mm Hg, and the alveolar P_{CO_2}, say, 30 mm Hg, i.e. lower than normal due to hyperventilation. The alveolar P_{O_2}, therefore, must be: $(140 - 47 - 30) = 63$ mm Hg. This is an oxygen pressure just sufficient to maintain the pilot orientated and in control of his aircraft, but as altitudes above 40,000 ft (12,000 m), it is

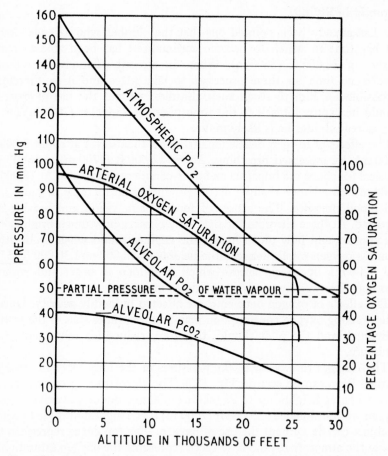

FIG. 15.6. Curves showing (1) the atmospheric P_{O_2}, (2) the arterial oxygen saturation, (3) the alveolar P_{O_2}, and (4) the alveolar P_{CO_2}; at all altitudes between sea-level and 30,000 ft (9200 m) (After Grow and Armstrong.)

necessary to raise the pressure by the use either of a sealed flying suit filled with oxygen under slight pressure, or a of sealed cockpit also under pressure. Using sealed cockpits, oxygen insufficiency ceases to be a limiting factor in flying at high altitudes.

The rarefied atmosphere at high altitudes produces certain other effects upon the body apart from the respiratory effects due to the low oxygen pressure. Speech has a nasal quality, which is partly due to the inability of the rarefied atmosphere to vibrate the vocal chords. Foreign bodies can only be expelled with difficulty, and a cough fails to dislodge particles from the respiratory mucous membranes, so that the cause of the coughing remains and pilots under these circumstances are subjected to continuous irritation. The low barometric pressure causes distention of abdominal organs, which contain gas; this may cause pain and discomfort. Severe frontal sinus pain may develop for the same reason.

CYANOSIS

Cyanosis may be defined as the bluish coloration imparted to the skin and mucous membranes by the presence of reduced haemoglobin in the blood of the superficial capillaries. It depends on the *absolute* amount of reduced haemoglobin in the capillary blood and not on the relative proportions of reduced haemoglobin and oxyhaemoglobin. It has been found that 5 g of reduced haemoglobin per 100 ml of capillary blood, or an oxygen unsaturation of 6·7 ml per 100 ml, is about the threshold level at which cyanosis appears. An anaemic subject, therefore, who has a total of less than 5 g of haemoglobin per 100 ml—i.e. an oxygen capacity of less than 6·7 ml per 100 ml—does not ordinarily become cyanotic. Thus the presence of cyanosis means that the tissues are hypoxic, although the absence of cyanosis does not necessarily indicate that there is no hypoxia.

The **causes** of cyanosis are numerous and are most important from the standpoint of diagnosis and treatment of the patient.

(1) **Conditions in which the Alveolar Po_2 is Reduced.** We have already discussed the problem concerning the mountaineer and the aviator at high altitudes where the lowered oxygen pressure of the air breathed causes hypoxia which may be severe enough to produce cyanosis through a diminished alveolar Po_2. Another cause is a reduced respiratory minute volume due either to failure of the respiratory mechanism or to obstruction of the airway. The respiratory centre is depressed, for instance, by overdose of sedative drugs; peripheral respiratory failure occurs as a result of degeneration of the lower motor neurones to the muscles of respiration as in poliomyelitis. Obstruction may be caused by foreign bodies lodging in the trachea or bronchi. In the case of complete obstruction of a bronchus to one lobe, absorption of air behind the obstruction gradually takes place leading to *collapse* of the lobe. The blood passing through the lobe will not therefore be oxygenated. *Asthma* is another form of partial obstruction of the airways so that the movement of air in and out of the lungs is hindered by contraction of the bronchial muscle.

(2) **Conditions in which there is Impaired Diffusion across the Alveolar Membrane.** This occurs in pathological states in which the alveolar membrane is abnormally thick due to inflammatory processes. The presence of oedema fluid in the alveoli also hinders diffusion and, in

consequence, increases the gradient of the oxygen pressure between alveolar air and arterial blood. A similar state of affairs occurs in *emphysema* in which there is destruction of many of the septa between alveoli causing a reduction in the area available for gas exchange.

(3) **Conditions in which there is Abnormal Reduction of Haemoglobin in the Systemic Capillaries.** This may be due either to an increase in oxygen utilization by the tissue or to a decrease in blood flow through it. The latter is the more usual cause of cyanosis in this group and gives rise to stagnant hypoxia. It may occur *locally* as a result of intense vasoconstriction through cooling a part of the body, or it may be *generalized* as in advanced heart failure and other conditions in which the peripheral circulation is abnormally sluggish.

(4) **Conditions in which there is an Abnormal Mixture of Arterial and Venous Blood.** In many forms of congenital heart disease, there is cyanosis due in part to direct mixture of venous with arterial blood through abnormal communications between the left and right sides of the heart. In other conditions which have already been referred to, such as obstruction to the air passages involving a part or whole of one lung, arterial blood will be a mixture of oxygenated and venous blood if the pulmonary blood flow through these areas is maintained. In point of fact, the pulmonary circulation gradually closes down in the collapsed part of the lung thereby reducing the volume of venous blood mixing with arterial blood and hence diminishing the cyanosis.

(5) **Conditions in which there is Alteration in the Haemoglobin.** A number of drugs and poisons are capable of converting the iron in the haemoglobin from the di- to the trivalent form causing the formation of *methaemoglobin.* This is dark in colour and so gives rise to cyanosis. In contrast with all the conditions giving rise to cyanosis enumerated in (1) to (4) above, the arterial Po_2 in methaemoglobinaemia is normal and, in consequence, there will be no stimulation of respiration reflexly through the chemoreceptors. The oxygen-carrying power of the blood is, however, reduced in proportion to the amount of methaemoglobin present. *Carbon monoxide poisoning* may also be mentioned here, since there is a similar loss of oxygen-carrying power of the blood. There is, however, no cyanosis, since carboxyhaemoglobin is red in colour. Carbon monoxide combines with haemoglobin with an affinity about 250 times that of oxygen: 0·1 per cent in the air produces a concentration of 15 to 20 ml per 100 ml in the blood. Very small concentrations in the air are therefore sufficient to produce severe symptoms in thirty to sixty minutes.

The Therapeutic Value of Oxygen

In treating certain forms of hypoxia, the administration of high concentrations of oxygen is a measure of the utmost value. By increasing the alveolar Po_2 the haemoglobin saturation of the blood leaving the pulmonary capillaries will be increased in conditions such as those in which the alveolar Po_2 is reduced and in which there is impaired diffusion across the alveolar membrane. There is relief of the cyanosis and a lessening of the dyspnoea associated with these conditions. Oxygen is also of extreme value in carbon monoxide poisoning for the high oxygen pressure displaces carbon monoxide from the blood.

In other forms of hypoxia, oxygen therapy is of less value. In anaemic hypoxia, for instance, the blood leaves the lungs with its haemoglobin fully saturated with oxygen, so the only benefit would be derived from the increased amount of oxygen carried in physical solution in the plasma. For a similar reason, oxygen is usually of less use in stagnant hypoxia.

Hyperbaric Oxygen Therapy. Attempts are now being made to treat certain conditions in which the tissues are hypoxic, by increasing the quantity of oxygen in the blood higher than can be achieved by administering 100 per cent oxygen. This is done by increasing the ambient pressure to 2 atmospheres. The patient is put in a cylindrical chamber large enough to accommodate an operating team as well, and is given oxygen to breathe. The quantity of oxygen dissolved in the plasma increases linearly with the arterial Po_2 by 0·003 ml oxygen/mm Hg Po_2/ 100 ml blood; breathing 100 per cent oxygen at 1 atmosphere pressure (alveolar Po_2 of 673 mm Hg) it increases to 2·0 ml/100 ml blood, while breathing oxygen at 2 atmospheres it is about 4·2 ml/100 ml blood at an arterial Po_2 of about 1,400 mm Hg. The arterial oxygen content, being the volume of oxygen chemically combined with haemoglobin plus that dissolved in the plasma, is $19·5 + 4·2 = 23·7$ ml/100 ml blood breathing 2 atmospheres of oxygen compared to $19·5 + 0·3 = 19·7$ ml/100 ml blood in the patient breathing room air at one atmosphere pressure. This method is proving beneficial in the treatment of coronary thrombosis, various forms of peripheral vascular disease and coal gas poisoning.

Respiration at High Atmospheric Pressures

When a man exposes himself to air at high pressures, he may develop certain symptoms either during exposure to the increased pressure or when he has returned to normal atmospheric pressure.

Increased air pressure is met in deep sea diving, in caissons and in submarine escape apparatus (the pressure within the submarine is at one atmosphere). Every 33 ft of sea-water means an additional pressure of one atmosphere, so that as a diver exposes himself to increased pressure the volume of respiratory gases *dissolved* in his blood plasma and tissues increases in proportion to the raised partial pressures of these gases in the alveolar air (Henry's law). Thus at two atmospheres pressure, twice as much gas will be dissolved in his blood and tissues as at one. The gases we have to consider are oxygen and nitrogen; the alveolar P_{CO_2} remains almost constant, and so carbon dioxide is not a gas which presents serious problems in this connexion.

Nitrogen. The dangers of nitrogen under increased pressure arise from two facts: (1) Nitrogen diffuses relatively slowly through living membranes, and (2) it is about five times as soluble in fat as in water. Consequently, not only does it take a considerable time for the body to absorb the extra nitrogen at any given high atmospheric pressure, but the elimination of the extra nitrogen when decompression occurs is also prolonged. If a diver ascends too quickly to a lower pressure, the nitrogen may come out of solution and form bubbles of gas in his blood and tissues, in particular in the central nervous system on account of its high fat content. These bubbles are apt to lodge in capillaries and obstruct the flow of blood giving rise to localized symptoms due to asphyxia and to distension of the tissues. These symptoms are pains in the muscles and joints, loss of cutaneous sensation and paralysis through involvement of the central nervous system ("caisson disease," "bends," "divers' palsy"). The severity of the symptoms depends on the pressure attained, the length of time spent by the subject at that pressure and on the rate of ascent. In severe cases, death may result from multiple air emboli in the heart and brain.

In order to prevent sudden evolution of gas, divers must ascend slowly, so that the tissues have time to get rid of their excess nitrogen via the lungs, without the formation of bubbles. Treatment of a case of caisson disease involves recompression in a pressure chamber, to dissolve the gas bubbles, followed by slow decompression to atmospheric pressure.

Another method of preventing the formation of nitrogen bubbles is to replace atmospheric nitrogen by helium, since helium is an inert gas and less soluble in fat than is nitrogen. In practice the diver is given a helium-oxygen gas mixture to breathe. This has another advantage, namely, it lessens "nitrogen narcosis," a condition associated with the onset of euphoria, hilarity, impaired mental activity and an increased difficulty in concentrating on and performing an allotted task. These effects, though they are very slight, are observed when air is breathed at 3 atmospheres pressure; they begin to handicap the subject at 4 atmospheres, and may rapidly make a man helpless at 10 atmospheres.

A similar condition of bends may occur in occupants of high-flying aircraft. Machines which are intended to fly at high altitude are fitted with pressurized cabins in which the pressure is maintained at an equivalent altitude of about 8,000 ft (2440 m) (barometric pressure 560 mm Hg). This enables an adequate oxygen pressure to be maintained in the lungs of the crew and passengers. Should an accident occur, resulting in the pressure in the cabin being suddenly reduced to the ambient pressure, oxygen and nitrogen bubbles may form in the blood, and cause caisson disease.

Oxygen. Gas mixtures containing up to 60 per cent of oxygen may be inhaled without danger. Pure oxygen (100 per cent) breathed for more than twenty-four hours may produce mental dullness and evidence of pulmonary congestion. Newborn infants are particularly susceptible to oxygen poisoning: there is proliferation of the retinal vessels into the vitreous humour with excess formation of fibrous tissue (retrolental fibroplasia), which may lead to permanent blindness. When oxygen is to be used in infants for resuscitation purposes, the concentration should be limited to 40 per cent in the inspired air.

Inhalation of pure oxygen at four atmospheres pressure produces signs and symptoms of oxygen poisoning which include convulsions and a fall of blood pressure. These were thought to be due to the increased amount of oxygen dissolved in the blood, so that when the blood passes through the tissues, less oxygen is lost from combination with haemoglobin. As we have seen in Chapter 10, haemoglobin becomes more acid when it combines with oxygen and is, therefore, less ready to surrender base for carbon dioxide combination. This results in a reduction in the amount of carbon dioxide removed from the tissues so that the effects of oxygen excess may be due to accumulation of carbon dioxide in the tissues. If this is the correct explanation, the carbon dioxide pressure should rise in the venous blood. More recent work indicates that, at these high oxygen pressures, the carbon dioxide pressure in cerebral venous blood, and hence in brain tissue, does rise, but that the rise is small and can in fact be excluded as an important contributing cause of oxygen poisoning in man. A direct toxic effect of oxygen on tissue enzyme systems, in particular those containing sulphydryl groups, is the most likely explanation.

CHAPTER 16

ARTIFICIAL RESPIRATION AND CARDIAC RESUSCITATION

Artificial Respiration

THERE are many circumstances in which respiratory movements cease temporarily. Death will follow from asphyxia unless fresh oxygen can be supplied, and the excess carbon dioxide washed out, by some means of artificial ventilation of the lungs. The cause of the respiratory failure can often be removed in this way, and complete recovery results. Common instances of such circumstances are drowning, electric shock, asphyxia from smoke, etc., in fires, carbon monoxide poisoning, certain diseases of the central nervous system which result in paralysis of the respiratory muscles, and the failure to breathe of the new-born.

In patients undergoing certain surgical operations it is desirable to produce complete muscular "relaxation" which is done by administering a drug which blocks transmission at the neuro-muscular junction. Since all skeletal muscles, including the diaphragm and intercostal muscles, are paralysed by such drugs, respiration must be maintained artificially.

In the emergencies mentioned above, it is usual for respiration to fail before the heart stops beating. As asphyxia gradually develops, however, not only does it adversely affect the heart, but it also depresses the medullary vasomotor centre. It is absolutely essential, therefore, that oxygen should be supplied to the tissues as quickly as possible to prevent deterioration of the heart and circulation, and to give the respiratory centres every opportunity of recovering their normal rhythmic activity. Before starting artificial respiration in such emergencies, however, it is necessary first to ensure that the patient's airway is not obstructed; no time should be wasted before loosening clothing and removing foreign bodies and water from the mouth and upper respiratory tract.

Emergency Methods

(1) *Expired air or "Mouth-to-mouth" method* (Fig. 16.1). This is now recommended by the St. John Ambulance Association of the Order of St. John and the British Red Cross Society as the method of choice in an emergency.

In this method, first practised by Elisha (2 Kings, Chap. 4, verse 34), the operator blows air into the patient's lungs intermittently. The operator kneels to one side of the head of the patient who is lying in the supine position. With one hand resting on the patient's forehead and occluding his nose, the patient's head is fully extended, the object of this manoeuvre being to prevent the tongue falling back and occluding the airway. The other hand pulls the chin downwards so as to open the patient's mouth.

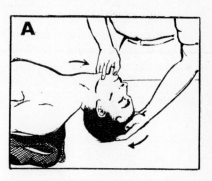

FIG. 16.1. The mouth-to-mouth or expired air method of artificial respiration. *A*, the patient's head is fully extended to prevent the tongue falling back and obstructing the airway. *B*, the operator pulls the chin down to open the mouth with his right hand, pinches the patient's nose with the other, and applies his own mouth to the patient's at the same time forcing air into the lungs. The operator then removes his mouth to allow the patient to passively exhale. *C*, an alternative way of occluding the patient's nostrils by means of the operator's cheek. (From First Aid Manual, St. John Ambulance Association of the Order of St. John).

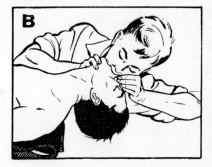

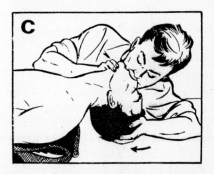

The operator then takes a deep breath and applies his *wide open* mouth to the patient's and blows air into the patient's lung. During expiration, the operator withdraws his head so as to enable him to take another breath and to allow expulsion of air from the patient's lungs by means of the elastic recoil of his lungs and chest wall. The cycle is then repeated about 15 times per minute. The main advantage of this method is that one knows immediately if there is any obstruction in the patient's airway; further-more, one can tell from movements of the patient's chest wall approxi-mately how much air is entering the lungs.

(2) *Arm-lift back-pressure (ALBP) method of Holger-Nielsen* (Fig. 16.2). This method has certain advantages (see below) and is as effective in ventilating the lungs as the mouth-to-mouth method. It may have to be used in cases involving facial injuries. The patient lies in the prone position with his arms above his head and elbows flexed so that one hand rests on the other; his head, turned to one side, lies on the uppermost hand. The operator kneels on his left knee at the patient's head, with his right foot near the patient's left elbow (A). Grasping the patient's arms

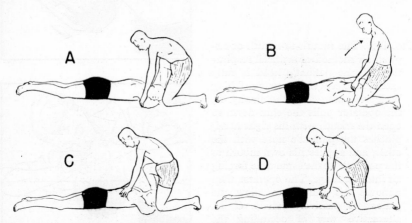

Fig. 16.2. Holger-Nielsen method of manual artificial respiration. A, placing hands for arm lift. B, arm lift. C, placing hands for back pressure. D, back pressure.

just above the elbows, the operator rocks backwards, raising the patient's arms until a resistance is felt (B). The arms are then dropped, and the operator, placing his hands just below the scapulae (C), rocks forwards keeping his arms straight, until his arms are in a vertical position, at the same time maintaining a steady pressure on the patient's chest (D). The movements of lifting and compression occupy about $2\frac{1}{2}$ seconds each and should be repeated about 15 times a minute.

(3) *Silvester's method.* When for any reason the mouth-to-mouth method cannot be used, Silvester's method may be carried out as an alternative. It has the advantage that it allows external cardiac compression to be carried out conveniently and at the same time if required.

The patient is laid on his back and the operator kneels astride his head, grasps his wrists and crosses them over the lower part of the chest. At the same time the operator rocks his body forward and presses down on the patient's chest. The pressure is then released and with a sweeping movement the patient's arms are drawn backwards, upwards and outwards as far as possible. This sequence is repeated about 15 times per minute.

These methods of artificial respiration have been established as the best of many which from time to time have been advocated in emergencies. The two main criteria on which success of a particular method is based are firstly, it must be capable of producing an adequate pulmonary ventilation as indicated by direct measurement with a spirometer and by estimations of the arterial blood Po_2, Pco_2 and pH. Secondly, the method must be capable of being carried out by non-medical personnel for prolonged periods of time, so that it should be simple and not require excessive physical effort on the part of the operator. In this connexion, it is of interest that the oldest established method has been proved experimentally to be the best.

When applying artificial respiration, the administration of oxygen may be beneficial. The addition of small quantities of carbon dioxide, however, is not recommended; patients requiring resuscitation almost certainly have a high arterial blood Pco_2, and to administer to them more carbon dioxide may depress the respiratory centres, rather than stimulate them, due to its narcotic action in high doses.

An important consideration in the choice of method of artificial respiration is its effect on the patient's circulatory system. Any method adopting the principle of intermittent positive pressure breathing, whether applied by means of a pump, or by the "mouth-to-mouth" emergency method, causes the mean intrapleural pressure to rise *above* atmospheric pressure and, in consequence, abolishes the "thoracic pump" aiding venous return to the heart. As a result, the cardiac output falls considerably, particularly if the patient is in a state of shock. In the mouth-to-mouth method, it is essential therefore not to over-inflate the lungs. On the other hand, any method adopting the principle of inflating the lungs by expansion of the thorax *alone* from without, thereby making the intrathoracic pressure more "negative," as for instance in raising the arms in the Holger-Nielsen method, improves venous return to the heart, and hence increases cardiac output.

Cardiac Arrest and Resuscitation

The term *cardiac arrest* is used to mean failure of the heart's action to maintain a circulation of blood.

Sudden cessation of the heart beat is a dramatic and often catastrophic emergency. The urgency with which attempts should be made to restart the heart beating again is directly related to the susceptibility of the brain to hypoxia. The brain cannot withstand cutting off its blood supply for any length of time. It has a high oxygen consumption, $3 \cdot 3$ ml/min/100 g cerebral tissue, and a high rate of blood flow equal to 54 ml/min/100 g or about 15 per cent of the resting cardiac output. Thus cessation of the cerebral circulation in man leads to loss of consciousness in a few seconds; after 3 minutes, cerebral damage occurs which may result in personality changes and physical disability, the severity of which increases with the duration of hypoxia. It will be evident therefore that it is of paramount importance to institute resuscitation therapy immediately.

One form of cardiac arrest is spontaneously reversible. An example of this is excessive vagal stimulation due to pressure over the carotid sinus regions in sensitive individuals. Such cases do not require any immediate treatment, because the heart starts beating spontaneously.

A second form of cardiac arrest is not spontaneously reversible and can occur as a result of many causes, viz., coronary thrombosis, pulmonary embolism, electrocution, drowning, during administration of anaesthetic agents, and in anaphylactic shock. In all these cases, the heart stops beating in one of two ways, cardiac asystole or ventricular fibrillation. In asystole, the heart is motionless, soft, relaxed and blue in colour. The coronary veins are engorged with dark blood and are very prominent. In ventricular fibrillation on the other hand, there is ventricular movement, not as a co-ordinated beat, however, but as a fine or course irregular uncoordinated writhing of the whole of the muscle, which can be felt as a "bag of worms" when the fibrillation is vigorous. The heart muscle is pale and cyanotic giving it a lavender hue. In both cardiac asystole and ventricular fibrillation the blood pressure rapidly falls to about 20 mm Hg or less, and there is complete cessation of blood flow. Outwardly the only way of distinguishing between these two forms of cardiac arrest is by studying the electrocardiogram.

Diagnosis. Cardiac arrest may occur quite suddenly and unexpectedly. Thus this condition must be suspected when a person suddenly loses consciousness and collapses. The absence of the pulse in a large artery, such as a carotid artery, is the essential feature in making the diagnosis. A convulsion may be the first phenomenon noticed, and the pupils are often dilated initially. The heart sounds are absent and respiration may have ceased or may be of a gasping type. The skin will have a greyish-white appearance due to cessation of the cutaneous circulation. The blood pressure will not be recordable. It must be stressed, however, that in the event of the carotid pulse being absent in a collapsed patient, resuscitation should be started immediately.

Principles of Treatment. When cardiac arrest has been diagnosed it it must be ascertained whether failure of respiration has occurred as well. Then the treatment of such a patient must be carried out with three principles in mind: (1) The circulation of the blood must be assisted artificially by compressing the heart rhythmically; (2) oxygenation of the blood must be carried out by any immediately available method, and then (3) attempts should be made to start the heart beating spontaneously.

Closed-chest Cardiac Compression

The technique of closed-chest cardiac compression is now the recommended method in emergencies. It has the advantage that it can be carried out without the use of any equipment and by people with little experience. In principle, the heart is rhythmically compressed between the sternum and the vertebral column thereby squeezing the blood into the pulmonary artery and aorta.

In practice the first thing the operator should do is to apply three sharp blows with the closed fist over the sternum. This *may* restart the heart

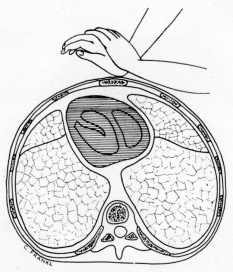

FIG. 16.3. Cross-section of the thorax showing how pressure on the sternum compresses the heart against the vertebral column. (Milstein, 1963, "Cardiac Arrest and Resuscitation" Lloyd-Luke: London.

when cardiac asystole is present, especially in the absence of gross heart disease or hypoxia. The operator then kneels to one side of the patient who is placed in the supine position on a rigid surface, preferably with the legs elevated to aid venous return. The heel of one hand is placed over the lower end of the sternum and the other hand is pressed vertically downwards on top of it and at a rate of about once a second (Figs. 16.3 and 16.4). The pressure should be sufficient to move the sternum 3–4 cm towards the vertebral column and the operator may find that the best position is one in which he can use his own body weight in applying the pressure. Between each compression pressure is removed to allow the chest to expand and the heart to refill. It is important not to perform cardiac compression too fast or there will be insufficient time for adequate filling.

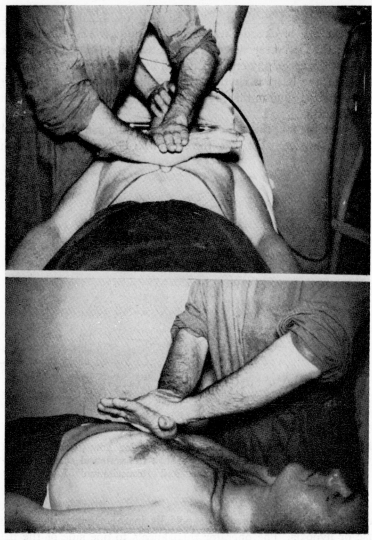

FIG. 16.4. Two views showing the method of applying closed-chest cardiac massage. The clavicles, sternum, xiphisternum and costal margins are outlined. (Milstein, 1963 "Cardiac Arrest and Resuscitation" Lloyd-Luke; London).

In children it is usually sufficient to apply this form of resuscitation by gentle pressure with the palm of one hand only, and in infants pressure with the thumb alone is adequate.

When failure of respiration occurs at the same time as cardiac arrest, an emergency method of artificial respiration must be carried out as well as external cardiac compression because the latter alone produces a quite inadequate pulmonary ventilation. Thus a single-handed operator should start by inflating the patient's lungs with two or three breaths by the mouth-to-mouth method and then commence cardiac compression with interruptions every minute to ventilate the lungs again.

In summary this method of closed-chest cardiac compression has the advantages that it can be applied anywhere, without the use of any equipment and by a first-aid worker; it is not necessary to open the thorax so that if spontaneous respiratory movements are re-established, the patient can breathe normally.

It is not without its disadvantages however. Firstly, various complications may arise: (1) Fractures of ribs or costal cartilages, especially in patients suffering from diseases of the skeleton and in those with a very rigid chest wall. This damage is relatively unimportant if a death is prevented. Fractures are usually due to the method being applied incorrectly; (2) bruising of the cardiac muscle and even rupture of the heart; and (3) laceration of the liver by exerting too much pressure over the xiphisternum, resulting in a fatal haemorrhage.

Secondly, the method will not correct ventricular fibrillation if present. It is then necessary to use a "defibrillator" which consists of passing an electric current through the heart with two electrodes, one placed on the upper end of the sternum, the other just below the left nipple. In principle, electric defibrillation renders all the fibrillating muscle fibres refractory at the same time. There is then a short period of asystole before a pacemaker initiates a co-ordinated contraction from which a normal cardiac rhythm ensues.

The cardiac output produced by external cardiac compression is considerably below the normal resting level even under optimal conditions, and the blood pressure may only rise to 60–70 mm Hg systolic. It is inevitable that the heart receives some bruising by the very nature of the procedure, so that the sooner a spontaneous heart beat can be restored the better. Nevertheless cases are recorded where external cardiac compression has been performed for up to 2 hours and the patients have left hospital physically well.

Transthoracic or Direct Cardiac Compression

An alternative method of artificially assisting the circulation is immediately following cardiac arrest to open the thorax and apply compression directly to the heart. But whereas closed-chest cardiac compression can be carried out by anyone trained in the use of the technique, direct cardiac compression should only be attempted by medically qualified personnel. It also requires efficient and careful control of the airway and ventilation of the lungs, and it cannot be practised outside the environment of a hospital.

Direct cardiac compression should be employed in cases in which the closed-chest method is being ineffective, or if ventricular fibrillation is suspected and no defibrillator is present.

A long incision is made with a scalpel in the fourth intercostal space on the left side and the ribs forced apart to gain access to the heart. To carry out cardiac compression the heart is grasped from behind with the right hand and compressed against the deep surface of the sternum. The left hand is placed over the sternum so that counter-pressure can be applied. Rhythmic compression about once a second is carried out and this usually produces an adequate cerebral circulation. The heart may start beating after 20–30 such compressions, but if not, the pericardium must be opened, and the ventricles compressed between the palmar surfaces of the two hands. It is necessary to pause between each compression to allow diastolic filling of the heart.

Restoration of the Heart Beat

When it is evident that closed-chest compression is being successfully applied, there being a reasonable pulse felt in the carotid region, attention should be given to restoring the heart beat. This is best done after removing the patient to hospital because treatment depends on whether the heart is in a state of asystole or is fibrillating, for which an electrocardiogram is required to distinguish between the two. When the heart is asystolic, a spontaneous beat may be induced by injection of calcium chloride (5 ml of a 10 per cent solution) or adrenaline (0·2–1·0 ml of a 1 in 1,000 solution) into the heart of intravenously administered during closed-chest cardiac massage. Adrenaline, however, has the disadvantage that it may cause ventricular fibrillation. Since cardiac arrest causes a rapidly increasing metabolic acidosis, attempts to restart the heart are often more successful if preceded by an intravenous infusion of 100 m. equiv. of sodium bicarbonate.

Electric defibrillation. In cases of ventricular fibrillation, the best method of restoring the heart beat is to "defibrillate" it by means of an electric shock. Defibrillation may be carried out externally as described above. An alternative but much less commonly used method is to open the chest through a rib space, and to apply the electric shock by means of two large electrodes placed on either side of the heart. (for details, see p. 130).

Section 6
THE NERVOUS SYSTEM

Chapter 17

NERVE

MESSAGES can be sent in the body by one of two systems, rapidly along the nerves, or slowly by hormones, "chemical messengers," in the blood. All messages from sensory receptors on the surface of the body or deep inside reach the brain along nerve fibres, and the detailed orders which the brain issues to the muscles and to most other effector organs (glands, etc.) are also sent along nerves. Hormones in the blood act more slowly and are used for more generalized and diffuse types of control (e.g. thyroid hormone) or in the control of specific and localized mechanisms when the pathway of control does not need to include the central nervous system (e.g. the stimulation of acid secretion in the stomach by gastrin).

In the study of peripheral nerve the ultimate object is to give a complete account in terms of physics and chemistry of how signals are transmitted along individual nerve fibres during normal activity in the living body. Direct investigation of single fibres in intact animals is, however, almost always impracticable. The majority of experiments have of necessity been done on isolated nerve trunks containing many nerve fibres. Fortunately there is good evidence that the mode of functioning of nerve fibres is not seriously upset when they are carefully dissected out of the body. Also the disadvantages of using a multi-fibre preparation are offset by the well-founded belief that individual nerve fibres function very independently; the sciatic nerve, for instance, contains motor fibres to very many widely separated muscles, and sensory fibres from a large area of skin. The fact that we can move a toe without any other muscles in the leg contracting, and that sensations from the toe are never confused with those from elsewhere in the leg, shows that the insulation between fibres must be excellent. These and other even stronger but more elaborate pieces of evidence give us every reason to suppose that when all the fibres in a large nerve trunk are excited together by an electric shock their

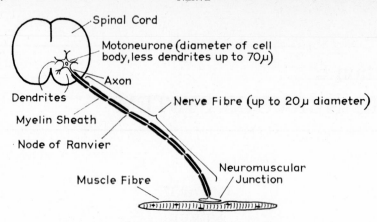

FIG. 17.1. Diagram of a nerve fibre.

A nerve fibre is a tubular process, often very long, arising from a nerve cell. The nerve cell protoplasm inside the tube is called axoplasm. In the diagram diameters are grossly exaggerated, with the true sizes roughly indicated (1 μ = ·001 mm).

The cell depicted is a motor nerve cell, or motoneurone, whose nerve fibre, or axon, ends on a skeletal muscle fibre. Only a single muscle fibre is shown but, in fact, a single motor nerve fibre by extensive branching inside the muscle may supply 50 or more muscle fibres. A motor nerve fibre with all the muscle fibres belonging to it is called a "motor unit."

Sensory nerve fibres, running to sense-endings in the skin and elsewhere, look precisely similar to motor fibres. Their cell bodies, however, are in the dorsal root ganglia (see Fig. 19.1), not in the spinal cord. A peripheral nerve trunk, such as the sciatic nerve, is a bundle of large numbers of motor and sensory fibres (together with sympathetic fibres; see Chapter 22) enclosed in connective tissue.

In vertebrates all nerve fibres (except the very smallest) are covered for most of their length by an electrically insulating fatty layer, the myelin sheath, the cell membrane being exposed only at the nodes of Ranvier, spaced about 1 mm apart. To start with, however, the complications introduced by the myelin sheath can safely be ignored and the nerve fibre considered simply as a tube of cell membrane containing axoplasm.

The nerve fibres of invertebrates, often used for experiment because of their large size, are non-myelinated but are otherwise essentially similar in structure and mechanism to vertebrate myelinated fibres.

individual behaviour will not be very different from usual, while the summing of all their effects makes observations much easier.

The Nerve-muscle Preparation

Many of the most important properties of excitable tissues were first discovered, and are still most conveniently demonstrated, upon a nerve-muscle preparation from a frog, usually the gastrocnemius muscle with the sciatic nerve attached. Ever since the end of the eighteenth century when Galvani discovered the electric current with his celebrated experiments on the excitation of the frog's leg by contact with metals, the frog's nerve-muscle preparation, stimulated electrically, has been the conventional object of neurophysiological enquiry. Many other agencies than electricity can be used to stimulate the nerve: local heating, pinching or tapping, the application of very hypertonic solutions and of various chemical substances,

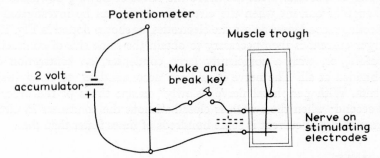

FIG. 17.2. Apparatus for stimulation of nerve by interrupted direct current.

> The muscle and the nerve in the trough are covered with Ringer's fluid. Contractions of the muscle are detected by watching it. The electrodes are of silver wire rendered non-polarisable by coating electrolytically with silver chloride. If ordinary wire is used with direct current the back electromotive force (E.M.F.) due to electrolytic polarization of the wires causes the threshold to wander unpredictably.
>
> To slow the rate of rise of current a condenser (shown dotted) may be connected across the electrodes. With an ordinary low resistance potentiometer a condenser of the order of 10,000 microfarads would be necessary, but smaller and more convenient values could be used if a resistance were inserted in one of the leads between the potentiometer and the condenser.

and in fact almost anything which is likely eventually to injure it. But the electrical stimulus has always been preferred to these, not only because of the convenience with which its timing and its intensity and duration can be controlled, but because unless quite unnecessarily strong it appears to cause no injury to the nerve. We now know that this is no coincidence because, as we shall see later, nervous conduction is itself electrical so that the electric current is the nerve's natural stimulus.

The simplest method of exciting a nerve electrically is to pass low-voltage direct current into it, using a circuit such as that shown in Fig. 17.2 to make and break the current and to alter its strength. With this equipment the main facts of nerve excitation are readily demonstrated.

Accommodation

In the first place it is observed that contractions can only be obtained at the moment when the stimulating current is made or broken and not when it flows continuously. This illustrates a very important general property which nerve shares with many irritable tissues: that a sudden change of stimulus is more effective than a slow or maintained alteration. We are familiar enough with this in the case of our sensations; it is always difficult to detect a gradual change in the brightness of a light or in the loudness of a sound. With the nerve the effect of slowing down the rate of change of current when the circuit is closed can be investigated by connecting a condenser across the electrodes, as shown dotted in Fig. 17.2. A larger current is then necessary to obtain the same size of contraction as before, or, with a sufficiently large condenser, no contraction can be obtained at all. The nerve is said to "accommodate" to slowly rising currents. With peripheral nerve "slowly" means times of the order of 1/50 second; when the switch is closed without the condenser in circuit the rate of rise of current is some hundreds of times faster than that.

Threshold

Another characteristic of nerve excitation by all kinds of stimuli is that nothing happens at all in the muscle unless the stimulus reaches a certain strength, no matter how abruptly it is applied. This is expressed by saying that the nerve has a "threshold" for the stimulus and unless the threshold is exceeded the nerve does not conduct. Such behaviour is quite different from that of many more familiar kinds of conduction; for example, if the output from the potentiometer of Fig. 17.2 is connected to an ordinary galvanometer, some current will flow in the galvanometer however small the voltage applied. It may be difficult to detect but it will be there all right. If, however, the nerve of a gastrocnemius-sciatic preparation is laid on the electrodes as before and the effect of making and breaking the current tried while the voltage applied to the nerve is gradually increased, nothing whatever happens in the muscle until the potentiometer is set to give perhaps half a volt, after which the muscle contraction increases rapidly in size as the voltage is further raised. The absence of response below half a volt is genuine and not merely due to a difficulty in detecting very small contractions. No matter how sensitive the equipment no response at all can be detected below the threshold.

The threshold of a nerve is not fixed but depends, among other things, on the rate of rise of the current, and also on its duration if this is less than about 10 milliseconds (1/100 second). As the duration of the current pulse is reduced below 10 milliseconds the strength of current necessary to excite rises progressively. The experimentally determined relationship between pulse duration and threshold current is known as a strength-duration curve. With pulses shorter than about 1 millisecond the quantity of electricity (i.e. the product of current strength and pulse duration) necessary to excite becomes a constant. This is because the nerve membrane behaves like a leaky electrical capacity. It is known that the condition for excitation by short pulses is that a certain length of nerve membrane should be depolarized by a certain number of millivolts. Hence, for durations of pulse so short that leakage current does not significantly discharge the capacity, a fixed quantity of electricity must be supplied in order to reach threshold.

Site of Excitation

A third fundamental property is that only current leaving the nerve excites it. In the ordinary convention current flows from anode to cathode. Current will thus enter the nerve in the neighbourhood of the anode, flow along the nerve in between the electrodes, and leave under the cathode, which in Fig. 17.2 is the electrode nearer the muscle. It is found that the nerve may be cooled, anaesthetized, or crushed either at the anode or between the electrodes without affecting the threshold when the current is switched on. But any of these operations at the cathode causes a very large increase in threshold, showing that excitation occurs under the cathode.

Break Excitation. As mentioned above the muscle also contracts when the current is broken. Similar evidence shows that in this instance excitation occurs under the anode. Anode break excitation is not a phenomenon of great significance. Many tissues, such as freshly dissected frog muscle, do not show it; even the frog's sciatic nerve does not do so if its circulation is intact. It seems to occur particularly in deteriorating preparations in which the fibres are somewhat depolarized. The explanation appears to be that anodal current repolarizes the fibres, but when the current stops they depolarize again rapidly and this excites them.

Conduction Velocity

So far we have only described how the nerve is excited and said nothing about transmission of the excitation to the muscle. Modern understanding of the nerve impulse began with Helmholtz's demonstration in 1850 that the influence, whatever it was, that passed down the nerve from the point of stimulation to the muscle and made it contract, travelled at a definite velocity, which he measured. In the frog it is about 60 miles per hour (25 metres per second). For one form of this experiment Helmholtz invented a myograph similar to that still widely used in the classroom (Fig. 17.3). The muscle pulled upon a lever to which was attached a long pointer writing on a revolving smoked drum. Thus a graph of contraction against time during a twitch was automatically drawn in the lampblack. The nerve was stimulated by an induction coil, it being arranged that the stimulus occurred at the same point on the tracing on each occasion. The stimulus was first applied to the nerve at a point near the muscle and a tracing of a twitch obtained. It was then moved to the end of the nerve distant from the muscle and a twitch again recorded. The second twitch was the same shape and size as the first but the whole tracing was shifted along the drum away from the point corresponding to the time of opening of the contact breaker.

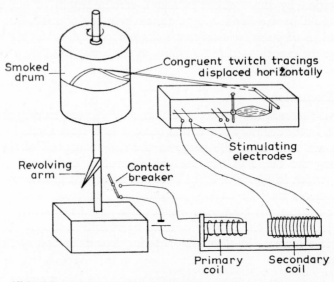

Fig. 17.3. Measurement of the conduction velocity of frog's nerve.

A sciatic-gastrocnemius preparation lies in the trough covered in Ringer's fluid. The tendon of the muscle pulls on a pivoted lever to which is attached a writing arm; the inner end of the muscle is fixed by a pin through the knee.

Stimuli are given by an induction coil, a device similar to a motor-car ignition coil, having a primary coil of few turns and a secondary coil of many turns, which delivers a brief high voltage pulse when the current in the primary is suddenly broken by a contact breaker. The strength of shock is adjustable by altering the separation of the primary and secondary coils.

Stimuli can be applied to the nerve either through a pair of electrodes on the end of the nerve, or through another pair close to the muscle. The contact breaker of the induction coil is knocked open by an arm attached to the shaft of the myograph drum. Thus the stimulus is always delivered at the same point of rotation of the drum.

Clearly the second twitch arises after a longer latency than the first and this is due to the time taken for the nervous influence set up by the shock to travel from the end of the nerve to the point near the muscle where the first stimulus was applied.

Helmholtz's experiment was of importance because it showed that the process of conduction in nerve was amenable to physical measurement and was not some mysterious and intangible influence passing with "the speed of thought." Helmholtz soon extended his measurements to both motor and sensory nerves in healthy human beings. For the motor fibres he stimulated the ulnar nerve at the shoulder and at the elbow and measured the difference in the latency of contraction of the muscles in the ball of the thumb. For sensory fibres he measured the difference in the time a subject takes to react to electric shocks applied, say, to the foot and the loin. This method involved the unproven assumption that no factors other than nerve conduction time cause the difference in reaction time from the two sites, but the answer it gave has been confirmed by modern methods. The conduction velocities of the fastest motor and sensory fibres are roughly similar and are about 50 metres per second in human limbs. Helmholtz also discovered, on the human subject, that nerve conduction is much slowed in the cold. A 10°C fall in temperature slows conduction by a factor of 1·7. Human limbs are often surprisingly cold in

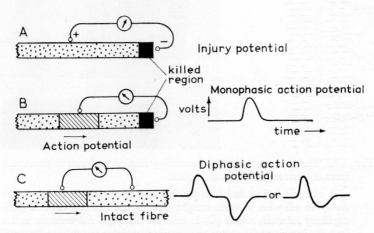

Fig. 17.4. Mode of recording injury and action potentials from a nerve fibre.

A. When the fibre is cut across the killed end shows a negative potential difference with respect to the intact part.

B. As an action potential (itself a region of negativity) passes under the electrode on intact nerve it causes a brief reduction in the potential difference. The appearance of the action potential recorded in this way on a cathode ray tube oscilloscope is shown to the right. The action potential fades out in the killed region and does not reach the end of the fibre. Hence the action potential is only detected as it passes the electrode on intact nerve, and the record is "monophasic."

C. With electrodes on an intact fibre a potential change, first in one direction and then in the other, is recorded as the action potential passes under each electrode in turn. This gives a "diphasic" record. Often the two phases run into each other giving the appearance shown on the extreme right.

winter and even in summer seldom reach "body temperature" (37°C or 98·4°F).

The Resting Potential

At about the same time that Helmholtz was measuring conduction velocities, du Bois Reymond and others were investigating the electrical

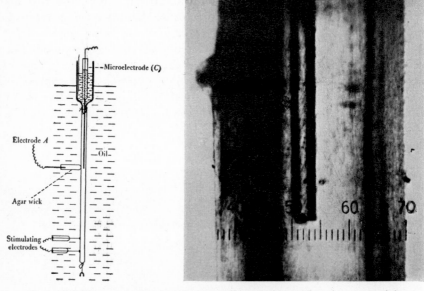

Fig. 17.5 The arrangements for recording resting and action potentials from a giant nerve fibre of a squid.

> A cannula is inserted into the cut end of the axon, which hangs freely in oil with a small weight tied to the bottom end. A glass capillary microelectrode (C) is inserted through the cannula as far into the interior of the axon as is desired, usually several centimetres. Contact with the outside of the axon is made by means of a wick soaked in sea water (electrode A).
>
> The photograph shows a microelectrode inside a living squid axon. The axon is seen as a clearer band surrounded by undissected connective tissue and smaller fibres. Each division of the graticule equals 33 μ; the axon is thus 500 μ ($\frac{1}{2}$ mm) in diameter and the electrode 130 μ. (Hodgkin and Huxley, *Nature*, vol. 144, p. 710, 1939.)

phenomena of nerve and muscle which led eventually to the electrical theory of nerve conduction. It was found that when a nerve or muscle was cut across, the cut end showed a negative potential difference of a few hundredths of a volt relative to the intact tissue. This is because the interior of nerve and muscle fibres is negative to the exterior with a potential difference across the cell membrane; normally the cell membrane surrounds the whole fibre, so that if two electrodes are placed on the surface at different points no potential difference is found. But cutting the fibre allows contact to be made with the interior and so we get the "injury potential" (Fig. 17.4). The magnitude of the injury potential recorded in this way is less than the true resting potential because, at the cut end, fluid and dead tissue, inevitably present, provide a current path between the inside and outside of the fibre

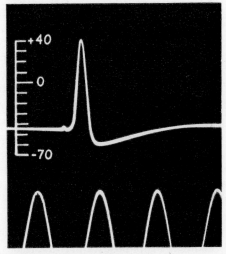

Fig. 17.6. Resting and action potentials from a single nerve fibre of the squid *Loligo forbesi*, recorded with an internal microelectrode by the method illustrated in the previous figure.

The potential difference between the inside and outside electrodes has been amplified by a direct-coupled valve amplifier and displayed on a cathode ray tube oscilloscope. The vertical scale indicates the potential of the internal electrode in millivolts (mV), the sea water outside being taken as zero potential. Time markers at 2 millisecond intervals.

The record reads from left to right. The potential to start with is the resting potential of -45 mV. The first small deflection of 2–3 mV is an artefact caused by the stimulus. It is followed by the action potential which overshoots zero and rises to $+40$ mV. (Hodgkin and Huxley, *Journal of Physiology*, vol. 104, p. 176, 1945.)

which short-circuits the resting potential and locally depolarizes the fibre The electrode on the cut end therefore makes contact with the axoplasm at a point where the potential difference is smaller than the true resting potential.

The true resting potential can be measured by thrusting a fine glass capillary electrode along the inside of an axon until the tip is well clear of the depolarized region. This was first achieved in 1939 using giant axons from the squid. The method used is illustrated in Fig. 17.5 and a record of potential made in this way is shown in Fig. 17.6. The resting potential of isolated squid nerve is about 50 millivolts (·05 volt). For fresh vertebrate nerve and muscle fibres the value (obtained by analogous methods) is about 90 millivolts.

The Action Potential

du Bois Reymond discovered that when a nerve is stimulated, the resting potential, recorded at the other end of the nerve, diminishes. At the time only slow galvanometers were available, but when rapid recording instruments were developed it was confirmed that the reduction was due to a brief wave of negativity which travelled along the nerve from the stimulating electrodes. As this wave passed under the electrode which was on intact nerve, it caused a temporary reduction in the potential difference between that electrode and the one on the cut end (Fig. 17.4). This electrical wave is called the action potential or, because of its shape, the spike potential. It used to be thought that during the action potential the resting potential was abolished, so that an electrode over the active region and one on the cut end would ideally record zero potential difference. Hence the action potential was spoken of as a wave of depolarization. In 1939 it was discovered that, when true potential differences are recorded by an electrode inside the nerve fibre, the action potential is larger than the resting potential (Fig. 17.6). It not only cancels the resting potential but overshoots by some 30–40 mV so that the inside becomes actually positive to the surface of a region at rest. The implications of this revolutionary observation will be considered later.

The Class of Disturbance to which the Nerve Impulse belongs. The All-or-none Law

A very important question which has attracted much interest from the earliest days is the relationship between the nervous impulse (defined as whatever process it is that passes down the nerve and makes the muscle contract) and the action potential. Is the electrical change an inherent part of the nerve impulse? In spite of much experimentation no one has ever been able convincingly to separate the two. It is found that they have the same threshold, propagate at the same velocity, are blocked at the same time if the nerve is frozen or compressed, and so on. Evidence of this kind shows that the nerve impulse and the action potential are so closely related that they cannot be dissociated. We now ask a further and a different question. Granted that the action potential is an inherent part of the nerve impulse, is it essential to the actual mechanism of propagation, or is it merely an invariable accompaniment of that mechanism? The evidence so far given permits, and perhaps encourages, this theory, but would be equally consistent with the view that the essential process is some chemical reaction which is always accompanied by electrical changes; the action potential would then be, as it were, merely the noise of the engine. Before describing Hodgkin's experiments which refuted this last possibility and proved that nervous conduction is electrical it will be convenient to bring forward various other facts which throw light on the kind of process that nervous conduction is, and which show how the particular hypothesis of conduction that he tested came to be proposed.

The action potential is, as we have seen, a travelling wave of electric change; in frog's nerve it moves at about 2,500 cm/sec and lasts about 1/1,000 of a second, so that the active region is confined at any instant to about $\frac{2,500}{1,000} = 2.5$ cm length of nerve. Hence in a nerve as long as the sciatic of the frog, stimulated at the end, all activity has ceased at the point of stimulation well before the action potential arrives at the muscle. The action potential is, thus, quite a localized affair and nervous conduction must be wholly unlike what happens in an ordinary telegraph wire; the common analogy drawn between nerves and telegraph wires is only very superficial.

As this region of electrical disturbance moves down a long nerve in uniform surroundings it neither decreases in size, nor travels more slowly. This suggests that the nerve impulse obtains the energy it needs for propagation locally as it goes along and not, like a rifle bullet, from the stimulus that starts it. This fits in with older observations that the stimulus does not have to be larger when it is applied to the nerve further away from the muscle, and that the impulse cannot be made to go faster by using a larger stimulus than is necessary just to excite.

Not only does the energy for propagation appear to be acquired locally, but local conditions also determine its rate of release. If a section of nerve is cooled the impulse goes more slowly in that length, but speeds up to its original rate when it reaches warm nerve again. Thus the conduction velocity in each stretch is determined only by the conditions in that stretch and not at all by the previous history of the impulse.

Such behaviour would be most simply explained if the impulse was self-propagated by the active region exciting the next section ahead, like a flame passing along a train of gunpowder. The characteristics of the response at any point would depend only on local conditions and not on the response of the next door sections that excited it. This theory is clearly a good one to explain the above observations on conduction velocity but it carries the implication that the size as well as the velocity of the impulse ought to be independent of the size of the stimulus. If release of energy for propagation is a purely local affair, one of the things determined locally should be the size of the impulse. At any point either you should get a full-sized impulse or none at all; it should not be possible to get a half-sized impulse by carefully grading the size of the stimulus. Behaviour of this kind is referred to as "all-or-none," and tissues which display it are said to obey the "all-or-none law." All-or-none behaviour was first observed in the contraction of the heart by Bowditch in 1872.

On the face of it, nerve does not obey the all-or-none law. As we have said earlier, if the nerve of a nerve-muscle preparation is stimulated with stimuli of increasing strength, first threshold is reached, but above threshold the contractions of the muscle for some time increase in size as the stimulus increases; so the preparation as a whole clearly does not behave in an all-or-none manner. An obvious explanation is that each individual motor nerve does obey the all-or-none law, but because the nerve to gastrocnemius contains many fibres with different thresholds they are excited one after another and so the relationship is concealed. This explanation was shown to be correct by Keith Lucas in 1909. He simplified the problem by using a very small muscle, the cutaneous dorsi muscle of the frog, which has only 8 or 9 motor nerve fibres. When the motor nerve is excited with steadily increasing strengths of shock the size of the contraction resulting does not increase smoothly but in a series of abrupt steps (Fig. 17.7). The number of steps is never more than the number of motor nerve fibres to the muscle. Each step clearly represents the excitation of one of the motor fibres, and the fact that each fibre has a sharp threshold, and that there is no further increase in the size of contraction until the next step, is interpreted to mean that, in each fibre, the size of the impulse does not increase with increasing shock size, once the threshold is passed. This experiment, it should be noted, establishes the all-or-none law for nerve, not muscle. The muscle fibres to which the nerve fibre is connected only come in as indicators of the arrival of a nerve impulse.

Nowadays the all-or-none law is readily observed on the single giant nerve fibres of invertebrates. With the arrangement shown in Fig. 17.5 it is found that, as the stimulus is increased from zero, at first the trace on the cathode ray tube remains quite flat, except for a small stimulus artefact, until suddenly the picture shown in Fig. 17.6 appears. Further increase in the stimulus causes no increase in the height of the action potential. No amount of adjustment of the stimulus strength ever results in a half-sized action potential. Thus the size of action potential is independent of the stimulus strength once this has reached threshold.

The all-or-none behaviour of the nerve impulse is important not only because of the light it throws on the nature of nervous transmission, but because it imposes the signalling code for the whole nervous system. Information and instructions can only be sent along a nerve fibre by altering the frequency of nerve impulses and not by altering their size. This system of frequency modulation rather than amplitude modulation, to borrow radio terminology, has very great advantages for long distance signalling—as radio engineers have discovered. It makes nerve signalling independent of local conditions; all that counts is the number of impulses that get through, and it does not matter if cold or pressure or shortage of oxygen slows them up or reduces their size, as long as conduction does not

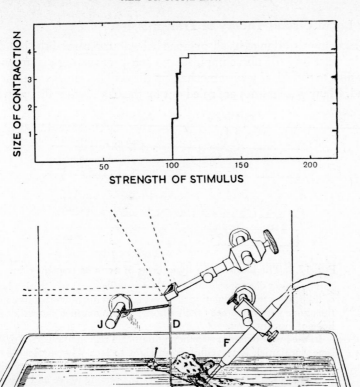

FIG. 17.7. Keith Lucas's apparatus for demonstrating the all-or-none law, using the dorso-cutaneous muscle of the frog.

The piece of skin into which the muscle, C, is inserted is cut free and attached to the lever, D, which carries a mirror. The muscle is lightly stretched by a spring between the lever and the support J. F, stimulating electrodes applied to the motor nerve. Contractions are recorded photographically by means of a beam of light reflected from the mirror.

Above is shown the relationship observed between strength of stimulus (threshold taken as 100) and the size of contraction. The number of steps was never more than the number of motor nerve fibres. (*Journal of Physiology*, vol. 38, p. 113, 1909).

fail altogether. Likewise it is responsible for the independent functioning of the many fibres bundled together in nerve trunks, for although the electric current generated by an impulse in one fibre will reach its neighbours, it is far too small to excite impulses in them (let along to extinguish impulses already there) and unless it does this it will not interfere with their signalling at all.

The Local Circuit Theory of Transmission

The demonstration of its all-or-none behaviour removed the last difficulties in regarding the nerve impulse as a self-propagating disturbance. We have now to consider by what mechanism the active region excites the region ahead. Many possibilities are ruled out by the observation that nerve fibres

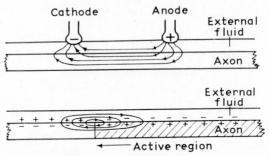

FIG. 17.8. The local-circuit hypothesis of nervous transmission.

The upper diagram shows a single nerve fibre, covered with a layer of fluid, with two stimulating electrodes. Current enters the fibre near the anode and leaves near the cathode, in the manner shown by the lines of current flow.

In the lower diagram an action potential, a region of reversed membrane potential, is travelling from right to left. The surface of the active region is negative with respect to the surface of the resting nerve ahead. Current therefore leaves the resting nerve and flows in the outside fluid down the potential gradient to the active region. The local circuits are completed via the axoplasm, where the same argument applies in reverse.

Thus in front of the active region current leaves the nerve fibre, just as it does under a stimulating cathode. These currents will tend to excite the nerve in front of the active region. The hypothesis is that they do in fact do so, and that this is how the action potential propagates.

(The spatial distribution of local currents along a nerve near a stimulating electrode, or ahead of an action potential, is determined by the cable-like properties of nerve fibres, as will be explained on p. 273. Such a distribution of current spread is termed *electrotonic* to distinguish it from ordinary *electrical* spread in a homogeneous medium that characterizes e.g. the lines of current flow between two electrodes immersed in a beaker of saline. The distinction need not be understood to follow the present argument.)

(whether sensory or motor) transmit equally well in either direction. If a length of nerve is excited in the middle the action potential spreads in both directions with equal velocity. Whatever it is that excites locally during propagation must therefore pass with equal ease up or down the fibre. Either diffusion of a chemical substance or the flow of electric current might serve; but diffusion looks like being too slow a process to account for conduction at 60 miles per hour, while there are obvious reasons for preferring an electrical hypothesis; electric currents very easily excite; the action potential produces an electric current; moreover the polarity is correct, for it is the cathode which excites and likewise the active region is negative.

The hypothesis is, then, that propagation occurs because the active region causes local currents to flow in the inactive region ahead (Fig. 17.8). These currents are in the same sense as the currents that flow when a

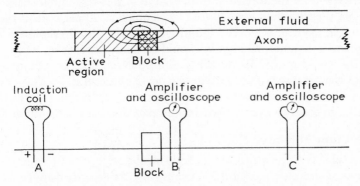

Fig. 17.9. Evidence for electrical transmission in nerve.

A frog's sciatic nerve is blocked by freezing a short length. When the nerve is excited by a shock from an induction coil applied through the electrodes at A, no action potential gets through to the recording electrodes at C, but immediately after an action potential from A arrives at the blocked region electrodes at B record small local currents spreading through the block. The upper diagram shows, for one fibre, how current spreads through the blocked region, just as it spreads in front of a normal impulse (compare with Fig. 17.8).

The electrodes at B can also be connected to an induction coil and used to measure the threshold of the nerve, the appearance of an action potential at C indicating that the threshold has been reached. Immediately after an action potential arrives at the other side of the block a transient fall in threshold can be detected at B. The fall in threshold occurs at the same time and has the same spatial distribution along the nerve, as the local currents set up by the blocked impulse. (After Hodgkin, *Journal of Physiology*, vol. 90, p. 183 and p. 211, 1937.)

cathodal stimulus is applied from an external electrode and excite for the same reason. There are no observations which are inconsistent with the local circuit theory and since the end of the nineteenth century it has been the most widely accepted hypothesis of propagation, but until 1937 no one knew whether it was true or not. The difficulty is that the action potential recorded from a nerve as it conducts is so very much smaller than the voltage that has to be applied through external electrodes in order to stimulate it. Certainly the local currents flow in the right way to excite, but the unanswered and critical question was: Are they in fact large enough to do so?

Hodgkin solved this question in the following way. In a frog's sciatic nerve he blocked conduction by freezing a short length (Fig. 17.9). Immediately after an action potential had arrived at the block, small currents of the kind expected from the local circuit theory could be detected spreading several millimetres beyond the block. Test stimuli showed that at the same time the threshold of the nerve in this region fell sharply. On occasion, the threshold was reduced by as much as 90 per cent. If the local currents in front of a blocked impulse can lower the threshold by 90 per cent those from a normal impulse would certainly lower it by 100 per cent, i.e. they would excite. Hence the action potential does constitute a large enough electrical stimulus to excite the nerve ahead of it. It is now known, in fact, that the normal action potential is five to ten times larger than it has to be in order to excite. Electrical propagation has a large safety factor.

Conduction Velocity

The velocity of propagation depends on the strength of current flowing in the local circuits ahead of the active region. As described above, because the nerve membrane has capacity, any current must flow for a certain time in order to excite; the larger the current the shorter the time for which it has to flow. Hence the larger the local currents, the sooner the section of nerve ahead of the active region is excited and the higher the conduction velocity. The strength of the local currents depends, amongst other things, on the electrical resistance of the outgoing path (i.e. the longitudinal resistance of the axon) and the resistance of the return path through the external fluid. The longitudinal resistance of the axon decreases as the cross sectional area of the axoplasm increases. It is true that an increase in the diameter of the axon also involves an increase in the area and, hence the capacity, of the membrane; but doubling the diameter only increases the capacity by a factor of two whereas the resistance (inversely proportional to area) decreases by a factor of four. Hence the decrease in resistance wins and large nerve fibres conduct faster than small ones. The increase of speed to be obtained by increasing diameter clearly has survival value, for several animals have evolved very large nerve fibres. The squid escapes from its enemies by contracting its mantle, which drives it rapidly backwards through the water. To do this as fast as possible it has developed its giant nerve fibre of up to 1 mm diameter, which conducts at some 25 metres/sec.

In the body nerve fibres are effectively surrounded by a large volume of fluid, so that there is little scope for increasing conduction velocity by lowering the resistance of the return path. In isolated fibres, however, the conduction velocity can be altered by changing the resistance of the return path, an experiment which provides powerful evidence for the electrical theory of propagation. Hodgkin laid a giant axon in air on a grid of platinum strips; electrodes were also provided for stimulating at one end and recording at the other, so that the conduction velocity could be measured. The ends of the platinum strips could be plunged into a trough of mercury, in order to connect them all together electrically. This had the effect of suddenly reducing the longitudinal resistance outside the nerve and, at the same moment, the velocity of the action potential was seen to increase. The fact that conduction velocity can be altered instantaneously by making electrical connections right away from the nerve would be almost impossible to explain unless conduction was itself an electrical process.

The Ionic Basis of Nerve Action

The foregoing experiments establish that the action potential propagates by local electric circuits, but although they tell us how it propagates they reveal nothing about the nature of the potential change itself. By what mechanism does the potential difference across the nerve membrane suddenly reverse and almost equally rapidly return to its resting state again, as it is seen to do in Fig. 17.6. The answer is: by movements of charged ions across the nerve membrane. This essential step of linking nervous activity with the movement of ions was taken by Bernstein in 1902. Bernstein proposed, correctly, that the resting potential, from which the action potential takes off, is a consequence of the unequal distribution of potassium ions across the nerve membrane, and that the action potential is due to movement of sodium and potassium ions down their concentration gradients. He got the details wrong because he thought that the action potential merely cancelled the resting potential whereas, in fact, it reverses it, but the modern Hodgkin-Huxley theory, to be described, rests on Bernstein's principles. Before describing how the potential difference across the membrane is reversed by ionic currents during the action potential, it is first necessary to look into the nature of the resting potential, already described in Chapter 1, in greater detail.

The Resting Potential

In sea water and in the blood and extracellular fluid of animals the chief ionic constituents are sodium and chloride ions. There is some potassium, but potassium ions only represent about 2·5 per cent of the total cations. Inside living cells, with few exceptions, the situation is reversed; there is a lot of potassium (roughly as much as there is sodium outside) but little sodium and chloride (Table 17.1). Although there is this small amount of chloride, by far the greater part of the internal anions consists of organic molecules (in the case of squid nerve mainly amino acids and other small organic acids) carrying net negative charges. Thus, outside cells, we have chiefly sodium ions (Na^+) and chloride ions (Cl^-) and inside, potassium ions (K^+) and organic anions. In solutions of such strength, sodium chloride is completely ionized and does not exist as a compound. Similarly there is good reason to believe that all, or very nearly all, the internal potassium also exists as free ions. It is misleading and, in a sense, incorrect to speak of cells as containing "potassium proteinate," as is sometimes done.

Leaving to one side the question of how these striking differences in the composition of the cells and the fluid bathing them arise in the first place, let us accept them and consider how they are maintained. One very simple way of keeping the K^+ in and the Na^+ and Cl^- out would be to have an impermeable cell membrane. But such cells as have been examined prove to be permeable to K^+ and Cl^-, although they are much less permeable to Na^+ and the organic ions. It might be thought that if the

TABLE 17.1

Approximate concentrations of potassium, sodium and chloride in nerve and muscle fibres and in the fluid bathing them (artificial sea water or Ringer's fluid).

1 m-mole/l $= 10^{-3}$ gram-molecules per litre

Tissue	Potassium		Sodium		Chloride	
	Inside m-mole/l	Outside m-mole/l	Inside m-mole/l	Outside m-mole/l	Inside m-mole/l	Outside m-mole/l
Squid axon .	400	10	50	460	110	540
Frog nerve and muscle .	120	2·5	15	120	3	120
Mammalian muscle .	140	4	10	150	—	140

cell membrane were permeable to K^+ and Cl^- the only way to keep the K^+ concentration high and the Cl^- low inside the cells would be to pump the K^+ back as it leaks out and pump the Cl^- out as it comes in. But this is not the only way, for the tendency of the K^+ to diffuse out can be offset by an electrical potential difference across the membrane. As potassium ions are positively charged, the inside of the cells must be negative relative to the outside in order to attract any potassium ions that try to leave. Since chloride carries an opposite (negative) charge the same potential difference will serve to keep out the chloride ions too. In fact in all cells on which measurements have been made (mainly nerve and muscle) a resting potential of roughly the expected size has been found. Thus K^+ and Cl^- are (to a first approximation) in equilibrium across the membrane, the tendency of the ions to diffuse down the concentration gradients across the membrane being balanced by the potential gradient.

The value of the "equilibrium potential" which just balances the tendency for a univalent ion of internal concentration C_i to diffuse out into an external fluid containing a concentration C_o is given by the expression $E = \dfrac{RT}{F} \log_e \dfrac{C_i}{C_o}$ where T is the absolute temperature, R is the gas constant (as in the gas equation $PV = RT$), and F is Faraday's constant (96,500 coulombs, the amount of electricity needed to deposit 1 gram equivalent of a substance at an electrode). Inserting numerical values of R, T and F and converting to logarithms to base 10 we get:

$$E \text{ (in millivolts)} = 58 \log_{10} \frac{C_i}{C_o} \text{ at } 20°C.$$

In fresh squid nerve and in vertebrate nerve and muscle the ratio $\dfrac{C_i}{C_o}$ for potassium is about 35, giving a potassium equilibrium potential of $58 \log 35 = 90$ mV, which is not far from the observed values of resting potential.

An important point that must be grasped in order to understand the ionic mechanism of nerve is that relatively very few ions indeed have to move in order to produce the changes of potential involved. The potential change caused by a certain movement of charge is proportional to the capacity of the structure into which it flows (1 coulomb flowing into a capacity of 1 farad changes the potential by 1 volt). The nerve membrane has a capacity of about 1 microfarad per square centimetre and the resting potential is roughly 100 mV = 1/10 volt. To change the potential difference of 1 cm^2 of membrane by 1/10 volt therefore needs 1/10 microcoulomb $= 10^{-7}$ coulombs of electricity. Now 1 gram molecule (mole) of a univalent ion carries a charge of 96,500 coulombs, say 10^5 coulombs, so that 10^{-7} coulombs corresponds to only 10^{-12} mole of a univalent ion. In a 500 μ squid axon the volume of axoplasm covered by 1 cm^2 of membrane is approximately 1/100 ml. Squid axoplasm contains some 0·4 mole o potassium ions per litre so that the amount of potassium in 1/100 ml is $0·4 \times 10^{-5}$ mole. Thus the axon contains $\dfrac{0·4 \times 10^{-5}}{10^{-12}} = 4$ million times more potassium ions than would have to pass across the membrane to alter the potential difference across it by 100 mV.

We are now in a position to understand by means of a hypothetical model just how the resting potential arises (Fig. 17.10). Let us in imagination make up something to represent extracellular fluid by dissolving some sodium chloride and, say, 1/20th of that amount of potassium chloride in water. The inside of the cell will be represented by a solution of the potassium salt of some amino acid (for the sake of definiteness say aspartic acid), together with 1/20th of the amount of sodium chloride. The total concentrations are chosen so that the two solutions have the same osmotic pressure. We now pour the two solutions into a chamber divided into two parts, which we will call inside and outside, by a membrane permeable to K$^+$ and Cl$^-$, but not to Na$^+$ or aspartate. Because of the concentration differences K⁺ at once begins to pass from the inside to the outside and Cl⁻ from outside to inside. Owing to their large charge, however, few ions have to pass before a potential difference is set up large enough to oppose these movements. (The reader is left to confirm that because the chosen proportion of KCl outside is the same as the proportion of NaCl inside almost the same difference is required to restrain the movement of K⁺ out and of Cl⁻ in.) Thus a membrane potential rapidly builds up, but the movement of ions necessary is so small that if

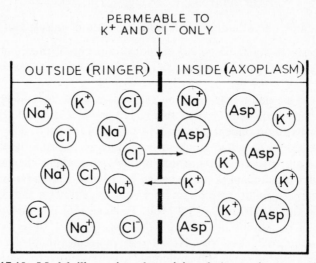

FIG. 17.10. Model illustrating the origin of the resting potential. A hypothetical partition permeable to K⁺ and Cl⁻ but not to Na⁺ or to organic ions, represents the nerve membrane. The solution in the compartment labelled "outside" is a simplified Ringer's fluid of NaCl with a small proportion of KCl. Axoplasm "inside" is represented by a solution of potassium aspartate with some NaCl, isotonic with Ringer.

samples of the two fluids were withdrawn and analysed no change in composition could possibly be detected. The movement of ions necessary to give the inside a negative potential relative to the outside would be, as we have seen, of the order of a millionth part of the total.

All cells that have been investigated so far have resting potentials in which the interior of the cells is negative to the surroundings. It is important to remember that this fact could not have been foreseen from a knowledge of the ionic compositions of the cell contents and the external fluid. If instead of being permeable to K⁺ and Cl⁻ and impermeable to Na⁺ the reverse had been true, there could have been an equally good equilibrium but the inside would have been positive. This can easily be understood with the above model. When the solutions are poured into the compartments, Na⁺ now being the only ion that can move, some sodium ions immediately move inwards. As they carry a positive charge the inside becomes positive and the outside becomes negative. Soon the potential difference becomes sufficient to prevent any further movement of Na^+ down the concentration gradient and equilibrium is established with the inside positive.

This situation is not of merely hypothetical interest. As we shall see later, at the height of the action potential the nerve membrane does become predominantly permeable to Na^+ and the potential difference across it is close to the equilibrium potential for Na^+, with the inside positive. Secondly, even at rest, the membrane is slightly permeable to Na^+. This complicates matters. The simplest way of looking at it is to regard the resting membrane as consisting of a large area of membrane permeable to K^+ and Cl^- and a small area permeable to Na^+. Each area tries to reach its own equilibrium potential but fails. The resultant potential is near the equilibrium potential for K^+ and Cl^-, but shifted some millivolts towards the Na^+ potential, i.e. the inside is less negative. Such a system cannot be in equilibrium. Since the membrane potential is less than the K^+ equilibrium potential, K^+ will diffuse out; and similarly Na^+ enters as the potential is very far from the Na^+ equilibrium potential. Left to itself such a system would slowly run down until the ionic concentration differences levelled out. That it does not do so in living cells is due to an active pump, driven by metabolic energy, which pumps Na^+ out and K^+ in. Thus cells maintain a steady state, but they do not have a simple membrane equilibrium, because energy has to be supplied to maintain their ionic composition.

In general, the potential across the membrane at any time depends on the relative permeabilities to Na^+, K^+ and Cl^-. Other ions to which the membrane is permeable are present in much lower concentrations and make little impression. Normally the membrane of nerves and muscles is moderately permeable to K^+ and Cl^- and almost impermeable to Na^+. So the resting potential is close to the K^+ and Cl^- potential. At the height of the action potential the membrane becomes extremely permeable to Na^+ and the potential difference is the Na^+ potential. Other conditions are also found, as we shall see subsequently; thus the muscle end-plate under the action of acetylcholine becomes very permeable to both Na^+ and K^+ and the membrane potential therefore nearly vanishes.

Bernstein's idea that the resting potential arises because of the K^+ concentration difference for many years rested mainly on the fact that raising the external K^+ concentration reduces the injury potential. It was also known that muscle fibres were permeable to K^+ but not to Na^+; they take up K^+ if the external concentration is raised but not Na^+. Thus if a muscle is placed in hypertonic sodium chloride it shrinks permanently, but if the bathing solution is made hypertonic by dissolving solid potassium chloride there is temporary shrinkage but the fibres soon regain their original volume and are found to have taken up extra K^+ and Cl^-. But quantitative evidence was lacking, partly because the absolute value of the resting potential was uncertain, and partly because in conventional tissues such as frog nerve and muscle it is difficult to get reliable estimates of the Na^+ and Cl^- concentrations inside the fibres; the concentrations inside are rather small, but very large in the extracellular fluid, so that a small error in estimating the amount of the latter produces very large errors in the internal concentrations.

Since 1945, work on single fibres, principally the squid giant axon, has given the necessary data. The permeabilities of the membrane to Na^+ and K^+ have been measured by observing the rate of uptake and of loss of radioactive Na^+ and K^+ by the axon. Furthermore the axoplasm of squid nerve can be squeezed out from the cut end like toothpaste from a tube, uncontaminated by extracellular fluid, so that accurate values for internal Cl^-, Na^+ and K^+ have been obtained. The value for the resting potential calculated from the permeabilities of the membrane to Na^+ and K^+ and from the concentrations of these ions inside and outside the axon, given in Table 17.1, agrees closely with the actual value, measured with an internal electrode.

The measured internal Cl^- concentration, however, is greater than it should be if the distribution of Cl^- is determined only by the resting potential. It has been shown that the high concentration is because Cl^- is actively pumped into the fibre by a pump similar to but distinct from the sodium pump described below. Among excitable animal tissues a chloride pump has so far only been demonstrated unequivocally in squid axon. The advantage to the squid of raising the Cl^- concentration in its giant axon is not clear.

Any possible doubt that the resting potential is determined by the concentrations of the ions and the passive permeability properties of the membrane was finally removed when it proved possible to squeeze all the axoplasm out of a squid axon and then to re-inflate it and perfuse it with solutions of known composition. With sea water outside and an isotonic solution of a potassium salt inside, the resting potential has normal values (50–70 mV) and the axon conducts action potentials of normal size for many hours. This is so even if the axon is perfused until more than one hundred times its volume of isotonic potassium sulphate has passed through. Hence the axon can have no secret soluble ingredients it requires to produce normal resting and action potentials. With isotonic potassium salt outside and isotonic sodium chloride inside the resting potential reverses, the inside of the nerve becoming 50–60 mV positive to the external fluid.

The Sodium Pump

The mechanism which pumps sodium out of cells and potassium in, was first discovered in red cells. In blood that is stored in a refrigerator the red cells gradually lose K$^+$ and gain Na$^+$. When they are incubated with some glucose the Na$^+$ content falls again and the K$^+$ rises. These movements are against the concentration gradients and since the movements of two similarly charged ions in opposite directions cannot both

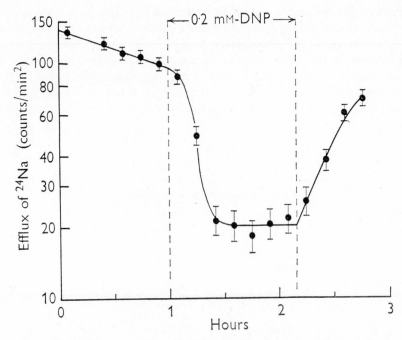

FIG. 17.11. Extrusion of radioactive sodium by a squid giant axon.

An internal microcapillary similar to that shown in Fig. 17.5 was used to inject a small quantity of solution containing ^{24}Na into the axoplasm. The sea water bathing the outside of the fibre was changed at 10 min intervals and the amount of radioactivity in successive samples, due to extruded ^{24}Na, measured in a Geiger counter. Quantity of radioactivity is expressed in counts/min and the units of rate of efflux are, therefore, (counts/min)/min.

The addition of 0·0002 gram-molecules per litre (0·2 mM) dinitrophenol (DNP) to the sea water outside the fibre reduced the efflux by a factor of 5. The pump recovered when the DNP was washed away. (Hodgkin and Keynes, *Journal of Physiology*, vol. 131, p. 592, 1956.)

be due to the potential difference across the red cell membrane (which, incidentally, has not been measured) it is clear that an active pump using metabolic energy is involved. A similar mechanism has been shown with great clarity in giant single nerve fibres from the squid. Hodgkin and Keynes pushed a fine glass capillary into a squid axon in the usual way but, instead of recording potential differences, it was used to inject a very small quantity of radioactive Na$^+$. Within a few seconds radioactivity began to appear in the fluid bathing the fibre. Most of this loss of radioactivity was due to active extrusion of Na$^+$, for the rate of loss dropped steeply if the pump was poisoned with dinitrophenol (Fig. 17.11) or by cyanide or azide.

Energy for the pump comes from hydrolyzing the phosphate bonds of "energy-rich" phosphate compounds such as adenosinetriphosphate (ATP). The above poisons stop the production of energy-rich phosphate compounds in the mitochondria. The pump can be restarted again by an injection of ATP down the internal microcapillary. The pump is also poisoned by the cardiac glycosides, the digitalis group of drugs; the one commonly used in experimental work is ouabain. The cardiac glycosides

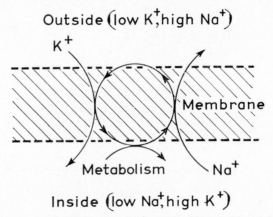

FIG. 17.12. Diagram of the supposed mode of action of the sodium pump.
(After Hodgkin and Keynes.)

inhibit the adenosine triphosphatase (ATPase) in the membrane. Thus they stop the pump by interfering with the utilization of ATP.

At one time it was thought that the pump need only extrude Na$^+$. If we imagine a cell initially containing a lot of Na$^+$ and Cl$^-$ and a little K$^+$, similar, that is, in composition to the outside fluid, and proceed to pump out the Na$^+$, then removing the Na$^+$ will leave the inside negative, so that K$^+$ will be drawn in and Cl$^-$ pushed out. Thus by merely pumping Na$^+$ a situation not unlike that found could certainly be arrived at, with low internal Na$^+$ and Cl$^-$, and high internal K$^+$. It appears, however, that the resting potential in nerve and muscle is a little lower than the equilibrium potential for K$^+$, i.e. there is a little more K$^+$ inside than could be drawn in by the resting potential. It could only get there against the electrochemical gradient by means of a pump. More direct evidence is provided by the finding that K$^+$ influx, measured with radioactive K$^+$, is reduced by poisoning the pump with ouabain.

Uptake of K^+ proves to be coupled to extrusion of Na^+ in a single sodium-potassium exchange pump (Fig. 17.12). The most direct evidence for the coupling of the two processes is that removing K^+ from the external fluid inhibits extrusion of Na^+ from inside the fibre. The only straightforward explanation of this finding is that the pump has to be able to take in K^+ in order to extrude Na^+.

In red cells Glynn and Post and their co-workers have shown that enzymic hydrolysis of ATP not only provides the energy for the pump but is an intimate part of the pumping mechanism itself. The main evidence is: (1) many cell membranes, including squid axon and red cells, possess a special ATPase which only operates in the presence of K^+ and Na^+. (2) like the pump, this ATPase is inhibited by ouabain. (3) in red cells the K^+ must be outside the cell and the Na^+ inside otherwise the ATPase is not activated (i.e. removing K^+ from the external fluid inhibits the hydrolysis of ATP, just as it inhibits the pump). (4) most remarkable of all, if red cells are prepared with a high K^+ content and no Na^+, and are suspended in saline containing no K^+, the very adverse concentration gradients resulting drive the pump backwards and it synthesizes ATP from ADP and inorganic phosphate. This synthesis is ouabain sensitive.

The ionic differences between the cell and its surroundings which the sodium pump maintains, are the basis of the excitable properties of nervous and muscular tissues. Whether in evolution this is the reason for them is not known, but nearly all cells whether excitable or not accumulate K^+ and expel Na^+, and a fair proportion of the basal metabolism of the body is devoted to driving the pump by which they do so.

The resting permeability to Na^+ is so low that when the pump is poisoned, large nerve and muscle fibres run down so slowly that the resting and action potentials are not altered significantly for hours. The pump is only necessary for maintaining the composition of the cells over long periods or in recovery after activity. It is important to be clear that the pump is not directly involved in the mechanism of the action potential. The concentration differences of Na^+ and K^+ across the membrane can be regarded as furnishing ionic batteries from which large brief currents can be drawn during the action potential. The pump only recharges the batteries and has nothing to do with turning on the currents during the action potential—which continues quite unaltered if the pump is poisoned.

The Action Potential

Up to the present we have spoken of the permeabilities of the nerve membrane to Na^+ and Ka^+ as if they had fixed values. But in fact they depend on the potential difference across the membrane and if this is altered by passing an electric current the permeabilities change. They both change in the same sense, namely that as the membrane potential is reduced the permeabilities increase, but the time relations differ. When the membrane is suddenly depolarized and held at the new value, the Na^+ permeability rises at once; but the increase is short-lasting and within a few milliseconds the Na$^+$ permeability has fallen away again. The K$^+$ permeability, however, rises only slowly but the increase is then maintained as long as the depolarization lasts. These facts were discovered by experiments on squid fibres in which the membrane potential was displaced by a known number of millivolts and "clamped" at the new value by an electronic device. The current flowing across the membrane, which is a measure of its permeability to ions, was recorded. If the fibre is in a special solution containing no Na$^+$, practically all the current is carried by K$^+$. Hence the record gives the change of K$^+$ permeability with time. With sea water outside the record gives the sum of the Na$^+$ and K$^+$ permeabilities, from which the time course of Na$^+$ permeability alone can be obtained by subtraction. Recently it has been shown that tetrodotoxin (the highly potent toxin of the puffer fish from the China seas) in concentrations of the order of 10^{-8} molar, selectively blocks the increase in Na$^+$ permeability without affecting the delayed rise in K$^+$ current when the nerve is depolarized. (Tetrodotoxin is an extremely useful tool for it has this action in all, or very nearly all, the tissues in which it has been tested, except in the puffer fish itself and related organisms, which are relatively resistant.)

When an action potential is set up by an electric stimulus the sequence of events is as follows. Current leaving the fibre under the stimulating cathode causes a voltage drop to develop across the electrical resistance offered by the membrane. This voltage drop is of the opposite polarity to the resting potential and hence it causes a depolarization of the membrane. The Na$^+$ permeability at once rises and Na$^+$ enters, driven both by the concentration gradient and the potential difference. The entry of positively charged sodium ions tends to make the inside of the fibre less negative with respect to the outside, i.e. it still further depolarizes the membrane. This depolarization resulting from Na$^+$ entry turns on still more Na$^+$ permeability. Thus a self-regenerative increase in Na$^+$ current develops, which very rapidly depolarizes the membrane, and gives the rising phase of the action potential. The inward flow of Na$^+$ ceases when the membrane potential reaches the equilibrium potential for Na$^+$ with the inside of the fibre positive to the outside (see p. 262); this marks the peak of the action potential. By this time the Na$^+$ permeability is already falling, for as we have said the increase caused by depolarization is only transient. If nothing else happened the potential would stay near the Na$^+$ potential until Na$^+$ permeability fell to ordinary levels. The potential difference across the membrane would then be very far from the equilibrium potential for K$^+$, so that K$^+$ would leave the fibre. K$^+$ current would continue to flow until the inside of the fibre was sufficiently negative with respect to the outside to prevent K$^+$ leaving, i.e. until the resting potential was reached again. In fact the falling phase of the action potential begins earlier and proceeds more rapidly than this, because the delayed rise in K⁺ permeability, which begins to make itself felt soon after the peak, allows much larger K⁺ currents to flow and greatly accelerates the whole process. The falling phase of the action potential is thus due to an outward movement of K⁺. The movements of Na⁺ and K⁺ during the action potential are shown diagrammatically in Fig. 17.13.

The self-regenerative increase in Na⁺ permeability during the rising phase of the action potential is what gives rise to the all-or-none property of nerve. After a stimulus is applied either the membrane goes all the way to the top of the action potential or it sinks quietly back to the resting

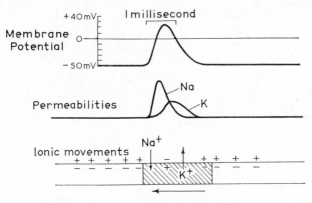

FIG. 17.13. Diagrams showing the movements of Na⁺ and K⁺ during the action potential.

At the top is an action potential record, as in Fig. 17.6. Below are shown the Na⁺ and K⁺ permeabilities during the action potential. The rising phase and peak of the action potential are caused by a large but transient rise in Na⁺ permeability. The falling phase is due to a delayed rise in K⁺ permeability.

In an action potential advancing along a fibre (bottom) Na⁺ current entering at the front part of the active region reverses the potential across the membrane; K⁺ leaving the fibre in the rear re-establishes the resting potential.

potential if the stimulus is too small. As the rising phase is self-regenerative it can never go only part of the way. The threshold, or level of depolarization at which self-regeneration begins, is set by the resting K⁺ and Cl⁻ permeabilities. If when the stimulus ends the Na⁺ current inwards tending to depolarize is greater than the sum of the K⁺ and Cl⁻ currents tending to repolarize, then the regenerative cycle will occur, otherwise not. If the resting K⁺ and Cl⁻ permeabilities are raised not only is the critical level of depolarization raised but by Ohm's Law a larger stimulating current is needed to produce any given depolarization, because the resistance of the membrane (which is inversely proportional to the sum of all the ionic permeabilities) is lowered. As we shall see, one form of inhibition in the central nervous system is brought about by increasing the permeability of neurones to K^+ and Cl^- thereby making excitatory currents less effective.

The most striking piece of evidence for the sodium hypothesis is the

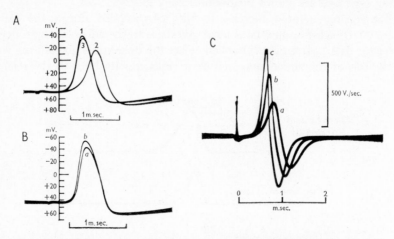

Fig. 17.14. Effect of varying the concentration of Na^+ in the external fluid on the height and rate of rise of the action potential in a single giant squid axon.

An internal electrode (Fig. 17.5) was used for recording the potential difference across the nerve membrane.

A. Sodium-deficient solution. Record 1, response in sea-water. Record 2, in a solution composed of 50 per cent sea-water, 50 per cent isotonic dextrose (Na^+ concentration 0·5 times that of sea-water). Record 3, after reapplication of sea-water.

B. Sodium-rich solution. Record a, response in sea-water. Record b, in sea-water in which additional sodium chloride has been dissolved to make the Na^+ concentration 1·56 times that of sea-water.

C. Records showing directly the rate of change of membrane potential, obtained by electronic differentiation of the ordinary action potential record. The height of the first peak in each record is proportional to the maximum rate of rise of the rising phase of the action potential (in volts/second). Record a, fibre in 50 per cent sea-water as in A. Record b, in sea-water. Record c, in enriched sea-water containing 1·56 times the normal Na^+ concentration as in B. (Hodgkin and Katz, *Journal of Physiology*, vol. 108, p. 37, 1949.)

effect of changing the Na^+ concentration in the fluid bathing the nerve. It is a direct consequence of the theory that the height and rate of rise of the action potential should vary with the external Na^+ concentration. Fig. 17.14 shows records of action potentials with low, normal and high Na^+ concentrations. The height and rate of rise of the action potential in different Na^+ concentrations are in quantitative agreement with the hypothesis. When the Na^+ concentrations are the same inside and outside the nerve the action potential should just not overshoot zero potential difference, for the sodium equilibrium potential would then be zero. This is found to be so. In a sodium-free medium no action potential can be obtained at all. These results have been extended to many other tissues. Frog sciatic nerve will conduct for an hour or more after it is immersed in a sodium-free fluid; but this is because the perineurium (the sheath around the outside of the nerve trunk) is a barrier to diffusion and prevents Na^+ getting out. Isolated nerve fibres dissected from the frog's sciatic are blocked within a second in sodium-free media. Block is also rapid in the spinal nerve roots which have no sheath.

These experiments made it highly probable that sodium ions carry the current across the membrane during the rising phase of the action potential, but the matter could not be regarded as settled until Na^+ had been shown to enter the fibre during activity. This was achieved using radioactive Na^+; from the radio Na^+ entry during a prolonged train of impulses the number of sodium ions entering during a single impulse was calculated and was found to carry a large enough charge to account for the change in potential difference during the action potential.

In all tissues where it has been tried lithium replaces sodium in the action potential (but the sodium pump will not extrude lithium). In squid axon a small quantity of calcium (Ca^{++}) enters during the action potential; roughly 0.1 per cent of the inward current is carried by Ca^{++}. In mammalian smooth muscle the proportion may be larger. Thus it is claimed that arterial smooth muscle will give action potentials both when the external fluid contains Na^+ but no Ca^{++}, and when it contains Ca^{++} but no Na^+. In a very few tissues Na^+ does not carry any inward current. Crayfish and barnacle muscle give action potentials in which the inward current is carried by Ca^{++}. In giant plant cells (*Nitella, Chara*) the rising phase of the action potential is due to an outward movement of Cl^-.

Refractory Period

A consequence of the regenerative increase in Na^+ current during the action potential is that the nerve cannot be excited again until some time after the regenerative cycle is finished. Obviously a second regenerative process cannot be superimposed on the rising phase. After the peak, Na^+ permeability is low ("inactivated" is the expression used) and only recovers as the nerve repolarizes. The regenerative process can be made to occur again when inactivation has diminished sufficiently for it to be possible by depolarizing to obtain a Na^+ current larger than the sum of the K^+ and Cl^- currents tending to repolarize. A larger stimulus than usual will be necessary until the nerve returns to its resting condition for three reasons; firstly inactivation makes it more difficult to turn on the Na^+ current, secondly until K^+ permeability returns to normal a larger Na^+ current will be needed to exceed it and cause regenerative action, thirdly by Ohm's law a larger current than usual will be needed to depolarize by a given amount because the membrane resistance is lowered so long as the K^+ permeability is raised.

The practical effect of these events is that during the spike no stimulus will excite; this is the "absolute refractory period" lasting about 1 millisecond in frog nerve. Then for about another 5 milliseconds (the "relative refractory period") a larger stimulus than usual is necessary. During the relative refractory period the same factors that raise the threshold also decrease the rate of rise of the second spike, reduce its amplitude and cause it to be conducted more slowly.

The refractory period is important because it sets an upper limit to the frequency at which nerve fibres can carry impulses. The limit is about 800 per second in the frog and perhaps 1,600 per second in mammals. The frequencies met with in life are usually much lower than this, probably because the above values only apply to the first few impulses. If a prolonged train of impulses is set up cumulative factors enter and later impulses require much larger stimuli. Hence for a sustained discharge, only much lower rates are possible.

Accommodation

If a subthreshold current is applied to a nerve the resulting depolarization, although insufficient to set off a regenerative change, does result in some inactivation of the Na^+ permeability mechanism and turns on the delayed rise in K^+ permeability. The threshold therefore rises for exactly the same reasons that it is raised during the relative refractory period; these changes are thought to be the cause of accommodation—the process which makes the nerve inexcitable by slowly rising stimuli.

It has been known for a long time that excitable tissues lose their accommodation if placed in solutions without calcium; the threshold falls and small constant currents will cause the discharge of a continuous series of impulses. Eventually impulses arise spontaneously. Calcium ions have been shown to have a profound effect on the permeability mechanisms for sodium and potassium in squid and frog nerve.

Clinically the failure of accommodation in motor fibres is the cause of the spontaneous contractions of muscles, particularly those of the hand and foot (carpo-pedal spasms), that occur in states of low blood calcium; for instance when the parathyroid glands are damaged accidentally in the course of an operation on the thyroid. Accommodation also fails in nerves recovering from anoxia. This is the cause of the spontaneous discharge of sensory nerves called "pins and needles" when a tourniquet is removed from a limb, or when the legs are uncrossed after sitting still for some minutes. In the latter case the peroneal (lateral popliteal) nerve is deprived of its blood supply by pressure where it passes round the head of the fibula.

Accommodation is not equally rapid everywhere in an axon. In sensory nerves it is slow near the sensory end organs, so that slowly rising generator potentials arising in the end-organ give rise to trains of nerve impulses. Similarly it must be slow or absent at the origin of the motor fibres in the ventral horn, because a steady depolarization of the motoneurone cell body causes a maintained discharge of impulses in the motor fibre. The basis of these differences in accommodation at the ends of axons has not yet been investigated in terms of the sodium and potassium permeability mechanisms.

Saltatory Conduction in Myelinated Nerves

We have already seen that increasing the strength of the local currents spreading in front of the action potential by increasing the diameter of the fibre, increases the conduction velocity. This is why invertebrates have developed giant fibres. The vertebrates obtain much higher velocities with smaller fibres by another method, making use of the property that local circuits can be made to spread further ahead of the active region by increasing the electrical resistance of the membrane. This can easily be understood by analogy with a submarine telegraph cable; if the insulation is bad the signal will not reach the other end but will be lost in local circuits through the insulation; the better the insulation the further the signal will travel. All nerve fibres behave like leaky telegraph cables, with an insulating surface layer surrounding the relatively low resistance core of axoplasm. Because of this the local currents set up by an active region of membrane spread much further along the nerve than they would in a homogeneous system in which the surface layer had the same specific resistance as the axoplasm. Such spread determined by the cable-like properties of the fibres is termed *electrotonic*. (The spread of local currents beyond the frozen region in Fig. 17.9 is electrotonic, and would be abolished if the cable structure were interrupted by squeezing the frozen region with a pair of forceps.) For a nerve axon of given diameter the extent of electrotonic spread clearly depends on how good the insulation is. In the squid giant axon and other invertebrate nerves the insulating layer is always thin. Vertebrates improve the insulation by laying down thick layers of myelin around the fibres, only leaving the membrane exposed at the nodes of Ranvier, spaced roughly every millimetre along the fibre. The action potential is confined to the nodes, the part of the fibre covered in myelin being inexcitable. A high conduction velocity is obtained because the currents produced by the active region, instead of being used to excite the section of nerve immediately ahead, are used to excite the next node some 50 fibre diameters further on. This is possible only because the insulation conferred by the myelin sheath ensures that the local currents get that far and do not leak away through the membrane first. Myelinated fibres transmit about ten times as fast as non-myelinated fibres of the same outside diameter at the same temperature. A typical figure is 90 metres per second for a 15 μ myelinated fibre at 37°C.

Evidence that the myelin is an insulator and that activity only occurs at the nodes has been obtained using single fibres dissected from frogs' nerves, a technique that has only been mastered by a handful of physiologists. It has been shown that the threshold is much lower when the stimulating cathode is opposite a node, and that, during the rising phase of the action potential, inward current (i.e. sodium current) only flows through the nodes. By recording from one node after another it was shown that the action potential jumps from one node to the next with a brief delay in between, hence the description "saltatory" from the Latin *saltare*, to leap. The saltatory theory met with opposition from those who believed that there were no nodes in the myelinated nerve fibres of the central nervous system. Ranvier himself said there were none, but they were seen by Cajal and their presence has been amply confirmed by recent investigations.

Another advantage of saltatory conduction, apart from the increased speed, is that the amounts of sodium gained and potassium lost during activity are much decreased, owing to the very much smaller area of active membrane. The amount of sodium entering per impulse is about 300 times smaller in frog's nerve than in an unmyelinated fibre of the same size. Hence the metabolic energy needed for recovery is much less and the fibres are practically indefatigable. There is, however, a debit side to the evolutionary balance sheet. Myelinated fibres, as we shall see shortly, are much more easily blocked by lack of oxygen than non-myelinated fibres, and they also appear to fail first in various pathological conditions, alcoholism, diabetes, infections of various kinds, intoxication with lead or thalidomide, and so on. We may surmise that even if their nerves were subjected to the insults which human nerves suffer it is unlikely that neuritis would be as common a cause of morbidity in squids as it is in man.

Nerve Fibre Diameter in relation to Function

Under the microscope a vertebrate nerve trunk proves to contain myelinated nerve fibres of all sizes from roughly 20 μ down to 1 μ in diameter. There are also numerous small non-myelinated fibres, mostly under 1 μ in diameter, which in many nerves outnumber the myelinated fibres. The relative numbers of myelinated fibres of different diameters varies from nerve to nerve, and between cutaneous and muscular nerves. The fibre spectrum of a cutaneous nerve from a cat is shown in Fig. 17.15.

As we have already seen on p. 258, large nerve fibres conduct faster than small. They also have a lower threshold and give rise to larger action potentials. Both these properties, like their higher conduction velocity, depend on the lower longitudinal resistance of the larger axons. The

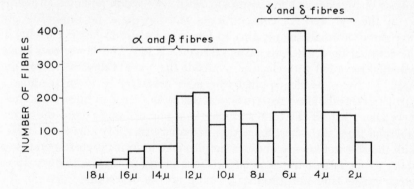

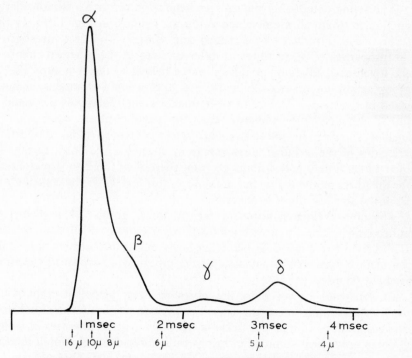

FIG. 17.15. Fibre spectrum and compound action potential of a cat's saphenous nerve.

The graph at the top of the page shows the numbers of myelinated nerve fibres of different diameters in the saphenous nerve (a cutaneous nerve) of the cat.

Below is a tracing of the action potential obtained from the same nerve. The conduction distance was 6 cm. The diameters of the fibres responsible for the various parts of the compound action potential are indicated under the time scale. (Modified from Gasser and Grundfest, *American Journal of Physiology*, vol. 127, p. 393, 1939.)

voltage change across the membrane during the action potential (which is set by the Na$^+$ and K$^+$ concentrations and has the same amplitude and time duration in all the myelinated fibres) gives rise to larger currents in the external fluid when the axon resistance is low, and hence to a larger potential recorded with electrodes outside the nerve. Conversely, with the larger axons, a smaller applied voltage is necessary in order to cause a current of threshold strength to flow in them. As a result of these properties, if we take a length of nerve, stimulate it at one end and record the action potential from the other, the action potential just above threshold arrives with the shortest latency and is a simple spike in form; it corresponds to a volley in the largest fibres. A larger shock brings in the next slower fibres which arrive later and produce a hump on the descending phase of the original spike; and so on with larger and larger shocks.

The action potential of the cat's saphenous nerve, with a stimulus large enough to excite all the myelinated fibres, is shown in Fig. 17.15. In the terminology introduced by Erlanger and Gasser, who first investigated the properties of nerve fibres of different sizes in the nineteen-twenties, the myelinated fibres of peripheral nerve belong to the A group. The A group action potential is subdivided into a, β, γ and δ elevations, as indicated in the figure. Because of their smaller action potentials the γ and δ fibres, although more numerous than the a and β fibres, make a much smaller showing in the compound action potential. The conduction velocities of the a and β fibres run from 90 metres/sec down to say, 45 metres/sec. The γ and δ fibres go from there down to 2 or 3 metres/sec for the fibres of about 1 μ; but in the record in Fig. 17.15 the contribution from the smallest fibres is not seen.

The non-myelinated fibres are termed the C group. Their diameters are roughly 0·2 to 1·0 μ, with conduction velocities of about 1 metre/sec. If the record in Fig. 17.15 had been taken on a much slower time scale the main C fibre action potential would appear as a very small elevation at about 60 msec.

In cutaneous nerves there are fibres of every size that respond to mechanical stimulation of the skin. The lightest touches (of the kind that evoke sensations of itch and tickle in man) give rise to impulses in δ and C fibres only; firm stimulation brings in a fibres. Painful stimuli appear to be signalled both by slow conducting A fibres, and by C fibres. Warming and cooling the skin also cause impulses in the slower A fibres and in C fibres.

In muscular nerves the motor fibres that cause the muscle to contract belong to the a group. There are also γ motor fibres that run to supply the small muscle fibres in the muscle spindles—one of the types of sensory ending in muscle (see p. 332). The sensory endings in muscle are connected to both fast and slow conducting A fibres.

The fine myelinated preganglionic fibres in the white sympathetic rami, and elsewhere in the autonomic nervous system (Chapters 22 & 23), are put in a special group, the B group. They are similar in size and conduction velocity to δ fibres of the A group. The non-myelinated postganglionic sympathetic fibres belong to the C group.

Fast conducting nerve fibres take up more space and use up more metabolic energy than small ones. This must be one reason why not all nerve fibres are large. It seems clear enough why some touch fibres and motor fibres have to be large, and why fibres conveying ill-localized aching pain can afford to conduct slowly. But much remains to be discovered particularly about the allocation of different modalities of sensation to the different groups and the reasons for it.

Nerve Block

Conduction in nerve fibres is blocked by many substances with a general anaesthetic action, such as alcohol, morphine, and ether or chloroform vapour. More powerful and convenient than these is cocaine, and its safer derivatives, procaine, etc., dilute solutions of which are widely used in medicine for local anaesthesia. Cocaine blocks small nerve fibres before large; hence the well-known paradox that cocainized surfaces may be insensitive to pain and yet able to feel the brush of a wisp cotton wool.

Nerves also cease to conduct if deprived of oxygen, but anoxia blocks the myelinated A fibres before the smaller unmyelinated C fibres. Hence in human limbs deprived of blood (ischaemic), touch and motor power fail before sensitivity to pain. When a tourniquet, or, better, the pneumatic cuff of a blood-pressure measuring machine (sphygmomanometer) inflated to a pressure above systolic, is applied to the upper arm, the first symptoms of block are numbness of the finger tips coming on after about 14 minutes followed by loss of touch sensation in the fingers and hand, and paralysis of the small muscles of the hand. Subsequently anaesthesia and paralysis slowly ascend the arm. After an hour the whole arm from the cuff down is anaesthetic to touch and paralysed; but pin pricks are still perceived as painful, although the sensation is delayed by a fraction of a second. This persisting, delayed pain is due to unblocked, slowly conducting C fibres. Ischaemia for longer than an hour is not advised (although periods of $1\frac{3}{4}$ hours have been used for experimental purposes, so far with impunity) because of uncertainty as to the time of onset of the disastrous irreversible changes in ischaemic muscles, akin to rigor mortis, occasionally seen in limbs constricted by splinting or plaster. When the circulation is restored after occlusion for an hour or less, recovery of sensation and movement begins within half a minute and proceeds rapidly. The familiar "pins and needles" follows.

It was proved by Thomas Lewis and his co-workers that the cuff blocks conduction because it cuts off the blood supply to the nerve, and not because of the pressure it exerts on the nerve fibres. Thus provided the pressure is always above systolic blood pressure, block develops in the same time whether the cuff be inflated to 150 or to 300 mm.Hg. Again if a cuff be applied just above the elbow until, say, the hand is anaesthetic to touch, and then a second cuff be inflated on the upper arm above the first and the first cuff removed, there is no recovery in the hand. The pressure has been removed from the original length of nerve without recovery; hence it cannot be the pressure that is relevant to blocking, but the ischaemia that is maintained by the second cuff.

It was also shown that anaesthesia and paralysis are due to conduction block in the proximal part of the nerve, and not to the effect of ischaemia on sensory endings and on the muscles. Thus, if one waits until the hand is anaesthetic and its intrinsic muscles paralysed, and then inflates a cuff round the wrist, subsequent removal of the cuff on the upper arm results in full recovery of sensation and power in the hand, although the hand remains ischaemic. Clearly the block lay in the stretch of nerve between the upper cuff and the wrist. The reason that the proximal part of a nerve fibre is more susceptible to ischaemia than the distal part is not known; neither is it known why the longest fibres suffer first so that symptoms appear first in the finger tips.

SUMMARY

A nerve trunk is a bundle of nerve fibres. Each fibre can easily be excited by a brief electrical pulse, which must reach a certain strength, the threshold, in order to excite. When a nerve fibre is excited a wave of electrical change, the action potential, passes along the fibre in both directions. In the largest nerve fibres the speed of the action potential is about 20 metres per second in the frog at 20°C, and about 120 metres per second in mammals at 37°C. The action potential lasts about a millisecond.

In each fibre the size of the action potential is independent of the size of the stimulus, once the stimulus reaches threshold. This is called all-or-none behaviour. It implies that the energy for propagation is obtained locally, as it is in the flame that passes along a train of gunpowder.

Propagation proves to be due to local electric currents by which the action potential in one section of the fibre excites the next section ahead. In non-myelinated fibres the process is continuous, but in myelinated fibres the action potential jumps from one node of Ranvier to the next.

Microelectrodes thrust into nerve and muscle fibres show that there is a standing potential difference across the membrane, the resting potential, the inside of the fibre being negative with respect to its surroundings. The resting potential is about 50 mV in squid giant axons and about 90 mV in vertebrate nerve and muscle.

During the action potential the resting potential is reversed; the inside of the fibre becomes about 40 mV positive with respect to the outside.

The inside of nerve and muscle fibres has a high concentration of potassium ions (K^+) and a low concentration of sodium ions (Na^+). The reverse is true in the extracellular fluid.

The resting potential arises mainly because the fibre in its resting state is permeable to K^+ and relatively impermeable to Na^+. K^+ therefore diffuses out, leaving a negative charge on the inside, until a potential difference large enough to restrain further movement is set up.

The permeability of the fibre membrane to Na^+ and K^+ depends on the potential difference and on time. If the membrane is depolarized (either by an electrical stimulus or by an approaching action potential) there is an immediate but transient rise in Na^+ permeability followed by a delayed rise in K^+ permeability.

With a sufficient depolarization the increase in Na^+ permeability leads to an inward Na^+ current which itself depolarizes. The depolarization thus becomes self-regenerative; this gives the rising phase of the action potential. Na^+ continues to enter until a potential difference is set up, with the inside positive, sufficient to restrain further movement. This marks the crest of the action potential, by which time too, Na^+ permeability is spontaneously falling. The delayed K^+ current then restores the resting potential; this is the falling phase of the action potential.

Vertebrate nerves contain myelinated fibres of all sizes from 20 μ down to 1 μ and non-myelinated fibres of 1 μ down to 0·2 μ in diameter. Different functions are served by the different groups of fibre size.

Nerve fibres are blocked by many agencies, but especially easily by local anaesthetics or by cutting off their blood supply.

CHAPTER 18

NEUROMUSCULAR AND SYNAPTIC TRANSMISSION

Neuromuscular Transmission

THE evidence that propagation of the impulse along nerve fibres is electrical is now overwhelming and its mechanism has been described. What happens when an impulse reaches the "end plate" where the nerve terminates on the surface of a muscle fibre by dividing into a spray of fine non-myelinated filaments? After a delay of about a millisecond an action potential, similar in nature to that in nerve, arises in the neighbourhood of the end plate and propagates by local circuits in the ordinary way along the muscle fibre membrane in both directions. How does the nerve impulse set off a muscle action potential? The arrival of the active region, which is negative with respect to the rest of the nerve, is equivalent to applying a weak cathodal stimulus to the muscle fibre at the end plate. This will tend to depolarize and excite the muscle fibre, but does it succeed? The answer is, no. Quantitatively the electrical stimulus is not strong enough. The nerve fibre does not supply nearly sufficient current to depolarize the very much larger area of the muscle fibre membrane. Instead, when the impulse arrives, the nerve ending secretes a very small quantity of the chemical substance acetylcholine. Acetylcholine has practically no effect on nerve or on most of the muscle fibre, but at the end plate, opposite the nerve ending, the muscle fibre membrane is highly sensitive to acetylcholine, to which it responds by an immediate and very large increase in permeability to both sodium and potassium ions. The effect is equivalent to making a minute hole in the membrane through which ions can pass freely and, as with a mechanical puncture, the resting potential disappears at that point. This depolarization of the end plate has the same action as applying a strong cathodal electrical stimulus to the muscle membrane around it, which thereupon is rapidly depolarized and excited. Within a millisecond or two the acetylcholine is destroyed by an enzyme, choline-esterase, present in high concentration in the end plate, which hydrolyses it into inactive acetic acid and choline. Thus acetylcholine and the nerve action potential itself both act in a manner which would tend to depolarize the muscle fibre. The difference is that in practice any depolarization due to the nerve action potential is too small to be detected, whereas that due to the acetylcholine excites by a comfortable margin. The chemical mechanism can be regarded as a device for amplifying the electrical effect of the nerve impulse by making a temporary chemical puncture in the muscle membrane.

Conclusive evidence for chemical transmission by acetylcholine has only recently been obtained. The story goes back to Claude Bernard's experiments with the South American arrow poison, curare, in 1850. Curare paralyses striated muscles. Bernard showed that it does so by blocking the passage of the nervous impulse from nerve to muscle. After curare a nerve-muscle preparation no longer contracts when the nerve is stimulated, but it does so again if the stimulating electrodes are moved on to the muscle itself; hence curare does not act by making muscle fibres inexcitable. Nor does it act on nerve fibres, for after painting curare on the nerve alone the muscle contracts in the ordinary way when the nerve is stimulated. Therefore there must be a region with special properties between nerve and muscle, now identified as the end plate, where curare has its effect. Curare was later found to act by rendering the muscle membrane at the end plate insensitive to acetylcholine; acetylcholine is still released by the nerve impulse but no depolarization of the muscle membrane follows. For a hundred years curare remained a physiological curiosity and tool, but recently the purified active constituent, curarine, and other drugs with analogous actions have come into extensive use in surgery for assisting muscular relaxation at operation and thereby permitting a lighter general anaesthesia.

At the beginning of this century Langley showed that the neuromuscular junction is specially susceptible to chemical excitation as well as to block. In most muscles the end plates lie near the centre of the fibres and in parallel-fibred muscles they form a band across the middle of the muscle near the point where the nerve enters. When dilute nicotine solution is applied locally to the end plate region prolonged twitching of the muscle results, but not when it is put on the nerve-free parts of the muscle or on the nerve itself. The chemically excitable structure revealed by nicotine appears to be the structure that the nerve impulse normally excites, for like the nerve impulse, nicotine action is blocked by curare.

These results would naturally suggest that the nerve fibre itself might excite the muscle by means of a chemical substance liberated at the nerve ending. As a matter of fact the idea of chemical transmitters had already arisen in connection with the autonomic nervous system (Chapters 22 & 23). It was known that injection of adrenaline, a substance isolated chemically from the adrenal glands, into the blood, gave rise to many of the effects of sympathetic nerve stimulation, (cardiac acceleration, rise of blood pressure, etc.). Similarly, injection of muscarine, the poison of a common toadstool, mimicked parasympathetic nerve action, (slowing of the heart, salivation, etc.).

Definite proof that the nerve impulse does liberate a chemical transmitter was first achieved by Otto Loewi in 1921. He showed that when the isolated frog's heart is slowed by vagal stimulation the perfusion fluid that comes from it will cause slowing of a second heart (Fig. 22.1).

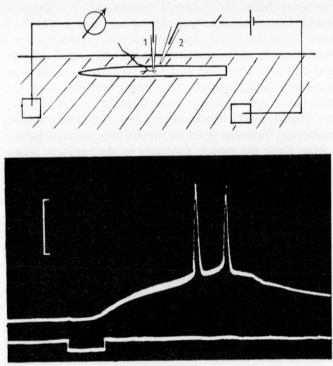

FIG. 18.1. Effect of applying acetylcholine to a motor end-plate in frog muscle.

The diagram shows the experimental arrangements. A glass micro-pipette (1), containing potassium chloride solution, is inserted into a muscle fibre at the end-plate region and used to record the membrane potential. A second micropipette (2) containing a solution of acetylcholine, is manoeuvred as close as possible to the outside of the end-plate; an outwardly directed pulse of current ejects acetylcholine from the tip of this electrode by electrophoresis. The electronic equipment used to produce brief current pulses is represented in the diagram by a battery in series with a make-and-break switch.

In the record, the step-like deflection in the lower trace signals the current pulse through the acetylcholine pipette. After the pulse, the potential record (upper trace) shows a slow depolarization of the end-plate membrane (an *end-plate potential*) on which are super-imposed two propagated action potentials.

Vertical calibration line, 50 mV. The current pulse lasts 17 milli-seconds. (Katz, *Bulletin of the Johns Hopkins Hospital*, vol. 102, p. 275, 1958.)

The transmitter secreted by vagal endings was identified by Dale and his colleagues as acetylcholine. Refined pharmacological tests had to be developed, for the amounts involved were far too small for chemical methods (Fig. 22.3). Dale and his colleagues afterwards applied similar methods to detect the even more minute amounts of acetylcholine in the blood coming from stimulated skeletal muscle; for this pharmacological *tour de force* the choline esterase in the muscle, which otherwise would have destroyed the acetylcholine immediately after release, was inhibited by the drug eserine.

These and other experiments made it clear that acetylcholine acts as the transmitter of excitation across the neuromuscular junction. The details of how it works have now been unravelled by modern microelectrode techniques, mainly in the hands of Katz and his co-workers. They employed a method of applying small doses of acetylcholine direct to the motor end plate by electrophoresis from a micropipette containing the drug. Another similar micropipette filled with KCl solution was inserted into the muscle fibre nearby and used as an electrode to record the potential difference between the inside and outside of the end plate membrane (Fig. 18.1). A squirt of acetylcholine, delivered by passing a brief pulse of current through the acetylcholine pipette, gives rise to a depolarization of the end plate, the end plate potential, which, if it is large enough, triggers off a muscle action potential (Fig. 18.1). Acetylcholine has no effect if it is applied to the inside of the end plate membrane after the micropipette has been pushed through the membrane into the muscle fibre. With the pipette outside the effect falls off rapidly if the pipette is moved along the fibre away from the end plate. Even with the most careful positioning the pipette cannot be got as close to the muscle membrane as the nerve terminals, which lie in little troughs of membrane on the surface of the fibre, so that a larger quantity of acetylcholine is necessary than a nerve impulse secretes, and the concentration at the membrane rises and falls more slowly. The end plate potential due to a nerve impulse is a much briefer affair and the depolarization is so rapid that it may be difficult to see where the muscle action potential takes off (Fig. 18.2).

It is not known how acetylcholine causes the greatly increased ionic permeability which depolarises the end plate. The changes in permeability to sodium and potassium ions are certainly quite different from those that occur during an action potential. The basis of the action potential is first that the permeabilities to sodium and potassium ions only alter when the potential difference across the membrane alters and secondly, that these changes are separated in time, the brief rise in sodium ion permeability preceding the rise in potassium ion permeability. At the end plate, however, the permeability changes are simultaneous and independent of membrane potential. Thus if a muscle is placed in an isotonic solution of a potassium salt, the resting potential vanishes because the concentration of potassium ions is the same inside and outside. In this condition the muscle and nerve become completely inexcitable, but electrophoretic application of acetylcholine to the end plate although it causes no potential

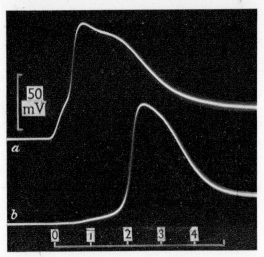

FIG. 18.2. Neuromuscular transmission in frog muscle recorded with an intracellular microelectrode.

A glass microcapillary is used to record the membrane potential of a single muscle fibre as in Fig. 18.1. The records show what happens after a nerve impulse, set up by stimulating the motor nerve at a distance from the muscle, arrives at the muscle end-plate.

Record *a*, with the microelectrode in the end-plate region, shows a rapidly rising end-plate potential from which an action potential takes off. The point at which the action potential arises is marked by a "step" on the rising phase. (A more conspicuous "step" is to be seen in Fig. 18.3, A). End-plate action continues during the action potential and causes a "hump" on its falling phase.

In record *b* the microelectrode in the same muscle fibre, 2·5 mm away from the end-plate, picks up the propagated muscle action potential travelling away from the end-plate. The longer latency before the action potential corresponds to the time taken for conduction from the end-plate region. At this distance there is little sign of the end-plate potential.

Such records show, first that the end-plate potential is a local nonpropagated response and, secondly that the propagated muscle action potential arises from the end-plate region.

Time scale in milliseconds. (Fatt and Katz, *Journal of Physiology*, vol. 115, p. 320, 1951.)

change still results in a large increase in permeability, as evidenced by a fall in the electrical resistance of the membrane. The membrane resistance is measured by passing a known current through the membrane from an internal micropipette, observing the alteration in membrane potential produced and applying Ohm's law.

Quantal Release of Transmitter. When internal microelectrodes were first used to study electrical events at the end plate it was discovered that, even when no nerve impulses are arriving, the end plate is

not electrically silent: small spontaneous potential changes are recorded
from time to time as shown in Fig. 18.3; they are similar in shape to
ordinary end plate potentials but only about 1 per cent of the size (0·5 mV
instead of some 50 mV). The time of occurrence of these miniature end-
plate potentials is normally completely random, precisely as is the time

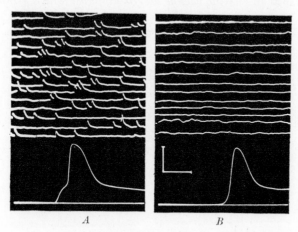

FIG. 18.3. Spontaneous miniature end-plate potentials in frog
muscle.

An intracellular microelectrode was used to record the membrane
potential of a single muscle fibre as in Figs. 18.1 and 18.2.

In A, the electrode was at the end-plate region. The upper part
consists of a number of records taken at slow speed and high amplification, showing the small depolarizations (miniature end-plate
potentials) which go on irregularly all the time in the absence of
stimulation. In B, the electrode was inside the same muscle fibre
2 mm away from the end-plate. No miniature end-plate potentials
are seen.

The lower parts of A and B show the response to nerve stimulation,
recorded at a lower gain and on a faster sweep from the same sites. In
A there is a conspicuous end-plate potential from which the action
potential takes off. No end-plate potential is visible in B. These
records, therefore, confirm that the microelectrode was at the end-
plate in A (compare Fig. 18.2).

Voltage and time calibrations are given by the L-shaped scales in
B. For the upper records the scales represent 3·6 mV and 47 msec.;
for the lower records, 50 mV and 2 msec. (Fatt and Katz, *Journal of
Physiology*, vol. 117, p. 109, 1952.)

of breakdown of the atoms of a radioactive element. An obvious explanation would be that the miniature potentials are due to accidental leakages
of single molecules of acetylcholine from the nerve terminal. They appear,
however, to be very much too large for that. For this and other reasons it
is believed that they represent the simultaneous release of a very large

number of acetylcholine molecules in a packet. This is certainly a surprising notion but electron microscopy has revealed that the nerve terminals contain numerous "vesicles," to be seen in Fig. 18.4, which are strongly suspected to contain the packets of acetylcholine in question. Pharmacological tests have shown that motor nerve fibres contain acetylcholine and also an enzyme *choline acetyltransferase* which synthesizes it.

How the packets of acetylcholine get out is not known but the rate at which they do so is found to depend on the potential difference across the

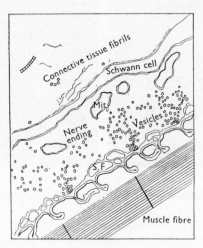

FIG. 18.4A. Outline drawing showing the principal structures visible in the electron micrograph, Fig. 18.4B.

The picture shows a fine terminal filament of the motor nerve fibre lying in contact with the surface of the muscle fibre. The area of contact is increased by folding of the muscle fibre membrane at intervals of some 0·4 μ. A Schwann cell covers the outside of the nerve fibre, and fingers of the Schwann cell (S.F.) protrude into the space between nerve ending and muscle fibre. The nerve ending contains vesicles (thought to contain acetylcholine) and mitochondria (Mit.)

(Birks, Huxley and Katz. *Journal of Physiology*, vol. 150, p. 134, 1960.)

nerve terminal membrane. If the nerve terminal is depolarized by passing a small direct current through it the rate of occurrence of miniature potentials rises steeply; it is estimated that a depolarization of 15 millivolts raises the rate by a factor of ten. Whatever the rate, the size of the miniature potentials remains the same; acetylcholine appears always to be released in packets of the same size. When a nerve impulse arrives, it causes a large and rapid depolarization of the terminal which for a millisecond or so raises the rate of release of acetylcholine packets so high that a hundred or two miniature potentials occur on top of each other.

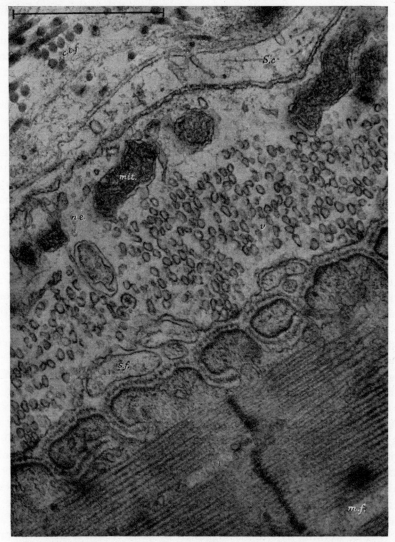

FIG. 18.4B. Electron micrograph of the neuro-muscular junction of a frog's sartorius muscle. Longitudinal section of the muscle. The scale at the top is 1 μ long.

They add up to give a single large end plate potential.

Depolarization of the nerve terminal does not act by causing sodium entry, for the increase in the rate of miniature potentials during depolarization produced by passing current through the ending is quantitatively the same after treatment with tetrodotoxin, which blocks the regenerative sodium mechanism (p. 268). The presence of calcium ions in the extracellular fluid is, however, essential; lowering the calcium ion concentration or raising the magnesium ion concentration (magnesium antagonizes the action of calcium at the neuro-muscular junction) reduces or stops the release of quanta of transmitter induced by depolarization. (It is of interest to note that calcium ions are also an essential co-factor in at least two other processes initiated by membrane depolarization: the regenerative increase in sodium permeability during an action potential, and the activation of the contractile mechanism in muscle fibres). Release of transmitter can also be prevented by botulinum toxin, the extremely potent and long-lasting exotoxin of the bacteria responsible for botulism, a rare but very fatal type of food poisoning. Botulinum toxin does not interfere with the response of the end plate to iontophoretically applied acetylcholine, as does curare, nor does it appear to deplete the stores of acetylcholine in the nerve terminal, but miniature end plate potentials cease and there is no end plate potential when a nerve impulse arrives.

The mechanism by which depolarization of the nerve terminal releases quanta of transmitter is not understood. One of the clues to be followed up is the recent discovery that transmitter release does not immediately follow depolarization. By placing an extracellular microelectrode close to a terminal nerve filament (in frog muscle) it has proved possible to record from quite a localized region of the end plate and to show that after the arrival of a nerve action potential there is an appreciable delay before an end-plate potential is set up at that point, and that this delay has a large temperature coefficient. The minimum delay measured from the first peak of the diphasic action potential to the start of the end-plate potential is 0·5 milliseconds at 20°C, but roughly 5 milliseconds at 2°C. Most of this time is occupied with the release of transmitter from the nerve and not with the time taken by the transmitter to diffuse to the muscle or to act on the muscle fibre when it arrives, for when acetylcholine was applied iontophoretically to the same point the first sign of an end plate response was seen within 0·2 milliseconds at 2·5°C. (The technique of application was similar to that in Fig. 18.1 but using briefer pulses.) When brief electrical pulses are applied to the tetrodotoxin treated ending there is likewise a definite latent period before release of transmitter starts (Fig. 18.5). The working hypothesis suggested by these results is that depolarization allows calcium to penetrate the surface membrane of the nerve terminal; once inside calcium takes part in a reaction, which, after a latent period, causes a rise in the rate of release of quanta of transmitter.

Effects of Denervation of Muscle. When the motor nerve to a muscle is cut and allowed to degenerate, the muscle, over a period of months, wastes away. Denervated mammalian muscle fibres are spontaneously active, individual fibres twitching repetitively and independently. The phenomenon is called fibrillation. It cannot be seen through the skin but if the muscle surface is observed directly it can be seen to be in shimmering movement. The action potentials of fibrillating muscle fibres

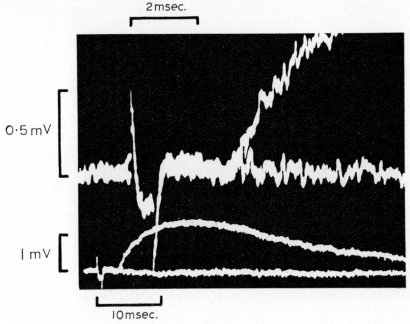

FIG. 18.5. Release of transmitter by an electrical stimulus at the
tetrodotoxin poisoned end plate.

The experimental arrangements were similar to Fig. 18.1, but
micropipette 2 contained sodium chloride and was used to depolarize
a small area of nerve terminal by passing current through it. The
resulting end-plate potentials were again recorded intracellularly by
micropipette 1. Temperature 4·5°C.

Recordings were made simultaneously on a fast time scale at
high gain (upper set) and on a slow time scale at low gain (lower
set).

A pulse of current lasting 0·68 milliseconds applied to micropipette
2 caused the "artifact" at the beginning of the records. Two superimposed records were recorded, at the same stimulus strength; in
one the stimulus caused the release of a single quantum of transmitter after a delay of 3 milliseconds; in the other it had no effect. To
facilitate recording, prostigmine, a cholinesterase inhibitor, was used
in the bath to increase the size of the end-plate potential.

Repetition of the experiment showed that, although the latency
of the end-plate potential varied from stimulus to stimulus, it was
never less than 2 milliseconds. (Katz and Miledi, *Proceedings of the
Royal Society, Series B*, vol. 167, p. 23, 1967.)

are easily detected in man by a needle electrode thrust into the muscle and
are diagnostic of degenerating muscle.

Degenerating muscle is hypersensitive to acetylcholine and gives a
larger and more prolonged contraction than usual when a small quantity
of acetylcholine is injected into the artery supplying the muscle. (The

hypersensitivity to acetylcholine does not appear to be responsible for fibrillation. The evidence is that fibrillation is unaffected by curare, which, of course, abolishes the action of acetylcholine on muscle.) Electrophoretic application of acetylcholine to hypersensitive muscle has shown that the phenomenon is not due to an increased sensitivity of the endplate to acetylcholine but to an extension of acetylcholine sensitivity over the whole muscle fibre. In an embryo the muscle fibres are at first sensitive to acetylcholine all over but later the sensitive region retreats from the ends of the fibres and shrinks onto the end-plate.

Thesleff and his colleagues have shown that muscle poisoned with botulinum toxin (see above) becomes hypersensitive to acetylcholine as fast as muscle that is denervated. Like denervated muscle it also fibrillates and wastes, and will accept innervation from an alien motor nerve grafted into it. (A supernumerary motor nerve grafted into a normally innervated muscle does not succeed in forming end plates in it.) Since the known action of botulinum toxin is, as we have seen, to block release of transmitter, the simplest conclusion from the above results is that the manifold effects of denervation on the muscle are due to acetylcholine deprivation. This may be so, but there is some evidence that substances other than acetylcholine with a "trophic" rather than a transmitter action may be involved; if so the release of such substances from the nerve ending must also be blocked by botulinum toxin.

Effect of Innervation on Speed of contraction of Muscle. In adult mammals two kinds of striated muscles are found, "pale" or "fast" muscles with brief twitches and high tetanic fusion frequencies and "red" or "slow" muscles with long twitches and low fusion frequencies. In man there are slow and fast muscles but the colour differences are inconspicuous. In the new-born kitten all the muscles are equally slow, the adult condition being reached in about four months by a speeding up of contraction in the fast muscles. In the adult, grafting the motor nerve from a slow muscle (e.g. soleus) into a fast muscle (e.g. flexor digitorum longus) in exchange for its own nerve, effects a fairly complete conversion of the fast muscle into a slow muscle. The opposite cross innervation, e.g. of soleus by the nerve to flexor digitorum longus, results in some speeding up of contraction, but conversion to the fast type is incomplete. It is suspected, but not established, that these highly intriguing phenomena are due to "trophic" substances liberated from the nerve terminals.

Neuromuscular Block. When a prolonged train of nerve impulses arrives at a neuromuscular junction the end plate potential set up by each impulse gradually gets smaller, until it may become inadequate to excite the muscle fibre. The decrease in size of the end plate potential is primarily due to a decrease in the amount of acetylcholine liberated by each impulse. In healthy subjects there is good evidence that at the frequencies met with during prolonged reflex or voluntary activation of muscle, say 20–40 impulses per second, neuromuscular block does not occur, at least until the contractile mechanism is itself almost exhausted. Fatigue in ordinary life is, therefore, not due to neuromuscular block, but to failure of the muscle fibres to contract when an action potential passes along them. Electrical excitation of motor nerves at higher frequencies may, however, induce neuromuscular block before the contractile mechanism is exhausted.

Neuromuscular block develops much more quickly in isolated frog muscle than in mammalian muscle with intact blood supply, hence neuromuscular block can readily be demonstrated in fatigued frog muscle in the class room.

Synaptic Transmission

Neuromuscular transmission is only a special case of the general process of the transmission of electrical activity from one excitable cell to another. In the nervous system, as elsewhere, the living units are cells, here called *neurones*, each a mass of cytoplasm bounded by a cell membrane and possessing a nucleus. When any part of the cell is separated from the nucleus it dies. The cell theory applied to the nervous system is called the *neurone theory*. Nerve fibres are processes of neurones and when separated from the cell body, containing the nucleus, e.g. by section of a peripheral nerve, they die and disintegrate. The process is called Wallerian degeneration after Waller who first described it in 1850.

For other tissues the cell theory was accepted as soon as the microscope and microscopical staining techniques were sufficiently developed to show clearly the individual cells and the membrane surrounding them. In the nervous system, however, the cell processes may be several feet long, so that it is not possible in general to see the whole of a single cell and be satisfied that it is marked off by a cell membrane from all other cells. As a result the neurone theory was still in dispute at the beginning of this century. Modern electron microscopy has confirmed that the cell membrane is continuous over the surface of the neurone.

The problem of how activity in one neurone influences activity in another, therefore appears to boil down to the question of how electrical changes at the surface of one neurone can cause electrical changes in another. Such interaction is thought to occur largely, but perhaps not exclusively, at special sites where processes of two neurones come almost into contact with each other. Such a site is called a *synapse*, from the Greek word meaning contact. In the central nervous system synaptic action has chiefly been studied in the neurones of the spinal cord that give rise to the motor nerve fibres to skeletal muscle, the motoneurones. The basic anatomy of the pathways ending synaptically on motoneurones is depicted in Fig. 18.6.

It may seem odd that the discussion of synaptic action, the study of which aims at explaining how the central nervous system works, precedes the chapter describing what the central nervous system does. In fact although we believe that what we know about synapses will one day take its place in any full explanation of nervous activity, this synthesis is in most directions so distant that the observations on synapses stand on their own. It is as if, faced by a large computer, we have probed into its works and discovered the mode of action of its "hardware", resistances, condensers, transistors, etc., and the basic circuits composed of them. This would be important knowledge but, if our object was to understand how the machine extracted a square root, we might not feel much the wiser. On the other hand a satisfying answer might be immediately obvious to someone who knew nothing whatever about the hardware but who was familiar with the logical structure of the machine—what sort of basic mathematical operations it performed, how numbers were represented in it, and so on—a logical structure conferred on the machine, of course, by the way in which the basic component circuits were connected together. In the central nervous system a beginning has been made on the hardware, but knowledge of the "logical structure" is almost entirely wanting.

Excitatory Synaptic Action on Motoneurones. The synaptic endings of the large spindle afferents on motoneurones (Fig. 18.6) are excitatory and their mode of action is closely similar to that of the neuromuscular junction, according to the evidence obtained by recording the membrane potential of the motoneurone with an internal microelectrode. This technical feat was first achieved by Eccles and his co-workers in 1951. Using anaesthetized cats they first removed the back muscles and the bony roof of the spinal canal to expose the spinal cord; the spinal column of the animal was then held rigidly by clamps to a massive steel frame, on which was also mounted a special micromanipulator carrying a capillary microelectrode filled with potassium chloride solution. The microelectrode was pushed through the spinal cord from the dorsal surface blindly into the ventral horn where the motoneurones lie. The motoneurones are among the largest nerve cells in the mammalian central nervous system, with a diameter of some 70 μ, and they offer a reasonable target. Impalement with a microelectrode of tip diameter about 0·5 μ does not apparently damage them, for they show a steady resting potential of roughly 70 mV. When one of the smaller neurones of the grey matter is entered, however, the resting potential is apt to decline rapidly. A cell is identified as a motoneurone by stimulating the ventral root of that segment. This sends a volley of impulses backwards (antidromically) up the motor nerve fibres into the ventral horn and if the electrode is in a motoneurone an action potential is recorded (Fig. 18.7G). The action potential of the motoneurone overshoots zero potential and in general appears to be similar in nature to the action potential in the peripheral motor fibre that arises from it.

When a volley of impulses in the large spindle afferents arrives at the synaptic endings, the motoneurone suffers a rapid depolarization which,

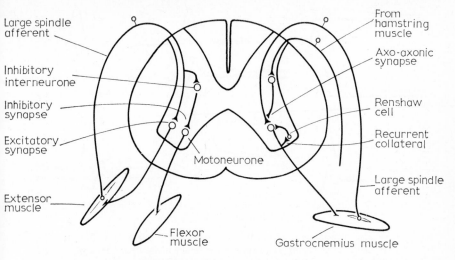

Fig. 18.6. Diagram of the excitatory and inhibitory pathways in the spinal cord studied in this chapter.

On the left is shown a pathway from one of the types of sense organ in muscle, the muscle spindles, to motoneurones. The larger afferent fibres from the muscle spindles are the only fibres entering the cord via the dorsal roots that send branches direct to the motoneurones to make synaptic contact with them. (All other afferents end on interneurones.) This *monosynaptic* pathway is excitatory to the motoneurones of the muscle in which the spindles lie. It is the basis of the stretch reflex, described on p. 328, and is most conspicuous in extensor muscles.

The large spindle afferents from extensor muscles also branch to excite interneurones whose axons form inhibitory synapses on the motoneurones of flexor muscles acting at the same joint. (The flexor motoneurones will actually lie in a segment of the spinal cord several segments posterior to the extensor motoneurones in question, although this fact is not conveyed in the diagram.)

On the right two other inhibitory pathways are shown. *Renshaw inhibition* (not confined to gastrocnemius motoneurones) is due to Renshaw interneurones, which are excited by the motoneurone recurrent axon collaterals. *Presynaptic inhibition* is thought to be due to other inhibitory neurones which form axo-axonic synapses on excitatory terminals; the particular connections shown, from hamstring muscles onto large spindle afferents from gastrocnemius are those relevant to Fig. 18.12. This presynaptic inhibitory pathway is shown with one interneurone, but may in fact consist of a chain of two or more interneurones in series.

There are, of course, very many other pathways, some of which involve branches, which are not shown, of the afferent fibres in the diagram. Only what is needed to follow the text has been included.

Each muscle is shown as having only one motoneurone, and each pathway is represented by a single synapse. In fact there are many motoneurones for each muscle, and each excitatory and inhibitory axon divides many times to end in numerous minute synaptic knobs that cover the cell bodies and dendrites of the motoneurones and interneurones. An account of general spinal cord anatomy appears at the beginning of Chapter 19.

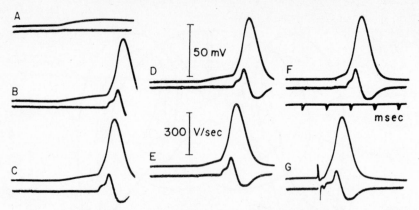

FIG. 18.7. Potentials recorded from a motoneurone in the cat spinal cord
with an intracellular microelectrode.

The animal was anaesthetized with pentobarbitone (nembutal).
In each of the records A–G the upper trace is the membrane potential.
Upward movement of the trace from the resting potential represents
a depolarization of the cell. The 50 millivolt calibration applies to the
upper trace. The lower trace is a differentiated record (cf. Fig. 17.14)
showing the rate of change of internal potential. The 300 volt/second
calibration applies to the lower trace.

The cell is identified as a motoneurone in record G, which shows
its response to an antidromic impulse set up by stimulation of the
ventral root. The shock artifact is followed, after a latency of only a
fraction of a millisecond, by a large action potential.

Records A–F show the response to volleys of increasing size in
the large spindle afferents, set up by stimulating a muscle nerve. In
record A the response is merely a small EPSP (other EPSPs are
shown in Fig. 18.12). In records B–F the EPSP rises more and
more steeply (due to "spatial summation" of synaptic action) and an
action potential takes off from it earlier and earlier, but at a roughly
constant level of depolarization of about 6 millivolts.

The rising phase of the action potential itself is not smooth but
but has a knee at about 30 millivolts depolarization. The knee
separates an initial slower phase, identified on other evidence as the
response of the initial segment (the IS spike), from a second more
rapid phase (the SD spike). The two phases show up more strikingly
in the differentiated records. Both the orthodromic action potentials
(B–F) and the antidromic (G) show the IS component, which is
thereby clearly distinguished from the EPSP. (Records of Coombs,
Curtis and Eccles. In, Eccles, "The Physiology of Nerve Cells":
Baltimore and London, 1957).

provided it is not large enough to excite an action potential in the motoneurone, can be seen to last for some 10 milliseconds. This is called an
excitatory post-synaptic potential (EPSP); it looks like and is similar in
mechanism to an end-plate potential in muscle. Thus by passing current
through the motoneurone membrane from an internal electrode and

measuring the change in potential difference produced, it is found that the membrane resistance falls steeply at the start of the post-synaptic potential. Other evidence suggests that this fall in resistance and the depolarization that accompanies it are both due to an increase in ionic permeability to sodium, potassium and probably other ions, similar to that which occurs at the end plate.

It is presumed that these permeability changes are due to a similar type of chemical puncture of the membrane under the synaptic endings by a chemical transmitter released from them when a nerve impulse arrives. Electron microscopy reveals numerous "synaptic vesicles" in the synaptic knobs, very similar in appearance to the vesicles in the nerve terminals at the end plate, which also are suspected to be packets of transmitter. Convincing electrophysiological evidence has also been obtained that release of the excitatory transmitter occurs in "quanta". Spontaneous synaptic potentials, similar in appearance to miniature end-plate potentials, are recorded with a microelectrode in a motoneurone. In the isolated spinal cord of the frog (which survives well in oxygenated Ringer's solution) the frequency of these spontaneous potentials is little altered when all action potentials are abolished by raising the potassium concentration in the bath. Hence, like miniature end-plate potentials, they are believed to represent the spontaneous release of single quanta of transmitter. In the cat the small EPSPs produced by stimulation of one or a few spindle afferents dissected from a muscle nerve have been shown to be compounded of a small number of these unitary synaptic potentials.

The chemical nature of the transmitter from large spindle afferents is not known except that it is not acetylcholine. Acetylcholine is ruled out on strong indirect evidence. It appears that a nerve fibre which liberates acetylcholine at its terminals, a *cholinergic* nerve in Dale's terminology is cholinergic throughout. Acetylcholine and choline acetylase, the enzyme that synthesises it, can be detected not only at the terminals but all along the nerve fibre. Thus ventral roots contain acetylcholine and choline acetylase. But dorsal roots contain neither, and since dorsal roots contain large numbers of the fibres that run from muscle receptors to excite motoneurones it is clear that these fibres are not cholinergic. Iontophoretic application of drugs to the motoneurone from a micro-pipette has confirmed that it does not respond to acetylcholine or its derivatives. A large number of other substances have been tried of which derivatives of the acidic amino acids (e.g. cysteic, glutamic and aspartic) were the most hopeful candidates; but much remains to be done to establish their relation to natural excitatory transmitter substances.

Although the details of the depolarization under a single nerve terminal are very similar in both the motoneurone and the end plate, synaptic transmission in the spinal cord is otherwise arranged very differently from the neuromuscular junction. In mammals each muscle fibre bears only one or two end plates supplied by a branch or branches of a single motor nerve fibre. Except in extreme fatigue every motor nerve impulse gives rise without fail to a muscle action potential, for each nerve impulse causes an end-plate potential several times larger than is needed to excite the muscle membrane. As the all-or-none law implies, the nervous system can only alter the strength of contraction in a muscle fibre by altering the rate at which nerve impulses reach it. Gradation of response occurs because although each nerve impulse gives rise to a similar all-or-none action potential in the muscle fibre, the contractile mechanism activated by the muscle action potential is not all-or-none; it is a graded process. A single muscle action potential results in a partial and long-lasting contraction; a following action potential causes a further contraction which, if it begins within a certain interval, summates with the first. The degree of summation is determined by the frequency of muscle action potentials and thus frequency determines strength of contraction. In the moto-neurone strength of excitation is also related to frequency of arrival of nerve impulses at the synaptic endings; but the graded, non-all-or-none stage where summation takes place is the membrane potential of the motoneurone. In contrast to the end plate potential the post-synaptic potential due to an impulse arriving at the synaptic knobs on a moto-neurone belonging to a single afferent fibre is very small, the depolariza-tion being far below the threshold needed to excite an action potential in the motor axon; but it lasts for some 10 milliseconds so that another impulse arriving within a few milliseconds can add a further post-synaptic potential to it, and so on. Thus the frequency of arrival of nerve impulses at the synapse determines the level of depolarization of the motoneurone. A similar effect can be obtained at the muscle end plate by treatment with curare, using a dose which reduces the size of the end-plate potential until with a single nerve impulse it is no longer large enough to excite the muscle fibre. With two or more impulses at intervals of a few milliseconds, the end-plate potentials summate and reach a level sufficient to excite.

Another difference from a muscle fibre is that a motoneurone has synaptic connections with not one but a large number of afferent fibres. The degree of depolarization of the motoneurone thus depends both on the number of afferent fibres sending impulses (spatial summation) and on the frequency of impulses in them (temporal summation). In experi-mental work where the afferent fibres are excited by electrical stimuli applied to a muscular nerve, spatial summation is demonstrated by varying the size of the volley (Fig. 18.7) and temporal summation by varying the interval between two volleys. Whenever in either of these ways the depolarization of the motoneurone reaches a threshold value an action potential is excited. In more natural circumstances, when for example pulling on a muscle sets up a continuous asynchronous discharge of impulses in many afferent fibres, both types of summation occur

together and result in a more or less steady depolarization of the motoneurone; with a sufficient depolarization a continuous discharge of motor
impulses is set up in the axon (Fig. 18.8). The frequency of discharge rises
as the level of depolarization increases. A similar discharge is observed if
direct current is passed through a motoneurone in such a direction as to
depolarize it. Myelinated nerve fibres do not in general respond to constant
current by repetitive firing in this way; they accommodate. Clearly there

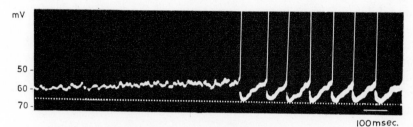

Fig. 18.8. Intracellular records during reflex excitation of a motoneurone,
in an unanaesthetized spinal cat.

The membrane potential (given by the scale at the left) was
initially 58 millivolts (the inside of the cell being negative with
respect to its surroundings). Mild reflex activation by moving the
hind limb caused a slow depolarization to 51 millivolts at which
level rhythmical discharge of action potentials began. The top of the
action potentials is cut off. Time bar, 100 milliseconds.

At other times during this experiment the resting potential of the
cell (i.e. the potential in the absence of action potentials) varied from
65 to 52 millivolts, the average level for initiating discharge being
51 millivolts. The dotted line is drawn at 65 millivolts. After each
action potential the membrane potential comes down to about this
level. This *after-hyperpolarization* is due to a temporary increase in
potassium permeability, lasting about 100 milliseconds, which
renders the cell refractory, i.e. more difficult to depolarize. The
frequency of discharge is governed by the time it takes the excitatory
synapses to depolarize the cell to the firing level in the face of the after-
hyperpolarization and of any other influences tending to hyperpolarize the cell (e.g. Renshaw inhibition, described below). (Kolmodin
and Skoglund, *Acta physiologica scandinavica*, vol. 44, p. 11, 1958.)

must be some part of the motoneurone or the axon near it, a "trigger zone",
which does not accommodate. The axon near certain sense organs is known
also to behave in this way.

There is indirect evidence that the trigger zone is, in fact, the unmyelinated part of the nerve axon as it leaves the motoneurone (referred
to by Eccles as the initial segment or IS) which is thought to have a lower
threshold than the cell body proper (the soma) and the dendrites (Eccles's
SD). When the neurone is depolarized by synaptic action, or by current
injected down the intracellular electrode, the action potential arises first

in the initial segment, the threshold depolarization required in a cat under barbiturate (e.g. pentobarbitone) anaesthesia being about 10 millivolts. Almost simultaneously the first node of Ranvier on the myelinated part of the axon is excited and an action potential departs down the motor fibre. The action potential then spreads back into the soma and dendrites, the threshold depolarization for the soma and dendrites being about 30 millivolts. The purpose of a low threshold trigger zone at the output end of the motoneurone is presumably to allow a concensus of the excitatory and inhibitory actions in the different parts of the soma and dendrites to determine whether the neurone fires. If, for example, the dendrites had the lowest threshold, local excitatory action on one dendrite could fire the whole cell and send an impulse down the axon, regardless of what was going on in the other dendrites. This presumably is undesirable. In computer jargon the motoneurone is required to function as an "and" rather than an "or" device. That is the basis of spatial summation.

This picture of how a motoneurone acts would not be inconsistent with the possibility that action potentials are set up in the finer dendritic branches, provided that they fade out before they reach the soma and leave only a subthreshold contribution to depolarization of the cell body (like the blocked impulse in Fig. 17.9). Some such elaboration will be necessary to explain how events in distant dendrites, which may be only 1 μ in diameter and more than 1 mm away from the cell body, could cause enough current to flow to exert any influence on the trigger zone.

Inhibitory Synaptic Action on Motoneurones. Synaptic endings which depolarise the motoneurone and tend to excite it are not the only kind. There are also inhibitory synaptic endings on the motoneurone whose action is to cut short or oppose excitation. For instance, impulses in the large spindle afferents from extensor muscles, which, as we have just seen, excite the motoneurones of their own muscles, cause inhibition of the motoneurones of flexor muscles acting at the same joint (one of the reflex actions involved in reciprocal innervation, see p. 368). When impulses reach the inhibitory synapses the membrane potential of the motoneurone commonly increases; there is a transient hyperpolarization of the membrane (Fig. 18.9), called an inhibitory post-synaptic potential (IPSP). The IPSP lasts for about the same time as the EPSP: they are, in fact, roughly mirror images of each other. The IPSP is due to a large increase in the permeability of the motoneurone membrane to chloride and potassium ions, but not to sodium ions. As explained on p. 269, the effect of this is to hold the membrane at the resting potential and reduce the efficacy of currents tending to depolarize. Thus inhibitory synaptic action makes the motoneurone more difficult to excite, by reducing the effect of excitatory synaptic action.

The intensity of inhibitory action is not gauged, as is excitatory action, by the size of the post-synaptic potential. In cat motoneurones there is normally an IPSP when an inhibitory volley arrives, but if the resting potential happens to be close to the equilibrium potentials for potassium and chloride ions, as it sometimes is, there may be none. Nevertheless the decrease in membrane resistance due to inhibitory synaptic action still renders excitatory currents less effective, i.e. still inhibits. The decrease in membrane resistance during the IPSP was demonstrated by passing a pulse of current of known intensity through the motoneurone membrane via an internal electrode. The change in membrane potential produced by a pulse during the IPSP was less than that caused by a similar pulse in the resting state; hence, by Ohm's law, the membrane resistance is less during the IPSP.

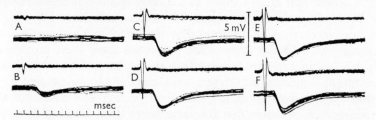

FIG. 18.9. Inhibitory post-synaptic potentials (IPSPs) recorded with an intracellular electrode from a hamstring (knee flexor) motoneurone.

The inhibitory volleys were set up by electrical stimulation of the nerve to quadriceps (the knee extensor). Each record is formed by the superposition of about 40 faint traces. The upper trace in each record shows the size of the afferent volley, as recorded by a surface electrode on the sixth lumbar dorsal root (negativity of this electrode signalled downwards). The lower traces are the intracellular records. Downward deflections signify an increase in membrane potential. The 5 millivolt calibration applies to the lower traces only. The size of the incoming inhibitory volley was increased progressively from record A to record F. (Records of Coombs, Eccles and Fatt. In, Eccles, "The Physiology of Nerve Cells": Baltimore and London, 1957.)

The discovery of the nature of central inhibition and the elucidation of its ionic mechanism was the most spectacular result from Eccles' development of the technique of intracellular recording from motoneurones. The increase in permeability to chloride ions during the IPSP was shown by artificially increasing the Cl^- concentration inside a motoneurone by electrophoretic injection of Cl^- ions from a KCl filled microelectrode. If the IPSP is associated with an increase in permeability to Cl^- tending to move the membrane potential towards the equilibrium potential for Cl^-, then raising the internal Cl^- concentration (initially low) ought first to arrest this movement, and then, when the equilibrium potential for Cl^- becomes less than the resting potential, to reverse it. This is precisely what was observed; injection of Cl^- ions converted the

IPSP to a depolarizing potential, an EPSP, which, if large enough, excited the neurone.

The injected anion does not have to be Cl⁻. Almost any small anion has the same effect as Cl⁻. Hence the membrane, during the IPSP, must develop a large non-selective permeability to small anions. The evidence for a simultaneous increase in permeability to K^+ is indirect; it appears to be quantitatively less important than the anion mechanism.

There is good but not conclusive evidence that the terminals of the large spindle afferents from extensor muscles do not themselves end directly in inhibitory synapses on flexor neurones. Rather they excite interneurones, which in turn inhibit the flexor neurones (Fig. 18.6). It is for this reason that after a volley in the large spindle afferents the IPSP in a flexor neurone begins about 0·8 milliseconds later (allowing for differences in conduction distance) than the EPSP in a extensor neurone. Interneurones with the appropriate properties have been provisionally identified by microelectrode recording at the base of the dorsal horn. (Intercalated neurones are known with certainty to be present in the pathway for Renshaw inhibition, described below.) The reason for these interneurones is probably that the same nerve fibre does not liberate an inhibitory transmitter from some of its terminals and an excitatory transmitter from others (to do so would violate Dale's principle), hence on the inhibitory pathway an extra neurone must be interposed to change from excitation to inhibition. This line of argument would, however, fall to the ground if it were shown that, in mammals, the same transmitter could both have inhibitory and excitatory effects at different synapses, as acetylcholine has been found to have in molluscs.

The chemical nature of the transmitter at inhibitory synapses on the motoneurone is not yet known. It has been shown, however, that both strychnine and tetanus toxin block inhibitory synaptic action on the motoneurone and this is suspected to be why they cause convulsions. Other convulsant drugs do not act in this way. In crustacea γ-amino butyric acid (GABA) is a proven inhibitory transmitter. In mammals GABA is present in, and confined to, the central nervous system. Applied electrophoretically to neurones it has a powerful inhibitory action; but this action is not antagonized by strychnine (or, for that matter, by picrotoxin; see below under Presynaptic Inhibition).

Renshaw Inhibition. Although, as we shall see in the next chapter, stimulation of the central end of a cut ventral root does not cause sensation or reflex movement or any other distant effects, antidromic impulses in motor fibres are by no means without influence in the part of the spinal cord where they arrive, as was first discovered by Renshaw in 1941. The most notable action of antidromic impulses in the motor fibres to a particular muscle is to inhibit the discharge of impulses (reflexly or voluntarily excited) to that muscle or to other muscles with

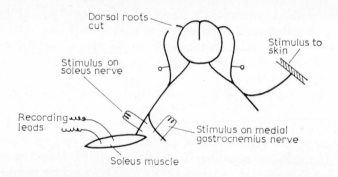

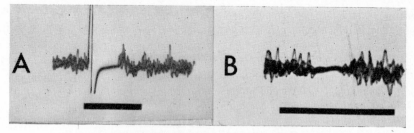

FIG. 18.10. Antidromic block and Renshaw inhibition.

The diagram above gives the experimental arrangements. All dorsal roots supplying one hind limb of a cat are cut, and the electrical activity of the soleus muscle is recorded. Contraction of soleus is elicited reflexly by pinching the skin of the opposite flank. An electrical stimulus to the nerve supplying soleus causes a large synchronized action potential in soleus (which is too large to be recorded properly) followed by a period of quiescence (record A) known as antidromic block. A stimulus to the cut nerve to the medial gastrocnemius (record B, from another experiment) results in a similar pause in motor discharge to soleus, which is not preceded by any increased discharge to soleus and cannot therefore be due to a refractory state of soleus motoneurones. This is Renshaw inhibition, which is an important element in antidromic block.

Each record is formed by the superposition of five traces. Time bars 100 milliseconds. (Holmgren and Merton, unpublished records.)

similar actions acting at the same joint (synergists). A convenient muscle in which to demonstrate this effect is soleus. In order to be certain that the effects observed are due to antidromic motor impulses and not to impulses in afferent fibres, which are unavoidably excited when the motor nerve is stimulated, it is necessary to cut all dorsal roots that might contain such fibres. Reflex contractions of soleus can still be set up by stimulation applied to the opposite side of the body. If, during such a contraction, the motor nerve is stimulated, the reflex discharge of motor impulses ceases for perhaps 50 milliseconds (Fig. 18.10A). This will be partly due to a refractory state of the motoneurones consequent on their invasion by antidromic action potentials causing an after-hyperpolarization (see Fig. 18.8), but that another potent factor is at work is shown by the fact that an antidromic volley in the nerve to the medial gastrocnemius (a synergist of soleus) causes an indistinguishable inhibition of the discharge to soleus (Fig. 18.10B).

As to the mechanism of this inhibition, Renshaw found that an antidromic volley excites a burst of action potentials of extremely high frequency, up to 1,500 per second, in interneurones (now known as Renshaw cells) lying in the ventral part of the ventral horn of grey matter (Fig. 18.11). Intracellular recording from the inhibited motoneurones has shown that they display ordinary IPSPs (e.g. reversed by increasing the intracellular chloride and blocked by strychnine), which appear to correspond with Renshaw cell discharge. Hence it is believed that an anti-

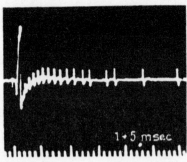

FIG. 18.11. Repetitive discharge in a Renshaw interneurone in the cat spinal cord, following an antidromic volley in motor fibres, recorded with an extracellular electrode in the ventral horn. The large potential at the start is the antidromic action potential in nearby motoneurones picked up by the recording electrode. (Renshaw, *Journal of Neurophysiology*, vol. 9, p. 191, 1946.)

dromic volley first excites Renshaw cells, which then, in turn, inhibit motoneurones.

The nerve fibres from motoneurones, or at any rate some of them, give off a branch before they leave the grey matter, which turns back into the grey matter. These recurrent collaterals are thought (on not perhaps much evidence, but with great plausibility) to be the route by which antidromic impulses excite Renshaw cells (Fig. 18.6). It is worth mentioning that recurrent axon collaterals are very widely distributed in the central nervous system, e.g. the axons both from pyramidal cells in the cerebral cortex and from Purkinje cells in the cerebellum often bear several. Hence mechanisms based on axon collaterals, of which Renshaw inhibition of motoneurones is the only one that has so far proved amenable to analysis, are likely to be of widespread importance.

It is believed that normal, orthodromic, discharge of motoneurones activates the Renshaw cells via the axon collaterals in just the same way that antidromic impulses have been shown to. Hence Renshaw inhibition can be thought of as a local negative feedback loop onto synergic moto-neurones, activity in which is a normal accompaniment of motor activity.

The presumed synapse from motoneurone collateral onto Renshaw cell is claimed to be the synapse in the central nervous system for which the chemical transmitter is most securely identified. On Dale's principle it ought to be acetylcholine, and much evidence has been obtained in support of this prediction. Acetylcholine has been detected, by bio-logical assay, in venous blood from the spinal cord after antidromic volleys in motor fibres have been sent in. Renshaw cells are excited by iontophoretically applied acetylcholine and this action is blocked by dihydro-β-erythroidin (one of the cholinergic blocking drugs and the most potent of them in this situation). The excitatory action of an anti-dromic impulse is prolonged by choline esterase inhibitors and abbrevi-ated by dihydro-β-erythroidin. Even large doses of dihydro-β-erythroidin, however, do not prevent a nerve volley from causing one or two action potentials in the Renshaw cell, a fact not yet satisfactorily explained.

The significance of Renshaw inhibition is not known. It is conspicuous in slow acting "tonic" muscles such as soleus and weak or absent in some rapidly acting "phasic" muscles, e.g. the diaphragm. Where it is present inhibitory feedback is bound to modify and may possibly stabilize in some way the discharge of synergistic groups of motoneurones, in a manner analogous to the action of negative feedback in modifying and stabilizing the characteristics of an amplifier. But as well as being excited by the motoneurone recurrent collaterals, it is known that Renshaw cells are subject to excitation and inhibition by afferent dorsal root fibres from the skin and muscles of the same and the opposite sides of the body and by fibres from the brain. Hence the Renshaw cells may be involved in the mechanisms that determine which muscles are to contract and how hard they are to contract as well as in regulating how they do it.

Presynaptic Inhibition and Dorsal Root Potentials. In addition to the type of inhibition previously described, effected by inhibitory synapses on the motoneurones themselves, there is another powerful and very much longer-lasting type of inhibition which acts upstream of the moto-neurone by reducing the amount of transmitter released from the ex-citatory synaptic endings and is hence called *presynaptic* inhibition. The evidence for its existence is that stimulation of certain peripheral nerves, which by themselves give rise to no IPSPs, no resistance or threshold change and no other detectable electrical alteration in the motoneurone under observation, causes a prolonged reduction in size of the EPSPs set up in that motoneurone in the ordinary way by stimulation of its large muscle afferents (Fig. 18.12). The technique of minimal afferent stimulation (described above in connection with the EPSP), has

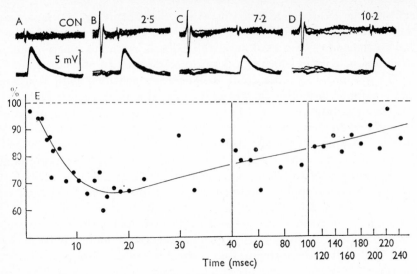

FIG. 18.12. Presynaptic inhibition of excitatory post-synaptic potentials (EPSPs).

In records A to D the lower traces show EPSPs recorded intracellularly from a gastrocnemius (ankle extensor) motoneurone. They were evoked by volleys in the large spindle afferents in the gastrocnemius nerve. Each record is formed by the superposition of five sweeps. In records B, C and D the volley in the gastrocnemius nerve was preceded by a volley in the nerve to a portion of the hamstring muscles (posterior biceps with semitendinosus) at intervals of 2·5, 7·2 and 10·2 milliseconds respectively. These hamstring volleys can be seen to reduce the size of the EPSP without causing any IPSP. A is a control record. The upper traces are from an electrode on the seventh lumbar dorsal root, and give an index of the size of the afferent volleys entering the cord (and also of the time scale from the known intervals between volleys in B, C and D).

The graph below plots the time course of presynaptic inhibition for the same experiment from which records A to D were taken. The ordinate gives the size of the EPSP as a percentage of the control size for various intervals between the inhibitory and the excitatory volleys. Inhibition is greatest with an interval of about 15 milliseconds, and persists for at least ¼ second. The vertical lines mark changes in the horizontal scale. (Eccles, Eccles and Magni, *Journal of Physiology*, vol. 159, p. 147, 1961.)

confirmed that, in the circumstances under consideration, inhibition is truly presynaptic; the number of quanta of transmitter released by a single afferent volley is reduced, while the size of the EPSP due to a single quantum, the "unitary EPSP" is unchanged.

Presynaptic inhibition is prolonged by moderate doses of barbiturate anaesthetics such as pentobarbitone (nembutal), an important finding to which we return below. The convulsant drug picrotoxin (which is without effect on the IPSP) diminishes presynaptic inhibition, and also reverses the action of nembutal. (Picrotoxin is used clinically in the treatment of barbiturate poisoning.) Strychnine is without effect on presynaptic inhibition or, rather, it enhances it. Thus the pharmacology of the two kinds of inhibition is quite distinct, and so, presumably, are the chemical transmitters involved.

The time course of presynaptic inhibition is similar to that of the large, slow potential changes (dorsal root potentials) that can be recorded from dorsal roots after the arrival of an afferent volley. A causal connection between the two phenomena is strongly suspected but not yet proved. It is, for example, obviously significant that dorsal root potentials, like presynaptic inhibition, are prolonged by barbiturates, and reduced in size by picrotoxin.

To record dorsal root potentials a length of root is gently freed and lifted onto two electrodes in air or in a layer of paraffin oil. When an afferent volley set up by an electric shock or by a natural stimulus, such as a tap on the skin, arrives at the cord a monophasic potential change is recorded lasting about a tenth of a second (Fig. 18.13). The electrode closer to the spinal cord goes negative with respect to the distal electrode.

What is the nature of the dorsal root potential? It is not due to action potentials propagating into the root, for it is largest when the proximal electrode is close to the cord and falls off rapidly (roughly by a factor of two for each $1\frac{1}{2}$ mm) as the electrodes are moved away from the cord. Propagated action potentials would stay the same size as the electrodes moved. The attenuation of the dorsal root potential along the root suggests that it is due to local currents spreading electrotonically from a site of depolarization in the cord. This interpretation is confirmed by the observation that the dorsal root potential vanishes if the root is squeezed with forceps between the cord and the recording electrodes (see the explanation on p. 273).

The region of the afferent fibres whose depolarization is responsible for the dorsal root potential appears to be the fine terminal branches in the grey matter of the cord. Further observations give clues as to the mechanism of this depolarization. If a row of dorsal roots is cut and a volley sent into the cord by stimulating the end of one of them, dorsal root potentials are observed in roots several segments in front and behind the one stimulated. In the immediately neighbouring roots the potential is about as large as it is in the root stimulated. Hence the slow depolarization is not confined to the terminals of the fibres along which the volley enters, and, indeed, is not specially large in these fibres. Sizeable dorsal root potentials are also produced by stimulating a dorsal root on the opposite side of the cord. Since no fibres entering the cord in a dorsal root cross to the other side, this fact, and other evidence, shows that interneurones are involved in the production of the slow depolarization. It is thus envisaged that

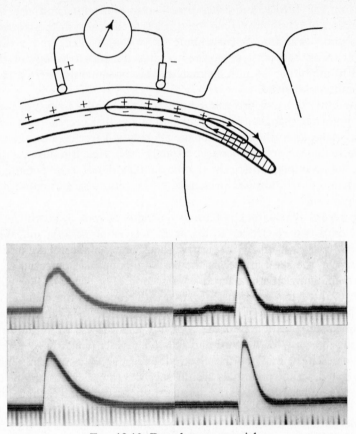

FIG. 18.13. Dorsal root potentials.

Above is shown diagrammatically the position of the recording electrodes on a cut dorsal rootlet. A single nerve fibre is drawn with its terminal portion inside the cord, which is depolarized, shaded. Local currents flow in the sense shown (see also Figs. 17.8 and 17.9) and give rise to a potential difference along the root which is picked up by the electrodes. (In fact, of course, fibres entering the cord divide into many terminal branches as well as giving branches that run up and down the cord, see p. 348).

In the records below, the dorsal root potentials illustrated are due to impulses entering by roots adjacent to the cut rootlet to which the recording electrodes are applied. Upward movement of the trace signifies that the electrode near to the cord became negative to the distant electrode. Time markers at 20 and 100 millisecond intervals.

Top left, frog, stimulus a light tap on the toes on the same side of the body as the rootlet recorded from. *Top right*, cat, the same. *Bottom left*, frog, electrical stimulus to a neighbouring rootlet. *Bottom right*, cat, the same. (Barron and Matthews. *Journal of Physiology*, vol. 92, p. 276, 1938.)

impulses in afferent fibres synaptically excite interneurones, whose axons end on the terminal branches of other afferent fibres and depolarize them (Fig. 18.6). At about the time this proposal was made electronmicroscopists obligingly revealed suitable axo-axonic synaptic endings in the spinal cord (the ordinary kind are called axo-dendritic). But a search with microelectrodes has not so far revealed interneurones which fill the bill for the dorsal root potential as convincingly as the Renshaw cells do for Renshaw inhibition.

As we have said already the time course of the dorsal root potential closely matches that of presynaptic inhibition, and the two are similarly affected by barbiturates and by picrotoxin. A plausible hypothesis is that depolarization of the excitatory terminals reduces the height of an arriving excitatory action potential (by causing inactivation of the sodium permeability mechanism; see p. 268) and so diminishes the amount of excitatory transmitter released. If the relation between change of membrane potential and rate of transmitter release is as steep as it is at the neuromuscular junction (see p. 286), large inhibitions would only entail a reduction of the action potential by a few millivolts. There is much work to be done, however, before this hypothesis can be regarded as established. The ionic mechanism underlying the depolarization of the afferent terminals is wholly obscure.

Wall has evidence that impulses in non-myelinated afferent (group C) fibres act in the opposite manner to the larger myelinated fibres we have been considering. They hyperpolarize the terminals of other fibres, appear to increase their synaptic efficacy, and, if stimulated alone (a difficult technical feat) give a dorsal root potential of inverted polarity. The significance of these observations is, as yet, uncertain, but they contribute to the belief that the dorsal root potentials are an index of the working of some important nervous mechanism in the cord—a belief reinforced by the recent discovery that large dorsal root potentials can be evoked by stimulating certain areas of the cerebral cortex and the brain stem.

Synaptic Transmission elsewhere in the Central Nervous System. The types of synaptic action described above cover the main varieties so far found in other parts of the central nervous system. As regards transmitter substances, it is almost certain that some of the endings on cells in the cerebral cortex, and in the cerebellum, are cholinergic. There is no adrenaline in the central nervous system, but substantial quantities of noradrenaline and dopamine (which is noradrenaline less a hydroxyl group) exist in the brainstem, where their presence in nerve fibres and synaptic endings has been mapped by Fuxe and his colleagues, using their property of fluorescence in ultra-violet light. The same elegant technique has also revealed a concentration of 5-hydroxytryptamine (serotonin) in a small midline nucleus in the brainstem. Of substances unrelated to transmitters found outside the central nervous system, of which there must be many, is ergothionine, which has an excitatory action on neurones in low dosage and is found in the cerebellum and the optic tract, and the acidic amino acids and their derivatives, previously mentioned.

Electrical Synapses. It is worth remarking that not all synapses employ chemical transmitters. As we saw, the chemical mechanism at the end plate is a device to allow a small structure to excite a large one by amplifying the depolarizing current. The same is obviously true of the excitatory synaptic knobs on a motoneurone. But if two structures are of comparable size there is no reason why one should not excite the other electrically if a low resistance path for depolarizing current is provided where the two membranes come together. Such electrical synapses were first demonstrated in crayfish where the giant nerve fibre excites smaller motor nerves; the same fibres have ordinary chemical synapses elsewhere. Synaptic excitation of the giant neurones of goldfish (Mauthner cells) has since been shown to have an electrical component. More remarkably still, an inhibitory electrical synapse has been discovered that operates on the Mauthner cell axon at its origin. Nature may prove to have been equally opportunist in the mammalian central nervous system.

One-way Transmission. A characteristic of all synapses in the vertebrate central nervous system yet investigated is that excitation only passes in one direction across them. (Two-way electrical synapses of a highly specialized kind are found at the intersegmental junctions on the giant nerve fibres of the earthworm, and in the parasympathetic ciliary ganglion of the chick.) In chemical synapses the transmitter is only liberated by one side of the synapse and only acts on the other side. Electrical back-excitation does not occur because no low resistance path exists across the synapse. In the crayfish electrical synapse one-way conduction is ensured by an electrical rectifying action of the synaptic membranes; current only flows easily in one direction. It is because of this one-way property of synapses that all nerve fibres, yet recorded from, normally carry impulses in one direction only. One-way synapses and one-way impulse traffic are only to be expected in the sensory nerves and tracts carrying sensory messages into and within the central nervous system, and in the motor tracts and motor nerves taking orders back to the muscles. These are the parts of the nervous system about which most is known at present. Once again there is no guarantee that elsewhere in the central nervous system all synapses will prove to be one-way or that all nerve fibres will be found to carry one-way traffic. So much remains to be discovered about the nervous system that generalization beyond what is established by experiment is always unsafe.

SUMMARY

Neuromuscular Transmission. Nerve fibres are so much smaller than muscle fibres that when an impulse in a motor nerve arrives at the neuromuscular junction it is not able to cause sufficient current to flow to depolarize the muscle fibre and excite it electrically. Excitation is achieved by a chemical mechanism that has the effect of providing a greatly amplified depolarizing current. When the nerve impulse arrives at the end-plate, the nerve terminal secretes a small quantity of acetylcholine. The muscle fibre membrane opposite responds to acetylcholine by a large increase in permeability to both sodium and potassium ions simultaneously. This causes a brisk depolarization, which excites the surrounding muscle fibre membrane.

The nerve terminal releases acetylcholine in packets or "quanta", each consisting of many thousand molecules of acetylcholine. A few quanta escape even when no nerve impulses are arriving, causing spontaneous "miniature" end-plate potentials. Depolarization of the nerve terminal increases the rate of quantal release; the nerve action potential releases a large burst of quanta because it transiently depolarizes the terminal.

The muscle fibre membrane is normally only sensitive to acetylcholine at the end-plate, but if the muscle is chronically denervated the fibre becomes sensitive to acetylcholine over its whole length.

Synaptic Transmission. Excitatory synapses on spinal motoneurones operate similarly to the neuromuscular junction, but on a relatively smaller scale, so that many have to be activated to excite an action potential in a motoneurone. Transmitter release is again in quanta. The chemical nature of the transmitter is not known, but the permeability changes it causes are apparently the same as at the end-plate, and last for about the same time.

Inhibitory synapses on motoneurones operate (by another unknown transmitter) mainly through a brief selective increase in membrane permeability to chloride and other anions. This has the effect of shifting the membrane potential of the motoneurone towards the chloride equilibrium potential and clamping it there, in antagonism to the depolarizing action of excitatory currents.

Apart from reflex and other sources of inhibition, antidromic impulses in motor fibres excite interneurones (Renshaw cells) whose axons terminate in inhibitory synapses on motoneurones (Renshaw inhibition).

Long-lasting inhibition of excitatory action on motoneurones associated with a slow depolarization of the terminations of dorsal root fibres (recorded as the "dorsal root potential") is the result of a different inhibitory mechanism in which the amount of transmitter released by an excitatory impulse at its synaptic endings is reduced (presynaptic inhibition) without any action on the membrane of the motoneurone itself.

At the majority of synapses in the central nervous system the chemical transmitter is not known. Synapses operating electrically are known in fish, but not, so far, in mammals.

CHAPTER 19

THE CENTRAL NERVOUS SYSTEM: I

Anatomy

Because the anatomy of the central nervous system is commonly less familiar, even to medical readers, than that of the rest of the body, all the structures subsequently mentioned in this chapter are briefly described in this section or are depicted in Figs. 20.1, 20.2, 20.3 and 20.7. A more thorough knowledge can be acquired from the books listed in the Bibliography, but the non-medical reader who may be daunted by the large volume of detail in such works should remember that, although it is axiomatic that physiology must always rest on a firm basis of anatomy, so little of the physiology of the brain is under-

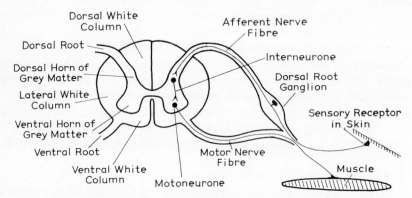

Fig. 19.1. Diagrammatic cross-section of the spinal cord showing the H-shaped grey matter, the columns of white matter surrounding it, and the components of a simple reflex arc.

stood at present that a relatively small amount of anatomical knowledge will be found adequate to support it. Outside the skull there are probably no organs or tissues in the human body of which the function or, in the case of rudiments, the significance is not understood, at least in a general way, but in the brain the student must not allow himself to be nonplussed to find numerous large masses of nerve cells for which factual information about function is negligible. He may be warned, however, that speculation on these matters, masquerading as fact, in anatomical and physiological texts, is an old if little recognized branch of science fiction.

The central nervous system consists of the spinal cord, the part within the spinal column, and the brain, the part within the skull. The spinal cord retains the segmental structure of the primitive nerve cord, giving rise in each segment to a pair of spinal nerves, each formed from separate dorsal (sensory) and ventral (motor) roots (Fig. 19.1). Inside the cord is a core of nerve cells (grey matter) surrounded by the tracts of nerve fibres (white matter) that carry nerve impulses up and down the cord. The spinal cord is the seat of various reflexes, protective, muscular, visceral, sexual, etc., and of various automatic nervous mechanisms concerned in standing, walking, etc. It also transmits sensory information to the brain, and executes the orders the brain sends it. In the higher vertebrates the spinal cord becomes increasingly subordinate to the brain, and the tracts of white matter running to and from the brain occupy a large part of it. The position of the principal spinal tracts is indicated in Figs. 20.2, 20.3 and 20.7.

The vertebrate brain develops from three hollow swellings at the cranial end of the primitive neural tube, the forebrain, midbrain and hindbrain vesicles. The olfactory and optic nerves take origin from the front and back respectively of the forebrain; all the other cranial nerves belong to the mid- and hindbrain (Fig. 19.2). The main external features of the mammalian brain result from

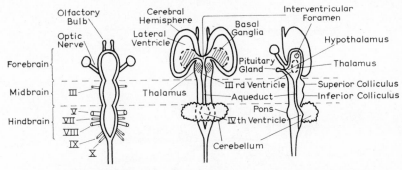

Fig. 19.2. Idealized mammalian brain in two stages of development. Left: the three primitive brain vesicles in horizontal section and the principal cranial nerves. Centre and right: a later stage, in horizontal and in midline section (cranial nerves, except optic nerves, omitted).

Cranial nerves: III (oculomotor) motor to most of the eye muscles; V and VII (trigeminal and facial) sensory and motor to face and mouth; VIII (auditory) consists of cochlear and vestibular portions from the organs of hearing and balance respectively; IX and X (glossopharyngeal and vagus) motor and sensory to the alimentary and respiratory tracts and to the heart.

elaboration of this basic structure in two regions. (1) From the front of the forebrain two further hollow swellings develop, the cerebral hemispheres (Fig. 19.2). The original cavity of the forebrain vesicle becomes known as the IIIrd ventricle and its extensions into the hemispheres are the two lateral ventricles. (2) In the roof of the front part of the hindbrain develops a large unpaired structure, the cerebellum. Tracts of nerve fibres running transversely to the cerebellum form a conspicuous bulge, the pons, on the ventral surface of the hindbrain. Behind the pons, where it tapers into the spinal cord, the hindbrain is known as the medulla oblongata, or medulla for short. The cavity of the hindbrain is named the IVth ventricle; it is connected to the IIIrd ventricle by the aqueduct, the narrowed cavity of the midbrain vesicle. The part of the brain around the IIIrd ventricle (the diencephalon), the midbrain and the hindbrain, excluding the cerebellum, are referred to jointly as the brainstem.

The cerebral hemispheres and the cerebellum are the parts of the brain that increase most in size as the evolutionary scale is ascended. In man they are so

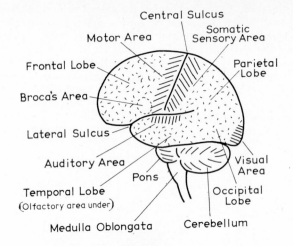

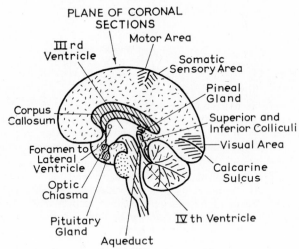

FIG. 19.3. Lateral view and median sagital section of the human brain, with "projection areas" marked.

Above the pituitary gland and optic chiasma the lateral wall of the IIIrd ventricle is formed by the hypothalamus, above that by the thalamus. The arrow indicates the plane of the coronal (frontal) sections in Figs. 20.2 and 20.7.

large that they hide most of the rest of the brain (Fig. 19.3). The cerebral hemispheres and the cerebellum are the only places in the central nervous system where grey matter lies on the surface forming a "cortex." Elsewhere the grey matter is in the middle with the connecting tracts of white matter around it. Underneath the cerebral cortex, thick bundles of white matter connect the parts of the cortex to each other and to other parts of the brain. A massive tract, the corpus callosum, runs between the two cerebral hemispheres above the roof of the IIIrd ventricle (Fig. 19.3). The main tracts connecting the cerebral cortex to the lower parts of the brain and to the spinal cord pass between the basal ganglia and the thalamus (see below), where they are known as the internal capsule, and emerge on the ventral surface of the midbrain to form the cerebral peduncles.

The basal ganglia, or corpus striatum, is a mass of grey matter that develops in the floor of the lateral ventricle. It is the highest centre for motor functions, apart from the cerebral cortex. The thalamus is a large group of nuclei in the wall of the IIIrd ventricle. It is the highest centre for sensory activity apart from the cerebral cortex. Below the thalamus the floor of the IIIrd ventricle descends to meet Rathke's pouch growing up from the roof of the buccal cavity, to form with it the pituitary gland. The grey matter in the walls of the IIIrd ventricle immediately above the pituitary constitutes the hypothalamus.

The brain stem contains a central core of grey matter, continuous with that in the spinal cord, from which arise the cranial nerves (Fig. 19.2), but the segmental origin and the division of each nerve into motor and sensory roots seen in the spinal cord are not in evidence in the cranial nerves. Among the cranial nerve nuclei and the other specifically named structures in the brain stem there is also a large region where small groups of cells lie in a network of nerve fibres running in all directions, hence known as the reticular formation (Fig. 20.7). This part of the brain is very fashionable among neurophysiologists, who do not always confine the term to the true reticular formation of the anatomists. Many functions are attributed to the reticular formation, some of which are discussed on pp. 362, 371 and 379. The respiratory and vasomotor centres are also claimed as part of the reticular formation.

Categories of Nervous Action

The central nervous system is the organ which directs the behaviour of animals, all those responses and activities by which an animal reacts to its environment and attempts to master it and flourish. In man and many other animals nearly all behavioural activities are carried out by the contractions of skeletal muscle. (This is not always so; the skunk and the electric fish have other ways of getting the better of their enemies.) In addition to its outwardly directed activities the central nervous system has the job of running most of the internal systems of the body; it controls, for instance, the endocrine, digestive, respiratory, blood circulatory and excretory systems. Most of these internal duties are discussed in the chapters dealing with those systems; in this chapter we are mainly concerned with the central nervous system as it determines the external behaviour of the animal through its muscles.

An animal's reactions to changes in its environment may differ greatly in complexity. Shining a light in the eye causes the pupil to constrict; this is one of the simplest of nervous reactions, and historically one of the first that was clearly understood to involve a nervous pathway from the sensitive surface to the central nervous system and back to the effector muscle. At the other end of the scale the production of a Ph.D. thesis may equally clearly be a response to a change of environment. Those reactions that seem to be automatic and immediate, such as blinks, knee jerks or sneezes, are termed "reflexes". The other main category of muscular actions is those that, because they involve conscious thought and decision, are called "voluntary movements." Typically a reflex is something the subject can't help doing, like coughing during a concert, or choking if someone touches the back of his throat with a feather, whereas voluntary actions are actions he could have refrained from if he had wished; hence the satirical definition of a voluntary movement as a movement a patient makes when he is told to by a neurologist.

The line between reflex and voluntary is very indistinct. There are all levels of behaviour between the most voluntary and unpredictable, such as writing a Ph.D. thesis, and the most automatic, such as the pupillary reaction to light. Reading a book is obviously a voluntary activity, looking up when someone enters the room is practically automatic, blinking when a threatening movement is made towards the face, although it may be possible to prevent it by a strong effort of will, is so automatic that it is generally considered a reflex, blinking when an object touches the cornea is an indubitable reflex.

No one knows whether the nervous mechanisms of the most elaborate voluntary actions and of the simplest reflexes differ in principle or only in complexity and detail. No rational classification of the activities of the central nervous system is therefore possible in the present state of knowledge, so whether we call some particular manifestation of nervous action voluntary or reflex, or by some other term, is purely a matter of descriptive convenience, and usages are bound to differ in so complex a subject.

An important category of semi-automatic reactions that are not usually called reflex is those involved in the expression of emotion. Emotional movements of the face are certainly different from voluntary movements in their nervous mechanism because, as we shall see, disease of the brain may paralyse voluntary movements of the face such as screwing up the eyes, baring the teeth, etc., and yet the patient may smile normally if amused.

So far we have spoken as if all behaviour were a reaction to some environmental stimulus direct or remote, but, of course, in ordinary life a good many of a man's or an animal's voluntary acts are likely to be in response to internal stimuli, thirst, hunger, and sexual and other instincts. Instances of simpler types of activity that appear to arise spontaneously, without any obvious external stimulus, are seen with blinking and with eye movements. Blinking may sometimes be reflex, as when something touches the cornea, or it may be a voluntary act. Blinking, however, goes on irregularly all the time while we are awake and for most of these occasions there is no apparent external stimulus and certainly no voluntary factor; its function is presumably to prevent the cornea from becoming dirty or drying up. Such blinking certainly appears to be spontaneous and, indeed, cannot for long be suppressed by the will. This urgency is even more in evidence with the incessant shifting of the direction of gaze that goes on all the time we have our eyes open. It is much more difficult to avoid moving the eyes than it is to avoid blinking. The need to move the fixation point at frequent intervals is probably connected with the fading of contrast which is observed if the retinal image is not allowed to move. At all events it cannot be because the world is full of interesting objects that provide a succession of irresistible reflex stimuli, for spontaneous eye movements if anything increase when looking at a blank surface; indeed, in the dark it appears to be impossible to keep the eyes still.

Nothing is known of the nervous mechanisms responsible for such apparently spontaneous actions, and they will not be discussed further. They are mentioned partly to emphasize that the nervous system may take a much more active part in shaping events than is implied in the simple idea of reflex action.

It will also be evident from the foregoing that there are nervous actions of which it is no use asking, is it a reflex?, expecting an answer yes or no. Thus, as we have seen, blinking may be reflex; more usually it is apparently spontaneous, but it may be voluntary or even emotional in origin. It is best thought of as just a specific type of muscular activity, that may arise in a variety of ways.

These remarks serve to introduce the ubiquitous and important subject of posture. Posture is maintained by the same muscles that are used to carry out the ordinary outwardly-directed behavioural activities (reflex, voluntary, etc.) of the animal, but otherwise it is more akin to the internal homeostatic mechanisms such as breathing. Readers will be familiar with Claude Bernard's teaching that stable surroundings for the cells of the body as regards temperature, pH, ionic composition, etc., are prerequisite for a life of unrestricted activity, but a land-living mammal is just as disabled if it cannot stand up as if, owing to faulty breathing, the pH of its blood is wrong. Correct posture is not so much a behavioural activity itself as an initial state which is necessary before an animal can act effectively. As with breathing, etc., it is best not to ask whether posture is reflex or spontaneous but to regard it as a state of the body which is controlled by automatic mechanisms sensitive to the direction of gravity, the pressure of the ground on the feet, etc., in the same way that breathing is controlled by the concentration of carbon dioxide in the blood, etc. No one thinks of breathing as a reflex response to a smack on the buttocks at birth, nor is standing merely a response to the sound of the breakfast gong. Both activities so long outlast the stimulus, that how they are maintained has become of much more interest than how they were initiated. (Standing is not a reflex response to gravity, for gravity acts very constantly and since animals sometimes lie down and sometimes stand up it cannot be gravity that determines which they do. It is true that when for other, usually inscrutable, reasons an animal stands up the direction of gravity determines how it does it, but that is not the same thing.)

Locomotion (walking, running, etc.) is another complex action whose mechanism deserves to be studied in its own right, quite apart from the stimulus that sets it going. It is closely related to posture and subsequently the two will be dealt with together.

This completes the introductory discussion of the types of nervous activity that have to be taken account of in this chapter. Nothing has been said of such things as social behaviour or psychology for the very good reason that we are so far from coming to grips with the neurological mechanisms involved that they are not yet part of the subject matter of physiology.

Since Sherrington's famous, but for many people almost unreadable, book "The Integrative Action of the Nervous System" (1906, reprinted 1947) it has been conventional to emphasize integration or co-ordination as functions of the central nervous system, so much so that some authors apparently feel that to describe a nervous centre as exercising an integrating or co-ordinating influence over some function or other absolves them from attempting any description of what it does. Sherrington himself, who was always prone to use words in highly specialized senses of his own, clearly used the word "co-ordination" with a very extended meaning, as the following sentences, with which he opens an article on the brain, show. "The nervous system has as its function the co-ordinating of the activities of the organs one with another. It puts the organs into such mutual relation that the animal reacts as a whole with speed, accuracy and self-advantage, in response to the environmental agencies which stimulate it." This quotation can be regarded as defining "co-ordination". For Sherrington, it is apparently that activity which is the function of the nervous system. Other passages show that he used "integration" in much the same sense. To avoid misunderstanding, the words "integration" and "co-ordination" are not used in this chapter.

Reflex Action

The word "reflex" implied originally that nervous messages travelling up sensory nerves were "reflected" in the central nervous system and passed out again into motor nerves. Ideas of this kind were current in the seventeenth century; an instance of reflection given by Descartes is the involuntary blink a man gives if a threatening gesture is made towards his face. Some of the first experiments were made by Stephen Hales, the perpetual curate of Teddington, Middlesex, in about 1730. He used a spinal frog, *i.e.* a frog that has been decapitated so that the spinal cord is the only part of the central nervous system remaining. When such a preparation is suspended the legs hang down limply, but if one foot is pinched that leg is drawn up as if to remove the foot from the injurious stimulus. This withdrawal reaction (the flexion reflex) is lost if the spinal cord is destroyed, a result which strongly suggests that the nervous pathway from the skin of the foot to the flexor muscles runs via the spinal cord.

Hales' experiment does not definitely exclude other more far-fetched possibilities, such as that the site of reflection is really in the lumbar nerve plexus but that the nerve plexus is under the influence of the spinal cord and ceases to reflect if the cord is destroyed. (Something not dissimilar is now known to occur in the axon reflex from skin on to cutaneous blood vessels.) But such alternatives were made superfluous by the celebrated experiments of Magendie and Bell on the functions of the spinal nerve roots, at the beginning of the 19th century. They showed that, if a ventral root was cut through, excitation of the peripheral stump caused widespread muscular contraction, but excitation of the central stump connected to the spinal cord was without obvious effect; in particular the animal exhibited no signs of sensation. The peripheral stump of a divided dorsal root gave no muscular movements (and, of course, no signs of sensation), but the central stump caused obvious pain and elicited muscular movements (which disappeared if the ventral roots were divided too). These experiments showed that the ventral roots were exclusively motor, with no sensory function, and that the dorsal roots were exclusively sensory but could excite movements by "reflection" in the spinal cord.

Before Magendie and Bell it was not clear that motor and sensory nerves were distinct. The real significance of their experiments was to show that the nervous system uses separate channels for input and output—the most important single principle in the organization of the nervous system. Nowadays the idea of motor and sensory fibres is so familiar that it is easy to forget that Magendie and Bell discovered their separate existence and did not merely demonstrate an anatomical fact about their mode of origin from the spinal cord. As regards reflex action, the fact that motor and sensory fibres maintained a complete separation of function until they reached the spinal cord showed that the connection between them, the site of reflection, must be in the cord.

The anatomical parts of the simplest idealized reflex pathway (Fig. 19.1) are: a sensory receptor connected to a sensory (afferent) nerve fibre running to the central nervous system, a motor (efferent) nerve fibre running from the central nervous system to a muscle, and a synaptic connection in the central nervous system between the sensory fibre and the motoneurone. This synaptic connection may either be direct or, more usually, via one or more additional nerve cells called interneurones. In all real reflex pathways, of course, many receptors and many sensory and motor fibres are involved.

The central connections between input and output are seldom simple enough to give the impression that sensory impulses are merely "reflected" into motor channels. An instance that might suggest reflection is the constriction of the pupil when light is shone into the eye. With the majority of reflexes, however, the pattern of discharge of motor impulses differs, often very widely indeed, from the pattern in the sensory nerves that excite them. A relatively simple reflex is the corneal reflex: a touch on the cornea, *e.g.* with a wisp of cotton wool, causes a blink. The sensory impulses for this reflex travel in the ophthalmic division of the trigeminal

(Vth cranial) nerve to the medulla (see Fig. 19.2), and motor impulses leave from nearby in the facial (VIIth cranial) nerve which supplies the orbicularis oculi—the muscle responsible for blinking. There is clearly a formal sense in which impulses may be said to find their way from the cornea via the facial nerve nucleus back to the orbicularis, but such a mode of description certainly tends to conceal the significant fact that a blink is an entity, almost an all-or-none event, a stereotyped pattern of motor discharge which differs little whatever type of stimulus is used to evoke it. Hence it is more illuminating to say that touching the cornea triggers off a blink, rather than that it reflexly excites the orbicularis. As Hughlings Jackson (1835–1911), the greatest speculative mind in the history of neurology, put it, even in the simplest reflexes the nervous system "thinks" in terms of movements, not muscles—the corneal reflex results in a blink, not just in some contraction of the orbicularis. Nothing is known of the details of the motor mechanism that organizes a blink.

Several examples of more complicated reflexes are found at the head end of the digestive and respiratory tracts, swallowing, vomiting, sneezing, coughing, etc. In swallowing the problem is to get a mouthful of food or drink rapidly into the oesophagus without any entering the nose or the larynx. The elaborate sequence of muscular operations by which this is achieved is described in Chapter 24. When voluntary activity is in abeyance, e.g. in stuporose human beings or in animals from whom the cerebral hemispheres have been removed (decerebrate preparations), reflex swallowing can be induced by placing small pieces of food on the back of the tongue. Vomiting, sneezing, etc., are also self-contained sequences of muscular acts which are triggered by sensory stimuli.

A different type of complexity is seen with micturition in the spinal dog. In a dog in which the spinal cord has been functionally separated from the brain by transection in, say, the thoracic region, the bladder, after some days, empties itself reflexly when it is full. Emptying of the bladder is itself another example of a definite act triggered by sensory impulses rather than a reflection of these impulses to the effector organ, but what is of particular interest is that the spinal dog, when it has finished passing its water, may wag its tail, just like any ordinary dog. Thus this elaborate gesture involving many muscles, none of them anything to do with the bladder, is clearly a part of the reflex act of micturition.

The examples so far discussed make it evident that on the motor side the reflex centres of the central nervous system deal in terms of complete muscular acts. It is natural to ask if there is any corresponding generalization to be made about the sensory side of reflex action. Take the case of the reflex blink in response to a threat. If we speak of this reflex as a matter of impulses finding a pathway from retina to orbicularis muscle we shall be on safe ground, but this formulation disregards the fact that only a spatiotemporal pattern of impulses in many thousands of optic nerve fibres which the brain recognizes as a threatening object rapidly approaching the face will evoke a blink. This is known to be a task that requires the highest centres for sensory interpretation in the cerebral cortex, for the blink to a threat from one side may be abolished by a small lesion of the opposite parietal lobe (see Fig. 19.3) which causes no detectable disturbance of vision (p. 345). Evidently in this reflex by far the most difficult part is the process of recognizing the threat; this is presumably why the delay after a threat is made before the blink occurs (variously known as the latent period or the reaction time) is of the order of 250 milliseconds, whereas the blink to a touch on the cornea takes only some 40 milliseconds. For the purposes of this reflex, therefore, impulses in the optic nerve are of no importance as such, but only become important when their message has been decoded into whatever pattern of nervous processes it is that constitutes the nervous representation of a threat; the threat is the significant thing, not the impulses. To adapt Hughlings Jackson, the central nervous system "thinks" in terms of the causative physical events not in terms of sensory receptors.

The blink reflex is an extreme example of this principle because the process of recognition is so complex and the motor mechanism relatively so simple, but at lower levels in the central nervous system sensory recognition is still important, chiefly in reflexes initiated from the skin. Elsewhere it is not so in evidence; *e.g.* when impulses from distension receptors in the bladder arrive at the spinal cord presumably they can only mean one thing; no problem of recognition arises. But the skin is played upon by many diverse influences, and the appropriate reflex responses can only be made if the central nervous system can distinguish the various stimuli.

In a spinal dog or cat two opposite reflexes can be elicited from the pads of a foot. Pressure by a flat object on the pads causes a brief powerful extension of hip, knee and ankle, the extensor thrust reflex (tentatively identified by Sherrington as an element in galloping), whereas pinching a pad (or any other form of painful stimulation) gives the withdrawal or flexion reflex of the limb, already mentioned in the frog. The stimulus for an extensor thrust presumably excites touch and pressure receptors. A pinch which elicits flexion excites pain fibres as well as touch and pressure. Experiment shows, however, that any noxious stimulus which is likely to cause pain will elicit the flexion reflex, so the essential thing about a pinch must be the pain, and this must be easy enough to recognize because it is carried by special pain fibres. Protective reflexes caused by noxious stimuli always seem to get priority in the nervous system (for obvious practical reasons), whence it appears that the recognition of pain carries with it an automatic refusal to recognize other stimuli (in this case touch and pressure) or in some other way to overrule them.

The recognition of the stimulus that calls for an extensor thrust is not so straightforward a matter, however. It is not merely a matter of impulses in touch and pressure fibres in the absence of pain. Sherrington never succeeded in eliciting an extensor thrust reaction by electrical stimulation of the sensory nerves supplying the pads although there is no reason to doubt that he was exciting touch and pressure fibres. (Pain fibres, being of small diameter, require a larger electrical stimulus so it is not difficult to avoid exciting them.) It seems likely that recognition of pressure on the pads depends on a distinctive pattern of discharge from touch and pressure receptors in different positions on the pads, and also perhaps on a distinctive distribution in time of the impulses from each receptor, and that electrical stimulation fails to imitate this spatio-temporal pattern of discharge.

At all events this difficulty in eliciting reflexes by electrical excitation of nerve trunks is a widespread and interesting phenomenon that has attracted attention since the middle of the nineteenth century. With large stimuli reflexes due to excitation of pain fibres are obtainable, but it is probably true to say that no other reflexes can be elicited by electrical stimulation of skin nerves (muscle nerves are different, as is discussed on p. 334). The explanation offered is that for most skin stimuli recognition depends on characteristic patterns of discharge in several nerve fibres which cannot be reproduced by electrical stimuli to nerve trunks; whereas pain stimuli are recognized because they travel in pain fibres and the pattern of discharge is unimportant; hence shocks large enough to excite pain fibres successfully excite pain reflexes.

Subjective observations by human subjects lend plausibility to this interpretation. Repetitive electrical stimulation of cutaneous nerve trunks is easily performed with an induction coil (Fig. 17.3) through pad electrodes applied to the skin over the nerve. With shocks that are not so large as to cause pain all that is felt is a vague tingling and sensation of tightness over the area of skin distribution of the nerve, not unlike "pins and needles". The feelings aroused never correspond to any sensation that could result from natural stimulation of the skin surface. This failure to evoke recognizable sensations cannot be due to any inadequacy in the total number of impulses but must be because of their unnatural arrangement. Apparently the reflex centres of the spinal cord likewise cannot make sense of the synchronous volleys of impulses that result from electrical stimulation of skin nerves and they therefore give no reflex responses. With stronger shocks the situation alters; in the human subject pain sensations are aroused which are recognized as similar to those caused by ordinary painful stimuli; likewise in animals ordinary pain reflexes are elicited.

The general conclusions from the foregoing are that the reflex centres only recognize patterns of afferent impulses which correspond to naturally occurring physical stimuli, and that these stimuli when recognized, only elicit definite movements each of which is an appropriate response to its stimulus. Nothing definite is known of the details of the connections between nerve cells that are responsible for the properties summarized in this paragraph.

Spinal Reflexes. The central nervous system is so immensely complex that to analyse how it works is bound to be extremely difficult. On the intact animal it is not possible to proceed by the classical scientific method of varying only one factor at a time while all others are held constant, because an animal's response to a particular change in its environment often depends on things that happened to it long before the experiment started. Even its reflex responses tend to be variable and unpredictable, and may furthermore be disturbed by apparently spontaneous activity. These difficulties can be minimized by confining attention to the reflex responses of the spinal cord after it has been severed from the brain to exclude voluntary and spontaneous interference.

For a time after spinal transection it is impossible to elicit any, or almost any, reflexes from the isolated part of the spinal cord below the section. This is called *spinal shock*. After shock passes off the reflexes tend to become brisker and more easily provoked than they were originally. The higher an animal is in the evolutionary scale the more profound the shock, the longer it lasts, and the smaller the number of reflexes that eventually reappear, although ultimately some of these reflexes may be greatly enhanced. The decapitate frog recovers from spinal shock in a minute or two. In the cat or dog some reflexes reappear in a matter of minutes; most of those that are going to appear at all do so in a few days, but the ease with which they can be elicited may go on increasing for months after. In the spinal monkey and in cases of accidental division of the spinal cord in man (spinal man) the return of responsiveness does not begin for several days and progresses very slowly.

The nature of spinal shock is still unknown; it is clear that shock is a bad name for something that may last for years and that grades imperceptibly into enhancement. It is not the mechanical damage that causes shock for, in an animal that has recovered from shock, a second section immediately behind the first causes no return of shock. Sherrington showed in the monkey that at a time when the lower limbs were entirely unresponsive to massive stimuli (such as repetitive electrical stimulation of large nerve trunks or extensive burning of the sole of the foot) which would normally cause violent limb reflexes, movements could still be obtained with ease by exciting electrically the tracts of the spinal cord exposed at the cut surface. This suggests that the spinal neurones are not so much inexcitable as deprived of excitation normally reaching them from higher levels in the nervous system. (This would explain why there is no trace of shock in any part of the nervous system in front of the section.)

The more advanced the animal the more its behaviour is dictated by its brain and the larger the deficit of excitation in the spinal cord after it is cut off from cerebral influences. During recovery certain reflex pathways, in some unknown way, increase their power of exciting and overcome the deficit. The larger the deficit the longer it takes to fill.

The reflexes that recover seem only to be those that in the ordinary life of the animal are little or not at all under voluntary control. In man almost every action is voluntary or requires voluntary permission, and a spinal man is left, below the level of the lesion, with little more than flexion reflexes (p. 324), tendon jerks (p. 332) and a number of visceral (sympathetic and parasympathetic) responses, notably automatic empty-ing of the bladder and rectum, sexual reflexes (erection and seminal emission) and vasomotor responses to pain and to a full bladder (see p. 665). Many of these become unnaturally brisk and easily provoked. In a proportion of cases the stretch reflex (p. 328) returns and after some years brief periods of spinal standing may be possible. In a spinal dog or cat, apart from similar visceral responses there are a large number of protective reflexes (of which the best known are the flexion reflex and the scratch reflex (p. 326)), some rather half-hearted attempts at standing and walking, several fragmentary reflexes of less easily recognizable purpose (such as the extensor thrust (p. 319) and the stretch reflex (p. 328)) which appear to be elements of postural or locomotor mechanisms or of the nervous mechanisms that control muscular contraction, and little else.

It is a price that the experimenter has to pay for getting all the variables of the experiment under his control that the isolated spinal cord of the ordinary laboratory mammals does not have a very large or interesting repertory of reflexes, but to offset this the simplicity of spinal reflexes has been turned to great advantage for purposes of analysis, and most of what is known of the detailed behaviour of nervous pathways has come from the study of a few spinal reflexes. Sherrington, who pioneered in this field in the last years of the nineteenth century, was impelled by the belief that reflexes were the units of nervous action and that more complicated types of behaviour would prove to be compounded of simple reflexes. Although what he and his pupils discovered about individual reflexes and the way reflexes interact (for instance the way in which the protective flexion reflex overrides, or inhibits, other reflexes) is of very great interest and importance, the attempt to show that complex acts like walking are made up of a succession of simpler reflexes was not equally successful and may (as is further discussed on pp. 328 and 339) prove to be mistaken. Hence the reader must not be disappointed to find that a knowledge of what goes on in the simpler spinal reflexes, of the nature of synaptic action and so forth, does not throw much light on the mechanism of more com-plex reflex actions, let alone on the mode of functioning of the higher parts of the brain.

The spinal reflexes which have been investigated in greatest detail and from which most generalizations about reflexes are conventionally drawn are the flexion reflex, the scratch reflex, and the stretch reflex.

The Flexion Reflex. The flexion or withdrawal reflex of the limb to a painful stimulus has already been referred to more than once; some of its characteristics as seen in the cat will now be described more fully. The reflex exhibits a threshold; to elicit it any stimulus must reach a certain intensity. The interval between the time of application of the stimulus and the start of the reflex contraction (the latency of the reflex) is of the order of 30 milliseconds, much longer and more variable than the latency of contraction when a stimulus is applied to a motor nerve. A stimulus is more effective the larger the area it covers and the longer it lasts (spatial and temporal summation). As the stimulus is increased in intensity the flexion movement becomes more vigorous and more extensive; thus a weak stimulus may cause movement of toes and ankle only, while with a very strong stimulus the knee and hip flex as well (irradiation). With strong stimuli the limb may remain flexed for a second or more after the stimulus ends (after-discharge). The words in brackets are the special terms introduced by Sherrington.

In the most clear-cut demonstrations of the above properties Sherrington and his colleagues used electrical stimulation of peripheral nerves to elicit the reflex and recorded the contractions of an individual muscle (tibialis anterior) by detaching its tendon from its insertion and connecting it instead to an isometric lever (p. 685). The reflex latency could be measured easily with this arrangement. After making allowance for conduction time to and from the spinal cord the delay in the cord itself was found to be a minimum of about 5 milliseconds (at times it is very much longer). Spatial summation was shown by applying shocks to two nerves, both shocks just too weak by themselves to elicit a reflex (subliminal), but successful if applied together. When both shocks were large enough to produce small reflex contractions, applying them together gave a tension greater than the sum of the tension produced by stimulating the two nerves separately (spatial summation again). When, however, both shocks were increased to give the largest possible reflex contractions, applying both together often gave a tension little greater than with either separately (occlusion), because the muscle was already giving a nearly maximal contraction with the single stimuli. Temporal summation was shown by applying two subliminal shocks in rapid succession to the same nerve; when the interval between them was less than some 20 milliseconds a reflex contraction resulted.

The fully developed flexion reflex is accompanied by extension of the opposite leg, the knee and ankle straighten out and the limb is thrust backwards at the hip. This *crossed extensor* reflex has a much longer latency (40–100 milliseconds) than the flexion reflex proper, and once it starts it takes a second or two to build up to its greatest strength (recruit-ment), in contrast to the rapid onset of flexion. Crossed extension still occurs when the dorsal roots of that limb have been cut. The crossed extensor reflex probably represents the first part of a step away from the noxious stimulus.

Temporal summation, as described above for the flexion reflex, implies that the first shock causes a change in excitability somewhere on the pathway of the reflex which persists for several milliseconds to summate with the effect of the second shock. Sherrington called this persisting change "central excitatory state". It seems to have been taken for granted that the alterations of central excitatory state during the flexor reflex took place in the motoneurones of the flexor muscles, in the motoneurone pool as it was termed. Electrical recording with fine electrodes inside the spinal cord has now shown, however, that the afferent nerve fibres that elicit the flexion reflex (and in fact all skin afferents), end on interneurones in the dorsal horn of grey matter (Fig. 19.1) and do not themselves run through to the motoneurones in the ventral horn.

A reflex contraction of tibialis anterior can be produced by exciting any one of a number of peripheral nerves in that leg. Sherrington pictured impulses from these various sources "converging" on to tibialis moto-neurones, which formed a "final common path". (As we have just seen the site of convergence is more likely to be the interneurones of the dorsal horn.) The concept of the final common path found wide application in his writings, but nowadays, although true in a certain formal sense, it is a less illuminating doctrine than it previously appeared. For one thing, by implying that in reflex action afferent impulses find their way through the spinal cord eventually to emerge via the motor roots, it speaks the language of simple reflection and therefore tends to distract attention from the view preferred here (and endorsed incidentally by Sherrington himself) that the spinal cord "thinks " in terms of organized movements; other objections will appear later (pp. 368–370).

Withdrawal reflexes in man can be elicited from the leg of a healthy subject by painful stimuli applied to the skin. Kugelberg and his co-workers have shown that the precise kind of movement obtained varies with the site of stimulation. As a convenient and reproducible stimulus they used a burst of high voltage electric shocks delivered through a pair of electrodes pressed against the skin. With the stimulus applied to the underside of the big toe the response obtained was flexion at all joints: upward movement of the toes, flexion of the ankle, knee and hip and forward flexion of the trunk, as illustrated in Fig. 19.4. When the stimulus was moved further back on to the sole of the foot the toes moved downwards instead of upwards, the other joints flexing as before. The same response can be obtained by firmly stroking the sole. With the electrical stimulus under the heel the toes again moved downward but now the ankle extended too, the other joints again flexing. With the stimulus on the buttock there was extension of the trunk and hip, some flexion of the knee, extension of the ankle, and downward movement of the toes, as shown in Fig. 19.4.

The effect of these movements in each case is to withdraw the stimulated point from the stimulus; but in addition they contain components

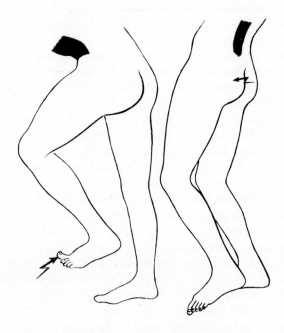

Fig. 19.4. Withdrawal responses to painful stimuli applied to the underside of the big toe and to the buttock. The filled-in areas mark the trunk muscles that contract. (Kugelberg, Eklund and Grimby, *Brain*, vol. 83, p. 394, 1960.)

which are clearly not part of the withdrawal, downward movement of the toes and extension of various joints. In a standing subject, the effect of these components of the reflex would be to press the toes downwards and assist to maintain standing. This only does not occur when the stimulus is applied to a toe, when it would be inconsistent with effective withdrawal. Hence it is thought that the reflex responses of the human leg to painful stimuli have the dual function of defence with maintenance of posture.

When the corticospinal motor tracts (p. 355) from the brain (without which a man cannot stand) are damaged, the components of the withdrawal response which appear to assist standing disappear. Electrical stimuli to the sole of the foot in such patients gave exactly the same response (i.e. upward movement of the toes and flexion at all other joints) as stimulation of the underside of the toe in healthy subjects. Firm stroking of the sole of the foot in such patients also causes an upward movement of the toes. The same response is found in infants before they begin to stand up, and before the corticospinal tracts receive their myelin sheaths.

In spinal man an upgoing big toe accompanied by flexion of the leg is one of the first reflexes to appear during recovery from spinal shock. Over a period of months the threshold of the reflex falls and flexion becomes more vigorous, until eventually violent flexion may result from trifling stimuli anywhere on the limb.

The response of the big toe to a firm stroke on the sole of the foot with a blunt point (the plantar response) is of great importance in clinical diagnosis, as an upgoing big toe is often the first unequivocal evidence of disease of the motor pathways (pp. 355, 358). The sign was first described by Babinski in 1896. An upgoing big toe is part of the general flexion reflex of the limb, but, although morphologically a movement of flexion, in anatomical nomenclature it is extension. Hence an upgoing big toe is referred to by neurologists as an extensor plantar response. A healthy plantar response is said to be flexor.

The Scratch Reflex. Some days or weeks after spinal section in the cervical region, a dog will respond to irritation of the skin over its shoulder by scratching at the place with its hind foot. The movements made (Fig. 19.5) closely resemble the familiar scratching of a normal dog, consisting of a series of rhythmical strokes of the whole leg at a frequency of about five per second. A good form of stimulus is a series of light touches with a pointed object. A single touch never succeeds; several dozen (at a rate of a few per second) may be necessary if they are all applied at one spot, but the total number diminishes if two or more spots are touched simultaneously; the most effective method is to touch a row of spots consecutively, thus imitating the pattern of stimulation normally caused by a moving flea. Once scratching has begun it continues for some seconds after the stimulus is withdrawn. (Readers are invited to apply to the above properties the Sherringtonian terminology given with the flexion reflex.)

The scratch reflex cannot be elicited by electrical excitation of cutaneous nerve trunks or of dorsal roots; apparently such volleys are not recognized as objects to be scratched at; but small shocks applied through a fine pin (electric flea) pushed just into the epidermis are successful. Not very surprisingly perhaps the frequency of scratching movements proves to be independent of the frequency of the electric flea bites that cause them. This is one of the usually quoted formal differences between (repetitive) movements elicited reflexly and by direct excitation of a motor nerve. Another is fatigability: if the scratch reflex is elicited several times from the same point of skin it becomes weaker and more difficult to obtain.

It may be useful to the animal to disregard a source of irritation it does not succeed in removing, so possibly the phenomenon is more akin to adaptation than to what is ordinarily thought of as fatigue. At all events the "fatigue" is not of the motor part of the reflex mechanism, for if the stimulus is moved to another point on the skin the reflex immediately returns in full strength. (It is not in general true that reflexes are readily fatigable. The cough reflex may persist with undiminished sensitivity after

SCRATCH–REFLEX

⅕ SEC.

FIG. 19.5. The scratch reflex in the spinal dog. The amount of the hip flexion recorded on a smoked drum by means of a string connected to the writing lever. The reflex was elicited by electrical stimulation of a point on the skin on the animal's back. The period of stimulation is shown by the descent of the signal line beneath the time scale. (Sherrington, "The Integrative Action of the Nervous System": New York 1906; Cambridge 1947.)

it has wholly exhausted the subject. The stretch reflex (p. 328) is also believed to be less fatigable than the muscles it employs.) If, during a scratch reflex, a painful stimulus is given to the leg, scratching immediately ceases and is replaced by a flexion reflex. This is an example of a protective reflex taking precedence by actively inhibiting a less urgent reflex.

The mechanism which generates the rhythm of scratching is not known. The frequency does not depend on the strength of the stimulus, or on the amplitude of the beat. Sherrington showed that if the amplitude is reduced by a carefully graded painful stimulus to a leg nerve, not quite strong enough to inhibit scratching completely, the frequency is unaltered. He also found that cutting the dorsal roots of the segments supplying the limb reduced the accuracy with which the scratching was directed to the point irritated, but did not alter the frequency. These experiments suggest that the rhythm is determined by a pacemaker in the spinal cord rather than by a sequence of flexor and extensor reflexes set up alternately by the moving limb itself; we shall see later (p. 339) that there is similar evidence for the slower rhythm of stepping.

The Stretch Reflex and the Tendon Jerk. So far we have dealt only with reflexes of obvious functional significance, elicited from the skin, the nose and throat, the cornea, the bladder, etc. In all cases the stimulus for the reflex would also have caused a conscious sensation in a normal human subject, pain, touch, tickle in the throat, etc. We now come to a very different reflex found in muscles. Muscles, like skin, are supplied with numerous sensory nerve fibres connected to sensory receptors, but unlike skin the impulses set up by these receptors do not give rise to conscious sensations. The knowledge we possess of the position of our limbs in space, position sense, comes from sense-endings in and around the joints, not from muscle.

The evidence for this statement is first, that the eyes, which, of course, have no joint receptors, are without position sense, as was clearly understood by Helmholtz a century ago. Modern work has shown that after thoroughly anaesthetizing the conjunctiva with cocaine, and holding the eyelids out of the way, the eyeball can be seized with forceps and rotated in the orbit without the subject being aware that anything is happening. Yet human eye muscles contain numerous sense-endings, including muscle spindles, which must necessarily be stimulated by these manipulations. Secondly, in the limbs, position sense is lost when the tissues surrounding a joint are rendered anaesthetic, even though the muscles acting at the joint, whose length alters when the joint is passively moved, are outside the anaesthetic region.

Strictly, receptors and nerve fibres that do not cause sensations should not be called sensory, but this usage is accepted along with "sensory root" for dorsal root, etc., and causes no trouble if care is taken to make the intended meaning clear when ambiguity might arise. Other familiar examples of sense-endings that do not affect consciousness are the blood-pressure receptors in the carotid sinus and the vagal receptors signalling inflation of the lungs.

Sense endings in muscles and those associated with joints were classed together as "proprioceptors" by Sherrington. The term is not used here as it tends to obscure the distinction that ought to be drawn between their functions.

The receptors in muscles elicit reflexes, but, again unlike the reflexes from the skin, they are not of unequivocal function. The most important and best understood muscular reflex is the stretch reflex: when a muscle is stretched by pulling on it a reflex contraction is set up which opposes the pull. The stretch reflex can be demonstrated on intact animals and human beings; it only reappears in the spinal dog after some weeks and in spinal man after a year or two. For analytical purposes it is usually studied on a decerebrate preparation, i.e. an animal whose cerebral hemispheres have been removed by making a hole in the skull under anaesthesia, cutting through the brain stem, usually just below the superior colliculi (Figs. 19.3 and 20.2), and scooping out the whole forebrain. Such a preparation has the advantage that the stretch reflex is present in the extensor muscles at once; indeed it is exaggerated, leading to a state known as *decerebrate rigidity*, which is mentioned again on pp. 337, 370. Decerebrate animals are also convenient because without a forebrain they cannot (it is generally accepted) feel pain and so no anaesthetic is required; also as the medulla is intact they breathe and maintain their blood pressure. The chief attention they require is to be kept at 38°C, because they have lost the automatic temperature control centres in the hypothalamus (p. 668).

In a decerebrate cat the stretch reflex is chiefly present in the extensors, the muscles that straighten the limbs. When such a muscle, e.g. the soleus, one of the ankle extensors, is cut away from its insertion and connected via its tendon to a device for measuring tension it is found that any attempt to elongate the muscle results in a rapid rise in the tension it develops, and at the same time electrodes on or in the muscle record numerous action potentials (Fig. 19.6). This active contraction is reflex, because it disappears if either the motor nerve to soleus or the appropriate dorsal or ventral roots are cut through. Stretching the muscle after cutting its nerve then only causes a much smaller rise in tension due to the simple passive elastic properties which muscle, like any other piece of soft tissue, possesses. It is clearly established by other experiments that it is the change in length of the muscle that excites the stretch reflex and not the change in tension. Except when reflex excitability is artificially raised the stretch reflex is private to the muscle stretched, no other muscles contract; and it persists in that muscle when the whole skin of the limb and every other muscle in the limb is denervated by systematic section of the nerves.

In human patients the neurologist detects the absence, presence or exaggeration of the stretch reflexes by assessing the "sense of passive resistance" he obtains when he moves the joints of the limb about while the patient relaxes and initiates no voluntary movements of his own. To express the results the somewhat unfortunate word "tone" is used. The normal degree of passive resistance is called normal tone; diminished sense of passive resistance is diminished tone, the muscles are hypotonic or flaccid; increased sense of passive resistance is increased tone with hypertonic or spastic muscles.

Opinions about the function of the stretch reflex are undergoing revision. It was once supposed that the stretch reflex was a characteristic of postural antigravity muscles, but it is now clear that the stretch reflex is active during reflex and voluntary as well as during postural contractions,

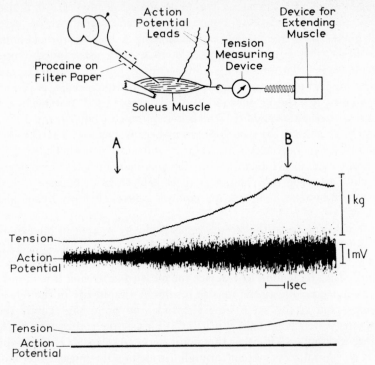

FIG. 19.6. The stretch reflex in the soleus muscle of a decerebrate cat.
The diagram above shows the experimental arrangements. The
bones of the leg are clamped to a stand and the severed tendon of the
soleus muscle connected to a device for recording muscle tension. To
stretch the muscle the whole tension recording device is moved by
means of a motor driven screw. The electrical response of the muscle
is led off by electrodes on the muscle. (The application of procaine
refers to Fig. 19.9.)

The records below show the rise in tension that occurs when the
muscle is extended 13 mm at a rate of 1·7 mm per second. Extension
starts at A and stops at B. At the same time a great increase in the
electrical activity in the muscle occurs, showing that the increase in
tension is associated with an active reflex contraction of the muscle.
The lower records, taken during a similar extension after the
stretch reflex had been abolished, show the absence of electrical
response and the much smaller rise in tension caused by the passive
elastic properties of the muscle. (P. B. C. Matthews, unpublished
records.)

and occurs in flexor as well as in extensor muscles. The view adopted here
is that the stretch reflex is part of the general nervous machinery controlling any muscular contraction and its function is discussed further under
that heading (p. 369). The rôle of the stretch reflex in posture is discussed
on pp. 338 and 368.

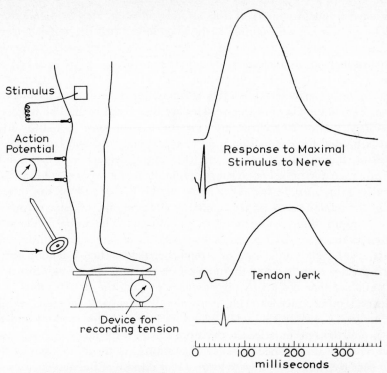

Stimulus

Action
Potential

Response to Maximal
Stimulus to Nerve

Tendon Jerk

Device for
recording tension

0   100   200   300
milliseconds

FIG. 19.7. The human ankle jerk. The reflex, which is obtainable in
almost all healthy persons, is elicited by striking the tendon of the
ankle extensors (the soleus and gastrocnemius muscles) a sharp blow
with a rubber-covered hammer; it consists of a twitch contraction of
these muscles. To record the contraction, the foot rests on a board
hinged under the heel; contraction of the ankle extensors causes an
increase in the downward pressure exerted by the front of the foot on
the board, which is recorded on a cathode ray oscilloscope. The
action potential of the extensors is led off by surface electrodes on the
calf and a record of it appears below the tension record.

The oscilloscope time base is triggered by contact of the hammer
with the skin over the tendon. The blow itself causes a brief rise in
tension which appears as a small hump before the reflex twitch
begins. The latency of the reflex in this subject, measured from the
contact of the hammer with the skin to the start of the action potential, is 47 milliseconds. Other evidence shows that of this some 35
milliseconds is nerve conduction time from the muscle to the spinal
cord and back again, together with a brief central delay.

For comparison a maximal motor twitch in the extensors, elicited
by an electrical stimulus to the motor nerves in the popliteal fossa, is
shown above. The time base in this record is triggered by the
stimulus. The latency is much shorter and the action potential and
twitch tension are larger. But the duration of the action potential and
the twitch are much the same as in the reflex jerk, showing that the
reflex discharge itself must be a highly synchronous volley of nerve
impulses. (P. A. Merton, unpublished records.)

A special manifestation of the stretch reflex is the tendon jerk, of which the best known example is the knee jerk. With the subject relaxed and his knee bent the tendon below the knee cap is struck a sharp blow with a rubber-covered hammer. The extensor muscles of the knee respond with a brief twitch-like contraction, the jerk. The jerk illustrated in Fig. 19.7 is an ankle jerk. The jerk is reflex, for it disappears if either the sensory or motor fibres to the muscles are interfered with. The latency is very short, about 20 milliseconds for the human knee jerk, little more than is needed for conduction time to the spinal cord and back. Experiments on animals show, in fact, that the central delay is less than a millisecond, time for only one synaptic junction to be passed. The afferent impulses which excite the reflex arise in the fleshy part of the muscle, not in the tendon; striking the tendon is effective only because it causes a sudden rapid slight elongation of the muscle. The initial rapidity of stretch is the essential feature; slower stretch of larger amplitude never elicits a jerk. The initial rate of stretch needed to elicit a tendon jerk is much greater than is normally imposed on the muscles by movements of the joints, or than is used by physiologists to elicit the stretch reflex.

Several other muscles with conveniently accessible tendons exhibit tendon jerks, notably the ankle extensors (the Achilles tendon) and the biceps and triceps muscles of the upper arm. The tendon jerks are of great clinical importance because alterations in them are one of the most sensitive objective indexes available of disease of the nervous system. They disappear if any part of their reflex arc is put out of action; and they are increased if the long motor tracts (pp. 355, 358) connecting the brain with the spinal cord are damaged, probably for the same (unknown) reasons that reflexes are augmented after complete spinal section.

More is known about the nervous mechanism of the stretch reflex than about any other reflex, but even here nothing like a complete account can yet be given and several fundamental properties still lack explanation. The receptors that excite the reflex are the muscle spindles. Muscle contains two special types of receptor; the Golgi tendon organs lie in the tendons and in tendinous bands and aponeuroses within the muscle and respond to a rise of tension whether this is due to contraction of the muscle fibres or to externally applied stretch. The muscle spindles are bundles of modified muscle fibres (intrafusal fibres) with sensory endings wrapped around a short length of the bundle (Fig. 19.8). Impulses are set up when the sensory portion elongates. The muscle spindles lie among the ordinary (extrafusal) muscle fibres and share their attachments; they therefore change length only when the muscle changes length. Hence they signal changes of muscle length. The muscle may shorten in length either because it contracts, in which case the tension rises, or because the load is reduced, in which case the tension falls. Thus tension and length can alter independently in an actively contractile structure (which

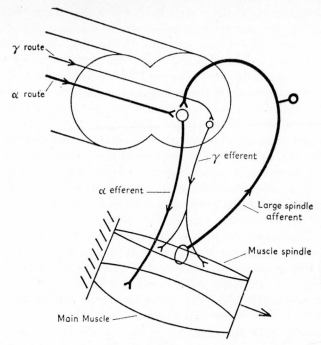

γ route

α route

γ efferent

α efferent

Large spindle afferent

Muscle spindle

Main Muscle

FIG. 19.8. Diagram of the mechanism of the stretch reflex. When the muscle is pulled on, the sensory portion of the muscle spindle is stretched. As a result impulses are sent up the spindle afferent fibre, which reflexly excite the motoneurone of the muscle. Impulses are thus sent down the large motor fibre (α efferent) to the muscle and it contracts.

The sensory portion of the muscle spindle (which is itself non-contractile), is also stretched when the contractile ends of the muscle spindle contract. This they do when motor impulses reach them via their special motor nerves, the γ efferents. Contraction of the ends of the muscle spindle, due to impulses arriving along the γ route, reduces the amount of externally applied stretch that has to be applied to elicit the stretch reflex; or it may even initiate contraction of the main muscle, via the stretch reflex pathway, without any applied stretch. (Hammond, Merton and Sutton, *British Medical Bulletin*, Vol. 12, p. 214, 1956.)

they cannot do in a passive structure such as a spring), so separate sense organs are needed to measure length and tension.

Impulses from spindle sensory endings travel in afferent fibres conducting with a wide range of velocities. The fast ones which are important in the stretch reflex are among the fastest in the body; they belong to the α division of the A group (p. 276), which also includes the motor fibres. These fast spindle afferents run right through the dorsal horn of grey matter to make synaptic contact directly with the dendrites and cell bodies of the motoneurones of the muscle from which they come, thus forming what is called the monosynaptic reflex arc. In a tendon jerk the sudden extension produced by the tap sets up a synchronous volley in the monosynaptic afferents which, when it arrives, excites a substantial fraction of the motoneurones belonging to the muscle stretched, and a twitch results.

A similar reflex occurs if the monosynaptic afferents are excited by an electrical stimulus instead of by a tendon tap. Such a *monosynaptic reflex* can seldom be obtained merely by applying electric shocks to a motor nerve, because a shock large enough to excite the monosynaptic afferents also excites the motor fibres which are in the lowest threshold, fastest conducting group too. As usual, impulses are propagated in both directions from the point of stimulation, so that as well as a volley to the muscle another passes backwards up the motor fibres to the spinal cord (an antidromic volley) at the same time as the volley goes up the monosynaptic afferents. The antidromic motor volley has the effect of inhibiting the motoneurones (antidromic block, see p. 300), so no reflex gets through. To avoid this in animal experiments it is conventional to cut the ventral roots so that the antidromic volley does not reach the cord, and to record the action potential of the reflex volley leaving the cord by placing electrodes on the central stump of the ventral root.

The stretch reflex also employs the fast conducting spindle afferents exciting the motoneurones monosynaptically. Thus both the tendon jerk and the stretch reflex are reflex responses to elongation of a muscle, and both employ the same reflex pathway, but with the stretch reflex an important elaboration makes itself felt, namely changes in muscle spindle activity produced by contraction of the spindle themselves. The intrafusal muscle fibres, except in the zone where the sense-endings lie, are essentially fine striated muscle fibres. They receive a motor innervation from motoneurones lying near the ordinary extrafusal motoneurones in the ventral horn, and when motor impulses reach them they contract. The sensory portion is non-contractile or less contractile, so that when the remainder of the spindle (the two "poles") contracts the sensory part is extended. This causes an increased discharge of sensory impulses, just as if the extension of the sensory ending had been due to extension of the whole muscle. (Contraction of the spindles does not cause the muscle as a whole to develop any appreciable tension, for the total cross section of intrafusal fibre is minute.) The motor nerve fibres that run to the intrafusal muscle are of smaller diameter than those going to extrafusal fibres. They belong to the γ division of the A conduction velocity group, and for this reason they are generally called "γ motor fibres"; those to the main contractile (extrafusal) muscle fibres are "α motor fibres."

Extensions of the sensory endings caused by contraction of the spindles and by stretch of the muscle are additive. It follows that, if the spindles are in a state of steady contraction owing to a stream of impulses reaching them by the γ fibres, less stretch ought to be necessary to elicit the stretch reflex than when the spindles are relaxed. Experiment has shown that this is so. It has been found by direct recording from single a and γ motor fibres, and in other ways, that even when a muscle is quite relaxed (no a discharge) there is a continuing discharge of impulses in γ fibres. The discharge is much more intense in a rigid decerebrate cat than in a spinal cat; the former has readily obtainable stretch reflexes, the latter little or none. The intermediate stages can be demonstrated elegantly by making use of the property of the drug procaine of blocking conduction in small

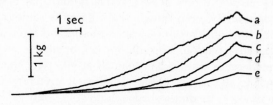

FIG. 19.9. The effect of paralysing the muscle spindles on the stretch reflex of a decerebrate cat. The figure shows superimposed tracings of the tension developed in the soleus muscle during a series of identical extensions, each of 15 mm at a rate of 1·5 mm/sec. The duration of each extension is indicated by the signal line beneath the records. The experimental arrangements were as in Fig. 19.6. The spindles were gradually paralysed by blocking the γ efferents with procaine. Procaine solution (0·2 per cent) was applied to the motor nerve to soleus on a piece of filter paper (see Fig. 19.6.)

Record a was obtained before applying procaine; records b, c and d were obtained when the nerve had been exposed to procaine for 4·5, 6·5 and 10 minutes respectively; record e shows the tension developed in the passive muscle when the stretch reflex had been completely abolished by another method.

After record d the tetanic tension developed by the muscle to electrical stimulation of the nerve central to the procaine block was no less than it was before applying procaine. Hence the diminution in the stretch reflex was not due to blockage of a motor fibres. (P. B. C. Matthews, *Journal of Physiology*, vol. 147, p. 547, 1959.)

nerve fibres before it blocks large ones (see also p. 277). When a drop of procaine solution of the right strength is put on a bared motor nerve it is possible slowly to block the γ fibres without affecting the a fibres. While the γ fibres to an extensor muscle of a decerebrate cat are being blocked in this way the extension required to elicit a stretch reflex increases progressively as block deepens (Fig. 19.9). The spindles are relaxing and a greater stretch is needed to produce the same rate of spindle discharge.

The degree of contraction of the spindles is said to control the "bias" of the stretch reflex. It is suspected that much of the unresponsiveness in spinal shock may be due to lack of bias, "spindle paralysis," due to a cutting off of excitation from the higher parts of the nervous system to the γ motoneurones; conversely, decerebrate rigidity is thought to be associated with "spindle cramp". Whether the increased stretch reflexes and tendon jerks found in muscles rendered spastic by disease of the long motor tracts in man are also due to increased spindle bias is not certain; there is some evidence that they are.

Although the stretch reflex and the tendon jerks are both exaggerated in decerebrate rigidity in animals or in spastic human muscles, and are both diminished if any part of the reflex arc (e.g. the dorsal roots) is damaged, they do not always behave similarly and that is why it is best to treat them separately, even though they share the same reflex pathway. In spinal shock, in light barbiturate anaesthesia, and after damage to the cerebellum (p. 364) tendon jerks of normal briskness may be present when the stretch reflex cannot be obtained at all. Why this should be is not understood; in all these conditions the loss of stretch reflex is probably due, at least in part, to diminished spindle bias, but relaxation of the spindles may have less effect on their response to a sudden jar. In addition there is evidence that the spinal cord may continue to respond to artificially synchronized volleys at a time when normal maintained responses to impulses arriving in an asynchronous stream are lost.

Another uncertainty concerns the part played by the Golgi tendon organs. Various pieces of evidence show that impulses from the tendon organs can inhibit the motoneurones of the muscle from which they come but it is not known to what extent this occurs in the normal stretch reflex. The nearly straight-line relation between extension of the muscle and the tension it exerts, seen in Figs. 19.6 and 19.9, has suggested that the function of the stretch reflex is not merely to pull back as hard as may be when the muscle is stretched, but is to set this particular relation between length and tension. How this is achieved is not known, but clearly a mechanism that causes the muscle to develop a particular tension at each length, might require information about tension from the tendon organs as well as information about length from the spindles. Such a function, however, is at the moment speculative; the accepted rôle for the tendon organs is in the non-linear properties of the stretch reflex. If the knee of a spastic man is forcibly bent at first the exaggerated stretch reflex resists powerfully, but at a certain point resistance collapses. This is called the "clasp-knife" response. A similar reflex response in chronic spinal or decerebrate animals is called the lengthening reaction; it is attributed to impulses from the Golgi tendon organs. There is some evidence that the inhibition acts on the γ motoneurones causing a sudden relaxation of the muscle spindles. The significance of the lengthening reaction is not clear; it is sometimes said to be protective against excessive tension, but this (as Sherrington himself saw) it clearly is not, for it may occur at tensions which must often be exceeded in ordinary life and are obviously not dangerous. The lengthening reaction has an inverse, the shortening reaction; if the bent knee is straightened out it is again found to resist bending; in other words the muscles have gone back to the initial state and the stretch reflex and lengthening reaction can be elicited once more. Much is obscure about the mechanism and significance of the lengthening and shortening reactions, but it is clear they have the tendency to make a limb stay put in whatever position it is made to adopt, in Sherrington's word, they render posture "plastic."

Posture and Locomotion

As already emphasized it is unrewarding to think of posture and loco-motion as reflex responses; how they are carried out is the interesting question, largely unanswered it is hardly necessary to add. The basic mechanisms for both standing and walking lie in the spinal cord, for spinal dogs and cats if allowed enough time to recover from shock will stand, and the hind limbs supported clear of the ground will perform indubitable walking movements in response to such stimuli as a pinch on the buttocks. Spinal standing and walking are imperfect performances; in order to stand and walk in a normal manner a cat or dog requires not only the spinal cord but the brain stem up to the front of the midbrain. In an ordinary rigid decerebrate preparation the midbrain is sectioned between the superior and inferior colliculi. If the section is in front of the superior colliculus, so as to leave behind the red nuclei (Fig. 20.7), decerebrate rigidity does not result and the preparation (known as a mid-brain animal) stands with a normal distribution of contraction between the extensors and flexors of the limbs. Why this should be is not known; decerebrate rigidity is discussed further on p. 370.

The midbrain is also necessary because it is involved in various reflexes that keep the animal balanced on its legs and restore it if it is thrown off balance. A spinal animal falls over very readily. These righting reflexes and other related reflex adjustments of posture are named after Magnus, who described them in detail in the nineteen twenties and demonstrated the various sensory channels they employ. In the midbrain animal the most important are the vestibular balance organs in the labyrinth of the inner ear; they reflexly cause the head to be kept upright. The body reflexly follows the head, but for this to occur the angle between head and body must be known; this is signalled by joint receptors in the neck vertebrae. With both labyrinths destroyed a midbrain animal can still right itself using information from pressure receptors in its flanks. In most intact animals the eyes are of at least as much importance as the balance organs for righting; the rabbit is an exception: its eyes are of no help. The foregoing applies to quadrupeds; in the monkey and in man the basal ganglia are necessary for effective righting and postural reactions to occur (p. 364).

Man has a more difficult balancing task than four-footed animals, particularly if he stands with his feet together; he uses his eyes and differential pressure sensations from the soles of his feet. If sensation in the feet is impaired (as it is for instance in alcoholic neuritis) the patient falls over if he stands with his feet together and then shuts his eyes (Romberg's sign). The labyrinths do not provide sufficiently sensitive information to enable him to balance in this situation. In fact, urban man is little disabled by loss of labyrinthine sense; he can walk and run normally, recover his balance if he is bumped into, and even ride a bicycle. His chief disabilities, as regards equilibrium, are difficulty in walking over uneven or soft ground, particularly in the dark, and a dangerous loss of orientation in water. Such patients are also apt to complain that they cannot see distinctly unless they stand still. This is because of the loss of the important vestibulo-ocular reflexes whose function is to steady the eyes by compensatory movements when the head turns, so that fixation of external objects can be automatically held.

Apart from the general brain stem reflexes concerned with balance there are also individual mechanisms in each limb for throwing the muscles into an appropriate state of contraction when an animal is placed on its feet. Thus when a midbrain animal is held up in the air its limbs hang limply, but as soon as a paw makes contact with the ground the whole limb stiffens into a standing posture; both flexor and extensor muscles contract to fix the joints. This is called the positive supporting reaction. The stimuli immediately responsible are pressure on the pads of the foot and stretch of the muscles to the digits and feet. The positive supporting reaction, however, is by no means just a stretch reflex, for many of the muscles that contract are not stretched at all.

The importance of the stretch reflex in standing has probably been overemphasized in the past. The attitude of a decerebrate cat was interpreted as an exaggeration of normal standing, and the fact that the extensor rigidity is due to greatly augmented stretch reflexes suggested that normal standing could be accounted for in terms of stretch reflexes of a more appropriate vigour. This argument has lost its force now it is known that there is another form of decerebrate rigidity, in which the attitude of the animal is the same, but which does not depend on the stretch reflex (p. 370). Furthermore decerebrate rigidity differs significantly from normal standing in that rigidity involves only extensors whereas both extensors and flexors contract in standing. The truth may prove to be that internal motor mechanisms, so far unknown, cause the appropriate muscles to contract and, as in many other actions (see p. 329), the contracted muscles exhibit stretch reflexes. The stretch reflex is obviously well adapted to oppose the forces that gravity applies to the muscles used in standing. On this view stretch reflexes remain of importance in standing but standing involves much more than the existence of stretch reflexes in extensor muscles.

For locomotion there is better evidence that the mechanism that produces the contractions of the flexors and extensors of a limb (in this case in sequence), does not depend on reflexes from the limb. A chronic spinal cat with all dorsal roots severed behind the spinal section except those belonging to the tail, will still make walking movements of the legs when the tail is pinched. This strongly suggests that the organization of walking is internal, and that walking is not of the nature of a chain reflex, in which movement of a limb forward sets up a reflex to carry it back and so on. Reflexes, however, are no doubt of great importance in modifying and making precise the movements of walking, although definite evidence as to how exactly they do it is lacking.

Chapter 20

THE CENTRAL NERVOUS SYSTEM: II

Voluntary Action

A voluntary action like picking up a pencil involves first seeing and recognizing the pencil and then making the appropriate movement to take hold of it. This description, it will be seen, is of the same form as the description of reflex action that was arrived at in the previous chapter Quite possibly it glosses over some essential difference between voluntary and reflex action, but it takes a good deal of the mystery out of both to emphasize their formal similarity. Of course, voluntary actions are often immensely more complex than reflex actions, and they are attended by consciousness. Physiology has nothing to say about the nature of consciousness except that it is something that seems to accompany the most elaborate reactions of an animal to its environment. It may mean that some fundamentally different kind of process is occurring or it may not. Whichever is the case it certainly makes voluntary actions, in spite of their complexity, easier to think about than reflexes because we have an immediate subjective awareness of the steps involved in a voluntary action (recognition, the decision to make a particular movement, etc.) that can only be reached by indirect argument in the case of a reflex.

In voluntary action the recognition of what is going on in our surroundings and the decision what to do about it both take into account an enormous store of memories of what the messages from our sense organs signified in the past and what the results of previous muscular efforts were. When a large number of factors have to be weighed up simultaneously in this way the brain seems to choose to do the job in a thin sheet of nerve cells the area of which, rather than the thickness, increases as the complexity of the problem increases. Such sheets of grey matter develop on the surface of the brain and are hence called "cortex," from the Latin word meaning outer shell. Conscious voluntary activity takes place, mainly at any rate, in the cerebral cortex; as the old writers put it, it is the organ of mind. In ascending the evolutionary scale the area of the cerebral cortex increases in step with increasing complexity of behaviour, ending with the enormous cerebral cortex of man.

The cerebral cortex has tackled its manifold tasks by subdividing and spreading them out over its surface, the more complex the task the larger the area devoted to it. In man there are large areas devoted to vision, hearing, muscular movement, sensations from the skin surface, etc. In picking up a pencil, there is evidence that seeing the pencil and recognizing it are associated with activity in and around the visual area of the cortex, and that the movements of the arm to pick it up are the responsibility of the area concerned with movement (the motor area). Thus it would appear that the steps into which we subjectively divide the action of picking up the pencil are in fact related to nervous processes occurring in distinct regions of the cerebral cortex. That this is so has only become clear within the last hundred years but already the facts of functional localization in the cortex are so familiar that it is easy to forget that they are not merely an anatomical matter. Just as the idea of separate motor and sensory nerves is now taken so much for granted that we are apt to forget that their discovery was not at the time just a matter of the anatomy of the spinal roots, so too we tend to think that modern neurology has merely answered the anatomical questions, where are functions A, B and C localized in the cortex? But a hundred years ago it was not known what the functions of the cortex were, nor whether they were generalized or localized, so the questions could not have been asked.

Thus the prime importance of the observations which showed a localization of cortical function was to reveal what kinds of function the cortex performs. The story, indeed, is by no means complete yet; there are large areas of which we only know in the most general way what they do, and some functions (e.g. vision) seem to be much more definitely localized than others (e.g. memory, which some people think is not really localized at all, see p. 374), but the main outlines seem clear enough. Roughly speaking the back part of the cerebral cortex is sensory in function and the front part motor, the dividing line being the central sulcus. In the back half of the cortex are areas devoted to vision, hearing, smell and taste, and to sensations from the skin and the body generally (somatic sensations). These areas (except smell and taste) are shown in Fig. 19.3. They are called the primary or receiving areas because messages from the respective sense organs are actually brought by nerve fibres to these areas. The cortex around and between the receiving areas seems to be concerned with interpreting what comes in, with building up a single picture of the external world from the information supplied by all the senses and with assessing the significance of what is going on. One highly specialized aspect of this general function with which special areas are associated is the comprehension of speech and the written word.

The front half of the cortex is concerned with the execution of motor acts and in a general way with planning. The detailed orders to the muscles to perform particular movements are sent out by the cortex just in front of the central sulcus. Again speech gets special treatment; its motor organization occupies a patch of cortex (Broca's area) in front of the main motor area, in the left hemisphere.

The motor area and the four sensory areas (somatic, visual, auditory and olfactory) are the only parts of the cortex which have large and obvious tracts of nerve fibres connecting them to other parts of the nervous system; for this reason they are often referred to collectively as projection areas; the parts in between, which are principally connected to other parts of the cortex, are called association areas; formerly they were called silent areas because electrical stimulation or surgical removal of these areas, particularly in animals, is often without obvious effect. In lower mammals the projection areas occupy a large part of the cortex but in man the proportion is quite small. A man's eyes, ears and hands are not much better than those of a chimpanzee, nor are the absolute sizes of the cortical areas to which they project greatly different; he is superior chiefly because of the far greater use he makes of the information from his sense organs and the far greater skill with which he uses his hands; this he owes to his enormously expanded association areas.

In man, and indeed in nearly all vertebrates, the most important source of information about the environment is vision. What we see occupies so much of our attention that with the great majority of mankind it can be assumed that if their eyes are shut they will not be attending to anything; conversely, though we can, by concentrating, disregard many sounds, smells and bodily sensations, it is very difficult indeed not to pay attention to what is passing before our eyes. The dominance of vision makes it natural to begin the more detailed discussion of the cerebral cortex with vision, more particularly since the anatomical peculiarities of the visual pathway have effects which are felt throughout the whole of the nervous system.

The Visual System

In man it is established with great certainty that damage to the occipital lobes causes blindness, and that lesions (i.e. areas of damage) elsewhere in the cerebral cortex never have this result. Hence we speak of a visual sensory area in the occipital lobes. When a lesion is small and circumscribed, blindness is limited to a particular part of the visual field. This result could not have been foreseen; for supposing, speaking metaphorically, the visual cortex had functioned like a lens to focus nerve impulses from the retina on to consciousness, then putting out of action one part of it would have caused a general dimming of the whole field and it would not have mattered which part was involved, only the total area would count. There may be functions of the brain, such as memory, in which the same disability might be produced by lesions in different areas of the cortex in this way and in these cases it is sometimes written that they are functions of the cortex "as a whole". We shall return to the question later but vision at any rate is very clearly not like that; blindness only results from cortical lesions if they are in the occipital lobe and blindness in a certain part of the field of vision can only be produced by a lesion in a certain area within the visual cortex.

Optic nerve fibres from the retina do not run direct to the visual cortex but go to the lateral geniculate bodies, two nuclei lying on the under side of each thalamus at the base of the cerebral hemispheres; from the neurones in them large tracts of nerve fibres arise, called the optic radiations, which curve backwards to the occipital cortex (Fig. 20.1). Now over most of the cerebral hemispheres the cortical grey matter is remarkably uniform in

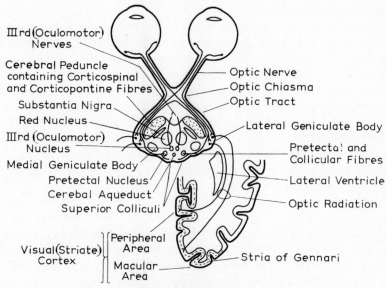

FIG. 20.1. The human visual pathways. Horizontal sections, roughly to scale, are shown of the right occipital lobe and of the upper part of the midbrain adjoining the thalamus. Some non-visual structures in the midbrain are also labelled.

The pretectal and collicular fibres are separate optic nerve fibres and not branches of geniculate fibres as the diagram has it.

naked eye appearance, consisting of a featureless sheet some 2 mm. thick, but the area to which the visual radiation runs is distinguished by a conspicuous white band (of nerve fibres) in the middle of the grey matter, called the stria of Gennari; hence the visual area is also known as the striate cortex. The function of the stria is unknown. In man, part of the striate area is on the tip of the occipital pole but the greater part is out of sight in the deep groove where the medial surfaces of the two hemispheres face each other.

By no means all optic nerve fibres go to the lateral geniculate bodies and thence to the cortex. In lower animals like fish, frogs and birds the main visual pathway runs to the optic lobes on the dorsal side of the midbrain, and even in man 20–30 per cent of all fibres from the retina go past the geniculate bodies and end in the same region of the midbrain, known in higher animals as the superior colliculi (superior corpora quadrigemina), or in the grey matter deep to the colliculi (pretectal nuclei). Animal experiments indicate that the pretectal fibres are responsible for the contraction of the pupil when a light is shone in the eye, but there is no evidence about the function of the very numerous collicular fibres in man. It is a fair surmise that they are involved in automatic control of eye movements but only a surmise. The visual projection to the cerebellum is via the superior colliculi.

Even in primitive vertebrates visual impulses from external objects to the right hand side of an animal are fed to the left half of the brain and vice versa. The reason for this crossing over, or *decussation*, is not properly understood although it is often thought to be a consequence of the reversal of the optical image caused by the camera-like structure of the vertebrate eye with its single lens. To remember the scheme on which the different parts of the retinae are projected on to the human visual cortex it is convenient to think first of an imaginary man with a single central eye. The natural method seems to be for the upper part of the retina to be connected to the upper part of the visual area and the lower part to the lower part; the right hand side to the right hand half of the visual area, i.e. to the right occipital pole; and the left hand side to the left occipital pole. The two real eyes both see almost the same field and each has the same connections as the hypothetical single eye, which means that fibres from the nasal halves of each retina have to cross in the optic chiasma. As a matter of fact things are not quite so simple because although it is true that fibres from the right hand halves of both retinae go to the right hand occipital cortex, with upper retinal fibres keeping to the top and lower to the bottom, a reversal has occurred such that the central part of the field (the macula) is not represented *medially* as it ought to be, if the above scheme were carried through, but *laterally* and the peripheral retina is represented medially, i.e. on the opposed surface of the hemispheres (Fig. 20.1). Thus if we imagine an object moving from left to right in front of a man who gazes steadily straight ahead, the area of cortical activity representing the object starts on the right striate cortex deep in the groove where it faces its fellow; it then moves posteriorly and laterally on to the tip of the occipital pole; when the object is dead ahead the active area jumps over to the opposite pole and moves medially and anteriorly down on to the medial surface again.

Part of the evidence for the above statements is that division of one optic tract, or removal of the whole of one occipital lobe in man, results in complete blindness of the opposite half of the visual field of both eyes (a hemianopia). The vertical division of the visual field between left and right cerebral hemispheres revealed in this way seems to be quite sharp and splits even the macula, the part of the retina we use when looking straight at an object, straight down the middle. It is perhaps rather surprising that, when a small object moves from one side to the other of the central line and its area of cortical representation jumps from one hemisphere to the other, there is no trace of discontinuity in our sensation. Of course the two visual areas are connected together by enormous numbers of nerve fibres running in the corpus callosum (Fig. 19.3), and these connections may be important in welding them into a functional whole (but see p. 374). But division of the whole corpus callosum has been performed several times in man with remarkably little effect at all, and in particular with no conspicuous visual symptoms.

We have seen that the retinae are, as it were, mapped on to the visual cortex, but nothing has been said as to scale. Here we come on the most notable instance of the general rule that the area of cortex devoted to a part of the body depends on its importance and not on its size. The total area of visual cortex is not far different from the area of the two retinae but something like half the total area of visual cortex is probably devoted to the macula, the central part of the retina about 1 mm. in diameter where visual acuity is highest. Thus the macula occupies a very much larger area on the cortex than it does on the retina.

When a lesion of the striate cortex causes a scotoma (a localized area of blindness) vision is lost as a whole in that area; it never happens, for instance, that colour vision is lost selectively, or that threshold to perception of light remains unaltered but objects cannot be perceived; all these functions are affected together, although in partially damaged areas not necessarily to the same degree. Scotomata, whether of cortical origin or due to damage to the retina or other parts of the visual pathway, can often only be found by careful examination, for patients are frequently unaware of them. Indeed with blindness of cortical origin they may deny that they have any trouble in seeing when they are grossly disabled. It is a general characteristic of cortical lesions, which goes under the name of anosognosia, that patients may lack insight into their condition and may not complain of their disability. This may seem less odd if we reflect that no one would expect a man who had had the whole of his cerebral cortex removed to realize how stupid he was. To remember what it was like to be intelligent he would have to be intelligent still. Similarly the visual cortex is not only the part of the cortex that does the seeing; it seems also to be the part that knows what seeing is.

The parts of the occipital lobe around the striate area and the posterior part of the parietal lobe adjoining it appear to be concerned with interpreting what we see with the striate cortex. The symptoms of disease in this region (collectively known as visual agnosia) are very various and fascinating, but there is only space to mention a few. To start with one that has been mentioned already, damage to the posterior part of the parietal lobe may abolish the reflex blink to a threatening gesture. Such a patient may have no detectable interference with vision and certainly sees a fist approaching, but his brain fails to interpret it as a threat, at any rate in time to do anything about it. Other lesions may upset judgement of distances. The patient may state that he clearly sees a chair placed in front of him, and yet when invited to step forward he walks straight into it and appears surprised to find it there. In these cases the disability may not be confined to a failure to judge distance, but may extend to a general inability to grasp the spatial relations of objects to each other and to himself. With his eyes open he may be unable to find his way about a house he has lived in for years, and paradoxically, may manage better blindfold, feeling his way. If five pennies are put on the table before him he cannot count them because, as it were, he never knows where he has got to. Another manifestation of disease in this region is the failure to recognize things which nevertheless are seen clearly enough. The patient when shown various common objects such as a box of matches or a pair of scissors, etc., may not be able to put names to them or describe what they are used for, although he can do so at once when allowed to handle them. The frequently associated inability to read will be discussed later under the subject of speech.

The ultimate problem of how the information contained in the optical image focussed on the retina is conveyed to the brain and handled there has begun to yield in recent years to the technique of recording from single neurones in the visual pathway. Retinal ganglion cells in the cat respond to, or are inhibited by, light falling on the receptors in a circular patch surrounding the cell, i.e. they have circular or concentric receptive fields (see p. 440). The next neurones on the pathway, the cells of the lateral geniculate body (whose axons end in the visual cortex) are likewise influenced from concentric fields in the retina. In the visual cortex, Hubel and Wiesel have discovered that the great majority of cells do not respond at all to general illumination of the retina, and only poorly to small circular patches of light, which are efficient stimuli for retinal ganglion cells and for the geniculate cells. For cortical cells the preferred stimuli are linear, bright lines of light on a dark background, or dark bars on a bright ground, or straight edges (boundaries between light and dark areas). Each cell responds best to a line stimulus with a particular orientation, and gives no response to a stimulus perpendicular to this optimal orientation. Cortical cells fall into two classes: "simple" cells, which respond to line stimuli (suitably orientated) presented at one particular position in the visual field only. Simple cells respond to moving line stimuli only when the line passes across this position. "Complex" cells are not so positionally sensitive. They respond to suitably orientated line stimuli anywhere within a certain area of the visual field. And they give a sustained discharge to such stimuli moving across this area.

Hubel and Wiesel also found that the visual cortex is divided into functional columns, each about half a millimetre across, extending through the whole thickness of grey matter. (No corresponding segmentation is to be seen microscopically.) All the responsive cells in a column have the same optimal orientation for line stimuli, but they differ in whether they prefer bright lines, dark bars, or edges. In each column some of the cells are simple and some are complex. The centres of their receptive fields are scattered over a region of retina comparable in size to the receptive field of a single complex cell. Neighbouring columns respond to stimuli in the same region of retina, but the preferred orientation varies randomly from column to column.

In the human subject, responses of the visual cortex to flash illumination of the whole visual field can be recorded with surface electrodes on the scalp. Similar "evoked responses", but of a much smaller voltage, can also be detected to movement of quite small continuously illuminated patterned objects (e.g. a grating of light and dark bars). To see these small responses clearly, repetitive stimulation is employed and successive responses are added up in a special computer. This multiplies the size of the evoked response while at the same time averaging out the spontaneous irregular activity of the brain. Such averaging techniques, originally developed by Dawson in 1951, are nowadays widely used for the study of small evoked potential changes in all parts of the nervous system.

The Auditory and Olfactory Pathways

The auditory area of the cortex is in the temporal lobe, in man in the part opposite the bottom end of the central sulcus (Fig. 19.3). Impulses from the ears reach the auditory cortex via the VIIIth nerve nucleus in the medulla and the medial geniculate body (Fig. 20.1). In addition to this geniculate pathway there are a large number of fibres that run to nuclei in the medulla and midbrain, notably to the inferior colliculus (Fig. 20.2). The automatic turning of the head and eyes towards a source of sound is suspected to be one function of these pathways (compare the visual fibres to the superior colliculus). The geniculate pathway is mainly crossed but a substantial fraction is not; each geniculate body and hence each auditory cortex is in connection with both ears. The result is that, in contrast to vision, damage to one auditory area or to the auditory pathway on one side does not cause marked deafness. As lesions large enough to affect both pathways are likely to be fatal, deafness is a rare symptom of disease of the brain. Because of this much less is known about hearing than about vision, even the position of the auditory area is not clearly delimited in man.

Electrical recording from the exposed cerebral cortex of the anaesthetized dog has shown that impulses excited by notes of different frequencies go to different points on the auditory cortex. The frequencies are spread out along a strip, high notes in front and low notes behind. Each octave occupies about 2 mm. of the strip. In man a jump of an octave in pitch gives the same subjective impression in whatever part of the scale it occurs. The frequency mapping in man may be quite different from that in the dog, but it is certainly very suggestive that in the dog a jump of an octave always moves the point of arrival of impulses the same distance along the cortex.

Signals from the balance organs of the inner ear play little part in conscious life, unless powerful stimulation makes us giddy or sea-sick (see also p. 337). The cortical area dealing with vestibular sense appears to be in the temporal lobe near the auditory area.

The parts of the cortex concerned with smell (and taste) are hidden away underneath the cerebral hemispheres. The olfactory nerves go to the olfactory bulbs under the frontal lobes and these are connected to the olfactory area of the cortex in the uncinate region under the temporal lobe. Smell is a relatively unimportant sense in man, and the olfactory parts of the brain are poorly developed. It still has survival value by occasionally giving an invaluable danger signal of a fire or a gas-leak, but loss of smell is a small disability compared with the loss of any of the other senses, although enjoyment of food is much diminished for it depends largely on the sense of smell. Uncinate epilepsy is mentioned later (p. 373).

Somatic Sensation

Afferent nerve fibres from sense-endings in the skin and the interior of the body are gathered together into peripheral nerve trunks and run to the spinal cord via the dorsal roots. The cell bodies of these nerve fibres lie in ganglia on the dorsal roots (Fig. 19.1). These particular cell bodies are merely trophic centres; nothing of nervous interest happens in a dorsal root ganglion, impulses just pass through as if it were an ordinary piece of nerve. On entering the cord afferent fibres divide into ascending and descending branches; from these branches arise collateral branches that run into the grey matter for reflex purposes.

Ascending branches that carry messages destined for the brain, to arouse conscious sensation, do one of two things (Figs. 20.2 and 20.3), either they immediately enter the dorsal column (on the same side they enter) and run straight up to the dorsal column nuclei in the medulla, or, after ascending for a segment or two, they terminate by making synaptic contact with nerve cells in the grey matter of the dorsal horn. The axons of these cells run all the way to the thalamus, the main sensory nucleus of the brain, which lies near the midline at the base of the cerebral hemispheres; to get there they cross the midline and run up the opposite side of the spinal cord in the ventro-lateral column of white matter. The tract is called the spinothalamic tract, but it is not a clearly demarcated area of white matter like the tracts in the dorsal columns. The fibres composing it are mixed in among a much larger number of descending fibres and other ascending fibres.

The axons that arise from the cells of the dorsal column nuclei in the medulla also cross the midline and run to the opposite thalamus. In the medulla they form a conspicuous slab-like band of white matter called the median fillet. Thus all nerve impulses that give rise to conscious sensation find their way to the opposite thalamus; either they run up the dorsal column on the same side as they enter the cord and cross over

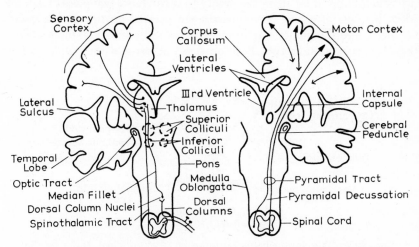

FIG. 20.2. Diagrammatic coronal (frontal) sections of the human brain to show the sensory and motor pathways. Plane of section indicated on Fig. 19.3. Roughly to scale except that the diameter of the brain stem and spinal cord is exaggerated. Some structures, shown here but not labelled, are labelled on Fig. 20.7. For spinal tracts see also Fig. 20.3. The outlines of the colliculi on the dorsal surface of the midbrain shown dotted. The median fillet is also known as the medial lemniscus.

immediately above the dorsal column nuclei, or they cross within a few segments of entering the cord and run up the opposite spinothalamic tract. These facts are important because the two pathways do not carry the same types of sensation. The spinothalamic pathway conveys sensations of pain, temperature and crudely localized mechanical contact. The dorsal columns are responsible for all the more refined types of touch sensation, such as we possess pre-eminently in our finger tips, and for sensations of position and movement of the limbs.

The result of this segregation of sensory pathways is that lesions of the spinal cord other than complete division seldom cause a complete loss of all forms of sensation in any part of the body, such as occurs when a peripheral nerve is divided. As a rule spinal disease causes a *dissociated sensory loss* in which some forms of sensation are lost and some retained. The clearest instance is when injury or disease sections either the right or the left half of the spinal cord, giving rise to what is known as Brown-Séquard's syndrome. Below the level of hemisection the patient suffers a loss of dorsal column sensation on the side of the lesion and a loss of spinothalamic sensation on the opposite side.

The dorsal column loss shows itself by an inability to localize contacts; if one of his fingers is touched the patient will feel it but be unable to say which finger it is; again the ability to distinguish two points from one when the tips of a pair of compasses are pressed on the skin is greatly impaired, and the points may have to be opened out several inches before they are recognized as two. Position sense is lost and the patient cannot

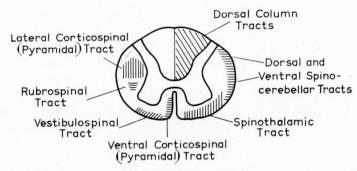

FIG. 20.3. The approximate positions of the principal tracts in the human spinal cord, ascending tracts on the right, descending tracts on the left.

say what position his joints are in or whether they are being flexed or extended by an examiner. The loss of discriminative tactile sense and the loss of position sense together prevent him from recognizing the size, shape and texture of objects which are put in his affected hand; this important symptom is called astereognosis and it makes the affected hand useless for most purposes.

The spinothalamic loss on the opposite side of the body makes the patient insensitive to pain, however aroused, and incapable of distinguishing hot from cold objects. No straightforward tactile loss is detectable for dorsal column sensation remains on that side but the loss of the spinothalamic type of tactile sensibility can sometimes be detected by the absence of sensations of itching and tickling. Itch and tickle are curious quasi-painful sensations that are believed to be carried in the spinothalamic tracts. The principal symptoms, therefore, are astereognosis and loss of position sense on the side of the section and loss of pain and temperature sensation on the opposite side—a dissociated loss. Simple contact, e.g. a brush with a piece of cotton wool, is felt everywhere because it can travel by either the direct or the crossed pathway.

Both the ascending sensory pathways eventually end in the ventral part of the thalamus; from these a large tract of fibres (forming the posterior part of the internal capsule) runs to the strip of cerebral cortex behind the central sulcus, the (somatic) sensory area (Fig. 19.3). Destruction of the sensory area in man causes a loss of sensibility over the opposite half of the body; but, whereas loss of one occipital lobe gives rise to permanent complete blindness in the crossed half-field (p. 344), even very extensive damage in the sensory area does not cause permanent complete anaesthesia on the opposite side of the body. Except, perhaps, for a day or two after an acute lesion such patients are found still to appreciate pain, differences of temperature, and ill-localized contact on the opposite side of the body. The interpretation of this phenomenon is controversial but the simplest view, originally put forward by Head and Holmes, is that consciousness of these sensations depends in some way on activity in the thalamus. All the more highly developed forms of sensation require the integrity of the sensory area of the cortex. Roughly speaking, sensations associated with the thalamus are of the type carried in the spinothalamic tracts, and sensations permanently lost after cortical damage are those carried in the dorsal columns. The former tend to be associated with feelings of pleasure or of unpleasantness, warmth, cold and pain (see pp. 358, 361 and 394 for further evidence that the central parts of the brain are concerned in emotion); but cortical sensations, such as distinguishing two compass points from one, are without emotional colour.

Lesions of the thalamus itself, besides causing a loss of sensation, may lead (after an interval of some weeks) to spontaneous and intractable pain, referred to the opposite side of the body; or it may happen that, without spontaneous pain, a stimulus such as a light pin-prick may cause disproportionately severe pain. Such symptoms, which constitute part of the *thalamic syndrome*, never, or almost never, occur with lesions of the sensory cortex (or indeed with lesions anywhere else in the brain), which is another reason for thinking that the thalamus is particularly concerned in appreciation of pain.

Lesions localized to a part of the sensory area cause loss of sensation in a particular part of the body in the same way that small lesions of the occipital cortex cause a localized patch of blindness in the visual field. In man the extent of the sensory area and the way the body is represented on it have been learnt mainly from the results of local damage, and by stimulation of the exposed cortex at operation. The brain substance itself and its immediate coverings are insentient, so that operations on the brain can be performed with only a local anaesthetic to insensitize the skin. It is then a simple matter to stimulate a point on the brain electrically by passing a low voltage 50 cycles alternating current between a round-tipped wire electrode resting on the cortex and an indifferent plate electrode on the skin elsewhere. When the electrode is on the post-central cortex the patient has a sensation which he feels in some part of the opposite side of his body. The electrical stimulus presumably does not imitate the normal pattern of activity caused by sensory impulses arriving at the cortex, for the sensation is indefinite and unfamiliar, not unlike the sensation from electrical stimulation of a cutaneous nerve (p. 320), but there is no reason to doubt that it indicates which part of the body normally sends sensory impulses to the point being excited. (With

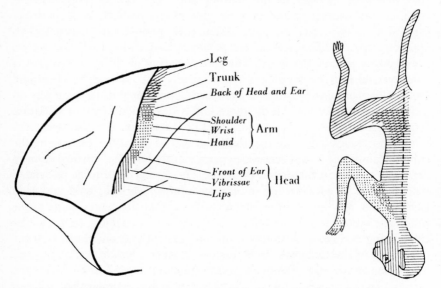

Leg
Trunk
Back of Head and Ear
Shoulder
Wrist } Arm
Hand
Front of Ear
Vibrissae } Head
Lips

FIG. 20.4. The somatic sensory area in a rhesus monkey, showing the large area devoted to the hand and face. The trunk region includes the back of the neck and head. (Adrian, *Journal of Physiology*, vol. 100, p. 159, 1941.)

strong stimulation the referred sensations may become painful, an observation which suggests that the cortex is not wholly unconcerned in the appreciation of pain.) In this way it has been found that the body is mapped upside down on the sensory area; messages from the foot and leg go to the top of post-central cortex, the middle region is concerned with the hand and arm, and the bottom with the face. As with vision the scale of mapping is very uneven; important parts, like the fingers, have a large area devoted to them, the skin of the back a very small area.

In animals the sensory area can be mapped by recording electrically the places which receive impulses when particular parts of the body are touched. The animal has to be fairly deeply anaesthetized to cut down the noisy background of spontaneous activity in the cortex. Then a fine

wire inserted into the cortex will detect sensory impulses arriving. Inter-
estingly enough although they have crossed at least two synaptic junctions
(in the dorsal column nuclei and the thalamus) the trains of impulses
from the sense-endings are little modified and what arrives at the cortex
is very much like what can be recorded from sensory fibres in peripheral
nerve. The difference is that with parts of the body, such as the back,
in which the cortex is not much interested, several or many sense-endings
may share a single projection fibre, so that touches at widely separated
points, supplied by different spinal nerves, all cause activity in the same
cortical fibre. Fig. 20.4 shows Adrian's map of the sensory area in the
monkey, which is not unlike that of a man.

In other animals the rule that only important matters get a hearing in
the cortex is sometimes even more obvious than in the monkey and man.

FIG. 20.5. The somatic sensory area in the pig. The whole area is
devoted to the opposite half of the snout. (Adrian, *Brain*, vol. 66,
p. 89, 1943.)

A pig uses its snout not only for finding its food but also for digging it
up; it is a pig's principal executive organ; the legs are little more than
props for the body. Adrian found that the snout, so far as he could tell,
was the only part of the body that sent sensory impulses to the cortex.
The whole somatic sensory area was snout (Fig. 20.5). And the absolute
area of cortex devoted to the pig's snout was larger relative to its size than
the area of human cortex concerned with the hand. Other mammals also
devote much of the sensory area to the nose and lips, particularly when they
bear vibrissae (the long hairs with which cats and rats feel their way in the
dark), but if the legs are used for fighting or digging they also are represented.

As regards the crossing over of sensory pathways by which sensory
impulses from one side of the body are carried to the thalamus and cortex
of the opposite side, the accepted explanation is that this occurs in order

that they should be dealt with on the same side of the brain that deals with vision for their side of the body. The mammalian brain is dominated by vision, and because the visual representation of external objects on the cortex is crossed (the left striate area dealing with the right half of the visual field and so on) everything that has to be correlated with vision crosses too; that includes not only somatic sensation but hearing and the motor pathways too. It lends support to the correctness of this view that when, exceptionally, somatic sensations are to be correlated with olfaction, whose pathway does not decussate, the somatic pathway remains uncrossed too. Thus Adrian found in ruminants (the sheep and goat) in whom smell is probably the main guide to what is to be eaten next, that the sensory area for the lips was uncrossed. The remainder of the body had a crossed representation as usual. In the cat and in other animals in which vision is used in feeding the cortical representation of the lips was crossed.

In man the symptoms of damage to the somatic sensory area, say the region concerned with the hand, are in the first place loss of all delicate, discriminative skin sensations by which objects are recognized and fine manipulations directed. The patient also tends to be inattentive to the affected hand, so that if quantitative testing of sensation is attempted, performance is irregular. If touched simultaneously on both hands he may fail to notice the touch on the affected hand, although he does so all right if it is touched alone. It seems that the affected hand tends to slip out of his mind; indeed with large lesions it may go out of his mind altogether, giving rise to the bizarre symptom that the patient when shown the affected hand denies that it belongs to him. He has apparently lost the part of the brain that deals with his conception of his hand. This is analogous to the patient with damage to the occipital lobes who is not aware that he cannot see. Needless to say a severe cortical sensory loss renders the hand useless, and, although it is not paralysed, to an onlooker it may appear to be, for the patient attempts nothing with it.

The Voluntary Motor System

The orders that the cerebral cortex issues to the muscles of the body leave from a strip of cortex in front of the central sulcus called the motor area (Fig. 19.3). If the motor area is damaged or removed the patient develops a voluntary paralysis on the opposite side of the body. He knows what he wants to do but when he tries to move the affected parts nothing happens. Lesions elsewhere in the cortex never have this result; this is the first reason for regarding the precentral cortex as an area specially devoted to voluntary movement.

Movements of different parts of the body are dealt with by different parts of the motor area; the arrangement matches that in the sensory area on the opposite side of the central sulcus, leg and foot at the top,

arm and hand in the middle and face at the bottom. Fig. 20.6 shows the
motor area of a chimpanzee. The human motor map is known to be very
much the same but a detailed map of a whole healthy human motor area
is not available. As in the sensory cortex there are large areas for important
parts like the hand and only small areas for parts like the buttocks which
have little to do directly with voluntary activities. Since on the whole
important parts are small and large parts unimportant it turns out that

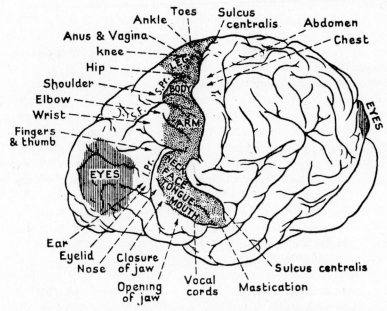

FIG. 20.6. The motor area of a chimpanzee mapped by electrical stimulation. There is much overlapping of the regions and their subdivisions which the diagram does not attempt to indicate.
Conjugate eye movements can be obtained by stimulating the
visual area in the occipital lobes and also from the frontal lobe in
front of the motor area. These movements (not mentioned in the
text) differ in their characteristics from movements obtained from the
ordinary precentral motor area. (Sherrington, "The Integrative
Action of the Nervous System": New York 1906, Cambridge
1947.)

roughly speaking the area of cortex devoted to a part of the body is inversely
proportional to its bulk. It is presumably because sensation, particularly
touch, is of such great importance in guiding movement that the cortical
area which controls the movement of a part lies next door to the area to
which it sends its sensory messages. In fact the motor and sensory areas
to some extent run into each other, for when stimulating points on the
exposed human cortex electrically it is found that sensations (referred to
the opposite side of the body) are sometimes felt when the electrode is

on the precentral cortex, and movement sometimes results when the electrode is on the postcentral cortex.

Movements of the opposite side of the body elicited by electrical stimulation are a hall-mark of the motor area. The ease with which movements can be obtained by electrical stimulation of the motor area, compared with the impossibility of obtaining movements from most other places in the cortex, is the second reason for linking the precentral area with the control of voluntary movement. The movements occur in the same part of the body which would become paralysed if the region of cortex around the stimulating electrode were excised. Thus the way in which the parts of the body are mapped on to the motor cortex can be discovered by electrical stimulation.

The motor area is connected to the spinal cord by numerous fibres running in the corticospinal or pyramidal tract (Fig. 20.2). The pyramidal tracts descend in the internal capsule between thalamus and basal ganglia; they occupy part of the cerebral peduncles on the ventral surface of the midbrain, pass through the pons and emerge to form two swellings, the pyramids (not shown in any of the figures), on the ventral surface of the medulla. Most of the fibres cross the midline in the pyramidal decussation to enter the opposite lateral column of the spinal cord (Fig. 20.3). A fraction (of unknown function) remain uncrossed and pass down the cord on the same side, mainly in the ventral column. Other fibres initially taking a similar course branch away to the motor nuclei of the cranial nerves (corticobulbar fibres).

The largest and fastest conducting fibres arise from exceptionally large neurones called Betz cells, of a size not found elsewhere in the cortex, but these are in a minority; by far the greater number of fibres from the motor area arise from ordinary small cortical cells. The pyramidal tracts (defined as the tracts that form the medullary pyramids) also contain very many corticospinal fibres (of obscure function) from the so-called premotor areas in front of the motor areas and from the sensory areas and adjacent parts of the parietal lobes behind them. In all there are more than half a million fibres in each pyramidal tract in man, but only some 30,000 Betz cells in each motor area.

The corticospinal and corticobulbar tracts represent only a small proportion of the efferent fibres from the motor cortex. There are also very large numbers of fibres carrying messages to the pons, for the cerebellum (p. 364), and other numerous *extrapyramidal* fibres to the motor nuclei at the base of the brain (p. 361 and Fig. 20.7).

The motor area was historically the first part of the cerebral cortex that was clearly shown to have a specific function. As so often in the central nervous system the first evidence came from the study of human patients. The central nervous system in its bony case is so difficult for the experimenter to get at and the results of operating on it are so difficult to evaluate in animals, who cannot be given instructions to attempt various movements or be asked to describe what sensations they have, that in many instances the first clues to the function of a part of the brain have come from the destructive experiments that disease performs in man. In fact to this day the parts of the brain about which we are most ignorant, such as the basal ganglia of the cerebral hemispheres or the olives in the medulla (see p. 361 and Fig. 20.7), are mainly those which do not suffer localized clear-cut destruction in disease.

The first definite indication of a localization of motor function in the cortex came with Broca's publication in 1854 of three cases of loss of speech associated with lesions in the lower precentral region of the left hemisphere. More precise information came from another direction. With the cerebral cortex it is not only destructive lesions that provide evidence, for the cortex is also prone to those paroxysmal bursts of over-activity which are the cause of epileptic fits (convulsions). This sort of instability seems to be peculiar to the cortical grey matter. The unsolved question of what happens in the cortex during an epileptic fit is a matter of physiology, not pathology, for anyone will have a fit if his brain is stimulated sufficiently violently. A convulsion triggered off by passing 50 cycles per second alternating current through the head is a standard and effective method of treatment in various psychiatric disorders, while in normal infants convulsions not uncommonly occur during teething, or ushering in an acute infective illness. In sufferers from epilepsy similar convulsions occur spontaneously. In a typical fit the whole cortex is involved more or less simultaneously, the patient loses consciousness and then has a generalized convulsion. Much less often convulsive movements begin in one part of the body only and spread to involve the remainder of that side of the body and then the other side.

Epilepsy is usually not associated with any changes in the naked-eye or microscopical appearance of the brain, but sometimes it is precipitated by obvious damage, a cerebral tumour or the scars of a brain injury. In the early 1860s Hughlings Jackson observed that convulsions starting uni-laterally (still known as Jacksonian fits) were associated with damage to the precentral region of the opposite hemisphere. When the fit began in the foot the lesion was at the top of the precentral region; with lesions in the middle the hand was involved first and so on. The commonest sites for the fits to start were the feet, the fingers and hand, and the corner of the mouth. From these facts Jackson inferred that the precentral gyrus is the cortical centre for movements, and that within it the body is represented upside down with the largest areas concerned with movements of the important "leading parts". The manner of spread of the convulsion, the "march" as he called it, reflected the spread of epileptic activity over the motor cortex, involving one area after another.

Jackson went further, and, in one of the very few successful predictions of new phenomena in biology, concluded that electrical stimulation of the precentral cortex in animals would be found to cause movements of the opposite limbs—an experiment soon afterwards successfully performed by Fritsch and Hitzig in the dog. Previous to this it had been generally held that the cerebral cortex was electrically inexcitable. Before the end of the century electrical stimulation had been used to map out the motor area in many species of animals and in man.

The paralysis caused by a lesion of the motor cortex is of a highly distinctive character and distribution. The actions lost or most severely weakened are the most voluntary and least automatic, the most accurately graded and individual movements in which the limb is usually employed, the sort of movements out of which skilled actions such as writing or driving a car are made up. Movements of this type employ predominantly the distal parts of the limbs, particularly the hands and it is here that the paralysis makes itself most felt, the proximal parts are less affected, while bilateral movements of the trunk are preserved. As already mentioned (p. 314), expressive and emotional movements of the face tend to be much less affected than movements made to order.

Within the hand itself the same principle applies; the most highly specialized movements are the most paralysed. The ability to move single fingers independently of the others is the first thing to go, so that the patient may lose manual dexterity completely while retaining a powerful grip. The same muscles move each finger whether they are flexed one at a time or all together, but the one movement is lost and the other is not. From this and many similar instances it is clear that it is not the muscles themselves that are paralysed but only certain movements carried out by them. The motor cortex, even more obviously than the spinal cord, "thinks" in terms of movements, not muscles.

Electrical stimulation of the human motor cortex exposed at operation under local anaesthesia causes fragmentary movements of just the type that are lost when the same area is removed. They predominantly involve the distal parts of the limbs, fingers and toes, wrist and ankle, and include a large proportion of discrete movements of the thumb and individual fingers of just the sort that a patient with a cortical palsy cannot make. Similar movements can be obtained after the grey matter has been removed, by stimulating the cut ends of the fibres in the white matter underneath; hence stimulation of the cortex reveals mainly the properties of the efferent pathways and if, as seems probable, the cortex itself has the function of organizing complete actions from combinations and sequences of these fragmentary movements, this activity is not put into motion by the type of electrical stimulation employed.

Some writers have argued that movements are represented in the motor cortex in the same sense that movements could be said to be represented in the skin; appropriate patterns of excitation can call forth elaborate muscular actions, but simple electrical stimulation of the skin or the cortex only discovers the most elementary. The analogy is a good one, for corticospinal fibres end mainly and cutaneous fibres end exclusively on interneurones and not on the motoneurones themselves. Both appear to activate the spinal mechanisms that synthesize functional movements out of contractions of individual muscles. The ease with which movements of the digits are obtained by cortical stimulation is partly a property of the spinal cord, for these are also the movements most readily obtained in spinal men and spinal monkeys by mechanical stimulation of the skin (e.g. the extensor plantar response, p. 325) or by electrical excitation of the sensory nerve fibres. Thus the great importance of the distal parts of the limbs in voluntary life is reflected in the spinal motor mechanisms, and it is the large area of cortex connected to these mechanisms that cortical stimulation reveals.

In man voluntary paralysis is commonly the result of rupture of fibres leaving the motor cortex by haemorrhage from a burst blood vessel near the internal capsule. The patient has an "apoplexy" or "stroke," i.e. suddenly has his senses and his power of motion taken from him, and is subsequently found to be paralysed down one side of his body (a hemiplegia). The plantar response (p. 325) on the paralysed side becomes extensor (upgoing big toe) from the onset. As usual after any sudden damage to the brain a good deal of recovery of function takes place in the next few weeks, possibly due to recovery of structures that were put out of action but not actually killed. Initially the paralysed limbs are quite flaccid, but if voluntary movements do not recover they gradually become stiff (spastic) owing to exaggeration of the stretch reflexes (p. 327), and the tendon jerks (p. 332) are increased. There is evidence that the spasticity is not due to destruction of corticospinal fibres; thus it is said that following division of the cortico spinal tract in the medullary pyramid in a monkey, the paralysed limbs remain flaccid. With a lesion in the internal capsule many fibres other than corticospinal fibres are divided. The important ones for spasticity may be those from the motor and premotor areas to motor nuclei of the extrapyramidal system. Why division of such fibres should cause spasticity is unknown. Spastic paralysis with increased tendon jerks also results from damage to the spinal cord short of complete division (paralysis in both legs due to a spinal lesion is called paraplegia). How this type of spasticity is related to that due to disease in the brain is not known. In view of these uncertainties, it is safest not to speak of spasticity and increased jerks, when they occur with lesions of the brain or spinal cord, as indicative of damage to the pyramidal tract, but to use some non-committal term such as "long motor tracts".

Another expression used is "upper motor neurone", dating from the days when the voluntary motor pathway was considered to consist of two types of neurones only, the upper motor neurone (the Betz cell in the motor cortex with its axon) connected to the lower motor neurone (the motor cell in the ventral horn of the spinal grey matter with its motor axon running to a muscle). Spastic paralysis with increased tendon jerks and an extensor plantar response are spoken of as signs of an upper motor neurone lesion. Lesions of the lower motor neurone (e.g. polio-myelitis) cause a flaccid paralysis with loss of tendon jerks and eventual wasting of the denervated muscles. There is no wasting to speak of in an upper motor neurone lesion.

As pointed out by Hughlings Jackson, destruction of nervous tissue can only be the direct cause of loss of function, of purely negative symp-toms such as paralysis. Positive symptoms such as spasticity and the change in character of the plantar response must be due to the action of surviving parts of the nervous system that are "released" from influences that previously controlled them. Release phenomena appear to fall into two categories, those that come on immediately after a lesion (e.g. the extensor plantar response after a stroke, or decerebrate rigidity after section of the midbrain in an animal), and those that develop after an interval of weeks or more (e.g. spasticity, and the thalamic syndrome (p. 351)). The hypersensitivity of denervated muscle to acetylcholine (p. 288) may also be considered as a release phenomenon of the second class. The relationship of clinical spasticity to the very similar state of the muscles in decerebrate rigidity in animals is not understood.

Speech. Speech is a form of motor activity peculiar to man. Inability to speak which is not caused by muscular paralysis or other local disease of the larynx, tongue, etc., is called aphasia. Patients with aphasia are often unable to understand what is said to them, or to read and write or to do arithmetic. These related disabilities are conventionally dealt with under the heading of aphasia. In right-handed persons aphasia is caused by lesions of the left cerebral hemisphere. Damage to the cortex in front of the motor area for the face at the bottom of the precentral gyrus (Broca's area, Fig. 19.3) causes a loss of speech with no loss of comprehension of other people's speech or of writing, a so-called motor aphasia. Damage to the parietal lobe in the region between the receiving areas for vision and hearing gives rise to a receptive aphasia; the patient cannot under-stand speech and may not be able to read. In this type of aphasia he may talk jargon and fail to recognize that what he is saying is meaningless. Instances of demonstrably pure motor or pure receptive aphasia are seldom met with in practice. Although difficult to assess in an aphasic it is thought that intelligence generally suffers. Thus aphasia may be only one symptom of a general inability to use symbols in thinking.

One of the many interesting things about aphasia is that the use of words to express emotion is often preserved. The patient who cannot get out the simplest sentence to express a thought, may yet be able to swear or to express approbation and disapprobation with a simple yes and no.

We have already noted that movements of the face to express emotion may likewise be preserved after damage to the cortical motor pathways.

The Frontal Lobes. The frontal lobes are the parts of the cerebral hemispheres extending forwards of the central sulcus. They therefore include the motor and premotor areas already discussed. Extensive damage or removal of one or both frontal lobes ahead of the motor and premotor areas does not cause any immediately obvious disability. Such a patient displays no defect of sensation, no paralysis of movement or loss of skill and no marked impairment of memory or intellect. Further observation, however, reveals that his personality has changed, the changes being much more conspicuous if both frontal lobes are involved. He is no longer able to plan ahead or to pursue any but the most immediate goals. Even if cautious and far-sighted before the operation he is now happy-go-lucky. His insensibility to the consequences of his acts may be embarrassingly apparent in his social behaviour. He makes jokes in bad taste, quarrels readily and may pass his water into his trousers, all with a blithe unawareness of the awkwardness he causes. These facts suggest that the frontal lobes are concerned with the long term planning of behavioural activity, with appreciating the consequences of various courses of action and with the emotional concomitants of this sort of activity, such as anxiety.

The operation of prefrontal leucotomy, cutting the white matter which contains the fibre tracts connecting the frontal lobes with the rest of the brain, may be of benefit to certain types of mentally sick patient. The general tendency of leucotomy is to make the patient carefree (see also p. 376).

Subcortical Motor Mechanisms

It is easy to gain the impression that there is little more to voluntary movement than the discharge of motor impulses down the pyramidal tract to the spinal motor mechanisms. The very large contribution that subsidiary mechanisms make to ensuring successful execution of the desired act tends to be lost sight of because, like the perfect servant, we are not conscious of it. The parts of the brain involved (*i.e.* all the subcortical motor nuclei and tracts, excluding the pyramidal tract) are referred to collectively as the extrapyramidal system. The cerebellum, which comes within this definition, is, however, usually treated apart. In addition there are automatic mechanisms based on spinal reflexes which appear to regulate the contraction of individual muscles in all types of activity, reflex and postural as well as voluntary.

The Extrapyramidal System. The structures comprised (Fig. 20.7) are the basal ganglia (the corpus striatum) and the brainstem nuclei closely connected with the basal ganglia, notably the sub-thalamic nucleus, the substantia nigra and the red nucleus, to which should probably be added some of the cells in the reticular formation of the brainstem (see also p. 370). In lower vertebrates in which the cerebral cortex is little developed the basal ganglia are the highest motor centres and the rubrospinal tract from the red nucleus is the principal tract to the spinal cord. As the cortex and pyramidal tracts increase in size the rubrospinal tract becomes less important and in man it is small. At the same time the amount an animal can do after the pyramidal tracts are sectioned in the medulla decreases. A cat moves about and performs many acts normally, but movements of individual limbs, pawing objects, etc., are lost. The monkey loses all delicate limb movements but after some weeks it can stand, and move about unwillingly. Man, no doubt, could manage even less.

These activities are little more than might from analogy with the cat and dog be attributed to action of the midbrain alone and scarcely seem to require the large development of the basal ganglia in primates. The evidence of disease in man suggests that the basal ganglia, having resigned the leading rôle in the motor system, have been taken into partnership by the cortex; but exactly what they contribute is very obscure. Brindley and Lewis recently showed that, after severing the pyramidal tracts in the medulla in a monkey, the motor map obtained by electrical stimulation of the cortex was the same as that found immediately beforehand; but that larger stimuli were required to obtain the movements. Each point stimulated gave movements in the same part of the body as before, but the threshold was higher. Hence we must envisage that the motor cortex has access to the musculature by two quite separate routes, pyramidal and extrapyramidal (of which the pyramidal route greatly increases in importance as we ascend the animal scale). Understanding of the extrapyramidal route is backward, largely because disease of the extrapyramidal system tends unfortunately to be diffuse and to affect unevenly many of the nuclei, partially destroying them. (It is clear at any rate that unilateral disease of the basal ganglia results in symptoms on the opposite side of the body. The rubrospinal tracts decussate in the midbrain.)

The commonest affliction of the extrapyramidal system is paralysis agitans (Parkinson's disease) in which the limbs become stiffened at all joints by contraction of both flexors and extensors and develop tremor at a frequency of three or four oscillations per second. The muscular contractions involve the stretch reflex but tendon jerks are not increased and the clasp-knife response is not obtained. This type of stiffness is called *rigidity* to distinguish it from the *spasticity* ensuing on damage of the long motor tracts (p. 359). What a physiologist calls decerebrate rigidity would be decerebrate spasticity to a clinical neurologist.

In Parkinson's disease the patient is disabled because he cannot get his voluntary movements going; all movements become cramped and slow and he walks with tiny shuffling steps. In the early stages the first things noticed even before rigidity and tremor develop are slowness in

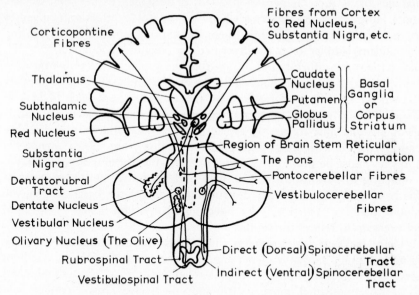

Corticopontine Fibres

Thalamus

Subthalamic Nucleus

Red Nucleus

Substantia Nigra

Dentatorubral Tract

Dentate Nucleus

Vestibular Nucleus

Olivary Nucleus (The Olive)

Rubrospinal Tract

Vestibulospinal Tract

Fibres from Cortex to Red Nucleus, Substantia Nigra, etc.

Caudate Nucleus
Putamen
Globus Pallidus

Basal Ganglia or Corpus Striatum

Region of Brain Stem Reticular Formation

The Pons

Pontocerebellar Fibres

Vestibulocerebellar Fibres

Direct (Dorsal) Spinocerebellar Tract

Indirect (Ventral) Spinocerebellar Tract

FIG. 20.7. The extrapyramidal system and the cerebellum. The nuclei are shown on a diagrammatic section of the human brain in the plane of the brain stem as in Fig. 20.2, with, here, the outline of the cerebellum and one dentate nucleus superimposed. Some structures not labelled here are labelled in Fig. 20.2; for spinal tracts see also Fig. 20.3.

The extrapyramidal nuclei are connected to each other and to the thalamus by numerous bundles of nerve fibres (not shown). The main tracts running to them are the dentatorubral from the cerebellum and fibres from the cerebral cortex to the red nucleus and substantia nigra. There appear to be relatively few direct connections between the cerebral cortex and the corpus striatum. Likewise the efferent connections of the extrapyramidal nuclei to the spinal cord arise mainly from the red nucleus and reticular formation. The reticulospinal tract (not shown) runs near the rubrospinal tract.

The olives are large nuclei of unknown function (only the left olive is shown), which receive large tracts of fibres from the neighbourhood of the red nuclei. They have efferent connections to the opposite cerebellar cortex and to the spinal cord by the olivospinal tracts (not shown), which run near the vestibulospinal tracts.

The cerebellum lies dorsal to the hindbrain connected to it by three peduncles (not distinguished in the diagram) on each side: superior, containing mainly the large dentatorubral tract and the indirect spinocerebellar tract; middle, the largest in man, consisting of pontocerebellar fibres from the pons; and inferior, containing principally the direct spinocerebellar tract, vestibulocerebellar fibres, and (not shown) fibres from the dorsal column nuclei and the olives to the cerebellar cortex, and efferent fibres (not shown) from the central nuclei other than the dentate to the medulla.

manual tasks, such as getting dressed, a dead-pan expressionless face, and a failure to swing the arms when walking unless attention is given to them. There is also an impairment of various postural and righting mechanisms similar to those described by Magnus in animals (p. 337). The patient has difficulty in turning from the supine to the prone position and in rising from the ground or from a chair. While standing he is easily thrown off balance by a push or by throwing his head back to look at something above him. It appears that many automatic elements in movement are lost and are slowly replaced by rigidity and tremor. Rigidity and tremor, in Hughlings Jackson's terminology, are release symptoms and they must be due to overaction of surviving nervous tissue. What is overacting in Parkinson's disease may perhaps be the surviving parts of the basal ganglia, for further destruction of one of the basal ganglia, the globus pallidus (Fig. 20.7), by injecting alcohol into it, has been found on occasion to relieve the rigidity.

There are facts which suggest that a patient with Parkinson's disease is not so much incapable of moving as prevented from doing so. It is of great interest that some gravely disabled cases may, if suddenly and powerfully motivated, move swiftly and effectively. Thus a patient who has great difficulty in feeding himself or walking may deftly catch a ball thrown to him, or jump out of the way of a car about to run him down. Gordon Holmes saw "a man who could scarcely walk in his waking state wander about easily in a period of somnambulism". Such dramatic temporary recovery would be unthinkable in patients with damage to the pyramidal pathways or the cerebellum.

In other patients disease of the corpus striatum results in involuntary movements of the limbs, which may take the form of elaborate writhing movements (athetosis) or of irregular jerkings (chorea), which may be of sufficient violence to damage the limbs. Which precise structures have to be destroyed to produce the rigidity-tremor syndrome and which the involuntary movements of athetosis or chorea is not known. This reflects the generally unsatisfactory and confused state of present knowledge of the basal ganglia.

The Cerebellum. The cerebellum appears early in evolution as a piece of private brain belonging to the vestibular-lateral line system of sense organs, which are believed to be important in the control of swimming. In primitive animals the cerebellum consists of two separate outgrowths, one on each side of the medulla, each connected to the vestibular nerve on that side. In higher animals they enlarge and fuse in the midline, but the connections to the cerebellum from sense-organs remain predominantly uncrossed, so that each half of the cerebellum deals with the half of the body on the same side.

In higher animals the cerebellum has become the civil service of the motor system; having started with the job of seeing that swimming was properly carried out having regard to all the circumstances communicated to it by the vestibular-lateral line system, it later took over the executive side of voluntary movements as well and uses a wider range of sense data to see that they are carried out properly too.

The cerebellum is a large organ in animals that conduct their lives in three dimensions, e.g. fish, birds and whales, as opposed to those operating essentially on a surface, e.g. frogs. But it reaches its greatest size in the higher mammals with their elaborate voluntary motor activities. In them it is not the vestibular parts of the cerebellum that have developed but mainly phylogenetically newer portions, the enlargement of which parallels the great development of the cerebral hemispheres. In man the vestibular parts are completely overshadowed.

In mammals the cerebellum receives afferent impulses from the vestibular organs, from the limbs and trunk (via the direct and indirect spino-cerebellar tracts (Fig. 20.7) and to a lesser extent via the dorsal columns), and from the eyes and ears. The visual and auditory connexions are via the superior and inferior colliculi respectively. Information about what the motor cortex is doing is sent by very numerous fibres that run near the corticospinal tract as far as the pontine nuclei whence fresh fibres forming the pons and the large middle cerebellar peduncle are distributed to the opposite cerebellar cortex. The cerebellar cortex consists of a uniform thin sheet of grey matter the area of which is enormously increased by deep and elaborate folding. The efferent fibres do not arise directly from the cortex but from central masses of grey matter, of which the largest are the dentate nuclei, one on each side. The principal efferent tracts run in the superior peduncles to the red nuclei; others go via the inferior peduncles to motor centres in the reticular formation in the medulla.

In the cat and monkey afferent impulses from the hind limbs go to the anterior part of the cerebellum (lobulus centralis and front part of culmen), from the fore limbs to the part behind this (culmen and sometimes part of lobulus simplex) and from the face to the part behind this again (lobulus simplex). Fig. 20.8 shows these areas in the monkey. The pathways to the cerebellum are uncrossed, the left fore-limb sends impulses to the left half of the culmen, and so on. Discharges to the limb areas are most easily produced by movement of joints and muscles and by pressure on the pads of the feet, but light touch is sometimes effective. The arrival of impulses is detected in the same way as in the sensory area of the cerebral cortex (p. 352). As with the cerebral cortex the pattern of impulses that arrives is very much like what it is in a peripheral nerve fibre. Auditory and visual stimuli cause activity behind the face area.

The cortico-ponto-cerebellar pathway as a whole projects to a larger area than the afferent pathways just described, but within this area the hind-limb, fore-limb and face areas of the motor cortex are connected to the cerebellar areas that receive afferent impulses from the same parts

of the body (Fig. 20.8). It is worth noting that the mapping of the body
on to the cerebellar surface continues across the morphologically important
division between anterior and middle lobes, which occurs between culmen
and lobulus simplex.

The cerebellum is wholly concerned with the execution of muscular
acts; it has no say in what is to be done, policy making is for the cerebral
cortex. The results of damage to the cerebellum are disturbances of
posture and disorganization (ataxy) of movement. If the lesion is on one

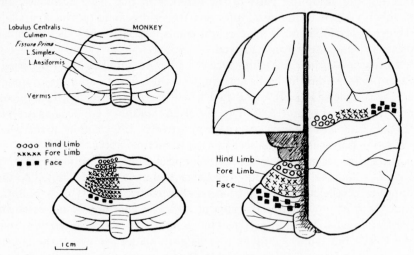

FIG. 20.8. Regions of the monkey's cerebellum connected with the
limbs and face, and with the motor cortex.

Top left, the anatomical divisions of the dorsal surface of the
monkey's cerebellum.

Bottom left, the regions in which impulses can be detected by
electrical recording when various parts of the body are moved or
pressed upon.

Right, the regions in which discharges originating in the limb and
face areas of the motor cortex can be detected arriving in the cerebellum via the cortico-ponto-cerebellar fibres.

(Adrian, *Brain*, vol. 66, p. 289, 1943.)

side of the cerebellum the symptoms are on the same side of the body.
In man nothing that goes on in the cerebellum reaches consciousness and
damage to the cerebellum does not affect memory, intelligence, character,
or any other aspect of our mental life. Although it is richly supplied with
afferent information, damage to the cerebellum causes no sensory loss.
Neither is the patient paralysed, he is not unable to initiate movements,
but the movements he begins do not come off properly. At rest little or
nothing is observed to be wrong. The characteristic disturbances appear
when the patient is asked to perform some action, e.g. to touch an object

in front of him with his index finger. He starts off without difficulty but his hand soon deviates from the correct line and may change direction and velocity several times in an irregular jerky manner. His finger may miss the target altogether, often by overshooting it, and wobbles irregularly as it approaches or even after it has made contact, a symptom called intention tremor (Fig. 20.9). The patient knows that his arm is moving

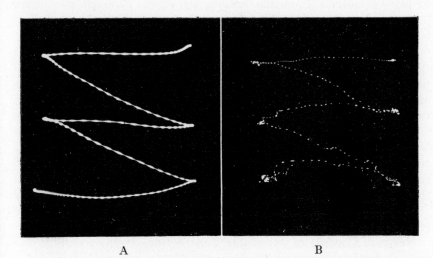

A   B

Fig. 20.9. Records to illustrate cerebellar ataxy. A flashing light was attached to the tip of a forefinger and its movements photographed in a dark room by leaving the camera shutter open. The light flashed 25 times per second; thus the record shows not only the track of the forefinger but also, by the spacing of the flashes, its velocity.

   The task was to move the forefinger accurately between two columns of illuminated points (which do not show up in the photograph), some 75 cm apart. The patient had right-sided cerebellar ataxy. A is the record from the unaffected forefinger, B that from the right forefinger. Record B shows intention tremor as each target point is approached, and irregularities of rate and direction in between. (Gordon Holmes, *Brain*, vol. 62, p. 1, 1939.)

incorrectly and may complain spontaneously that he is unable to control it; he tries to move it in one direction, he says, and it goes off in another. As already implied this is not due to loss of sensation in the arm; in particular it is not due to loss of position sense; the patient knows where his arm is well enough and he does not have to look at it to find out. Cerebellar ataxy is not aggravated by shutting the eyes, unlike the superficially similar sensory ataxy caused by lesions of the dorsal columns and elsewhere.

   Examination shows that the muscles in the ataxic limb are contracting and relaxing at the wrong moments and exerting the wrong force when they do contract (dysmetria). Much of the trouble is due to failure of the muscles to steady the shoulder girdle and the elbow; the arm swings like a barn door in the wind and the intention tremor is partly due to the patient's voluntary attempts to compensate for this lack of the normal postural fixation of the proximal joints. At rest the arm offers no resistance to passive movement; stretch reflexes are absent although the tendon jerks are normal (p. 332). These observations show that the cerebellum has the task of making the automatic modifications of posture that we take for granted when we make voluntary movements, and for arranging that the numerous muscles involved in a movement contract at the right time and with the right force. One possible way in which the cerebellum supervises muscular contractions is discussed on pp. 369–371. The cerebellum also ensures that successive components of a complex act run smoothly into each other; in cerebellar ataxy there is particular difficulty with alternating movements, delays occurring at each turning point; similarly, in speaking, words are broken up and each syllable pronounced separately (scanning speech). How deeply the cerebellum is involved in the actual learning of motor skills (e.g. playing the piano, or throwing a cricket ball), a task usually, but on little evidence, assigned tacitly to the cerebral cortex, is a question not yet answered.

Nervous Control of Muscular Contraction. Until recently it was often thought that orders from the cortex to carry out a voluntary movement were delivered by pyramidal fibres direct to the motoneurones of the muscles concerned, and that even in reflex action impulses in sensory nerves made their way straight to the motoneurones. We have seen that in general this is not so; most pyramidal and dorsal root fibres end elsewhere in the spinal grey matter and set in motion spinal mechanisms that elaborate the motor act. Almost nothing is known of how complex acts such as scratching and walking are produced, but evidence has been cited (pp. 327 and 339) that they are not in the nature of chain reflexes; the basic mechanisms seem to be built into the grey matter and can function after a fashion without impulses from the peripheral sense organs.

One common feature that stands out is that when a limb is moved the muscles in it that would oppose the movement are caused to relax. This is known as *reciprocal innervation*; it is seen very clearly if a flexion reflex is elicited in the leg of a decerebrate cat. The rigid extensor muscles of the knee immediately relax; this occurs even if the flexors of the knee are detached from their insertion so that the knee is not moved, or even if the motor nerves to the flexors are cut so that they do not contract at all. The mechanism of reciprocal innervation appears to be in the spinal grey matter, but it is assisted as usual by reflexes from the periphery. Thus intracellular recording from motoneurones (p. 299) has shown that impulses from muscle spindles in flexor muscles inhibit extensor motoneurones. Movements elicited by electrical stimulation of the motor cortex also exhibit reciprocal innervation.

Reciprocal innervation was of great importance in the development of neurophysiology because it revealed to Sherrington the large part played by inhibitory processes in nervous action. Not all types of muscular action, however, employ reciprocal innervation. It is very clear that flexors and extensors can readily be made to contract together by voluntary effort, and the same thing occurs automatically to fix the joints in standing (p. 338). In these instances the limbs are stationary; reciprocal innervation comes into play when they move.

Even the spinal mechanisms that arrange for the correct muscles to contract in the correct sequence may not act by directly exciting their motoneurones. There is evidence which suggests that in many instances they activate subsidiary mechanisms whose job it is to regulate the contractions of the individual muscles. As already mentioned on p. 330 muscles engaged in all kinds of contractions, reflex, postural and voluntary, are found to show the stretch reflex. There is evidence that when a muscle shortens impulses from the γ motoneurones make the muscle spindles shorten too, so that at whatever length the muscle reaches the stretch reflex remains active (see Fig. 19.8). In fact, in reflex contraction, direct recording from single nerve fibres has shown that the γ discharge begins before the α motoneurones start up. The first thing that happens, therefore, is that the spindles contract, which stretches the sensory region and sends impulses up the monosynaptic afferents. Such impulses are excitatory to the motoneurones and assist in causing them to discharge. It would be possible, of course, for the motoneurones to be caused to discharge by thus turning on the stretch reflex without any excitation reaching them from elsewhere, but whether contractions are wholly driven via the γ route in this way is not known. Probably not—some direct excitation of α motoneurones appears likely; the most that can be said is that in reflex activity in the decerebrate cat the γ route contributes a substantial fraction.

To an engineer the ordinary stretch reflex is a servo-mechanism tending to hold the muscle at a certain demanded length by using negative feedback from change-of-length detectors in the muscle. If the load varies it turns muscle tension on or off in an attempt to maintain the demanded length. This is very clearly seen in an extensor muscle of a decerebrate cat. A shortening of a muscle driven or assisted by spindle contraction is equivalent to changing the demanded length. Thus we arrive at the idea that this servo-mechanism based on the stretch reflex allows the motor centres to order a certain change of length, which furthermore will be carried out with the same automatic adjustment of tension to load that is observed in the ordinary stretch reflex. In many actions what is required is a change of limb position, i.e. changes of muscle length. A muscle, on the other hand, is essentially a device for producing tension; feedback from the muscle spindles on to the motoneurones appears to modify the characteristics of the system so that when excited via the γ route it tends instead to produce changes of length, by servo action.

If we are to regard the stretch reflex as a device for setting a linear relation between length and tension (p. 336), the above picture must be elaborated. The input does not demand a new length, but, instead, a new position of the length/tension line, a change of "bias" (Fig. 19.9). If the "gain" of the system is low, as, indeed, it appears to be in a decerebrate cat, this will be decidedly different in its outward effect.

There is certainly a great deal that is not yet discovered about the functions of muscle sense organs, and how they are employed to make the muscles do what is required of them. We are not likely to be led astray in thinking that one of their functions is to confer new properties on the muscle by feedback action (in the same way that feedback confers new properties on an amplifier), even if we are not yet sure quite what those new properties are. At all events this statement ought to make clear why the stretch reflex is coming to be thought of as part of the muscles' own nervous machinery; and why, when this machinery depends on excitation of the γ motoneurones, in addition to the α motoneurones, it is missing the point (if not exactly incorrect) to think of all reflex and voluntary pathways as converging on to the "final common path" of the α motoneurones.

Not all muscular contractions are based on the stretch reflex. It is well known that many spinal actions can be obtained after cutting all the dorsal roots to the moving limb, which necessarily abolishes all stretch reflexes in it. Examples already given are the crossed extensor reflex (p. 323), the scratch reflex (p. 326) and spinal walking (p. 339). Voluntary movements can also be carried out by a deafferented limb. In these instances all the excitation must be reaching the α motoneurones direct. Granit and his collaborators have now shown that even with the dorsal roots intact the nervous system has the choice of employing this direct α route instead of turning on the stretch reflex by exciting the γ motoneurones. Which route is employed appears to depend on the cerebellum. The evidence for this derives from experiments on decerebrate rigidity, which must now be discussed.

Decerebrate rigidity develops in the cat, dog, etc., when the mid-brain is sectioned behind the superior colliculus. As described by Sherrington in 1898, such rigidity disappears in a limb if the dorsal roots to that limb are cut, because, as we now know, it depends on exaggerated stretch reflexes. Much later it was observed that, if the anterior lobe of the cerebellum was removed too, an outwardly similar rigidity developed, but it was not abolished by section of the dorsal roots. It, therefore, could not be due to exaggerated stretch reflexes. The mechanisms in the brain stem and cerebellum responsible for these phenomena are not understood. (Magoun and Moruzzi and their colleagues have investigated the excitatory and inhibitory effects on spinal reflexes which can be obtained by stimulation of two regions in the reticular formation. An explanation of decerebrate rigidity is sought in terms of a disturbance in the balance of such antagonistic reticular influences.) At all events it is clear that there are two distinct kinds of decerebrate rigidity, and it turns out there are two kinds of reflex movements also. Single fibre recording has shown, as already described, that during reflex movements vigorous contractions of the muscle spindles occur in the ordinary decerebrate animal; after removing the anterior lobe of the cerebellum practically indistinguishable reflexes can be elicited but the spindles remain passive. Thus the reflex centres may activate the muscles in either of two ways. Probably varying combinations of the two routes are normally employed.

It is a matter of conjecture what the advantages of this double system are to an animal. The direct route may be better in rapid movements because of the extra delays involved in conduction time with the γ route. The desirable properties that the stretch reflex confers on a muscle have been emphasized already. It has been suggested that the dysmetria and failure of joint fixation in human cerebellar ataxy may be due to a loss of the type of contraction driven through the γ motoneurones, to spindle paralysis in fact. One of the ways in which the cerebellum supervises muscular activity may be by making sure that the best route, the α route or γ route, is used to activate the muscle. At all events it seems justifiable to consider the details of muscular contraction separately from the question of which muscles contract. The local spinal mechanisms belonging to the muscles and the cerebellar mechanisms that control them appear to be at the disposal of both reflex and voluntary, and probably of postural mechanisms as well.

CHAPTER 21

THE CENTRAL NERVOUS SYSTEM: III

Learning and Memory

A man's present actions may be influenced by what happened around him, by what he thought and felt, and by what he learnt to do many years ago. The question of how and where the brain stores memory traces of these things is of great general interest, but so far only hints of the answer are available. As regards how, no electrical phenomena, action potentials, changes in synaptic excitability, etc., have yet been discovered which last longer than a few seconds. It has therefore been suggested that memories depend on nerve impulses continually circulating over closed pathways, the nature of the memory being determined by the pattern of the pathway. This theory runs into the difficulty that memories cheerfully survive events such as profound anaesthesia or epileptic fits which would be expected to stop or disorganize the electrical activity of the brain. For these reasons it seems probable that long-lasting structural changes will prove to be involved, using the term in the widest sense to include such things as changes in the amount of an enzyme in synaptic terminals. The possible nature of these changes is a matter of speculation only at the present.

A fact that any theory has to account for is that recent memories are more easily lost than old ones. It is a commonplace that old people may recall endless details of their childhood after they can no longer remember the events of middle age, or even of a week ago. Similarly after a head injury with concussion the patient may remember nothing of the events leading up to the accident; he has what is called a *retrograde amnesia*; commonly it goes back a few minutes or an hour or two but in severe cases it may extend to several weeks or even years before the accident. Retrograde amnesia is one instance of a general principle, first clearly stated by Hughlings Jackson, that the most recently acquired and the most highly organized activities are the first to be lost when the brain is damaged. A hemiplegic loses the ability to write while he can still pick up his bread and butter. The extensor plantar response (p. 326) he exhibits represents a return to the infantile form of the reflex. The emigré who develops a degree of aphasia reverts to his mother tongue, which he may not have spoken for years.

In addition to their retrograde amnesia, patients recovering from head injury pass through a phase when, although behaviour is normal and consciousness not clouded in any way, they are not laying down new memories, and when fully recovered cannot recall what happened during this period of *post-traumatic amnesia*. A familiar instance is seen when a football player is mildly concussed. After a momentary loss of consciousness, followed by a short period of confusion, he rises and plays on, apparently normal. After the game it is found that he has a brief retrograde amnesia and, in addition, has no recollection of what he did for several minutes after he came to again. With more severe injuries there is a rough correlation between the durations of the retrograde and post-traumatic amnesias.

These facts suggest that all memory traces have a tendency to fade, but this is normally counteracted by a mechanism which consolidates memory traces. This mechanism is temporarily put out of action by head injury. No new memories are consolidated, and the least consolidated (i.e. the most recent) old memories fade irretrievably before the consolidating mechanism restarts. The fact that retrograde amnesia may be of any duration up to several years, shows that memories remain subject to consolidation indefinitely, and does not encourage a distinction between long-term and short-term memory.

There is evidence that the mechanisms that organize the formation and recall of memories are in the under part of the temporal lobes near the cortical area for smell and taste. (This is not to say, of course, that the actual memory traces are laid down in this region.) It has been known for a century that in epilepsy beginning in the under part of the temporal lobe (uncinate fits) the patient may experience feelings that what is going on around him is intensely familiar; it has all happened before (*déjà vu*). Or he may vividly relive incidents in his past life. Recently it has been found that if the anterior parts of both temporal lobes are removed (as was done in an attempt to cure epilepsy) new memories cannot be formed. The patient cannot remember what happened even a few seconds ago and lives literally for the moment. Intellect, sensation, and other cortical activities appear unaffected.

Loss of memory is an early symptom of generalized shrinkage of the cortical grey matter when it occurs in old age or in various forms of dementia. The demented patient forgets past events, names, faces, words, the time, where he is, what he was going to do next, and so on. He also loses his code of social behaviour, his power of reasoning and his ability to cope with new situations. One might say he has forgotten how to behave, how to think and how to adjust. Many of these disabilities are presumably due to loss of the learned activities of some of the special areas of the cerebral cortex already described. A patient with damage to the frontal lobes can be said to have forgotten how to behave. The aphasic cannot recall names or words. After damage to the parietal lobe a patient may forget where he is. Regional cortical lesions of this kind, however,

seem never to cause a loss of memory for past events. It is therefore sometimes suggested that memory for past events is a function of the cortex
as a whole.

Support for this view came from Lashley's experiments with rats in the
nineteen-twenties on the learning and retention of simple habits, such as
threading a maze to obtain food. He excised various parts of the cerebral
cortex and came to the conclusion that it did not matter which part he
removed; the impairment in learning appeared to depend only on the
total area of cortex removed. The only sign of localization was that tasks
involving visual pattern recognition required the visual areas. Lashley's
results could be explained if the learning process involved every part of
the cortex.

Information on this question and on other fundamental issues in
learning and memory has come from the split-brain preparation pioneered
by Sperry and Myers. In their leading experiment the main fibre connections between the two cerebral hemispheres of a monkey were severed
by midline section of the corpus callosum. The optic chiasma was also
divided in the midline. For the right eye this left only optic nerve fibres
running to the right hemisphere, and likewise for the left eye. One eye,
say the left, was covered with a patch while the animal was trained to
make some visual discrimination with the right eye, e.g. between a square
and a circle (see under Conditioned Reflexes below). When the patch was
then shifted to the right eye, and the same task was presented to the left
eye, there was no evidence of transfer of learning, i.e. it took as long to
train the animal to make the discrimination with the left eye as it did
originally with the right eye. Hence the memory traces of the task learnt
with the right eye were confined to the right hemisphere. When the
experiment was repeated without section of the corpus callosum, the
learning of the task transferred readily from one eye to the other.

Cutting the corpus callosum at various intervals after learning the task,
showed that the memory traces were at first confined to the hemisphere
into which the visual information came, but after some days another set of
memory traces had been laid down in the other hemisphere; for, after
cutting the corpus callosum at that interval, the task was performed
equally well with either eye. Such doubling-up, however, is not found
with all tasks in the monkey and is little in evidence in man, in whom the
hemisphere associated with speech is "dominant" to the other; e.g. a
patient whose corpus callosum has been divided can only read print which
he sees in the half of his visual fields belonging to his dominant hemisphere. (It is remarkable that, in man, division of the whole corpus
callosum, the largest fibre tract in the brain, gives rise to no disabilities
that obtrude into everyday life. Indeed, none were detected at all until a
few years ago.)

Conditioned Reflexes. Reflexes such as the knee jerk, or constriction of the pupil when light is shone in the eye, are innate, but many other automatic actions are learnt. If a dog is given food and at the same time a bell is rung and this is repeated several times at intervals of, say, five minutes, it is found that after some time the dog will salivate when the bell is rung, without any food being offered. The dog's nervous system has learnt to associate the bell with food and a new reflex is established. The famous Russian physiologist, Pavlov, called the process of acquiring such reflexes "conditioning" and the reflexes "conditioned reflexes". Innate reflexes were called "unconditioned". Most reflexes that depend on visual and auditory recognition by the cerebral cortex are probably conditioned, not innate. Salivation when food is placed in the mouth is an unconditioned reflex. In addition all normal dogs, if hungry, will salivate when merely shown meat. Pavlov showed that this is a conditioned reflex, for if dogs are reared without ever eating meat they do not salivate when shown it for the first time, although, if allowed to eat it, they salivate at once. In man such reflexes as the blink to a threatening movement, and an enormous number of other automatic responses to events signalled by the eyes and the ears, are doubtless conditioned reflexes established in childhood. Only the very simplest conditioned reflexes remain or can be established after removal of the cerebral cortex, but innate reflexes are not affected.

In the first half of this century Pavlov and his school intensively studied conditioned reflexes, working chiefly with reflexes causing salivation in the dog. One parotid duct was transplanted to the skin of the cheek so that the saliva could be collected, and its amount measured. Thus the experiments were made roughly quantitative. Conditioned reflexes are very easily prevented by any disturbance. Thus, if someone walks into the experimental room, or if a buzzer is sounded, the conditioned secretion of saliva to ringing of a bell is likely to fail on that occasion. For this, and other reasons, the dogs were put in soundproof rooms with the experimenter invisible outside, and all manipulations, etc., were done by remote control. The prevention of conditioned reflexes by miscellaneous interruptions is called "external inhibition". The other sort, "internal inhibition", occurs, for example, if (having established a conditioned reflex) the bell is rung at intervals but food never follows. After some repetitions the flow of saliva dwindles and ceases. It would not be very surprising if the association were lost under these circumstances, but there is good evidence that the reflex is not so much lost as actively suppressed. For instance, it recovers very rapidly if food is presented with the bell once or twice. This is called "reinforcement". It also recovers spontaneously if the dog is left for some hours. But most striking of all, it reappears at once if a stimulus, such as an electric buzzer, of the kind that usually causes external inhibition, is given at the same time as the bell. It seems that the first thing external inhibition acts on is the last thing the animal learnt, namely the association of the bell with no food which overrode the original reflex. Hence the conclusion that the original reflex was inhibited, not lost.

Animals can be trained to make sensory discriminations in their conditioned reflexes. For example, if a musical note of a certain pitch is established as a conditioned stimulus, then initially many other notes will also excite the reflex. But if the first note alone is reinforced (i.e. followed by food) while the others never are, sooner or later only the original note is effective. Pavlov thought of this as an internal inhibition to the other notes. When an indifferent disturbing stimulus is given, such as the buzzer, discrimination tends to be lost; a wider range of notes again causes the reflex (internal inhibition again counteracted by external inhibition).

If notes closer and closer together are used the animal eventually has difficulty in distinguishing them and when faced with the task of doing so may display symptoms very like those of human anxiety neurosis. In his later years Pavlov devoted much work to these experimental neuroses. It was the observation by Fulton and his associates in America that a chimpanzee with such a neurosis lost her anxiety after removal of the frontal lobes that led to the development of the operation of prefrontal leucotomy by the Portuguese surgeon, Moniz (p. 361).

In addition to Pavlovian conditioning of reflexes there is another type of experimental learning situation, originally called "trial and error" learning but now known as "operant conditioning" or "instrumental learning". When a hungry cat is placed in a cage with food outside, it will struggle to get out. If there is a lever which opens the door, sooner or later the cat will accidentally press the lever and get out. If this procedure is repeated over and over again, the time taken before the lever is pressed diminishes, until finally the cat operates the lever directly it is placed in the cage. This basic experiment lends itself to endless elaboration, e.g. the cat can next be trained to distinguish between a lever with a square end and one with a circular end.

Both conditioned reflexes and operant conditioning have been very widely used by experimental psychologists for testing the performance of sense organs in animals. If a dog can be trained to salivate to one note and not to another half a semitone below it, it obviously has pitch discrimination at least as good as that. It is important to note that the reverse does not follow. In this type of experiment the animal has not only to distinguish the two stimuli but also to remember the first stimulus for several minutes. Dogs happen to have an excellent memory for pitch, but many experiments claiming to show that various animals do not have colour vision may merely mean that they have no colour memory.

Pavlov's work was important because it was the first experimental investigation of higher nervous function in animals. He was careful not to use subjective words like perceive, desire, etc., in describing the results of the experiments. A great deal was learnt about the rules of habit formation in the cerebral cortex, but only recently has a start been made at investigating the neuronal mechanisms involved.

The Electrical Activity of the Cerebral Cortex

Nerve impulses can be detected arriving in the projection areas of the cortex and leaving the motor area, but what goes on in between is mysterious. When recording electrodes are placed on the surface of the brain potential oscillations are recorded all the time, even when no sensory impulses are arriving, unless the animal is deeply anaesthetized. In a

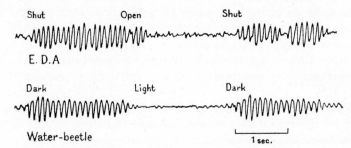

Fig. 21.1. The electroencephalogram of a human subject (E.D.A.), recorded with electrodes on the scalp, showing the prominent α rhythm at about 10 cycles/sec with the eyes shut, and its disappearance when the eyes are open.

The lower record shows the very similar rhythm obtained by leading from the optic ganglion of a water beetle in the dark, which again is blocked by allowing light to enter the eye. (Adrian and Matthews, *Brain*, vol. 57, p. 355, 1934.)

normal conscious man such brain waves can be detected through the skull by electrodes resting on the scalp; the record is called the electro-encephalogram (E.E.G.). Over most of the head it is usual to find regular more or less sinusoidal waves, some 50 microvolts (5×10^{-5} volts) in size with a frequency of about 10 cycles per second. These waves, known as the *alpha rhythm*, were first described by Hans Berger in 1929. The alpha rhythm is only present when the eyes are shut; with the eyes open it is replaced by lower voltage, irregular activity (Fig. 21.1). It appears that the alpha rhythm is characteristic of an awake but inattentive brain. Thus even with the eyes closed the alpha rhythm may disappear if the subject's attention is engaged, if he tries to do mental arithmetic, or if he is unexpectedly touched. Normally it is difficult to be inattentive with the eyes open, for vision is the dominant sense, but if the scene is made uninteresting, for example by wearing strong spectacles which blur everything, or by looking at a blank screen, the alpha rhythm returns. If inattention goes so far that the subject falls asleep, the 10-per-second rhythm disappears and is replaced by irregular higher voltage waves of much lower frequency, 1–3 per second. At intervals during any period of prolonged sleep these slow waves vanish and the E.E.G. exhibits low voltage fast activity, similar to what is seen in the waking attentive state. These phases, during which the subject remains deeply asleep (hence the name, paradoxical sleep), are discussed below.

The alpha rhythm must be due to the synchronized beating of very large numbers of cortical neurones, for if few neurones were involved or if large numbers were beating asynchronously at different frequencies the resultant potentials would not be large enough to detect through the skull. The detailed mechanism of the alpha rhythm is not understood, but it seems to be an example of a general tendency to synchronized rhythmical oscillation that is shown by many large masses of nerve cells when they are not doing anything in particular. Remarkably similar waves were recorded by Adrian from the optic ganglion of a water beetle, and, like the alpha rhythm, they disappeared when a light was shone into the eye (Fig. 21.1).

Nothing very definite can be made out in the cortex when attention is aroused by the arrival of a sensory message. Leading directly from the cortex in animals has shown that the synchronized activity of large regions is broken up and replaced by an indecipherable shifting pattern of waves of varying amplitude and frequency.

The human electroencephalogram is important in medicine. During an epileptic fit very large waves occur all over the brain. Many epileptics continue to show some abnormal waves in between attacks, and their discovery is often useful in diagnosis. Distinctive abnormalities also occur around cerebral tumours and other lesions, and assist in their location.

The cerebellar cortex also shows spontaneous rhythmical waves, but of a much higher frequency, some 250 per second. They cannot be picked up by electrodes on the skin in man.

Consciousness and Sleep

Throughout these chapters it is taken for granted that conscious happenings in the mind, sensations, emotions, voluntary efforts, etc., are associated with definite physical events in the brain. This is a reasonable working assumption until it is shown to be wrong and the resultant mixture of physical and psychological terms it encourages (as when we speak of a tract of nerve fibres conveying sensations of pain) saves space and is not likely to mislead unless it is taken out of context. The nature of the interaction between mind and brain is so far a matter for philosophers, but physiologists have something to say about what parts of the brain are involved in conscious life.

A distinction must be drawn between the state of consciousness, whether we are conscious or unconscious, and the content of consciousness, what we are conscious of. The content of consciousness appears to depend mainly on the normal activities of the cerebral cortex. We are ordinarily aware of what we see and hear and feel and of what we are thinking and doing, and so on. As described in previous sections it looks as if when the region of cortex dealing with one of these activities is lost that side of consciousness drops out. It is apparently wrong to picture the conscious self as a little man sitting in a room on the top storey answering telephones when he's rung up by the various sensory areas. This puts the difficulties one stage further off, but there doesn't appear to be such a stage. The sensory areas seem to be straight through to consciousness without having to ring up, and when one of them is lost the conscious self is that much diminished. Were all the cortex removed we should presumably be conscious only of the crude skin sensations attributed to activity in the thalamus; and with the thalamus gone too, of nothing. Thus the content of consciousness seems to depend mainly on how much of the cerebral cortex is there, or rather on how much of it is in a normally responsive state. It does not respond normally to sensory impulses arriving if an anaesthetic has been given or if an epileptic fit is in progress, and at these times the subject is unconscious.

In ordinary life our state of wakefulness or sleep seems to be determined by events at the level of the brainstem. It has been known for a long time that tumours growing in this region may cause pathological sleepiness and that mechanical interference around the midbrain at operation under local anaesthetic is liable to cause a rapid lapse into unconsciousness. On the other hand large pieces of cortex can be removed at operation under local anaesthetic without any apparent alteration in mental state. Probably it is for the same reason that a punch on the jaw which transmits the shock to the base of the brain is a much more effective way of knocking a man out than hitting him on the top of the head.

The precise location and mode of action of these lower centres is at the moment the subject of much research. Magoun and his followers urge the claims of the reticular formation of the brain stem to be the region responsible for keeping the cortex awake. The principal evidence is firstly that lesions destroying the grey matter around the aqueduct of the midbrain in animals leads to somnolence. This is not due to interference with the sensory tracts running to the thalamus, for it occurs when these are not damaged; conversely lesions interrupting the sensory tracts but not the reticular formation do not cause sleepiness. Secondly, electrical stimulation of this region in anaesthetized animals converts the electrical activity of the cerebral cortex from the pattern characteristic of sleep to that of wakefulness (see p. 377). Similar "arousal reactions" cannot be obtained from elsewhere in the midbrain.

There is evidence, then, for the view that normal wakefulness depends on the action of neurones in or near the reticular formation. What determines whether the reticular activating system is itself active or quiescent is at present unknown. In the nineteen-twenties Hess showed elegantly that stimulation of the lower part of the thalamus (and of several other regions at the base of the brain) could cause sleep. He used freely moving conscious cats with electrodes chronically implanted into the thalamus. Appropriate stimulation caused a cat to look sleepy, circle round, lie down and go to sleep, exactly like a normal cat going to sleep. There was no question that the cat was merely knocked unconscious by the current. These experiments suggest that falling asleep may be an active process. There is evidence in man too that falling asleep is more than something that happens when all sensory inputs are reduced to a minimum, although this assists. In the mysterious disease, narcolepsy, the patient is seized with irresistible drowsiness during the day, perhaps several times a day, and rapidly falls asleep. After a minute he can be aroused and is once more normal.

As was hinted in the previous section, sleep itself can no longer be regarded as a single state. Ordinary sleep, in which the subject makes no eye or limb movements and exhibits slow waves in his E.E.G., is interrupted several times a night by periods of paradoxical sleep, lasting for a few minutes, during which there are jerky movements of the limbs, roving eye movements under closed lids, and low voltage fast waves in the E.E.G. characteristic of wakefulness. But, judged by the intensity of stimuli necessary to wake him, the subject is more deeply asleep during paradoxical sleep than during ordinary sleep; it is also found by waking subjects up that paradoxical sleep is the time they dream. For these reasons ordinary sleep is also known as slow-wave sleep or light sleep; paradoxical sleep is also known as fast-wave sleep, rapid-eye-movement sleep, deep sleep and dreaming sleep.

During light sleep in the cat, the head is held up by a "tonic" contraction of the neck muscles (the activity in which can be monitored by recording their action potentials). On passing into paradoxical sleep, the head falls forward, electrical activity in the neck muscles ceases, and spontaneous eye movements, begin. Jouvet has made the remarkable discovery that a cat decerebrated by removal of the forebrain and midbrain after section of the brainstem at the level of the upper border of the pons and kept alive by skilled treatment, oscillates regularly for weeks between paradoxical sleep, with flaccid neck muscles and roving eyes, and a state of apparent wakefulness, during which the neck muscles are tonically active. No paradoxical sleep is seen, however, if the section is behind the pons. Hence there appears to be a centre for paradoxical sleep at pontine level. (There is also evidence for a centre capable of inhibiting the reticular activating system, and thereby causing the onset of ordinary, slow-wave sleep, in the same region of the brain. Its relation to the experiments of Hess, described above, is unknown.)

Summary of Chapters 19–21

The two main categories of nervous action are reflex and voluntary. Subsidiary categories are spontaneous and quasi-spontaneous actions (e.g. breathing, blinking), the expression of emotions, postural and locomotor activities.

Reflexes are of all grades of complexity, some (e.g. conditioned reflexes) involving the cerebral cortex; but they have usually been studied in the spinal cord, because of the relative ease with which the conditions of the experiment can be controlled.

If the spinal cord is sectioned, to cut off the hind portion from the unpredictable influence of the higher nervous centres, a state of spinal shock ensues, much more severe in the higher mammals than in the frog. There is no spinal shock, however, in the much used decerebrate preparation, in which after a section at the level of the midbrain, the forebrain is removed.

Sherrington and his pupils mainly drew their conclusions from experiments on a small selection of spinal reflexes: the flexion or withdrawal reflex (a manifestation of which is the Babinski or extensor plantar response in man), the scratch reflex of the spinal dog, and the stretch reflex (to which the clinically important tendon jerks are closely related). The most deeply analysed of these is the stretch reflex, evoked by impulses from the muscle spindles. The complexity of the stretch reflex is due to the fact that the muscle spindles themselves are under efferent control and contract during reflex action (and probably in voluntary and postural action too).

Righting reflexes and other postural reactions were described in detail by Magnus, but their internal mechanism is not known; and the same goes for the mechanisms responsible for locomotion.

Conscious voluntary action is the province of the cerebral cortex, different functions being localized in different parts of the cerebral hemispheres. The visual area, which receives impulses from the retina (via the lateral geniculate nucleus), is in the occipital lobe. Damage to the visual area causes blindness. The cortical area for hearing is in the temporal lobe; the area for taste and smell is underneath this lobe.

The important region that receives sensory messages from the body surface, etc., is in the postcentral gyrus. After removal of this cortical area in man, all delicate sensation on the opposite side of the body is lost; but crude sensations are retained. Impulses to the brain to arouse conscious sensation ascend the spinal cord in two pathways: fine tactile sense and position sense run uncrossed in the dorsal columns; sensations of pain, temperature and crude contact are conveyed in the crossed spinothalamic tract.

The motor area is in the precentral gyrus. Damage to this region causes voluntary paralysis on the opposite side of the body, while electrical stimulation gives movements of the same parts. The motor area is connected to the spinal cord by the large corticospinal or pyramidal tract. There are also large extrapyramidal pathways. Damage to these motor pathways (an "upper motor neurone lesion") causes spastic paralysis with exaggerated tendon jerks, an extensor plantar response, and no muscular wasting.

In front of the motor area on the left side (in right-handed people) is the cortical motor area for speech. The receptive side of speech is dealt with in the parietal lobe. Damage to any of these regions results in loss of speech, aphasia.

The function of the extrapyramidal motor nuclei (the basal ganglia, etc.) is not well understood. In Parkinson's disease, in which they are damaged, there is clumsiness and slowness in voluntary movement, with muscular rigidity and tremor.

The cerebellum in man is mainly concerned with the subconscious side of voluntary movement. Damage leads to a general disorganization of voluntary movement, with intention tremor and muscular hypotonia, known as cerebellar ataxy, the symptoms being on the same side of the body as the lesion.

All muscular movements (reflex, voluntary, etc.) have various lower level motor mechanisms in common, e.g. reciprocal innervation, and feedback mechanisms based on the stretch reflex.

Learning and memory are cortical functions which are not associated with specific areas. Memory theories have to take into account the clinical facts of retrograde and post-traumatic amnesia, and the results of experiments on animals and men after section of the corpus callosum.

Conditioned reflexes (and operant conditioning) are again mainly a cortical phenomenon, widely used for the study of sensation and learning in animals.

The electrical activity of the cortex can be recorded in man by electrodes on the scalp; the resulting record is the electroencephalogram (E.E.G.).

Although conscious life as we know it depends on activity in the cortex, the state of wakefulness or sleep is determined by centres at the base of the brain and in the brainstem. There appear to be two phases of sleep, ordinary light sleep being interspersed with periods of deep or paradoxical sleep.

Section 7
THE AUTONOMIC
NERVOUS SYSTEM

CHAPTER 22

THE SYMPATHETIC NERVOUS SYSTEM

THE autonomic (involuntary or vegetative) nervous system is often defined as that part of the peripheral nervous system which is independent of the control of the will. The designation of the system as "autonomic" or "involuntary", stresses this essential feature. The definition, however, like nearly all attempts at definition, is not strictly correct. Reflexes like the knee jerk are involuntary, but do not involve autonomic pathways. On the other hand, by recalling emotions or sensations, the will may exercise more or less control over smooth muscle and glands and in doing so stimulate autonomic fibres. There are, in addition, persons who can control one or another of the autonomic functions. They are able, by effort of will, to slow or to quicken the heart beat, to contract the smooth muscle of the skin or to constrict the pupil.

For our purpose, the autonomic nervous system is best defined as the efferent pathway to the viscera, including all nerve cells and fibres through which impulses are sent from the central nervous system to glands, smooth muscles and heart, that is, all the efferent fibres in the body except those to the striped (voluntary) muscles. The definition stresses two points, (a) the efferent character of the system, and (b) the fact that we are dealing with a peripheral nervous system. Afferent (sensory) fibres are usually excluded from the autonomic nervous system. When we use the term autonomic nervous system, however, in this restricted sense, we have to realize that most of our so called autonomic nerves, such as the splanchnic, the vagus, or the chorda tympani, are mixed nerves containing autonomic (efferent) as well as afferent (sensory) fibres.

Autonomic nerve fibres emerge from the central nervous system, mostly in the motor roots of the spinal cord and in some of the cranial nerves.

There are two major divisions of the autonomic nervous system, the *sympathetic nervous system* which emerges from the thoraco-lumbar spinal region, and the *parasympathetic nervous system* which emerges from the cranial and sacral regions. Many organs in the body are influenced by both sympathetic and parasympathetic systems, usually in opposing directions, but the definition of the two systems derives from the anatomical connections with different parts of the central nervous system, not with the way in which physiological function is changed.

There are some organs to which the double antagonistic innervation does not apply. For example, most of the systemic blood vessels are supplied by sympathetic vasoconstrictor fibres only, and centrally induced vasodilatation is brought about by inhibition of vasoconstrictor tone. Some vessels in skeletal muscles are supplied with vasodilator fibres, but these, also belong anatomically to the sympathetic system (p. 392 below). There is no parasympathetic innervation of the smooth muscles of the upper eyelid, of the hair muscles in the skin, of the uterus, of the sweat glands or of the adrenal medulla. Even when a tissue is provided with a dual antagonistic innervation, a too simplified conception of this antagonism is misleading. When light falls into the eye, the pupil constricts as a result of parasympathetic impulses. When the eye is in the shade the pupil dilates, not as a result of stimulation of the sympathetic fibres to the dilator muscle of the pupil, but because of diminished discharge in the parasympathetic system. On the other hand, the dilated pupil of a frightened person is mainly a sympathetically stimulated pupil and dilatation can occur despite the fact that bright light may shine into the eye.

To understand the difference in the working of the different parts of the autonomic nervous system the anatomical arrangements have to be considered. Efferent nerves in general can be subdivided into somatic and autonomic. The somatic nerves pass as medullated nerve fibres from the ventral horn cells in an uninterrupted pathway to the skeletal muscles. In contrast, the autonomic peripheral pathway consists, with one exception, of two neurones. This is illustrated in Fig. 23.4 (p. 402). Impulses emerging from the central nervous system into autonomic fibres thus have to cross a *ganglionic synapse* on their way to the periphery. The first neurone originates in a cell in the central nervous system and the axon (the *pre-ganglionic fibre*) terminates at a synapse near a cell in a ganglion. The ganglion cell with its axon (the *post-ganglionic fibre*), constitutes the second neurone which terminates at the peripheral effector structure. A preganglionic fibre may traverse one or several ganglia without entering into synaptic junction with a ganglion cell; each fibre may form a great number of synapses in a given ganglion or give off collateral branches terminating around the cells of different ganglia. By using *nicotine*, Langley was able to discover the endings of preganglionic fibres and the origin of the postganglionic ones. Nicotine has no action on nerve fibres, but stimulates, and later paralyses the ganglion cells. If it is painted on an autonomic ganglion, therefore, the nerve cells in the ganglion will be excited and give rise to impulses passing along the postganglionic fibres, thus indicating the origin of a postganglionic fibre to a given peripheral structure. Later on, these cells become paralysed and can no longer be excited when their preganglionic fibres are stimulated. This block will not occur when fibres merely traverse a nicotinized ganglion without entering into synaptic junctions. It is, therefore, possible by stimulating fibres proximal to a ganglion, painted with nicotine, to find out if they only traverse the ganglion or form synapses with its nerve cells.

Cell Stations.

The position of the cell stations or synaptic junctions in the autonomic path varies. Preganglionic fibres may be relatively short, relaying in ganglia near the vertebral column (vertebral or lateral ganglia), to long post-ganglionic fibres. Or the postganglionic fibres may be short and the long preganglionic fibres may terminate around ganglion cells situated within the tissue of the innervated organ (terminal or peripheral ganglia). Or the cell stations may have intermediate positions (collateral or prevertebral ganglia). There is this general difference. Parasympathetic preganglionic fibres relay in peripheral ganglia or in collateral ganglia (ciliary, spheno-palatine, submaxillary or otic ganglia) situated near the innervated tissue. Terminal ganglia, however, are the exception in the sympathetic path. Its main cell stations are the vertebral ganglia forming the paired sympathetic chains with their adjoining cervical ganglia in the neck. In addition there are many cell stations in collateral ganglia, like the coeliac and the mesenteric ganglia. There is one exception. The autonomic fibres to the adrenal medulla do not pass a cell station on their way to the periphery. The medullary cells and the sympathetic ganglion cells have a common origin. Both are probably derived from the same primitive masses of neuroblasts, but have followed different paths in their differentiation. The innervation to the adrenal medulla consists of preganglionic fibres of the sympathetic system, the postganglionic fibres, so to speak, having been converted into a gland of internal secretion.

Since the preganglionic sympathetic fibres are medullated when they emerge from the lateral horn cells of the cord into the ventral roots and pass as fine filaments to the sympathetic chain, these filaments have a whitish appearance (*white rami communicantes*). The fibres usually lose their myelin sheath near or at the ganglia; thus the connecting filaments containing the non-myelinated postganglionic fibres which are sent back to the spinal nerves of the trunk and limbs have a more greyish appearance (*grey rami communicantes*).

The term *intermediate ganglia* is given to sympathetic nerve cells which are not located in the ganglia of the paired sympathetic chains, but in the rami communicantes, often in close proximity to the motor nerves. They are of practical import-ance in surgery of the sympathetic nervous system. For instance, an operation of thoraco-lumbar sympathectomy, i.e. removal of the lower ganglia of the sympathetic chains, does not lead to complete sympathetic denervation of the skin in the lower part of the body.

The ganglia are distributing centres, in which impulses from a single preganglionic fibre may be relayed to many (twenty or more) post-ganglionic fibres. In the parasympathetic division the relays are situated in or quite near the innervated tissue and this limits the spread of the impulses beyond a restricted area. The position is different in the sympathetic system. Here the anatomical arrangement clearly favours diffuse distribution of the nerve impulse over wide areas. In addition, on stimulation of the sympathetic, hormones (*adrenaline* and *noradrenaline*) are secreted from the adrenal medulla into the blood stream, mimicking many of the sympathetic nerve effects, thus emphasizing the fact that the organism is not concerned with a limitation of sympathetic effects to restricted areas. The anatomical arrangements of the two divisions reflect the fundamental difference in the function of the two systems.

It is possible that some of the parasympathetic ganglia are weak automatic centres, independent of the central nervous system, from which impulses originate continuously. Such function is attributed to the cells of the nerve plexus in the wall of the digestive tract. To a lesser degree it may be a more general property of parasympathetic ganglia.

The adrenal medullary cells secrete adrenaline and noradrenaline as a result of the release of acetylcholine from the pre-ganglionic nerve endings (see p. 403). We must emphasize again the distinction between transmitter substances and hormones. The former are released from nerve endings and then modify or initiate the activity of cells in close proximity. The latter are secreted from gland cells, released into the blood, and act on cells which may be quite remote and in entirely different organs.

The Function of the Sympathetic System

The Emergency Function of the Sympathico-adrenal System

Removal of the paired sympathetic chains with their outlying ganglia, as far as it is technically possible, is compatible with life. Sympathectomized animals show, in fact, no signs of deficiency if kept in sheltered conditions, but when exposed to extreme cold, oxygen lack, carbon dioxide increase, hypoglycaemia, haemorrhage or anaesthesia they may succumb earlier than control animals. The sympathetic innervation fulfils an important function in making the animal fit for states of emergency. There is a widespread discharge of impulses in the sympathetic system in states of physiological stress, during severe muscular work, in situations of danger, in extreme temperatures, asphyxia, haemorrhage, under strong emotions such as fear or rage, or when in pain. The discharge affects also the fibres to the adrenal medulla leading to an output of adrenaline and noradrenaline, as is illustrated in Fig. 23.4, p. 402. This widespread discharge has been likened to a reflex action of the organism with the purpose of strengthening its powers of defence and producing those changes necessary for preparing the organism for "fight and flight". It is in this connection, that Cannon referred to the emergency function of the sympathico-adrenal system. Sympathectomized animals show signs of deficiency in many of these adverse circumstances, but the degree of deficiency varies in different species. The capacity for strenuous muscular exercise is definitely decreased in cats but not in dogs which remain excellent fighters.

The effects of sympathetic stimulation are easily understood and remembered, when seen in the light of a protective mechanism for emergencies. The dilatation of the pupil (contraction of the radial muscle of the iris) protrusion of the eye or *exophthalmos* (contraction of the smooth muscle at the back of the eye) and opening of the palpebral fissure (contraction of the smooth muscle fibres of the levator palpebrae) increase the perception of light. In animals an alarming appearance is produced by bristling of the hairs of the back and tail. Of this effect "goose flesh" alone has survived in man. Broncho-dilatation decreases the resistance to the passage of air into the alveoli of the lung. The movements of the digestive tract are inhibited and the sphincters contract. Glucose is mobilized from the liver. The spleen contracts and ejects its store of red blood cells. Fatigue in skeletal muscle may be counteracted. The heart beats more strongly and more frequently; the coronary arteries are dilated. Vasoconstriction occurs in the systemic vessels, mainly in the splanchnic area and in the skin which becomes pale. In the skeletal muscles, however, the blood vessels dilate, thus shifting the flow of blood from regions where it is not urgently needed to the active tissues. The redistribution of blood may occur with little or no rise in arterial blood pressure. No useful purpose would be served if the circulatory effects of sympathetic stimulation, as well as of adrenaline, consisted in an increased activity of the heart in order solely to eject the blood against a greater peripheral resistance. The main effect is redistribution of the blood volume with increased circulation rate. On the other hand, the vasoconstriction following severe haemorrhage tends to keep up or restore an effective arterial blood pressure by adapting the vascular bed to the reduced blood volume.

Adrenaline and Noradrenaline.

These hormones are apparently not always secreted in a constant proportion. They may be secreted by different cells which can be selectively stimulated from the central nervous system. Insulin hypoglycaemia, for example, increases the proportion of adrenaline secreted, while most other ways of evoking central stimulation of the adrenal medulla produce a preponderance of noradrenaline in the secretion. It is interesting to note in this connection that adrenaline has a much more powerful hyperglycaemic effect than has noradrenaline.

Cannon points out that a general sympathico-adrenal discharge may be harmful unless transformed into action. Heart and circulation may be worked just as hard from an armchair as from a rower's seat. "If no action succeeds the excitement and the emotional stress—even worry and anxiety—persists, then the bodily changes due to the stress are not a preparatory safeguard but may be in themselves profoundly upsetting to the organism as a whole."

a- and β-receptors (table 22.1)

The actions of the transmitters at the sympathetic neuro-effector junctions are illustrated diagrammatically in Fig. 23.4 (lower part). Nor-adrenaline makes smooth muscle contract, for example it produces vaso-constriction and a rise of arterial pressure. This is termed the a (alpha) effect and the drug is said to act on a receptors in the muscle. (These receptors correspond with the chemically excitable structure, or the "receptive substance" at the neuro-muscular junctions, and must not be confused with the "sensory" receptors). Isoprenaline in general produces

TABLE 22.1

a-receptors	β-receptors
Glycogenolysis	Vasodilatation
Dilation of the pupil	Relaxation of bronchi
Cardio-acceleration	Cardio-acceleration
Vasoconstriction	Increased force of heart beat
Relaxation of intestines	Relaxation of uterus
Pilo-erection	Rise in blood sugar

relaxation of smooth muscle, for example vasodilatation and, more import-ant therapeutically, dilatation of bronchioles. This is termed the β (beta) effect, the drug acting on β receptors. Adrenaline produces a mixed effect since it acts on both kinds of receptor, but in low (*i.e.* physiological) concentrations chiefly on the β receptors; this action is important in blood vessels of skeletal muscles, but not in those of other organs and tissues. Adrenergic blocking agents, like ergot extracts or dibenzyline, are especially effective in blocking all actions on the a receptors. Adrenaline in larger concentrations acts more on the a receptors than on the β receptors and produces vaso-constriction and rise of blood pressure; but when adminis-tered after adrenergic blocking agents, it produces vaso-dilatation and fall of blood pressure. The effects of sympathetic stimulation on tissues other than smooth muscle, for example increased frequency of heart beat or rise in the blood sugar concentration, are regarded as β effects, partly because isoprenaline has more action on them than has noradrenaline, and partly because of their responses to adrenergic blocking agents.

The Efferent Pathway of Reflexes to Organs Widely Distributed in the Body

The sympathetic system may act as a unit in conditions of physiological stress, but this is one aspect only of its function. It may also act as the efferent pathway for reflexes in which the blood vessels, sweat glands and hair muscles are the effector organs, widely distributed in the body. Sympathetic fibres are the sole connections between the vasomotor centre in the brain and the blood vessels; regulation of the calibre of the vessels is brought about by increased or decreased sympathetic discharge, the parasympathetic taking no part. It is true that the latter system contains vasodilator fibres to some tissues such as the salivary glands; these fibres, however, are not activated for the purpose of circulatory readjustments but for a specific organ function, salivation. Without a sufficient supply of fluid to the glands, salivation would not continue; accordingly the pattern of the salivary reflex incorporates a localized vasodilatation mediated by parasympathetic nerves. The regulation of heat loss through the temperature regulating centres (Chapter 39) is almost entirely dependent on the sympathetic system, whether by control of the calibre of the blood vessels in the skin and thus the skin temperature, control of the evaporation of sweat or, in animals, control of the erection of hair or feathers.

Sympathetic discharge to certain tissues is continuous. The heart, the arteries, arterioles, capillaries and probably venules, and the smooth muscles in and around the eye, are kept in a state of continuous although varying tonic contraction as a result of their sympathetic innervation. When this is interrupted, the blood vessels dilate, as was first shown by Claude Bernard when he cut the cervical sympathetic nerves on one side of a rabbit; the vessels of the external ear on the denervated side dilated and the skin temperature rose. When the sympathetic innervation to the eye is interrupted, the pupil contracts, the eye sinks into its socket (enophthalmos) and the upper lid droops (ptosis), giving the eye a sleepy appearance. The smooth muscles of the hairs, the sweat glands, the digestive tract and the medulla of the adrenal gland, on the other hand, receive sympathetic excitation only in special conditions, e.g. those of an "emergency".

It is not surprising, therefore, that different parts of the sympathetic system may act separately from each other and even antagonistically. The following instances will illustrate these points. (1) Emotional blushing is the result of inhibition of sympathetic constrictor tone of the skin vessels. This inhibition is limited and usually does not spread over the vessels of the whole body. In women who blush frequently and vividly, the "blush area" is usually confined to the face and to the V-shaped area in the neck, areas of skin exposed to sunlight by the cut of modern dress. (2) Sweating, limited to the skin around the lips and nose, may be evoked by gustatory stimuli such as chewing spicy foods. (3) When there is a sufficient rise in the environmental temperature, large areas of the skin become flushed and sweat beads appear. Again the flushing is due to reflex *inhibition* of sympathetic vasoconstrictor tone in the skin but the secretion of sweat is the result of *excitation* of the sympathetic secretory fibres to the sweat glands,

When the vasoconstrictor fibres are excited at the same time as the secretory fibres, as in extreme fright, "cold sweat" appears, the sensation of cold being brought about by the restriction of the blood flowing through the skin.

One of the main functions of the sympathetic system is its rôle in preserving constant internal conditions, the preservation of what Claude Bernard called the "milieu intérieur". The sympathetic system is in part responsible for man's great adaptability to life in different surroundings and for the conservation of his "inner climate" which he carries about with him. The constant changes in the distribution of the circulating blood volume to adapt the organism to changed environmental conditions and to the changing demands created by muscular activity are brought about, as far as nervous mechanisms are involved, through the sympathetic system.

CHAPTER 23

THE PARASYMPATHETIC NERVOUS SYSTEM

UNLIKE the sympathetic system with its widespread discharge the parasympathetic system is the main efferent pathway for those reflexes which are more localized and usually influence single organs without affecting others. These reflexes are abolished when the parasympathetic pathway is interrupted; for example, in the eye the pupillary reflexes to light and near vision (Chapter 25) are no longer obtained. When the parasympathetic pathway to the salivary glands is interrupted neither the presence of food in the mouth nor its sight or smell will induce salivary secretion. The reflex secretion of gastric and pancreatic juice and of succus entericus are dependent on the integrity of the parasympathetic fibres in the vagus nerve, stimulation of which in addition, causes increased bile flow and increased activity of the walls of the digestive tract and inhibition of its spincters. Cutting the parasympathetic fibres to the lacrimal glands abolishes reflex lacrimation. A continuous discharge is exerted through the parasympathetic fibres in the vagus upon the heart's action, as shown by the fact that the heart-rate in man may double when the vagal inhibition is removed, as after atropine. Vagal tone is weak at birth; in a new-born baby, atropine will increase the pulse rate only from about 140 to 160 per minute. The vagal tone to the heart in man is influenced continuously by many reflexes. The significance of this tone depends on the effect of heart rate on mechanical efficiency; the heart uses less oxygen to perform a given amount of work when it is beating slowly than when it is beating quickly.

The parasympathetic fibres from the sacral division are the efferent pathway for the reflex contraction of the urinary bladder and inhibition of its internal spincter in the micturition reflex. There is no sympathetic control of bladder activity, although sympathetic nerves regulate the blood flow in the bladder muscle. The contraction, produced by stimulating the sympathetic nerve of the muscle of the ureteral orifices and of the trigonum, is linked not with the micturition reflex but with the sex function. Section of the hypogastric nerves which contain the sympathetic fibres does not interfere with micturition whereas the bladder becomes paralysed after section of the pelvic nerves.

The cranial division of the parasympathetic contains vasodilator fibres to the salivary glands and tongue and the sacral division contains similar fibres to the erectile tissue of the external genitalia. The main rôle of these

TABLE 23.1

Summary of the Effects of Stimulation of the Sympathetic
and Parasympathetic Nerves

Organ	Sympathetic	Parasympathetic
Glands		
Sweat	Secretion	No innervation
Salivary, Gastric, Intestinal and Pancreas (acini and islets)		Secretion
Liver	Glycogenolysis	Increased bile flow
Lacrimal		Secretion
Smooth muscles		
of bronchi	Relaxation	Contraction
of oesophagus	Relaxation; usually contraction of cardiac sphincter	Contraction; relaxation of cardiac sphincter
of stomach	Usually relaxation	Contraction
of intestine	Relaxation	Increased tone and motility
of eye iris	Midriasis; contraction of dilator pupillae	Miosis; contraction of constrictor pupillae
ciliary	No innervation	Contraction
internal anal sphincter	Contraction	Relaxation
detrusor of urinary bladder	Relaxation	Contraction
trigone and spincter of urinary bladder	Contraction	Relaxation
vasa deferentia, seminal vesicles and prostate	Contraction (ejaculation)	No innervation
uterus	Relaxation; contraction when pregnant	No innervation
Blood vessels of		
salivary and lacrimal glands	Constriction	Dilatation
abdominal and pelvic viscera	Constriction	No innervation
external genitalia	Constriction	Dilatation (erection)
skin	Constriction	No innervation
skeletal muscles	Constriction. Dilatation during activity	No innervation
coronary system	Dilatation	Constriction (?)
Heart		
frequency of beat	Increased	Reduced
conduction of impulse	Quickened	Slowed
auricular contraction	Strengthened	Weakened
ventricular contraction	Strengthened	No innervation in mammals

vasodilators is, as mentioned before, linked with the specific functions of these organs, salivary secretion and erection of the generative organs respectively and not with general circulatory readjustments. Ejaculation is dependent on the integrity of the sympathetic system; its removal causes impotence in the male. Thus both divisions of the autonomic nervous system are involved in the mechanism of coitus (Chapter 36).

RELATIONS BETWEEN THE AUTONOMIC NERVOUS SYSTEM AND THE CENTRAL NERVOUS SYSTEM

A man's conscious activities largely consist in controlling his skeletal ("voluntary") muscles in response to information received through his "special senses" (chiefly vision and hearing) and controlled by his central nervous system. But he cannot do this properly unless his "auxiliary machinery"—cardio-vascular system, gastro-intestinal tract, etc.—is also operating properly, controlled in an appropriate manner by his autonomic nervous system; this, accordingly, is not really autonomous, as the name implies, but co-operates with all the other parts of the nervous system.

Some examples of this have been given in previous chapters. If the spinal cord is severed from "higher" parts of the nervous system, defaecation and micturition are controlled according to the distension of the rectum and bladder respectively. Gunshot wounds may sever completely the spinal cord in men. If this occurs in the cervical or upper thoracic region, disconnecting the sympathetic system from the higher centres, distension of the bladder causes a large reflex rise in blood pressure. If the section through the brain stem is such as to allow the medulla to remain connected with the spinal cord—as by decerebration, or by a gunshot wound in the lower thoracic region of the spinal cord, the blood pressure is well regulated and there is no rise when the bladder is distended. The baroreceptors are connected to the vasoconstrictor fibres of the sympathetic system through the vasomotor centres, and are able to control the cardiovascular system. In the whole normal animal, with intact nervous system, these and other "centres" are subjected to overriding influences from the rest of the nervous system, and their efferent discharges blocked or enhanced.

Little is known about this finer central integration which is necessary for keeping the internal environment constant. The most important structures through which it is exerted, however, lie in the **hypothalamus**. As mentioned in Chapter 32, the internal secretions of the adenohypophysis (anterior pituitary body), and hence those of many other parts of the endocrine system concerned in stabilizing the internal environment, are controlled through the hypothalamus. Here also are the "osmoreceptors" which control drinking and water diuresis through the neurohypophysis (posterior pituitary body), the centres controlling hunger and appetite and those controlling body temperature and the loss of heat. Electrical stimulation of the hypothalamus, through implanted electrodes in unanaesthetized animals, results characteristically in excitation of the sympathetic system with rise of blood pressure, dilatation of the pupils, erection of hairs and inhibition of gastro-intestinal movements and secretion; but parasympathetic effects may also be obtained—contraction of the bladder and increase in gastro-intestinal movements—according to the exact position of the stimulus and form of stimulating current. Stimulation of an appropriate area, may put the animal into a rage, snarling and biting, with staring eyes, hairs on end and general excitation of the sympathetic system, with perhaps urination and defaecation. A similar condition of "sham rage", ill-directed and short-lived, is produced by quite harmless stimuli in animals whose forebrains have been destroyed, leaving the hypothalamus intact.

Some structures in the hypothalamus, therefore, seem to be concerned in producing an abnormally irritable and aggressive type of behaviour, together with excitation and inhibition of many parts of the autonomic nervous system. These structures are normally held in check by higher centres which lie in the rhinencephalon, or "olfactory brain": this consists of structures which form a kind of arch, or "limbus" round the rostral brain stem and interhemispheric commissures, and is better called the "limbic system" since there is no good evidence that it is concerned with the sense of smell. The most important of these structures, in relation to emotion and temperament, appear to be the *amygdala*. If, instead of the whole forebrain, only the neocortex is removed, leaving the amygdala intact, cats become abnormally placid and show no signs of anger even when ill-treated; if the amygdala are then destroyed bilaterally, the cats become savage and malevolent. The evidence, however, is conflicting, since in other series of experiments, on cats and monkeys, removal of the amygdala has made the animals unusually placid; wild Norway rats also, ordinarily untameable, become gentle. Rather similar conflicting results have followed attempts to improve the condition of assaultive psychotic patients by making lesions in the amygdala. The organization of the limbic system is obviously very complicated, and much remains to be discovered.

CHEMICAL TRANSMISSION

The chemical transmission of excitation from motor nerves to skeletal muscles has been discussed in Chapter 18 and its intimate mechanism is most fully understood at these junctions. But historically, the theory of chemical transmission of the nervous impulse arose at the beginning of this century in connection with the autonomic system, to explain the striking similarity between the actions of adrenaline and of sympathetic nerve stimulation, on the one hand, and between the actions of drugs like pilocarpine and muscarine and of parasympathetic nerve stimulation, on the other hand.

Direct experimental evidence in favour of the theory was first produced by Otto Loewi in 1921. Fig. 23.1 shows a modification of his original method. Two frogs' hearts are supplied with Ringer solution from the same reservoir, the liquid being mixed by the pumping action of the hearts. On stimulating the vagi to the first heart, it is inhibited and may stop beating. When stimulation ceases and the heart starts beating again, a slight but definite inhibition occurs in the second heart which is connected with the first heart only by the Ringer solution. A substance must have been released into the liquid during stimulation of the vagus which on reaching the other heart causes the vagus-like effect. On stimulation of the sympathetic accelerans fibres to the heart an "accelerans substance" is correspondingly released.

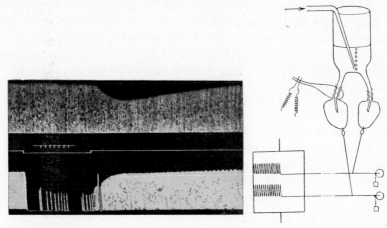

FIG. 23.1. Demonstration of chemical transmission of vagus effect on the frog's heart. Modification of Loewi's original experiment. (After Kahn.)

Similar experiments with stimulation of the vagus to the mammalian heart perfused with blood failed for a long time to demonstrate the existence of a "vagus substance", for the following reason. We now know that the substance released from the parasympathetic vagus nerve endings is **acetylcholine.** Once released, this is quickly hydrolysed by an enzyme *cholinesterase* into choline and acetic acid, both pharmacologically inert substances in comparison with acetylcholine. Choline has, in fact, actions like acetylcholine, but only if given in concentrations several thousand times as great. The amounts of choline set free, therefore, are too small to produce reactions and the hydrolysis may be regarded as an effective mechanism of inactivation. In warm-blooded animals the enzyme will have acted usually before the acetylcholine has had time to enter the capillaries. By the use of a tissue from a cold-blooded animal, and of Ringer solution instead of blood, Loewi had avoided this danger.

The effects of sympathetic stimulation have been described as rather, but not quite, like those of adrenaline and the name **sympathin** was given by Cannon to the "accelerans", adrenaline-like, substance or substances liberated at sympathetic nerve endings. When noradrenaline (adrenaline without its methyl group was identified in the adrenal glands, it was found to have actions resembling those of sympathin, particularly in those respects in which the actions of sympathin and adrenaline differed. Sympathin is now generally held to be a mixture of *adrenaline* and *noradrenaline* in different proportions at different sites of action. A third substance, *isoprenaline* (isopropylnoradrenaline) has been found to show those actions of sympathin in which it differs from those of noradrenaline. Isoprenaline has also been found in some mammals.

Sympathin is not as rapidly destroyed by blood as is acetylcholine, and as a hormone, the sympathin secreted by the adrenal medulla is transported by the blood stream to the tissues on which it acts. Sympathin released from nerve endings is probably partly destroyed before diffusing into the capillaries. By the action of an enzyme in the tissues, the hydroxyl group in the ortho position on the benzene ring is methylated; the compounds formed are pharmacologically inactive. Another enzyme (monoamine oxidase) may oxidize and deaminate the side chains. But some of the transmitter certainly reaches the blood stream in an active form and can and has been demonstrated there by its reactions on distant denervated tissues (denervation sensitizes the tissues to sympathin or adrenaline). For instance, when in cats the heart, pupil and nictitating membrane (a third eye-lid present in some species) are denervated and the adrenals removed, to exclude this source of sympathin, stimulation of sympathetic fibres to other tissues will cause quickening of the heart, dilatation of the pupil and withdrawal of the nictitating membrane, all of which are typical effects of adrenaline and noradrenaline.

It would be useless to employ similar methods for the detection of the released acetylcholine. Its enzymatic destruction provides an extremely efficient safeguard against any spread of the effects of the nerve impulse and thus makes acetylcholine particularly suitable as a transmitter for the peripheral effects of the parasympathetic division of the autonomic system with its restricted localized functions. In addition, the quick destruction will also ensure a short duration of the effect not outlasting the nerve impulse for any length of time. But how can the acetylcholine be detected if it is so quickly destroyed ? This has become possible by the use of eserine (physostigmine), which prevents the hydrolysis by cholinesterase. The released acetycholine may then escape into the blood stream and exert effects on distant organs in the same way as sympathin does in the normal course of events. This is illustrated by the experiment shown in **Fig. 23.2**

Before acetylcholine can be acted upon by the cholinesterase, it has to become attached to, or combined with, the enzyme; it is then at once hydrolysed and the enzyme becomes free again. Eserine (and related substances such as prostigmine) also combine with the enzyme and having done so, prevent acetylcholine from combining. Eserine, however, is hydrolysed slowly, if at all, and thus remains fixed to the enzyme. If, therefore, sufficient eserine molecules are available, all the enzyme molecules will, after a time, become blocked and unavailable for acetylcholine. An action such as that of eserine is called "competitive inhibition". There are certain organic phosphates which also are very potent inhibitors of cholinesterase. Some of them were originally prepared as war gases such as di-isopropylfluorophosphonate (DFP), others as insecticides such as tetra-ethylpyrophosphate (TEPP).

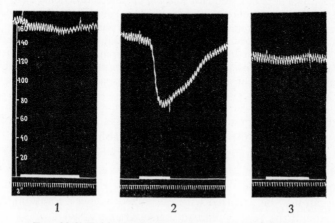

FIG. 23.2. Evidence for the Release of Acetylcholine.

Effect on the arterial blood pressure of an anaesthetized cat of three stimulations of the chorda-lingual nerve, which contains secretory and vasodilator fibres to the salivary glands and tongue.

In 1, there is no effect, since the local vasodilatation is insufficient to affect the general blood pressure. Between 1 and 2, eserine is injected intravenously. In 2, 10 min later, there is general vasodilatation, and a fall of blood pressure, as the released acetylcholine, escaping destruction, diffuses into the blood capillaries. Note the latency of some 10 sec, due mainly to the time taken for the blood to travel round the circulation.

Atropine is then given, and this abolishes the vasodilator action of acetylcholine. In 3, therefore, there is no depressor effect.

The amounts of acetylcholine released on nerve stimulation and available for analysis are far too small to be detected or identified by our present chemical methods. But acetylcholine has been identified chemically in extracts of the horse spleen, the human placenta and the ox brain and can be regarded as a substance occurring naturally and being formed in the body. Its identification when released on nerve stimulation is based on pharmacological methods using tissues which respond to minute doses of acetylcholine with characteristic reactions. Some tests in use for this purpose are shown in Fig. 23.3.

(a) Contraction of the muscle of the body wall of the leech, the effect being greatly increased in the presence of eserine. The reaction is very sensitive; it is induced by a concentration of acetylcholine of only one part in a thousand million.

(b) Contraction of the rectus abdominis muscle of the frog and the sensitizing effect of eserine on the action. Sensitive to about one in fifty million acetylcholine.

(c) Inhibition of the beat of the frog's heart. This was the first test used. The action is abolished by atropine.

(d) Depression of cat's blood pressure. The action is sensitized by eserine and abolished by atropine.

In each of these tests, the response to the unknown solution is matched with that of an appropriate dose of a standard solution of pure acetylcholine, and hence the apparent acetylcholine content of the unknown solution is determined. If the apparent acetylcholine content is found to be the same in all four tests, and, in addition, the unknown substance is unstable in alkaline solution and destroyed by blood in the absence of eserine, but not in its presence, the identity with acetylcholine is regarded as proved. Other choline esters produce qualitatively similar, but quantitatively different, effects on these tissues, acting relatively more on one than the other compared with acetylcholine.

In order to prove that a nerve impulse acts by the release of acetylcholine, the following three facts must be established.

(1) Acetylcholine is released into the tissues when the nerve is stimulated. The eserinized venous blood from a given organ may be collected and tested for acetylcholine, while the nerves to the organ are stimulated; or the organ may be perfused with eserinized Ringer's solution, the nerve stimulated and the venous effluent collected and assayed.

(2) The action of injected acetylcholine must be identical with, or approximate closely to, that of nerve stimulation, although we have to take into account the fact that the method of injection does not always imitate closely the release of acetylcholine by nerve impulses.

(3) Eserine, by delaying the destruction of the released acetylcholine, must potentiate and prolong the effects of nervous stimulation. In some instances, prolonged action of acetylcholine may paralyse a reactive structure; in that case the response to nerve stimulation should be affected similarly after eserine.

The identification of sympathin is based on similar lines of argument: similarity of the effects of sympathetic nerve stimulation with those of injection of adrenaline and noradrenaline, the actions of various drugs (as mentioned later) in modifying these effects, and pharmacological assay of adrenaline and noradrenaline in venous effluents during stimulation of sympathetic nerves.

The tests generally used are:

(a) rise of blood pressure in the cat or rat after destruction of the spinal cord (to prevent vasomotor reflexes) and treatment with atropine and hexamethonium.

(b) inhibition of the contractions of the rat's uterus, rat's colon, or hen's colon.

The tests can detect the presence of 1/1,000 to 1/100 of a milligram of adrenaline or noradrenaline, but no single test will differentiate between them with certainty.

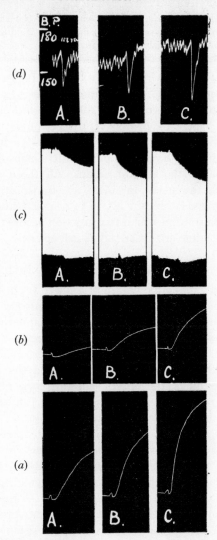

FIG. 23.3. Tests of Substance in Perfusion Fluid emerging from Veins
of Stomach during Stimulation of Vagus.

From below upwards. (a) Eserinized leech muscle; (b) Frog's
rectus abdominis; (c) Frog's heart[1]; (d) Cat's blood pressure. In each
case, A shows the effect of a suitable dose of acetylcholine, B shows
the effect of a dose of the perfusion fluid, adjusted to be proportional
to the dose A of acetylcholine. C is the effect of acetylcholine given
in twice the concentration of A. In each of the four reactions, the
effects of B are intermediate between those in A and those in C.

Concentrations of acetylcholine (A): (a) $1:280 \times 10^6$; (b)
$1:56 \times 10^6$; (c) $1:56 \times 10^6$; (d) 1 ml of $1:40 \times 10^6$. (After
Dale and Feldberg.)

[1] Owing to the slowness of the drum, the individual vertical lines representing
heart beats have overlapped. The vertical distances between the upper and lower
borders of the white patch nevertheless indicate the relative amplitudes of the heart
beat.

The different preparations, however, have very different sensitivities to adrenaline and noradrenaline, so that by using several tests in parallel the quantity of each in a mixture may be estimated. Adrenaline and noradrenaline may also be separated from one another, and from interfering substances, by the use of paper chromatography.

A systematic analysis of the effects of different nerves soon showed that chemical transmission is not confined to the autonomic nervous system, as is made clear in Chapter 18. Moreover, the peripheral pathway of the autonomic nervous system (except that to the adrenal medulla) consists of two neurones; transmission across the ganglionic synapses must be considered as well as that to the effector organs. All those nerve fibres or neurones from which the nerve impulses are transmitted to the next neurone, or the effector cells, by the action of acetylcholine are described as **cholinergic**; all those from which transmission occurs by the action of noradrenaline or adrenaline are described as **adrenergic**.

SOME PROPERTIES OF CHOLINERGIC AND ADRENERGIC NERVES

The adrenergic and cholinergic nature of a nerve is not confined to the endings but is an inherent property of the whole neurone. An adrenergic or cholinergic nerve contains noradrenaline and adrenaline, or acetylcholine, respectively, throughout the whole course of the nerve fibre; when the nerve impulse passes along it, minute amounts of the chemical mediators are released. The difference between the fibre and the ending is only quantitative. At the endings, the process shows a local intensification to ensure transmission to a contiguous cell. No function can yet be postulated for the release along the course of the fibre.

Cholinergic nerves have the ability to synthesize acetylcholine from choline, with the aid of an enzyme *choline acetylase*, not only at their endings but along the whole course of the fibre. The synthesis is a complex process in which adenosine-triphosphate and coenzyme A, the coenzyme for acetylation are involved. The acetylcholine so formed is not free but in loose combination with some cell constituent, probably protein; this complex is pharmacologically inactive and resistant to the action of cholinesterase. At the nerve endings, the nerve impulse releases the acetylcholine from the bound complex, so that it becomes diffusible and pharmacologically active; then it is at once destroyed by the true cholinesterase. About forty-eight hours after a cholinergic nerve is cut, the peripheral end loses its ability to synthesize acetylcholine and the acetylcholine store disappears; at this time the fibre is still able to conduct nerve impulses.

Another observation suggesting that the whole of a neurone is either cholinergic or adrenergic is based on regeneration experiments. When the known facts of regeneration experiments with cross-sutured nerves were reconsidered in the light of the chemical transmission theory, it became evident that cholinergic fibres could replace other cholinergic fibres and enter into functional connections with them and that adrenergic nerves could replace adrenergic ones, but a cholinergic fibre could not enter into functional connection with an adrenergic one or *vice versâ.*

The Distribution of Adrenergic and Cholinergic Neurones

This is shown diagrammatically in Fig. 23.4. Most of the endings of the sympathetic fibres with their effector cells are adrenergic, which explains the striking similarity between the effects of noradrenaline and adrenaline and of sympathetic stimulation. The endings of the parasympathetic fibres with their effector cells are cholinergic, a fact which explains the equally striking similarity between the effects of parasympathetic stimulation and of drugs like acetylcholine, pilocarpine or muscarine. The secretory nerves to sweat glands, and the vasodilator nerves to blood vessels in skeletal muscles, are peculiar. The endings of the nerve fibres on the effector cells are cholinergic and thus appear to belong to the parasympathetic system; but the nerves arise from ganglion cells which are situated centrally, not peripherally, and anatomically form part of the sympathetic system.

The synaptic transmission across the ganglia of the autonomic system, both sympathetic and parasympathetic, is cholinergic, and so also is the neuromuscular transmission at the motor end-plates of skeletal muscles (Chapter 18). Two rather different types of cholinergic nerve ending must be distinguished, associated with the two classes into which the pharmacological actions of acetylcholine can be divided.

(*a*) *The Muscarine-like Action.* Muscarine is a substance of known composition closely related to choline; it is found in extracts of a common toadstool (*Amanita muscaria*). Its effects are the same as those observed on stimulating the postganglionic parasympathetic fibres. These actions, whether induced by muscarine or acetylcholine, are abolished by atropine.

The muscarine-like action of acetylcholine is effective in the transmission to the peripheral structures from all postganglionic parasympathetic nerves, as well as from the cholinergic postganglionic sympathetic nerves; all these nerve effects are blocked by atropine (Fig. 23.4, upper part). After atropine, stimulation of the vagus no longer inhibits the heart, and stimulation of the sympathetic no longer causes sweating in human beings. Nevertheless the nerve impulses still release their acetylcholine. Atropine, although abolishing the effects of nerve stimulation, has no action on the nerves or nerve endings themselves, but renders the effector structure insensitive to the action of acetylcholine, whether released or artificially applied. Many other drugs can still act after atropine. We do not know why drugs like atropine render the cells insensitive to one kind of drug and not to another.

(*b*) *The Nicotine-like Action.* Nicotine first excites and subsequently paralyses the following structures: (1) the autonomic ganglia; (2) the cells of the adrenal medulla and (3) the motor end-plates of skeletal muscle. Similar actions can be obtained when acetylcholine is injected. The

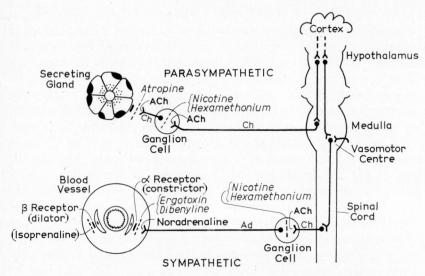

FIG. 23.4. Diagram showing Chemical Transmission in the Autonomic Nervous System and the distribution of cholinergic (Ch) and adrenergic (Ad) neurones.

    A secreting gland is taken as a typical effector organ innervated from the parasympathetic system; and the smooth muscle in a blood vessel as a typical effector organ innervated from the sympathetic system.

    At each junction the transmitter substance liberated at the nerve endings is labelled (ACh = acetylcholine); the receptor is shown by the thick short line; and the site of action of blocking agents, as labelled, shown by the interrupted line. As hormones, secreted by the adrenal glands, noradrenaline acts only on the α receptors, and adrenaline, in low concentration, more on the β receptors than the α receptors; in larger concentrations it acts chiefly on the α receptors.

    The parasympathetic receptors may be excitatory, as in glands and in smooth muscle cells of the alimentary canal, or inhibitory, as in the heart. The sympathetic β receptors in the blood vessels (when present) are not innervated; but in other kinds of receptor cell, such as the heart, they are thought to be innervated and may be excitatory.

nicotine-like effects are relatively insensitive to atropine. Acetylcholine has, in addition, stimulating and paralysing effects on cells of the central nervous system.

    The nicotine-like action of acetylcholine is effective in the transmission to the cells of the adrenal medulla, the nerve cells of the autonomic ganglia, and the end-plates of skeletal muscle. Transmission at these structures is not blocked by atropine, but is blocked by suitable amounts of nicotine; the motor end-plates, also, are blocked by curarine, the active principle of the poison curare. Nicotine acts on the ganglia, and curare on the end-plates, much as atropine acts on the heart, smooth muscles or gland cells. They prevent the nerve impulses from being transmitted across the junction, but do not prevent the release of acetylcholine at the nerve endings by the incoming impulses. The action is on the ganglion cells, or the end-plates, respectively. The postganglionic fibres in the presence of nicotine, and the muscle fibres in the presence of curare, respond as usual to direct electrical stimulation.

As mentioned in Chapter 18 drugs with a curare-like action are widely used in general anaesthesia to produce relaxation of skeletal muscles. Since one cannot breathe without active skeletal muscles, this would be dangerous unless the synthetic curarine substitutes employed had a shorter duration of action than the natural product. Correspondingly, since autonomic ganglia when paralysed have as their most widespread and dramatic consequence a profound vasodilatation and fall in arterial blood pressure, ganglion-blocking drugs are widely used in the treatment of patients with chronic high arterial pressure (hypertension). The actions of the short-lived acetylcholine and the prolonged nicotine would be unsuitable because of their initial stimulating action. Synthetic substances such as hexamethonium bromide have an uncomplicated blocking action which is inconveniently short-lived, but many other synthetic products are now available which have a longer-lived action in blocking the autonomic ganglia in hypertensive patients

Section 8
RECEPTORS AND SENSATIONS

CHAPTER 24

MECHANICAL STRAIN, TEMPERATURE, TASTE AND SMELL

No animal can act in a purposive way or control its own bodily functions unless it is supplied with enough information about the outside world and the state of its own body; it is the function of the receptors to supply this. Some of the information received by the central nervous system from receptors controls reflex responses; for example, receptors in the muscles of the limbs are continuously signalling the lengths of these muscles and in the absence of other activity they are kept, by reflex action, at a constant length. In ourselves, and by inference in other persons and in the higher animals generally, some of this information also reaches consciousness and underlies sensation.

Our own experience of receptor mechanisms is dominated, as was the early experimental work on the subject, by sensation. It is therefore important to understand the relation between a sensation and the activity of the receptor organs. This relationship is probably best illustrated by describing briefly the events that are going on when we are conscious of a sensation. Let us consider a visual example: electro-magnetic waves of widely varying wave-lengths are reflected from various parts of the object seen, different wave-lengths being reflected with greater or less intensity from the different parts; those wave-lengths within a certain narrow band, which we call light, are able to excite receptors in the retina and these set up nerve impulses; the activity in any one nerve fibre is combined with, and modified by, the activity of other nerve fibres at junctional regions; several such junctional regions, at each of which changes in the message will occur, are to be found before the information reaches those levels at which it is generally presumed, the entirely unexplained processes involved in consciousness and sensation takes place.

This illustrates certain things about a sensation. First, it is and can

405

only be a subjective response. Secondly, a sensation cannot include more information about an object or event than has been transmitted by the physical events outside the body and by the activity of the receptors and the nervous system. Thirdly, sensation may be a product, not only of the information from one particular kind of receptor, but also of that from other kinds of receptor of the same general type but differing in detail. Fourthly, the intensity and quality of a sensation depend on the nature and intensity of other sensations, on the general activity of the central nervous system at the time, and on its antecedent activity associated with previous experience. One can diminish a sensation of pain by applying a counter-irritant; one can fail to hear quite loud sounds if one is deep in thought; and one can fail to observe, by touch or sight, a familiar object in its accustomed place. The selection and synthesis by the central nervous system of the information transmitted to it from a variety of receptors forms the basis of the wide range and subtlety of sensation of which the human mind is capable. Sensations depend as much on the central nervous system as on the receptors, and great care must be taken to scrutinise the interpretation when sensation is used as an index of receptor activity.

The most striking thing about our sensations is their clarity and detail, but it must be remembered that there are real limitations; for example, "sounds" with a frequency greater than 20,000 c/s are inaudible, and the effect of doubling the intensity of a sound wave is not to increase its loudness by a factor of two, but by a variable factor, which is quite different for high and low notes. It is the purpose of this chapter to consider how the receptors are able to transmit so much information to the central nervous system and to describe also some of their limitations.

The Behaviour of Receptor Units

The first step in considering the problem of the transmission of information to the central nervous system is to consider the behaviour of the individual unit, the word unit being used to describe a single afferent (sensory) axon and the one or many receptors with which it is directly connected and the whole lying *in situ*. It seems probable that all types of unit, including those in the complex organs of the so-called "Special Senses," behave in fundamentally the same way; however, most experiments on single units have been done in places other than the organs of "special sense."

The Specificity of Receptor Units. Single afferent nerve fibres can be dissected out from nerve trunks and separated from other fibres which have different connections. When this is done, it is usually found that activity appears in response to excitation of the receptors from which the fibre is derived; and usually, it appears much more readily when one particular type of energy is used, e.g. mechanical, thermal, chemical or light, than when other types are used. Thus the receptors of the retina normally respond only to light, and those associated with the senses of taste and smell respond only to chemical stimulation. In general, therefore, each kind of receptor unit is specially sensitive to one form of energy: receptor units are *specific* in that each unit exhibits a particular pattern of sensitivity (Muller's Law). One class of unit which does not show big differences in its sensitivity to different forms of energy but shows a distinct sensitivity pattern of great importance, is that associated with the sensation of pain. These units may have different patterns of sensitivity but in general they respond to high intensities of stimulation by all types of energy—that is levels which are nearly or actually damaging. When receptor units, which are specially sensitive to one form of energy, are excited by a high intensity of some other form, the sensation aroused is that expected of the normal stimulus, demonstrating that the sensation is dependent on the connections of the unit and not on the nature of the stimulus that excited it. A good example of a sensation being aroused by an abnormal stimulus is to be found in the flash of light that is seen if the eyeball is struck, or if an electric current is passed through it.

The Response of a Single Unit. The response that can be recorded from a single afferent fibre when the area it innervates is stimulated, consists of one or many impulses. These impulses, like all nerve impulses, are all-or-nothing; it is clear, therefore, that information can only be carried either by the time relations of impulses in any one fibre, or by the interrelations of the activity of a number of different units. The simplest type of response is found in the signalling of steady states by certain units; these include temperature sensitive units, some mechanically sensitive units, some units in the retina and the chemically sensitive receptor units associated with smell. Such a unit, when in a steady state, sets up a train of impulses which lasts as long as the stimulus; the frequency of the impulses depending on the strength of the stimulus (Fig. 24.1). These frequencies are repeatable so that, for example, whenever a limb is in a given position, a given receptor in the joint capsule will discharge at a particular frequency. This is important, since the nervous system can only act consistently if the signals it receives are consistently related to the stimulus.

The response is not quite as simple as that just described if the stimulus is applied abruptly and then left constant; for example, if a muscle stretch receptor (muscle spindle) is suddenly stretched to a new length, the impulse discharge starts at a high frequency, which declines at first rapidly and then more slowly until the steady frequency associated with the particular degree of stretch is reached. This decline of frequency after the onset of a steady stimulus is called *adaptation*. The frequency at the beginning of such a discharge depends not only on the final size of the stimulus, in this instance the amount of stretch, but also the rate at which the final level is reached, in this example, the velocity of the stretch. Discharges from temperature receptor units which behave in this way are shown in Fig. 24.5.

A large number of receptors do not respond to steady stimuli at all. They respond to a suddenly imposed steady stimulus by a discharge at a frequency which is initially high but which falls rapidly to zero (Fig. 24.2); and often give another burst of impulses when the stimulus ends.

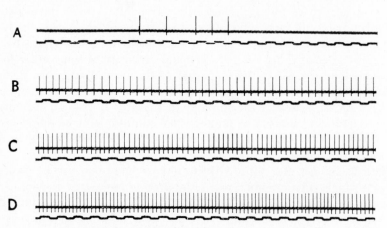

Fig. 24.1. The relation of frequency of discharge to stimulus strength. Records of impulses from a single fibre of the incisor nerve of an anaesthetized rabbit while different weights were hung from the tooth. A, 5 g (threshold). B, 10 g. C, 20 g. D, 50 g. All records one minute after the weight was applied. Note occasional irregular impulses in A.

Below each record are time marks in 1/10th second.

All the action potentials are seen to be of the same size, irrespective of their frequency and thus of the strength of stimulation, illustrating the all-or-nothing law. (From a record kindly prepared by Mr. A. R. Ness.)

As an extreme case, the large capsulated end organs, known as Pacinian corpuscles, often respond to a steady pressure with a single impulse at the moment the pressure is applied and another when it is released. Such receptors which respond only to a change of state are called "rapidly adapting," or *phasic receptors*; they are to be found both among those responding to mechanical stimuli and those responding to light stimuli.

A little thought about one's own sensations will immediately make clear the importance of signalling changes of state; one responds vigorously to sudden changes of sound, while being oblivious of a steady noise; and if one wants to feel an object carefully one keeps one's hand moving and allows the rapidly adapting receptors to respond as the hand passes over the small irregularities of the surface.

Receptive Fields. A single nerve fibre may come from a single receptor or from many; such a fibre may be excited from an appreciable area due either to spread of stimulus or to branching of the unit. The receptive fields of primary receptor fibres may therefore vary from a single point up to quite considerable areas; in the cat there are units sensitive to mechanical deformation which have receptive fields up to 5 cm by 9 cm in size. Receptive fields usually overlap.

10 msec.

FIG. 24.2. Rapid adaptation of a receptor discharge. Impulses recorded from a mesenteric nerve, while a single Pacinian corpuscle was stimulated by the movement of a piezo-electric crystal. The top trace (at left) indicates the amplitude and time course of the stimulus. (Gray and Matthews, *J. Physiol.*, 1951.)

Receptor Mechanisms

It is probably true to say that all receptors when excited set up changes in electrical potential, which, unlike the nervous impulses, are not all-or-nothing, but vary in size and duration with variations in magnitude, rate of change and duration of the stimulus (Fig. 24.3). These *Receptor Potentials*, which are localized in the receptor or its neighbourhood, are the immediate cause of the impulse discharge. The ways in which the various types of stimulus set up these potentials are not yet known with any certainty. However, whatever the mechanisms involved in setting up these potentials, they must be highly sensitive; a rod cell in the retina can be activated by a single light-quantum, i.e. the smallest possible quantity of light; movements of the basilar membrane of molecular or even atomic dimensions are adequate to set up impulses in responses to sound; the threshold movement on the outside of a Pacinian corpuscle (not on the sensitive element) is probably about $0.2\,\mu$—below the limit of resolution by the best light microscope.

In view of this high sensitivity, it is not surprising to find that the energy received by a receptor, in the form of light or mechanical work, for example, is too small to account for the electrical energy which is released by the receptor, and which can be recorded as the receptor potential. The external event must, therefore, release energy from an internal store. It appears that receptors store energy in the form of concentration gradients of ions across membranes. The stimulus causes a change in the permeability of this membrane and allows the ions to move down their electrochemical gradients. In general, this process is

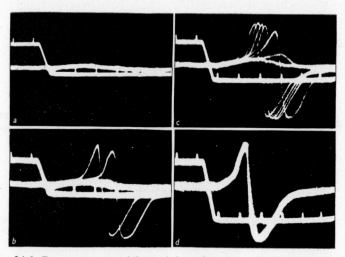

Fig. 24.3. Receptor potentials and impulses in a Pacinian corpuscle. Each picture is of twenty superimposed traces; the top beam (at the left) signals the amplitude and time course of the mechanical stimulus that was applied to the corpuscle and also shows 1 msec time intervals. The stimulus strength was increased between each record. The receptor potential can be seen to increase in size with the stimulus and the impulses increase in number. In (b) and (c) 2 and 5, respectively, of the stimuli gave rise to impulses, which "took off" at different values of the receptor potential, owing to slight variations of the threshold. In (d) every stimulus results in an impulse. (Gray and Sato, J. Physiol., 1953.)

similar to the release of electrical energy in the form of end-plate or synaptic potentials by a chemical transmitter.

The Transmission of Receptor Information

How can receptor units when working in large numbers provide enough information for complex sensations? Information on the strength and duration of a stimulus may be conveyed by the time course of the discharge in each fibre, but information about stimulus strength is also signalled by the number of units activated. The time course of the discharge can, however, convey nothing about the site of the stimulus or its nature; such information reaches the central nervous system through the organization of particular fibres, each of which has its own particular properties. There are thus two general ways in which information is signalled: in time, and by distinguishing between different units; or one can say in time and space. These two general ways are correlated with the two types of summation found in the central nervous system, temporal summation between successive impulses and spatial summation between impulses in neighbouring fibres.

It is now possible to summarize the variables available for transmitting information:

Factors depending on time.

(*a*) The intervals between impulses.

(*b*) The duration of the discharge.

Factors depending on the specific properties of the receptor units.

(*a*) The specificity of the unit to a particular type or types of stimulus and its rate of adaptation, which decides whether it is sensitive to a steady state or a change of state.

(*b*) The size of the receptive field and its position in the body.

(*c*) The sensitivity of each unit and, arising from this, the number of units active for a given stimulus.

A pattern of nerve impulses is therefore set up by each stimulus, however complex, and this pattern involves both the timing of each impulse in each fibre and also the spatial pattern formed by those units which are active and those which are not. For every stimulus, which can be distinguished from other stimuli, this pattern must be unique in that it must differ from the patterns set up by each of the other stimuli. The physical properties of the tissues in which the receptors lie perform a major rôle in distributing the energy of the stimulus amongst the different receptors and also in determining the time course of any disturbance occurring in the immediate vicinity of each receptor. Examples of this will appear in the following chapters. The mechanics of the ear determines the distribution of activation amongst the receptor units of the cochlea it will be seen that, as the intensity of the sound increases, the mechanical disturbance spreads further and so more units are activated; as the frequency of the sound wave changes, the position of the maximum disturbance moves. In the vertebrate eye the light is focussed by an optical system onto an array of receptors; each unit probably responds with an increasing impulse frequency to increasing intensity of illumination at that point; in some species, such as man, receptors having different sensitivities to different wave-lengths are intermingled and the combined output of groups of such different units enables the wave-length, as well as the intensity and position, of the light to be determined.

SENSATIONS ASSOCIATED WITH MECHANICAL STRAIN

There are many kinds of receptor which are activated, and discharge nerve impulses when distorted or deformed. The deformation may be produced by contact with objects in the outside world, by changes in the relative position of different parts of the body as a result of muscular contraction, or of movements and changes in orientation with respect to gravity. The stimuli to which they respond are thus essentially mechanical, so that it is convenient to group them together. Receptor units which can respond to mechanical stimulation are found in the skins or other integuments, in the muscles, and in the joints or other articulations, of species throughout the animal kingdom. There are many varieties of such units, and many of them are associated with special structures which make them particularly sensitive to certain kinds of mechanical deformation. The Pacinian corpuscle is one such structure, of a relatively simple kind, and others will be mentioned in the following paragraphs. In the ear, the associated structures are so elaborate that the receptor cells—which are not in themselves essentially different from other mechanically sensitive receptors—respond only to the changes in air pressure which constitute sound; and the whole arrangement makes up an organ of "Special Sense."

Touch and Pressure

The sensations experienced by human beings when they come into contact with objects outside them are often described as "touch" or "pressure." Such terms have value in any investigation in which a human sensation is used as a criterion, but are of little value when discussing the physiological processes which underlie the sensation. The information on which these sensations are based is received by receptors which are sensitive to mechanical stimuli, and which lie in the skin. The receptor units, even in one individual, vary in all the ways that have been mentioned in the last section: they vary in their sensitivity to the direction of the force; they vary in the time course of their responses and, associated with this, they vary in their responses to different rates of change of the applied force; they vary in position and in size of receptive field; and even when these factors are the same, they may still vary in their sensitivity to a force of given magnitude. The specialization of structure which can be seen under the light microscope, and is found among receptors in the higher mammals, may be associated with particular functional properties. It is certain, however, that great variation in the properties of receptor units can be found in species that do not show any gross morphological specialization of receptors; and even in those that do—man, for example—there are areas which contain no receptors specialized in this way but which are, none the less, associated with a full range of sensations. In any event this is not a matter of great importance in this context. What does matter is that there are, functionally, many types of receptor unit each with its own quantitatively characteristic properties.

A sensation of "Touch" implies several things. Change is an essential element and the sensation is normally only aroused at a moment of change. The change has position and can be localized fairly accurately; the change has other qualities, velocity, direction and final amplitude, all of which may be appreciated in a quantitative way. Since "Touch" is mainly concerned with change it is the phasic or rapidly adapting receptors which contribute most to it. The responses of such receptors are brief and the timing of impulses in individual units can play little part in the transmission of all the information needed to define the size, direction and position of the stimulus; this information depends on the distribution of activity amongst units having a range of characteristics such as that mentioned in the last paragraph. These differences may frequently fall within a single category of receptors as defined by gross morphology. Thus the sensation of "Touch" aroused by drawing a piece of cotton wool over hairy skin (a test used in clinical medicine) is much reduced if the hairs are shaved. There are receptors associated with the hair follicles and similar receptors in experimental animals have been shown to have the characteristics required; it is therefore likely that in this instance the hair follicle receptors are associated with the sensation. The "sensation of pressure" (which must not be confused with pressure in its other senses) is used to describe the sensation aroused by a maintained force, which, relative to those arousing a sensation of "touch", may be stronger and more widespread. The sensation is maintained and is probably associated at least in part with slowly adapting or tonic receptors.

Being sensations, "touch" and "pressure" are the products of the activity of the central nervous system as well as of that of the various kinds of receptor just described. Some of the attributes of such sensations can even be lost by lesions of the nervous system without affecting others; with certain lesions, for example, localization of the sensation may be lost, while sensitivity is retained.

Proprioception

Information about the position of the body and of its parts is provided by mechanically sensitive receptors of a variety of types which are stretched or deformed in various specific conditions. *Muscle spindles* provide information about the lengths of muscles; *tendon* receptors provide information about the tension set up by the muscles; receptors in *joints* indicate the angle or angles between the bones. Most of these receptors are able to signal a steady state, although they are all more active during a change. Information from these sources, together with that from receptors in the labyrinths (see below) and from the eyes, is used by the nervous system to control posture and movement; this information can also form the basis of a conscious appreciation of the orientation and movement of the body in space and the position of the limbs with respect to the rest of the body.

Lastly, the *baroreceptors* in the aorta and carotid sinus, sensitive to the arterial blood pressure and the stretch receptors in the *lungs* are all receptors sensitive to mechanical strain. The information provided by these is important for initiating cardio-vascular and respiratory reflexes, but rarely, if ever, forms the basis of conscious sensation.

The Labyrinths

Each labyrinth lies in the petrous bone in close anatomical relation with the inner ear, with which, however, it has no physiological connections (Fig. 26.5). It consists of three specialized structures, each containing mechanically sensitive receptors. (1) The *utricle* encloses a small calcareous body (the *otolith*) lying against the projecting filaments of the receptors (hair cells). The receptors are activated by the weight of the otolith and so provide information as to the orientation of the head with respect to gravity; they are also activated by linear accelerations. (2) The *saccule*, which also contains an otolith, is perhaps also concerned with signalling the position of the head in space. In the frog, the saccule is concerned only with the detection of low frequency vibration. In the cat, there are apparently two separate systems which signal tilts from side to side, and fore and aft, respectively, but they have not yet been identified anatomically. (3) The *semi-circular canals*, lying in three planes at right angles to each other, and filled with endolymph. Each canal contains a *cupola*, which consists of hair cells whose bases are embedded in a gelatinous matrix in which they are in contact with a number of nerve endings. When the head is rotated, the endolymph in the semi-circular canals, owing to its inertia, lags behind; the cupola is dragged through the endolymph and thus displaced and distorted.

Electrical studies have shown that the nerve endings in the cupola discharge impulses when the head is at rest. When the cupola is displaced in one direction the frequency of discharge is increased, and when it is displaced in the opposite direction, the frequency is decreased (Fig. 24.4). As a result, rotations in both directions may be signalled. In steady rotations, the discharge of impulses behaves as though the cupola were displaced during the period of acceleration, and then drifted slowly back to its resting position during the period of steady rotation. Suddenly stopping the rotation of the head will displace the cupola in the opposite direction, and although movements of the endolymph die down in about three seconds, the cupola seems to take about twenty-five to thirty seconds to return to its resting position. During this time the subject will experience a sensation of rotation in the opposite direction.

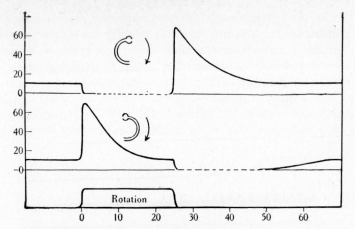

F<small>IG</small>. 24.4. Frequency of action potentials from the horizontal semi-
circular canal of a cat, when acceleration and deceleration are
separated by an interval of steady rotation.

There is a steady discharge during rest which is suppressed by
rotation in one direction, and augmented by rotation in the opposite
direction. Cessation of the rotation leads to an after discharge, or a
silent period according to the direction of the rotation. (Adrian.)

Reflexes based on information provided by the receptors in the labyrinths
are important, not only in the maintenance of posture, but also in controlling the position of the eyes, as will be discussed in the next chapter.

TEMPERATURE

Much of what has been said in the previous sections about the relationship between receptor units and sensation is also applicable to that between
the receptor units affected by temperature and the sensation associated
with temperature. Temperature sensitive receptors are found in all parts
of the skin and in some mucous membranes. Certain single units investigated in detail have been found to set up a steady discharge whose
frequency depends solely on the temperature of the receptor; for a given
receptor there is a temperature at which the frequency of the discharge
is a maximum, and the frequency declines at temperatures on both sides
of this maximum. There are two main groups of receptor, those which
have a maximum discharge around a temperature of 30°C, and those
which have a maximum around 40°C. A particular combination of frequency of discharge in each group of units is thus uniquely related to a
particular value of temperature. Information from a single group of
receptors having a temperature–frequency characteristic of the type
mentioned would always be ambiguous, since it gives the same frequency
of discharge at two separate temperatures. When a man is in a "comfortably

warm" state, the temperature of his skin ordinarily lies between 25° and 35°C, that of the temperature receptors being a few degrees higher: in these conditions, a rise of temperature causes one group of receptors to discharge more rapidly, and the other group to discharge less rapidly, while a fall in temperature has the converse effect. Both groups of receptor respond with a burst of impulses, over and above the steady response, if the temperature is suddenly changed; the "30°" receptors respond in this way to a sudden fall but not normally to a sudden rise of temperature,

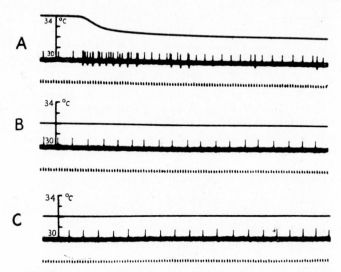

Fig. 24.5. The impulse discharge, in two nerve fibres from temperature receptors in a cat's tongue, showing adaptation. The upper line signals the temperature, which falls at the beginning from 34°C to 32°C. At the bottom are time marks in 1/50th second. The discharge in one fibre (diphasic potentials) adapts to zero, while the other (monophasic potentials) adapts to a steady frequency. The records were taken at the following times: A, zero; B, 1 minute; C, 15 minutes (Hensel and Zotterman, *Acta physiol. Scand.*, 1951.)

and the "40°" receptors respond to a sudden rise of temperature. These higher frequencies resulting from change of temperature decline rapidly and within seconds, or at most one or two minutes, have reached their steady level (Fig. 24.5).

Certain other points of interest arise if we consider the sensations aroused from human skin as a whole instead of considering the responses of single units from experimental animals. If an area of skin is tested for these sensations using metal rods with small tips (say, diameter 1·5 mm), which can arouse the sensation called "hot" or "cold", it is found that there are certain areas where it is especially easy to arouse either the sensation of "warmth" or that of "cold". In these areas the sensation is easily obtained in the centre, but less easily in the immediate surroundings. Provided that the testing rod is left long enough in contact with the skin, temperature differences can be felt on most parts of the skin owing to the conduction of heat to or from the sensitive spots. The areas associated with the sensation of "warmth" do not coincide with those associated with the sensation of "cold"; neither are they equal in number. Certain "mucous membranes" are relatively insensitive to stimulation by raising the temperature, so that it is possible, for instance, to drink liquids which are hotter than the skin can bear, and the same also applies to medicinal douches.

If one hand is placed in hot water and the other in cold, and if they are allowed to remain until the sensations of cold and warmth have subsided and then both hands are placed in tepid water, the hand that was in the hot water will now feel cold and the one that was in the cold feel hot. This effect is probably not due simply to an initial adaptation of the receptors themselves. Like some other peculiarities of the sensation of temperature, it may be due partly to the cutaneous vasomotor changes that accompany sudden changes in the temperature of the surroundings. The temperature of the deeper layers of the skin is rarely the same as that of the superficial layers, and the magnitude, and even sign, of the difference depends largely upon the rate of blood flow in the various parts of the cutaneous circulation. The temperature sensitive receptors in the two hands may thus be at different temperatures, even though both hands are in water of the same temperature. But it is possible, also, that there is some central adaptation; the sensation at any moment will not be determined solely by the signals sent in by the receptors at that moment.

PAIN

"Pain" is a sensation associated with high intensity stimulation of any type, though any particular "pain" is likely to have characteristics related to characteristics of the particular stimulus arousing the sensation. As stimulus intensity increases, the frequency of firing in certain individual tonic units increases; in any range of intensity only certain units will be in their working range, some will be sub-threshold and others may have already reached their maximum rate of firing. High intensities of stimulus are, therefore, signalled by the activation of those units having the highest working ranges and hence it is the activation of this group of units which is associated with the sensation of "pain". Unpleasant sensations may be aroused in other ways but these are not usually described as "pain"; for example vibrations of certain frequencies can be unpleasant even though each individual stimulus in the sequence is of very low intensity and is signalled as such by the receptor units.

Two types of pain, fast and slow, are usually described. This distinction was first made from results of subjective experiments, but analysis of the responses in single primary receptor fibres has shown that receptor units with a high threshold for all types of energy fall into two groups with different velocities of conduction of the nerve impulses. The faster group have a conduction velocity comparable to that of the slower low threshold mechanically sensitive units concerned in the sensations of "touch" and "pressure"; while the slower group are among the slowest of all sensory fibres.

A special word must be said about visceral pain. Most of the information from the visceral receptors never reaches consciousness, but on occasion a sensation of pain may be aroused; when it is, the pain may be referred by the nervous system to the skin belonging to the same segment as the visceral nerve responsible. This is known as *"referred pain"*. For example, gall bladder pains are often localized in the right shoulder; kidney pains in the groin. One finds that the receptor nerves to joints, to the muscles working those joints, and the covering skin are all supplied from the same spinal cord segment. In joint injuries it is usual to find impaired movement due to fixation by the muscles, and also pain in the overlying skin. Visceral sensations are usually painful and are of the same type whatever their origin. Two very common causes of visceral pain are (1) prolonged contraction of plain muscle such as occurs in a ureter when partly obstructed by a stone, and (2) the stretching of organs such as the mesentery.

TASTE AND SMELL

There are many different kinds of receptor which are sensitive to the presence of various chemical substances in the fluid around them. Many of these, such as the "chemo-receptors" in the brain and carotid body, concerned in the regulation of breathing and the "osmoreceptors" concerned in the control of the concentration of the urine, are of great importance in the life of man as well as that of all animals; their activities do not give rise to any definite kind of sensation. Certain specific chemical substances, however, when present in or near the appropriate kinds of receptor may arous the sensations of "taste" and "smell". In this respect, the two sensations are superficially related; but when examined in more detail, it is seen that there are very considerable physiological differences between them.

Taste

The mucous membrane of the epiglottis and soft palate, and of the tip, sides and root of the tongue, contain special receptor organs known as taste-buds. In these are the chemo-receptors associated with "taste". All "tastes" can be divided into four (or perhaps six) groups: the sour, the salt, the bitter and the sweet, to which are sometimes added the metallic and the alkaline. It is significant that although many substances give rise to mixed sensations of taste, it is nearly always possible to distinguish the components, and it is impossible to create an entirely new taste by combining any or all of the "pure" tastes. "Smell", as we shall see, differs very markedly in this respect. It must be remembered that in most cases the actual flavour of any substance present in the mouth depends upon the excitation of olfactory receptors almost as much as on the excitation of taste-buds.

Sourness is a sensation aroused by all solutions containing hydrogen ions in sufficient concentration. For the mineral acids, such as HCl, the threshold concentration is at a pH of about 4. The organic acids, such as acetic, and also carbonic acid, appear more sour than would be expected from their hydrogen ion concentration, probably owing to the greater ease with which they penetrate through cell membranes,

Saltness is a sensation aroused by the salts of the strong acids, particularly the monobasic acids. The least concentration of NaCl which can be tasted is about 0·02 M (0·12 per cent).

Bitterness is a sensation aroused by many substances with a very wide range of chemical composition, but above all of the alkaloids such as strychnine and quinine. Salts of magnesium, calcium and ammonium have a bitter taste, and so have ether and most glucosides. The threshold concentration for strychnine is about 0·00006 per cent.

Sweetness is a sensation aroused by the sugars, and also by a number of other completely unrelated compounds, e.g. beryllium salts, lead acetate, chloroform, many amino-acids and saccharin. The least concentration of cane sugar which can be tasted is about 0·5 per cent, whereas that of saccharin is only about 0·001 per cent.

These four sensations are not equally easy to arouse in all parts of the tongue, some being most easily aroused in some parts, and others in other parts. There are even substances such as magnesium sulphate and dulcamarin (the glucoside from bitter-sweet) that give rise to different sensations when applied in different places. The receptors through which comes the information on which these sensations are based must vary in their sensitivities to the different classes of substance; but records from single receptor units in various species of experimental animal indicate that there is not a distinct class of receptor for each of the four sensations. Thus in the cat, there are receptors responding predominantly to acids; others responding to acids and to salts; still others responding to acids and to substances like quinine; and some responding to sucrose. We do not know that the receptors in man have the same sensitivities as those in the cat, but such a pattern of sensitivities contains all the variability required to transmit the necessary information; there is a unique combination that responds to each class of substance. This is another example of a principle which is often found in the receptor nervous system, and which has already been referred to in connection with the sensation of temperature.

Smell

The organs for smell are situated in the upper parts of the nasal cavity. Odorous substances in the inspired air dissolve in the mucus covering the sensitive cells, diffuse into the hairs which protrude from the cells into the mucous layer, and so excite the receptors.

In contrast with the sense of taste, it is quite impossible to classify the various types of smell into definite components; each substance has its own distinctive smell. There are certain general resemblances, however, and it has been suggested that odorous substances can be grouped into the spicy, the flowery, the fruity, the resinous or balsamic, the burnt and the foul. Unlike taste, again, the combination of two or more smells may produce a completely new smell, which cannot be analysed into its components. One smell, again, can mask, or neutralize another (the action of perfumes in this connection is well known), and this can take place even if the two odorous substances are applied to different nostrils.

One of the peculiarities of the sense of smell is its rapid "fatigue"; air which initially has a powerful smell may seem quite odourless within a few minutes. Recovery is equally rapid. This "fatigue" only applies to the particular substance exciting it, and another substance, even though it has a very similar smell, may be perceived normally. Different substances "fatigue" the sensory apparatus at different rates, but for any given substance, the rate of "fatigue" increases with the intensity of the smell. Some people are completely deficient in the sense of smell and many are incapable of smelling certain substances which have a strong odour to others (hydrocyanic acid is a typical instance). This deficiency may be congenital or acquired.

Action potentials in the olfactory bulb and the olfactory area of the brain of experimental animals have been recorded by Adrian. These potentials indicate the activity of cells on which impulses from thousands of primary units have converged; this activity, therefore, represents a stage in the analysis of the information. Nevertheless, it seems clear that different kinds of odorous substance may affect preferentially different groups of receptor. The number of such different groups appears to be very large, and each group may respond to a number of different substances; there is no indication of the existence of any analysis in terms of a small number of "standard" components. It was found, however, that on the whole water soluble substances, such as acetone or amyl acetate, excite preferentially receptors in the anterior part of the olfactory epithelium (in the rabbit), while oily (lipoid soluble) substances, such as cedar wood oil or benzene, excite receptors in the posterior part. The discharge set up by oily substances, also, had a longer latency, a less abrupt onset, and longer duration, than those set up by water soluble substances. The discrimination of smells may thus depend both on the spatial distribution of the activated receptors, and on the temporal characteristics of the response. The rapid "fatigue" to the smell of any one substance appears to arise in the central nervous system; the receptors themselves appear to be able to respond indefinitely.

CHAPTER 25

VISION

LIGHT, that is those electromagnetic waves with wave-lengths between approximately 400 and 700 mμ, has a very special value in the transmission of information from a distance to an animal. This particular band of waves allows a high resolution and can be precisely focussed by simple optics. Other electromagnetic waves and sound waves do not compare with light. A receptor system, which can measure the intensity, position and wave-length of light is one which can give an animal a very large amount of detailed information about its environment. Our own experience of human vision, the conscious appreciation of information received through the eyes, can tell us immediately of the great amount of information we can derive in this way.

As in any receptor system the rôle of an eye is to set up patterns of nerve impulses in such a way that for every distinguishable pattern of light reaching the eye there is a pattern of nerve impulses different from that set up by any other light stimulus. The general situation has already been considered in Chapter 24. It was pointed out that the first stage is for the external energy, in this instance light, to be transmitted to and distributed amongst the receptors; in eyes, such as the human eye, this is done by the optical system which focusses the light on the array of receptors, the retina. The receptors almost certainly produce electrical changes related to the light intensity falling on them; in retinal receptors a stage in converting the light energy into electrical energy is the absorption of the light energy by a *photochemical* substance. The electrical changes in the receptors then set up the nerve impulses. Vertebrate eyes, as normally understood as anatomical entities, have the complication that they are more than receptor systems having the general task outlined in the first sentence of this paragraph and in both Chapters 24 and 26. These eyes contain, as well as the receptor system, other nerve cells and synapses which perform stages of analysis which in other systems are performed in the central nervous system. Furthermore, since all these cells and the receptors lie in the retina (Fig. 25.1), it has not yet proved possible to record directly the impulses occurring in the primary receptor units themselves.

In considering the rôle of the eye as a receptor system, the relation of human sensations to stimulus characteristics will be considered first; it is intended to establish certain overall properties which the system must

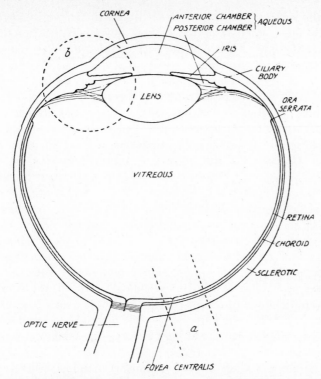

FIG. 25.1. Diagrammatic horizontal section of the human eye. (Parsons.)

possess. This is followed by a section on the optics of the eye and finally the development of the electrical changes and the initiation of impulse patterns are considered.

Human Vision

Threshold. Vision is the conscious sensation aroused by light and must not be confused with any other nervous activity associated with light. The threshold of vision varies according to conditions, in particular on the position on the retina on the wave-length of the light, on the state of dark adaptation of the eye, on the area of the test illumination, and on the duration of the test. Each of these will be considered in turn in the sub-sections which follow one dealing with the absolute threshold.

Absolute Threshold. By the absolute threshold is meant the smallest amount of light, which under ideal conditions can arouse a sensation. If a short flash of light is used to illuminate the peripheral parts of the eye it is possible to measure the least quantity of light energy, incident on the cornea, which can just be seen. The light has to pass through the parts of the eye shown in Fig. 25.1; it passes through the transparent cornea, through the aqueous solution (*aqueous humour*) behind the cornea, then through the lens and the transparent jelly-like material (*the vitreous body*) which fills the main part of the eyeball and finally reaches the retina, which lines the inner surface of the back of the eye. Measurement of the optical properties of these media shows that if we use the green light to which the eye is most sensitive, about one-half of the light incident on the cornea will reach the retina; and about one-fifth of that incident on the retina will be absorbed by the rods and its energy made available for their excitation. According to the Quantum Theory of radiation, light energy can be emitted or absorbed only in packets of a certain size, known as *quanta* (or *photons*); the size of each quantum increasing as the wavelength becomes smaller. Since we know the wave-length of the light used, we can convert the threshold quantity of light energy into the threshold number of light quanta. Now in threshold conditions, by definition, the light will be seen in about 50 per cent of the trials. But in these conditions, the number of quanta absorbed per unit area of the retina (about 250 per square centimetre in 0·1 sec) is very much smaller than the number of rods per unit area (about 14 million per square centimetre): thus, according to the laws of probability it will be exceedingly rare for any single rod to absorb more than one quantum—certainly in very much less than 50 per cent of the trials. Thus it must be possible for a rod to become activated if it absorbs a single quantum of light energy—the smallest amount which can exist.

There is no sensation of vision, however, unless several quanta— probably between 5 and 10—are absorbed within the retinal action time by a group of rods which are all connected together—i.e. are included in one receptor unit. This figure is based on rather indirect evidence and is still uncertain.

The Central and the Peripheral Retina. The central retina contains the fovea (Fig. 25.1), a small depression on to which the centre of interest of the visual field is normally focused. This part of the retina has the advantage of having less tissue in front of it than the remainder of the retina. Curiously vertebrate eyes, unlike the other group of "camera eyes" found in molluscs, have evolved with several layers of nerve cells and nerve fibres lying between the source of light and the receptors themselves, which are at the back of the retina. In the fovea the nerve cells and fibres tend to be displaced to the side, so giving more direct access of light to the receptors. In the human fovea these receptors are all cones, a name for one of the two main types of receptor; the others are rods. As one moves towards the periphery of the retina the proportion of rods to cones increases. It is the peripheral part of the retina which can give rise to a sensation at the lowest levels of illumination; a common experience is to see a faint light in the periphery of one's visual field and then to fail to be able to see it when one looks directly at it. There appears to be an association between low thresholds for sensation and the presence of rods;

nocturnal animals have a preponderance of rods in their eyes. On the other hand the human fovea which is purely cones has not got a low threshold for sensation. Cones appear to be associated with colour vision and rods incapable of providing the necessary information for such sensations; this is suggested by the reverse of the argument just given associating rods with a low threshold for sensation. Taken together, these and certain other facts imply considerable differences between vision at low intensities (*night vision* or *scotopic vision*) and high intensity vision (*day vision* or *photopic vision*). At low intensities we cannot perceive colour, detail is poor and the eye is most sensitive to light of a wave-length about 500 mμ (would give sensation of green); vision is best in the periphery of the visual field. At high intensities we can perceive colour and detail and the eye is most sensitive to light at 560 mμ (appears yellow); the fovea is the most important part of the retina for this type of vision.

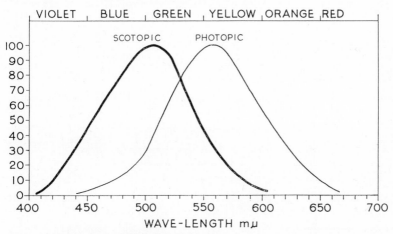

FIG. 25.2. Scotopic and photopic luminosity curves.

Abscissae—wave-length in mμ.

Ordinates—relative sensitivity of the eye, the sensitivity at the most effective wave-length (505 mμ for scotopic conditions, and 560 mμ for photopic conditions) being made, arbitrarily, equal to 100. (Crawford, and L. C. Thomson.)

Spectral Sensitivity. The eye can only detect a narrow band of electromagnetic waves and within the band there are big differences in sensitivity; sensitivity is the reciprocal of the intensity required to give a specified response. These differences are shown in Fig. 25.2. There are two curves given in this figure, that on the left for vision in dim light (rod vision) and that on the right for daylight vision (cone vision). It will be seen that in dim light the maximum sensitivity is at 505 mμ and that the sensitivity has dropped to about 25 per cent at 560 mμ, which is the wave-length at which sensitivity is maximum in daylight. The longer

wave-lengths, normally associated with sensations of orange and red, are
virtually undetected in dim light. The shape of the curves in Fig. 25.2
are almost certainly directly dependent on the properties of the photochemical substances found in the rods (scotopic) and cones (photopic).

Dark Adaptation. It is common experience that on going from light
to dark, dim lights cannot be seen, but that after a time they can be seen
with ease. This process is known as dark adaptation. When a subject has
been adapted to a bright light and this light is then turned off, his threshold
can be measured by exposing him to test lights. When this is done curves,

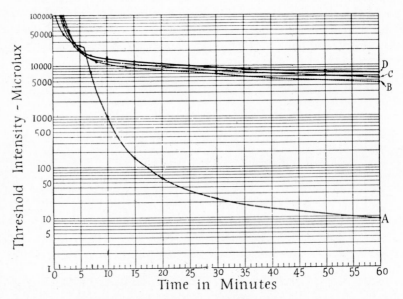

FIG. 25.3. Dark-adaptation curves of one normal (A) and three con-
genitally night-blind (B, C and D) subjects.

1 lux = 1 metre-candle = 0·1 foot candle (very nearly). (After Dieter.)

such as those in Fig. 25.3, are obtained. The different curves given in this
figure are for different individuals; they were all obtained away from the
fovea. The top part of the curve (0-5 min) is probably due to the adaptation of the cone vision. The second phase of the curve, (5-60 min), is
probably associated with rod vision. Only in curve A from the normal
subject is the second phase present; in the night-blind retina, rods are
absent. At long wave-lengths there is no dim-light vision and hence
almost certainly no excitation of rods; the adaptation curve to test
lights of these wave-lengths is of the pure cone type as found in the
fovea for all wave-lengths.

Fig. 25.3 illustrates the time course of adaptation on changing from light to complete darkness and it will be noted that changes are slow; full adaptation takes more than 45 minutes. Clearly one would expect

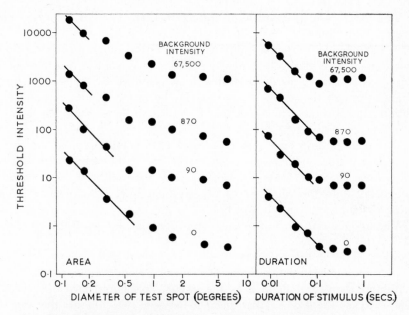

FIG. 25.4. Spatial and temporal summation in the human eye.

The threshold intensity, or the increment threshold, is plotted against the size of the test spot (on the left), the duration of exposure being constant at 0·93 sec; and against the duration of the test stimulus (on the right), the size of the test spot being constant, with an area subtending 27·6 deg² at the eye (diameter subtending 5·9 deg).

The sloping lines indicate the relation to be expected if the threshold were inversely proportional to the area (Ricco's law); or inversely proportional to the duration (Bunsen-Roscoe law). The brightest background had an illumination of about 1 lux, and was thus only moderately bright.

The intensities, both threshold and background, are expressed in units of 1,000 quanta (507 mμ) in each (degree)² arriving at the eye in each second. (From Barlow, redrawn.)

that for any constant level of general illumination there will be a steady level of adaptation. This may be observed by measuring what is known as the *difference threshold*, the smallest increase in intensity which can just be detected. This is considered further below in the section on visual discrimination.

It now appears certain that the large changes in sensitivity which occur during adaptation (Fig. 25.3) are largely due to changes in the nervous pathways. The bleaching of the photochemical substances was always thought to be the main reason for the decrease in sensitivity as light intensity increases and this may be a factor.

The Area and Duration of the Stimulus. The intensity of light required to stimulate decreases as area increases over small areas (Fig. 25.4 left). Under certain conditions the intensity (energy per unit time per unit area) is inversely proportional to area; i.e. for a constant time, energy is constant regardless of area. This is shown by the straight lines drawn through the points on the left of the figure. Under certain conditions this phenomenon is certainly a function of the nervous connections of the receptors.

A similar finding regarding the duration of a light is also shown in Fig. 25.4 (right). Again on the left of the figure the straight line shows where the intensity (energy per unit time per unit area) is inversely proportional to the duration of the stimulus; i.e. for a constant area, energy is constant regardless of time.

Visual Discrimination. Visual discrimination is concerned with the ability to distinguish one detail of a pattern of light and shade from another. The ability to make such a distinction will depend on their separation and the relative intensities reflected from the two parts.

Visual Acuity is defined as the angular resolving power of vision; that is to say the least angular distance between two contours that can be distinguished from each other visually. The best test of this is to use an array of parallel lines or rectangles alternately light and dark of equal width; there should be maximum contrast between them. The array can be viewed from different distances; or one can have different arrays in each of which the lines are of different width, all of the arrays being viewed from the same distance. With either method the angular separation of the light and dark lines subtended at the eye can be altered. If the eye looks directly at such a test object the image falls on the fovea. When tested in this way it is found that the smallest separation of lines which can be detected gives an image on the retina in which the lines are separated by a distance which is the same, or little more than, the diameter of a cone, about 3 μ. Assuming that the discrimination is truly simultaneous, the spacing of the cones would be expected to set one limit to visual acuity. (If the eye were to scan, in the way that is familiar from television, this would not necessarily be true). Since it is vision which is being tested, the information must be transmitted to the brain and it is likely that there are as many nerve fibres in the optic nerve carrying information from the foveal cones as there are cones. With this kind of test the acuity is little dependent on level of illumination over a wide range of relatively high intensities. Some test objects commonly used for measuring acuity are at the same time tests of a threshold and if these are used the level of illumination has a greater effect on the apparent acuity. "Landolt's C" and letter cards are of this type. The acuity achieved by the eye appears, therefore, to be very close to the limit set by the spacing of the array of receptors. It is interesting that the acuity achieved is also close to the limits imposed by the optics of the system.

In contrast to this high acuity achieved by the fovea, the acuity of the extra-foveal retina is much worse than either the optics or the fineness of the pattern of rods and cones would lead one to expect. The explanation must be that the information is lost between the receptors and the optic nerve. There are one hundred million receptors and only one million optic nerve fibres, so it is the latter which will limit the amount of information which can reach the brain.

Discrimination of one intensity from another is measured as a *difference* (or *incremental*) *threshold*; this is the smallest difference in intensity, from that of the background illumination, which can be detected. The relation between the difference threshold and the level of illumination is not simple except under special conditions. If the test field is large, the duration long and the background intensity greater than a thousand times the absolute threshold, then, usually but not always, the difference threshold, ΔI, is proportional to the background intensity, I. The ratio $\Delta I/1$ may under these conditions have a value of about 0·03. This figure is quoted, despite the qualifications, in order to give some idea of the order of intensity discrimination obtained in vision.

Colour Vision. The sensation aroused by a light needs three terms to define it, the brightness, the hue and the saturation. In this section we are concerned with the latter two. Hue is best illustrated by the sensation associated with a pure spectral colour, i.e. with a light of a single wavelength; this ranges from red through yellow and green to blue and violet. Hues of this kind are highly saturated; on the other hand white, grey and black are three brightness levels of the completely unsaturated situation, which consequently has no hue at all. Between the saturated hues of the spectral colours and the unsaturated neutral tone there are a series of shades of varying hues and varying saturations; for example there is a series of shades running from green through greyish green to greenish grey to grey. Human vision can distinguish 120 different hues and about 1,000 different shades.

There is one very important finding about colour vision, which dominates ideas in this field. If two lights, each of a single wave-length— one in the red and the other in the green, are shone on to a white screen and their intensities varied, it is possible to produce on the screen colours having any hue lying between these two in the spectral sequence. If a third, blue, light is added to the mixture it is possible to match, by an adjustment of intensities, almost any shade of light projected on to another screen; there are a few shades which cannot be matched. If one moves one of the three standard lights and mixes it with the "unknown" shade and then matches this mixture with the mixture of the other two standards, it is possible to match the few shades which could not be mixed before; this procedure simply introduces the possibility of a minus intensity. It is possible to use any three standards, but a red, a green and a blue are commonly used as with these the number of negatives is minimal and the accuracy of the matching is high. It must be emphasized that these experiments are concerned with the mixing of lights of known wavelength; the mixing of pigments involves many different questions. The

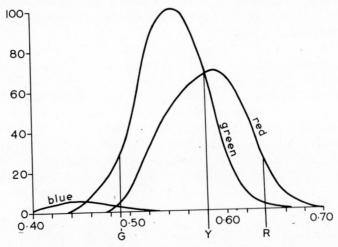

FIG. 25.5. König and Dieterici's suggested response curves for three channels in the mechanism for colour vision (corrected by Judd).

Abscissae—wave-length in μ.

Ordinates—relative sensitivities of three hypothetical receptor systems at different wave-lengths, the maximum sensitivity of the "green" system being made equal to 100. (From Walters: Proc. Roy. Soc.)

importance of such experiments is that the three characters of the sensation, its brightness, its hue and its saturation can be completely controlled by adjusting three knobs controlling the intensity of three lights. If a further control is added nothing further is achieved, since the new variable can always be exactly defined in terms of the other three. If the number of variables is reduced to two, it is not possible to match all shades. Thus there are three variables or degrees of freedom in the visual system connected with colour vision and there are not more or less. This means that there must be three independent channels in the mechanism taken as a whole from the receptors to the highest levels of the nervous system; it does not *necessarily* imply three types of receptor.

Attempts have been made to estimate the sensitivities of the three channels (Fig. 25.5). Such attempts can only indicate possibilities; they are based on matching experiments such as those described and others, including matching after adaptation to lights of particular wave-lengths. Vertical lines drawn on Fig. 25.5 indicate the relative sensitivities of the three mechanisms to certain particular wave-lengths. These curves are sensitivity curves (relative reciprocal of intensity to produce a standard response under different conditions, here wave-length). Response curves (relative size of response to a stimulus of constant intensity under different conditions) do not necessarily have the same shape. The curves presented do however indicate, in a general way, that each wave-length will arouse a unique combination of responses from the three channels.

The ability to match all shades with three standards does break down if very small fields (less than 30 minutes) of illumination are used on the fovea. Under these conditions colour vision is less good and two standards is sufficient.

Defects in colour vision do occur. There are those who are totally colour blind, but are rare. Many more are able to match all the shades they can see by mixing two, instead of three standards. They are dichromatic, instead of the normal trichromatic. In these people there appear to be only two channels available. Most cases are not as severe as this and have anomalous colour vision, possibly one or more of the channels having abnormal characteristics.

The detection of deficiencies in colour vision is not a task which can be undertaken light-heartedly, since there are all grades of severity, and when a defect is present in a mild form, it may only be possible to detect it when the conditions are made difficult. A subject may, for instance, show no signs until the area which he is required to recognize is very small, feebly illuminated, or the colour mixed with a lot of white light, as happens in a fog. In the Board of Trade test the candidate is required to name the colour of a small illuminated area of variable size. This is the basis of the Eridge-Green colour perception lantern. Another method is to present the suspect with a skein of wool, and ask him to pick out the one which matches it from a pile of variously coloured skeins. In the third method, which is the most convenient for rapid use, a series of cards ("Ishihara charts") are printed with figures in coloured spots on a background of similarly shaped spots, but in a colour which is liable to look the same as that of the figure to a colour defective. The background spots may also be arranged to include a figure which is not obvious to a normal person, but which may be seen clearly by a colour defective.

The Formation of the Retinal Image

The first step towards setting up patterns of nerve impulses which are related in a meaningful way to any particular light stimulus, is to distribute the light in a suitable manner amongst the receptors. In vertebrate eyes, as well as in many molluscs (e.g. octopus), this is done by forming a focused image on the retina. The focusing may depend largely on the corneal surface, as in man, or on a lens as in fishes and there are even a few examples of the image being formed by a spherical mirror (e.g. scallop). These eyes with focused images (excluding the few focused by mirrors), are sometimes called "camera eyes" to distinguish them from the "compound eyes" of, for example, the insects. The analogy to a camera is clear, but there is a difference. In a good camera the image must have a uniform high quality all over the film. In the human eye, as has been shown in the section on vision, only the fovea has the capacity to transmit further all the information available in a well-focused image; the fovea is moved over any area it is desired to look at in detail, as for example in scanning down a line of print. If there is a focussed image there must be a means of adjusting the focus for objects at different distances from the eye. In mammals, as will be described in the second sub-section, this is done by altering the shape of the lens. But this is not the only method found in animals; in some the eye is moved backwards and forwards as in a camera.

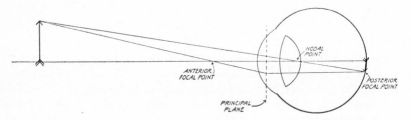

FIG. 25.6. The formation of the retinal image in the schematic eye.

In man the image is formed as a result of refraction at the corneal surface and in the lens.

It is important to remember that the strongly curved outer surface of the cornea is the chief refracting surface of the eye. The lens is very powerful if examined in air, but since it is suspended in fluids whose refractive indices are only a little less than its own, it loses most of its power when in the eye. The lens is concerned with the fine focusing of the image on the retina. Application of the laws of optics to the refracting surfaces and the refractive indices of the eye media shows that the retinal image must be inverted as in a camera. Such an inverted image can be seen in the excised eye of an albino rabbit by looking at it from behind through the non-pigmented sclera.

If the retinal image is reversed (i.e. made upright) experimentally, by means of reversing spectacles, the visual sensation is reversed. After some days, however, the sensation may reverse and appear upright again, despite the inversion of the retinal image from normal. This reversal is helped by clues from other senses.

Before reaching the retina the rays of light have to pass through the cornea, the intra-ocular fluid, the lens and the vitreous body. The absorption of visible rays by these eye media is small except in old age,

when there is an appreciable absorption of the shorter spectral waves by
the lens. Infra-red and ultra-violet radiations, both of which are capable
of damaging the retina, are absorbed by the eye media before reaching it.
Both these types of radiation are harmful to other structures in the eye.
The infra-red rays, for instance, can cause cataract of the crystalline lens
(e.g. amongst glass-blowers), whilst the ultra-violet rays cause intense
inflammation of the outside surface of the eye (film-star's eye, snow-
blindness). The retina is protected against intense visible radiation by
changes in the pupil diameter, the iris (Fig. 25.1) contracting reflexly under
these conditions and dilating again more slowly in the dark. Even when the
pupil is fully contracted, the absorption of visible light by the retina at the
site of a very bright image may lead to a rise of temperature sufficient to
cause a burn resulting in local blindness. This condition is not uncommon

FIG. 25.7. Figure for illustrating the presence of the blind-spot.
Look at the cross with the right eye only and hold the book at
about 22 cm. from the eye.

in those who unwisely observe an eclipse of the sun without adequate
protection by dark glasses.

The image on the retina is formed by what, in geometrical optics, is
called a "thick lens." The size and position of the image can thus be
calculated from a knowledge of the cardinal points of the optical system.
The most useful of these is the *nodal point*, an imaginary point at the
optical centre: it lies at the geometrical centre of a thin lens, but in the
eye it is in the crystalline lens near the posterior surface, 15 mm in front
of the retina (Fig. 25.6). A pencil of light directed towards the nodal
point behaves as though it had passed through undeflected, although this
does not mean that the pencil actually follows this path. Its use is in
calculating the size of the retinal image, when the size and distance of
the external object are known. The calculation is made by the use of the
principle of similar triangles. It can be applied, for instance, to the
calculation of the distance between the blind-spot (optic disc) and the
region of most distinct vision (fovea). A circle and, 60 mm to its left, a
cross are made on a piece of paper (Fig. 25.7), and, looking at the cross
with the right eye only, the paper is moved away from the eye. At about

220 mm distance the circle will be invisible because its image will fall on the blind-spot, at which point the sensitive elements in the retina are absent. By "similar triangles" we have:—retinal distance required: 15 mm: 60 mm: 220 mm. The distance between the fovea and the centre of the optic disc works out to be 4 mm, a result which agrees with histological observation.

The *anterior focal point* is 13 mm in front of the cornea, and a pencil of rays which has passed through it is refracted parallel to the optic axis when it meets the *principal plane*, which lies 2 mm behind the anterior surface of the cornea (Fig. 25.8). Using these quantities in conjunction with the nodal point, the position of the image within the eye can be determined.

The eye behaves like other optical instruments in that it is subject to some of their defects. Among these can be mentioned *spherical aberration*

FIG. 25.8. The Changes in the Purkinje images during accommodation.

A 3-point source of light forms mirror images at the anterior surface of the cornea and at the anterior and posterior lens surfaces. During accommodation (right) only the anterior lens image changes. Notice the contraction of the pupil. (Fincham.)

The power of a spherical lens is greater at the periphery than at the centre, that is to say, the image formed by its periphery is nearer to the lens than the image formed by its centre. In the eye the outline of the refracting surfaces is slightly hyperbolic and in this way spherical aberration is diminished. *Chromatic aberration* of a lens system is due to the fact that the short (blue) waves of the spectrum are bent at a refracting surface through a greater angle than are the long (red) waves, and so come to an earlier focus. Actually the eye, on looking at a point source of light, is focused on the middle wave-lengths, giving the light a halo of red and blue. These halos can be seen by looking at a small light through a piece of cobalt glass which transmits only blue and red rays.

The Focusing of the Image in Mammals. A normal mammalian eye, directed on a distant object, will focus the image on the retina; its *far point* of distinct vision is said to be at infinity, and this is the position of rest for the eye. When the eye is directed on to a near object the image is focused by altering the shape of the lens; the nearest point at which objects can be focused sharply on the retina is known as the *near point*. The process of altering the focus from infinity towards a nearer object is sometimes known as *accommodation*; when the eye is adjusted to focus the near point, it is said to be at *maximum accommodation*.

The changes that occur in the lens of the human eye can be observed by means of the Purkinje images (Sanson's images). These are images of a source of light, held slightly to one side of the subject's eye, formed by reflection at the principal refracting surfaces. The anterior surface of the cornea acts like a convex mirror and forms a bright uninverted image. The anterior surface of the lens functions similarly, but the image is faint and often very difficult to see, and normally is larger than that formed by the cornea. The posterior surface of the lens acts as a concave mirror; the image is inverted and much smaller than the others. When the eye focuses alternately for far and near objects a marked change occurs in the image from the anterior lens surface; there is a very slight change in the image from the posterior lens surface, and no change at all in the image from the cornea, showing that this structure is unchanged during focusing (Fig. 25.8). In order to focus near objects the curvature of the anterior lens surface is increased and consequently the mirror image formed at its surface becomes smaller. When the eye is focused on infinity, the radius of curvature of the anterior surface of the lens is about 10 to 12 mm; when focused on the near point, the radius of curvature is reduced to about 6 mm. The radius of curvature of the posterior surface changes only slightly, from about 6 mm to about 5·5 mm.

An excised lens has surfaces as highly curved as in the eye when accommodated for near vision. The reason for this is that the lens is an elastic body which, for distant vision, is stretched and flattened as a result of the method by which it is supported; and for near vision is released and allowed to thicken. The lens substance is held under pressure by a capsule, which is held around its edge by an elastic ligament. This pulls the capsule out in one plane, so tending to flatten the lens. If the tension provided by the ligaments, is reduced the lens becomes more curved. The capsule does not have a uniform thickness and hence the changes of curvature are greater in some parts than in others. The tension can be taken off the capsule by the contraction of a circular muscle running around the lens near the line of attachment of the ligament.

The increase in lens curvature during near vision is accompanied by a reduction in size of the pupil (Fig. 25.8). The reduction in the optical aperture improves the depth of focus. The eyes, in man and other mammals with binocular vision, converge slightly when viewing a near object. The change in lens curvature, the change in pupil diameter and the slight convergence and divergence of the eyes are maintained at any moment in correct adjustment by means of appropriate neural control systems. The pupil diameter is, of course, adjusted in relation to the light intensity as well as the distance of the object on which vision is focused. The muscles responsible for altering lens shape and pupil diameter are supplied by

parasympathetic fibres (in the IIIrd nerve) and the neuromuscular transmitter is in each case acetylcholine. This means that blocking agents such
as atropine and homatropine cause relaxation of the muscles and hence
the eye is focused at infinity and the pupil is dilated. These substances
are effective if dropped in the eye and hence are used in clinical practice.
eserine and pilocarine have the opposite effects and can be used to counteract the effects of atropine.

Faults in Image Formation. The range over which the human eye
can focus in young people (under 25) is equivalent to 10 dioptres (D). The
power of a lens in dioptres is the reciprocal of its focal length measured in
metres; convex (converging) lenses have positive values, while concave
(diverging) lenses are given negative values; the values are additive so that
when lenses are placed together their combined power in dioptres is the
sum of the individual values. With increasing age the lens hardens and
the range over which the eye can focus diminishes; by the age of 50, this
range has been reduced, on the average, from 10 D to 1·8 D. In a normal
young person the near point is around 10 cm, while at 50 it is around
55 cm. In some people the image of an object at infinity is not focused on
the retina with the eye relaxed. If this image is in front of the retina it
means that the focal length of the whole lens system needs to be increased
or the power in dioptres decreased, if infinity is to be focused. Such people
can focus near objects and are *near-sighted* (sometimes called myopic).
In the reverse situation the image of an object at infinity is, in relaxation,
behind the retina. Such people are therefore unable to focus near objects
and are known as *long-sighted* (sometimes hypermetropic). The optical
system may also be at fault in not being radially symmetrical. If the focal
length in the vertical plane is different from that in the horizontal plane,
there is an imperfect image and the eye is said to be *astigmatic*. All these
faults in image formation can be corrected by adding suitable lenses to the
optical system of the eye.

The Receptor System

Once the light has been distributed to the receptors, the next stage in
transmitting information about the environment to the brain is to convert
the light energy into electrical energy. This is the task of the retinal
receptors. It is probable that in the vertebrate retina, as in other receptor
situations, the receptors first produce a potential change whose size is
related to the intensity of light at the receptor; this graded potential change
is probably responsible for setting up nerve impulses. The pattern of these
impulses, both in time in any one fibre and on the spatial distribution
of active and inactive fibres, must be uniquely related to a particular
pattern of light intensity and wave-length reflected from the environment.
Direct records from receptors of the vertebrate eye have not been obtained
with any certainty and hence we must rely on less direct methods. The

energy of the light is absorbed by a photochemical substance and these are discussed in the first subsection. In the second section reference is made to light receptors in invertebrate eyes. In the final section the responses of the higher order cells in the vertebrate retina will be considered.

Photochemical Substances

The purpose of a photochemical substance is to provide enough energy for the next process in the chain to occur and to provide it when and only when it receives energy from the arrival of a quantum of light. There are a number of different substances known, but the one best known and studied in most detail is *rhodopsin* (visual purple) which can be extracted from the rods of a wide range of vertebrates. In studying this and other photochemical substances much use has been made of the *absorption spectrum* of the substance. Lights of different wave-lengths will have different effects on the molecules of the substance. Those wave-lengths which have the greatest effect on the molecule will be those that are giving up most energy in the substance, and hence are those for which least passes right through the sample. If a solution of the substance is put in a light beam from a source of monochromatic light, the absorption at each wave-length may be measured.

Rhodopsin. Rhodopsin is almost certainly the substance responsible for light absorption in the rods of man. Not only can it be extracted from the rods and is the only known photochemical substance to be extracted, but its absorption spectrum is very nearly identical in position and shape to the dim-light sensitivity curve (Fig. 25.2). The agreement is closer if the absorption spectrum of the substance is measured in situ, that is with the molecules highly concentrated and laid down in an organized way.

Rhodopsin consists of retinene with a protein called opsin. Retinene is formed by oxidation of vitamin A and is the aldehyde of this substance. Retinene has a number of isomers of which two are important in this context. The retinene attached to opsin in rhodopsin is known as 11-*cis* retinene. The absorption of light energy by rhodopsin is thought to change this to another isomer the all-*trans* retinene. All-*trans* retinene does not remain attached to opsin and the molecule breaks up. All-*trans* retinene as would be expected from this does not form rhodopsin in the presence of opsin. Rhodopsin is formed however by opsin in the presence of 11-*cis* retinene. The latter may be derived *in vivo* from vitamin A. An enzyme has been found to catalyze the change from the 11-*cis* to the all-*trans* form, but this does not appear to be important in the intact human eye.

Other Pigments. A most interesting recent finding has come from the development of a technique for measuring the absorption spectra of single cones in the isolated retinae of primates. Three types of cone each giving a different absorption spectrum were found and the peaks of the curves were at 445 mμ (blue), 535 mμ (green) and 570 mμ (red) (cf. Fig. 25.5).

If further investigation shows these to be homogeneous groups and does not reveal any further categories, it would seem that the number of channels required for colour vision is limited to three at the level of the photochemical substances.

Most of the photochemical substances found have come from rods, since the quantities in cones are generally much less and hence their pigments are not easily detected by extraction methods. In mammals the substances which have been found have all had maxima to their absorption spectra close to 500 mμ (cf. Fig. 25.2). Most freshwater fish have at least one photochemical substance with absorption maximum between 510 mμ and 550 mμ. An interesting group are the deep sea fish, many of whom have substances with maxima between 475 mμ and 490 mμ; it is these wave-lengths which are able to penetrate to great depths.

Photoreceptor Activity

Photoreceptor activity has been investigated in a single part of the compound eye of an arthropod called *Limulus*. In this the nerve cell is surrounded by a number of supporting cells, which appear to contain the photosensitive mechanism. It has been possible to record the electrical activity of the nerve cell in the region of the receptor and it has been found that this cell is depolarized when light falls on the receptor. These slow potential changes are related in a graded manner to the intensity of the illumination falling on the receptor, in a manner similar to that described for receptors in general in Chapter 24. It has been shown in these photoreceptors that the potential change results from a change in the permeability of the cell membrane and in this respect also they are like other receptors. Impulses are also seen to be discharged by these nerve cells and the frequency of the impulses is related to size of the slow potential change and hence to the intensity of the light. Electric currents related to illumination have also been found in the receptors of octopus eyes; in this case there are no supporting cells and this is clearly a response of the receptor itself.

Impulse Activity in the Mammalian Retina

It has already been pointed out that our knowledge of impulse activity from the retina derives from units which are not the primary receptor units, but from the nerve cells in the retina which are of higher order. These responses therefore are comparable to those of cells which occur in the central nervous system in the case of other receptor systems in mammals. Most of results come from the ganglion cells and their axons, which form the fibres in the optic nerve. The responses of these cells result from the interaction of considerable numbers of receptors.

The overall activity of the whole optic nerve can be observed by means of electrodes placed on it, in suitable kinds of experimental animal. As one would expect, the relation between the intensity of the stimulus (in this case light) and the number of impulses passing up the optic nerve in a given time is similar to that for other receptor systems. Within limits, the frequency of the optic nerve impulses appears to depend on the total *amount* of light stimulating the eye. In other words, in order to obtain a given response the product of the intensity of the light, the duration of the illumination and the area of retina illuminated, must be kept constant. This, as we have seen, applies also to the subjective sensations. The frequency of the impulses, moreover, rises with time after the start of the illumination, reaches a peak and then declines: the greater the intensity, the higher the peak, the sooner it is reached and the more rapidly it decays.

If special techniques are used to eliminate the effects of *all* eye movements the sensations of vision also decline. It is clear that a part of this adaptation must occur in the retina.

The subjective sensation of brightness (as observed in man) thus seems to follow in a general way the frequency of the impulses in the whole optic nerve (as observed in experimental animals). But the more detailed content of the sensation—the detection of spatial and temporal patterns, and of colour—must be conveyed by signals in the separate nerve fibres from different receptor units.

By the use of micro-dissection methods, and of micro-electrodes, it is possible to record the action potentials in single optic nerve fibres, the ganglion cells from which they arise, and (probably) the bipolar cells. These experiments have shown that in both the frog and the cat, there are two main types of response. The impulses may increase in frequency when the light is switched on, and decrease in frequency, or cease altogether, for a short time after the light is switched off (the "on" response, Fig. 25.9, A): or the impulses may decrease in frequency, or cease, when the light is switched on, and increase in frequency after it is switched off (the "off" response, Fig. 25.9, B). This "off" response can be suppressed immediately by turning the light on again. The impulses usually appear at a high frequency for a fraction of a second after the light is switched on, or off, and then settle down to a steady lower frequency, or may cease. Some nerve fibres give a short burst of impulses both at "on" and at "off" (the "on-off" response). This type of response is characteristic of the rapidly adapting type of receptor; the response is determined by the *change* in the illumination, whether this is an increase or a decrease, as for example, would accompany movements of light and shade across the retina. Such movements, particularly in the peripheral regions, are particularly effective in attracting attention.

Observations on single fibres have demonstrated conclusively a fact that may be inferred from other evidence, and has already been mentioned. The receptive field connected to a single nerve fibre in the optic nerve may be very large, and action potentials may be set up in a given nerve fibre by illuminating rods or cones spread over a wide area; the sensitivity decreases markedly towards the periphery of the field, so that it has no sharp boundary. Conversely, a very small spot of light, stimulating only a very few receptor cells, will produce impulses in several different fibres, so that the receptive fields of different units must overlap considerably.

If the eye is fully dark-adapted, there is summation between the effects of illuminating any one part of the receptive field with that of illuminating any other part; the threshold light intensity falls as the area illuminated rises in the central part of the whole receptive field by some units, but not by all. If the eye is not fully dark-adapted, the discharge set up by illuminating one spot in the receptive field may be inhibited when another

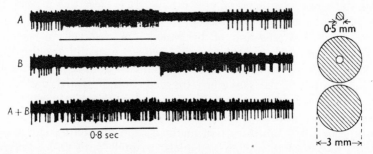

Fig. 25.9. Action potentials from a cell in the inner nuclear layer of a cat's retina.

A. On illuminating a spot 0·5 mm diameter in the centre of the receptive field of the cell; "on" response.

B. On illuminating a ring 3 mm diameter surrounding the 0·5 mm spot illuminating in A; "off" response.

A + *B*. On illuminating both the central spot and the peripheral ring; both responses are present but each is partially inhibited by the other.

The patterns of light falling on the retina are shown on the right of the figure. (Brown and Wiesel, 1959. *J. Physiol.*)

spot is illuminated simultaneously. The discharge obtained from a unit in the centre of the receptive field, when that part is illuminated, is regularly inhibited when the peripheral part is illuminated as well, and *vice versa*. This is illustrated in Fig. 25.9. In the cat, one and the same unit may give, say, an "on" discharge when the central part of its receptive field is illuminated, and an "off" discharge when the peripheral part is illuminated (as in Fig. 25.9), or *vice versa*. This does not affect the mutual inhibition.

Spectral Sensitivities. The least amount of light energy which will produce a just detectable response in an optic nerve fibre varies with the wave-length of the light. If the eye examined is dark-adapted, the spectral sensitivity of all the receptors has a maximum at about 500 mµ, the curve has much the same shape as the human scotopic visibility curve (Fig.

25.2), and is just what would be expected if rhodopsin were the photo-chemical substance in action. If the eye is light-adapted, and if the retina contains a sufficient proportion of cones, the spectral sensitivity of some of the units will have a maximum sensitivity at about 560 mμ, and the curve resembling the human photopic visibility curve. Granit, who has been responsible for much of this work on single optic nerve fibres, called these curves the scotopic and photopic *dominator curves*. But in addition, light-adapted eyes are found to contain units whose spectral sensitivity curves have more complex shapes, some with humps and others with sensitivity maxima at two different wave-lengths; some curves, also, even though they have only one peak, are much narrower than the dominator curves. These results are explained by Granit as being due to the existence of *modulator curves*, of which there are three kinds: those with maxima in the red part of the spectrum (about 600 mμ); those with maxima in the green (about 530 mμ); and those with maxima in the blue (about 450 mμ). The precise position of the maximum sensitivity varies somewhat from unit to unit, but always lies in one or other of these three regions. These complex responses from the ganglion cells may result from the interactions of responses from receptors containing the different photo-chemical substances referred to above (p. 437), one for rods and three for cones.

The Position of the Eyes

The eyes must be accurately directed if detail is to be appreciated in the visual image. The control of the eye position is chiefly initiated from signals from the retina itself. However, compensation must be made for movements of the head or of the whole body; the labyrinthine organs (Chapter 24) play a rôle in bringing about the necessary compensation of the position of the eyes.

The adjustment of the direction in which the eye is looking is extremely precise, but is never perfect, even though there are no complicating movements either of the head or of the object looked at. Unless special attention is given to maintaining an exact fixation, the image on the retina is continually shifting slightly, by a few minutes of arc at intervals of a few tenths of a second. This has, in fact, some advantages. Acuity of vision depends on the detection of small differences in the illumination falling on neighbouring cones but the electrophysiological evidence suggests that many of the receptor units behave as if they were rapidly adapting. Slight movements of the image from one to another would thus facilitate its detection. Colour vision, also, necessitates the illumination of relatively large numbers of receptor units, either simultaneously or in rapid sequence. The anomalous types of colour vision associated with very small areas of illumination can only be detected when fixation is very careful and deliberate.

Stereoscopic vision depends on the fusion of images from the two eyes. The sense of depth obtained depends on the slight difference of viewpoint, when the two eyes are both fixated on the same point. Precise positioning of the eyes is necessary if there is to be fusion of the image and double vision avoided. Accurate control mechanisms are needed for all these purposes. The detectors are the eyes themselves, the control mechanisms in the central nervous system and the effectors are the eye muscles.

CHAPTER 26

HEARING AND SPEECH

MANY events in the environment set up mechanical vibrations in the air (or water). A very effective form of distance reception developed in animals is the detection and analysis of these vibrations. In man, such vibrations can arouse the sensation of hearing and a particular use of the ability to analyse air vibrations has been developed—the ability to discriminate the subtleties of speech so providing a method of communication between individuals. The first steps in the reception and analysis of the information contained in these vibrations (or sound waves) are carried out in the ear.

The rôle of the ear in the reception of sound is to set up patterns of nerve impulses in such a way that for every distinguishable sound there is a pattern which is different from that set up by any other sound. These patterns are transmitted to the central nervous system. This has already been referred to in Chapter 24. It was pointed out that the first step is for the energy of the stimulus, in this case the vibrations in the air, to be transmitted to and distributed amongst the receptors. These receptors then produce electrical changes which are directly related to the mechanical changes in their immediate vicinity; these electrical changes set up nerve impulses in the fibres, which run in the auditory nerve. A major factor in determining the pattern of nerve impulses in the fibres of the auditory nerve is, therefore, the way in which the mechanical changes are distributed amongst the receptors.

In considering this problem, certain properties of sound waves will be considered first. This is followed by a section on the relation of human sensations to various sound waves with the intention of establishing certain overall properties which the mechanisms under consideration must possess. The transmission and distribution of the mechanical energy is then dealt with and finally the electrical changes and the initiation of nerve impulses in meaningful patterns are considered.

The Physical Properties of Sound

If a tuning fork is struck, the "prongs" of the fork are set into vibration, that is, they move backwards and forwards with great rapidity at one moment coming nearer to one another, at the next farther away. If, now, a small mirror is attached to one such prong, so that a beam of light

443

reflected from it moves with the prong, it will be possible, by arranging that this beam falls on to a moving strip of photographic film, to obtain a record of the movements of the prong over a given time. In other words, the record will constitute a graph showing the position of the prong (ordinates) against time (abscissae). Such a graph is shown in Fig. 26.1. The completed record is said to show the *wave-form* of the tuning fork vibrations, and the distance between the resting position of the fork and its position of maximum deflection gives a measure of the *amplitude* of swing of the fork; where this distance is large, the vibrations are said

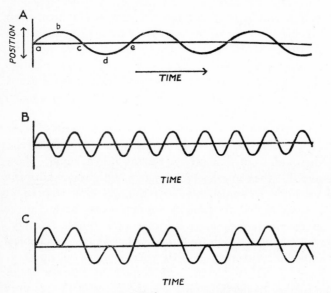

FIG. 26.1. Wave-form of vibrations of tuning forks

A. a b c d e constitutes one complete cycle.
B. Frequency of fork three times that of A.
C. Composite wave-form produced by sounding forks A and B simultaneously.

to be of large amplitude, and where it is small, of small amplitude. It is easily demonstrable that a fork vibrating at greater amplitude will produce a louder sound; the record from such a fork will show the same number of waves in a given time, but the amplitude of each wave will be greater. When the wave-form of a good tuning fork is examined in this way, it may be shown that the curve thus reproduced is almost exactly the same as that obtained by plotting the sine of an angle against the angle itself. Such a wave is thus known as a *sine-wave* and the vibrations of the fork which give rise to it as *sinusoidal*.

A similar record may be obtained without a mirror on the fork. When the prongs of the fork vibrate, air pressure changes are set up in their vicinity, and these in turn set up pressure changes near-by; thus the sound travels through the air in the form of waves, the direction of wave motion being the same as that in which the sound is travelling, unlike waves on the surface of water, whose motion is at right angles to their direction of travel; these propagated pressure variations are perceived by man as sound. These pressure changes can also be converted, by means of a microphone, into electrical changes having an identical time course; these electrical changes are easily amplified and displayed on a cathode ray oscilloscope. Such a record will be found to be exactly as Fig. 26.1 (A), except that in this case the ordinates represent *air pressure changes*. The number of complete cycles, a b c d e, in one second of time is known as the *frequency* of the fork or note and is usually measured in *cycles per second*. The wire set into vibration by striking the note "Middle C" on a piano has a frequency of 256 cycles per second, that is, it performs 256 complete double vibrations in one second.[1] Pitch is a quality of sensation

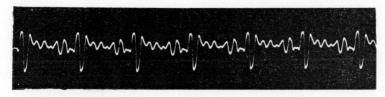

FIG. 26.2. Wave-form of an English Vowel of the type "ah."
(D. B. Fry from "Science and Speech.")

related to the frequency of the wave and the higher the frequency the higher is the pitch.

If, now, a fork of three times the frequency of the first fork be set into vibration, the resulting oscilloscope record will be as shown in Fig. 26.1 (B). Should forks of both of these frequencies be set going at the same time, the resultant wave will be that shown at (C). Thus, it is evident that the wave-form of the air vibrations set up by two forks sounding simultaneously is quite different from that obtained from either fork alone. Most of the sounds commonly met with in daily life have an infinitely more complicated wave-form than this, the *quality* of a sound depending on its wave-form. The wave-form of the vowel "ah" is shown in Fig. 26.2. According to Fourier's theorem, however, just as the relatively complicated wave-form of (C) is the result of adding together (A) and (B), so the wave-form of any periodic vibration, however complicated, may be resolved into a series of simple waves, consisting

---

[1] A frequency of 256 cycles for the note " Middle C " is traditional in physics. Pianos and other musical instruments are normally tuned to the international standard pitch (A = 440 cycles per second), corresponding, when adjusted for equal temperament, to a frequency of 261·6 cycles per second for middle C.

of a *fundamental* with the lowest frequency found, and a number of *overtones* or *harmonics*, whose frequencies are multiples of that of the fundamental. Each of these single component frequencies will be of the same wave-form as Fig. 26.1, i.e. sinusoidal, and in the case of highly complicated sounds, the number of these components may be very great.

The analysis of a complex wave-form into its sinusoidal constituents in the ordinary way requires much tedious mathematical manipulation; but mechanical and electrical frequency analysers have been developed which have made possible the estimation of the frequency and power of the fundamental and harmonics of most sounds commonly met with in daily life. The frequency of these harmonics will bear a simple numerical relationship to that of the fundamental. They are called second, third, etc., harmonics, according as their frequencies are respectively twice, three times, etc., that of the fundamental or first harmonic. A sound whose wave-form is not strictly periodic will be found upon analysis to contain components whose frequencies are not simple multiples of that of the fundamental. These components are called *anharmonics*. "Noises", whose wave-form is highly irregular, contain many such constituents.

When a sound is emitted from a source, power is radiated in the form of pressure variations in the surrounding air. The *intensity* of the sound is the amount of power (in watts) which passes through unit area (1 square centimetre) at right angles to the direction of propagation. In practice, it is more convenient to measure the variations in air pressure (in dynes per square centimetre), by means of a suitable calibrated microphone, for example; the sound power is proportional to the square of the pressure variation.

A just perceptible sensation may be produced by a sound whose intensity is somewhat less than 10^{-12} watt per square centimetre; the variation in air pressure is then about 10^{-9} atmosphere, and the air molecules vibrate with an amplitude less than one-tenth of their own dimensions. In quite ordinary circumstances, however, we are exposed to sounds with intensities between a thousand times and a thousand-million times greater than this. It is more convenient, therefore, to avoid the use of very large figures by adopting a logarithmic scale (analogous to the pH scale for hydrogen ion concentration). The unit is called the *bel*, and the difference in bels between the intensity levels of two sounds is the common logarithm of the ratio of the two actual intensities: a 10-fold increase in the intensity of a sound is an increase of 1 bel in the intensity level, a 100-fold increase is an increase of 2 bels, and so on. For practical purposes, however, such a unit is inconveniently large, and the *decibel* is more often used. This is simply one-tenth of a bel, and represents an increase in intensity of roughly 25 per cent. (This is, as it happens, about the least change in intensity that can ordinarily be detected.

Since the power and hence the intensity of a sound is proportional to the square of the variations in air pressure, the difference in intensity level between two sounds, in decibels, is given by twenty times the common logarithm of the ratio between the two sound pressures. (Since the pressure variations are alternately positive and negative, we define their magnitude in terms of the "root mean square (r.m.s.) pressure"; similarly, the voltage of an alternating electric supply is defined by the r.m.s., or "effective," voltage.)

It is to be noted that the decibel is a ratio and as such can have no meaning unless the standard from which it is measured is quoted. A number of different standards are commonly used for different purposes. One may use an arbitrarily chosen r.m.s. sound pressure, such as 0·0002 dyne per square centimetre, as conventionally used by acoustical engineers. But when measuring deficiencies in hearing, it is customary to use, as standard, the threshold intensity, at each frequency, of the average person with "normal" hearing, as given in Fig. 26.8 below: the "hearing loss" of the patient is then the amount in decibels by which the intensity must be increased before the patient can just hear the sound.

Frequency, wave-form and intensity are physical properties of the propagated waves of pressure change, whether they can be "heard" or not; pitch, quality and loudness are of psychological significance, and describe characteristics of the sensation evoked by a sound wave. Pitch and quality are, for all practical purposes, determined uniquely by frequency and wave-form respectively The pitch associated with a given frequency may, however, depend somewhat on the intensity, and the quality associated with a given wave-form may depend on both the intensity and the frequency of the fundamental component. The loudness of a sound of given intensity, on the other hand, may differ very considerably according to its component frequencies; and the discrepancy is of sufficient importance to require special discussion in the next section.

Auditory Acuity

Threshold. When the intensity of a sound is continuously decreased, it reaches a value where no sensation of sound is produced. The smallest intensity of sound required to produce a sensation is said to be on the *threshold of audibility*. As is shown in Fig. 26.3, the physical intensity (sound pressure level) of a threshold sound varies very considerably with its frequency. The ear is not uniformly sensitive throughout the range of frequencies; it requires a smaller intensity of sound at 1,000 to 4,000 cycles per second to produce a just perceptible sensation than it does at frequencies higher or lower than these. At 100 c/sec and at 10,000 c/sec the threshold intensity is nearly 1,000 times greater than it is at 3,000 c/sec.

The curve of threshold intensities given in Fig. 19.3 represents the average values obtained from a group of young people, aged 18–25, using one ear only and applying the sound through an earphone. This is the method ordinarily used for testing deficiencies in hearing. But we usually hear sounds in the open air, using both ears; in such "free field" conditions, the threshold of audibility is some 5 to 10 decibels (depending on the frequency) below the values plotted in Fig. 26.3.

If the intensity is adequate, a pure tone may be heard and recognized as such, if its frequency lies between some 20 and some 20,000 c/sec. Many kinds of animal, however, such as dogs, can hear notes with frequencies well above 20,000 c/sec, which are inaudible to man. Beyond these limits of frequency, a "sound," if sufficiently intense, may be felt

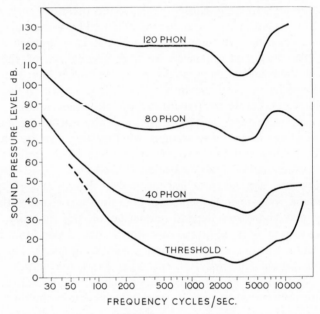

FIG. 26.3. The variation of intensity with frequency (a) for just detect-able (threshold) tones and (b) for tones of equal loudness (at three different levels).

    The intensity is measured in terms of the sound pressure level, in decibels above a pressure of 0·0002 dyne per square centimetre. (Robinson and Dadson, from Kaye and Laby, "Tables of Physical and Chemical Constants" 11th edition, 1957.)

by parts of the body other than the ear, but it will not, strictly speaking, be "heard." Within these limits of frequency, a very intense sound is not only heard, but also felt by the ear, often a somewhat painful sensation; it is then said to be on the *threshold of feeling*.

Loudness. The loudness of a pure tone may be measured in terms of the physical intensity of the tone, expressed in decibels above the physical intensity of the same tone when it can just be heard—i.e. at the threshold of audibility—as given, for example, by the lowermost curve in Fig. 26.3. Tones of different frequency, but of the same physical intensity, therefore, will not necessarily have the same intensity level each above its own threshold, and are not necessarily of the same loudness. We cannot, therefore, measure the loudness of a complex sound in terms merely of its physical intensity, since in general we do not know what its physical intensity would be if it were reduced in loudness to the threshold value; this will depend on the relative magnitudes of its component frequencies. This difficulty is avoided by using a pure tone of 1,000 cycles per second as a reference standard, and adjusting its intensity until it is judged, by a person with "normal" hearing (or a group of such persons), to have the same loudness as the sound or noise under investigation. The intensity of the 1,000 c/sec., tone is measured in decibels above a reference sound pressure, which for a 1,000 c/sec tone is just threshold. This then becomes a measure of the subjective loudness of a complex noise, for example, and is expressed in terms of a unit called the *phon*. For all frequencies other than 1,000 c/sec, and for complex noises, the subjective loudness (measured in phons) differs, often very considerably, from the physical intensity (measured in decibels above the reference pressure). This is indicated by the three upper curves in Fig. 26.3, each of which represents the relation between physical intensity and frequency for pure tones, which have the same subjective loudness of 40 phon, 80 phon and 120 phon, respectively. On the whole, the greater is the intensity of a sound, the less does its loudness vary with its frequency.

TABLE 26.1

Loudness in phon

Faintest audible sound (average normal person)		4
Whisper.	about	20
Quiet street	,,	40
Ordinary conversation	,,	60
Busy street	,,	80
Noisy engine room	,,	110
Painful sound	,,	130

In practice, loudness measurements are often made, not by subjective judgment, but by using a sound intensity meter (i.e. an instrument measuring sound power directly) whose frequency characteristic can be adjusted to match that of the ear. Such instruments are usually calibrated in decibels above a reference sound pressure level; loudness is thus very commonly expressed in "decibels", although the phon is the correct unit. Approximate values of the loudness of certain noises are given in Table 26.1.

Difference, or Discrimination, Thresholds. A normal man is capable of detecting quite small differences between the *frequencies* of two tones. The minimum perceptible difference (*absolute* difference threshold) is about 3 c/sec, independent of the frequency up to about 500 c/sec, and rising more or less in proportion to the frequency above about 1,000 c/sec. Expressed as a percentage of the frequency, the *relative* pitch discrimination threshold falls with increase in frequency up to about 1,000 c/sec, and then remains more or less constant, as is shown in Fig. 26.4. Up to a limit, the ability to discriminate between sounds of different frequency improves with increase in the intensity of the sound, as is indicated by

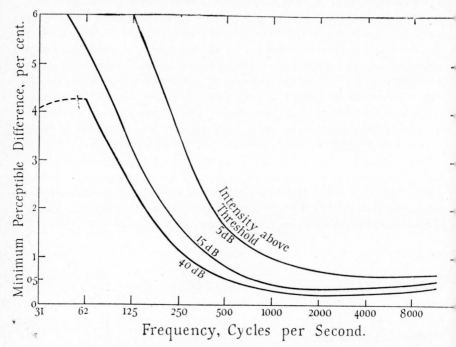

Fig. 26.4. The Minimum Differences in Frequency which can be detected at various frequencies and at various intensities above the threshold (expressed as a percentage of the frequency of the stimulus). At intensities greater than 40 dB, the changes in sensitivity are small. The values given are for listening with one ear; if both ears are used, the minimum perceptible differences are smaller. (From data by Shower and Biddulph.)

the three curves in Fig. 26.4. If the pitch is fairly high, therefore (frequency greater than 1,000 c/sec), a difference of about 1/20 semitone can be detected: if it low (say, 100 c/sec) about 1/2 semitone. Over the whole range of audible frequencies there are about 1,600 perceptible changes in pitch.

The acuity of the ear for differences in sound *intensity* is much smaller than its acuity for differences in frequency, the fractional increase which can just be detected under the best conditions being between 5 and 10 per cent. Intensity discrimination is not so good for low notes or low intensities; at a frequency of 60 c/sec and at a moderate intensity, a change of 20 per cent is just perceptible, whilst at low intensities an increase of as much as 200 per cent is necessary.

Masking. It is a common experience that the presence of one sound reduces our ability to hear other weaker sounds, which are then said to be masked. Suppose that we are listening to some particular sound whose intensity is at about the threshold value, and other sounds or noises then begin. In order just to hear the sound that we are interested in, we should have to increase its intensity to a value which is about 10 to 30 decibels below that of the interfering sounds. The threshold of audibility is thus raised by an amount which increases with increase in the intensity of the masking sounds. But much depends on the frequencies of the sounds considered; a loud sound of any particular frequency masks others with a higher frequency much more than it does those with a lower frequency. If we study the masking effect of a pure tone, we find that if its intensity is not very large (say up to about 40 dB above threshold), only notes immediately above and below it in frequency are appreciably affected; the threshold of audibility of these is raised to a value which is about 10 dB less than the intensity of the masking tone. Notes which have frequencies of 2X or 0·5X or more away on each side are not affected. If the intensity of the masking tone is raised, however (say to 80 or 100 dB above threshold), the effect spreads increasingly to notes of all frequencies above it, whilst notes of much lower frequency, 0·5X or more below it, remain unaffected; the threshold of audibility of all the masked tones is now raised to a value which is about 30 dB below the intensity of the masking tone.

These masking effects are to be expected from the properties of the cochlea as discovered by direct observation and by electrophysiological studies; they affect, also, the intelligibility of speech in the presence of much background noise and they affect the relation between the quality of a complex sound and its wave-form. Suppose, for example, that we produce a complex sound consisting of a fundamental frequency A together with notes of progressively increasing frequency a, b, c, etc. If the intensity is small, all the constituents may be heard: if the intensity is doubled, A may mask a; if it is redoubled, A may mask both a and b; and so on until nothing will be heard but the single note of frequency A, which therefore gains in prominence as the sound is amplified.

The Localization of Sound. The ability to recognize the direction from which a sound proceeds is poorly developed in man. Under the best conditions it is rarely possible to localize the direction of a sound more accurately than within 10 degrees in the horizontal plane and considerably more in the vertical plane. Man's ability to localize sound is due to two factors. First, sound has a finite velocity, so that unless a source of sound is equidistant from the two ears, a given vibration will not arrive at both ears simultaneously; a sound from a source at an angle of 45 degrees from the sagittal plane, for example, will reach one ear approximately 0·4 millisecond before it reaches the other. If the two ear pieces of a set of headphones are wired separately, so that clicks may be presented to the two ears with a small time difference between them, it is found that the direction from which the sound appears to come varies with this interval, provided that it is not greater than about 1 millisecond. Secondly, for high frequency tones, above 3,000 c/sec, there will be a difference of intensity at the two ears due to the "shadow" effect of the head; the sound is localized to the side where it is loudest. Both methods are probably used together for localizing the most common sounds, which contain components of many different frequencies.

Many animals have another way of localizing sounds. They rotate their pinnae until the apparent intensity is greatest, when the pinnae will be facing the source of sound.

Auditory Fatigue. If the ear be subjected to prolonged loud sounds, it suffers a transient loss of sensitivity, i.e. it becomes fatigued. This means that the intensity of a note, if it is just to be perceived, must be made greater after such stimulation than before. A sufficiently intense stimulus, applied to a single ear only, causes a loss of sensitivity in both ears; that is to say, the fatigue is binaural. The loss in the nominally unstimulated ear is not produced by the residue of sound reaching it (due to bone conduction, slight leaks, etc.), as is shown by the following experiment. Suppose a sound of intensity only 70 decibels above the threshold be applied to the right ear, then no loss of acuity will be found in either right or left ear. If, however, the intensity of the fatiguing sound is raised, although still applied only to the right ear, the left ear, as well as the right, will suffer a loss of sensitivity. Yet the residue of sound reaching the left ear is at least 60 decibels below that in the right ear, and thus can exert no fatiguing effect on it. It follows, therefore, that stimulation of one ear, if sufficiently intense, lowers the sensitivity of both ears; this effect is probably central. The loss in the stimulated ear, however, is somewhat greater than that in the unstimulated one. The greater fatigue of the stimulated ear is presumably due to a loss of sensitivity in more peripheral mechanisms.

In general tones of frequency above 1,000 c/sec produce much more fatigue than do tones of frequency below this.

Deafness. The tests for deafness normally employed are the spoken voice, whisper, the tick of a watch, and tuning forks of various frequencies. Such tests are inaccurate, but in experienced hands can give a fair indication of the degree of loss of hearing. A more accurate instrument, with which the sensitivity over almost the whole auditory spectrum may be tested, frequency by frequency, is the *audiometer*. In this, pure tones produced electrically are led to the ear by a high quality earphone; the intensity of the tone may be altered at will, and that point at which the patient no longer hears the sound is readily estimated.

The threshold of audibility, for tones of 10,000 cycles per second and above increases rapidly with increasing age, even in "normal" people, who have no particular disorder of hearing; there is usually, also, a smaller loss of sensitivity to frequencies down to 1,000 c/sec.

More serious deafness may result from several types of disorder.

(a) *External Ear Obstruction.* The external auditory meatus is obstructed by a wax plug, by dirt, or by inflammation and swelling of the meatal wall (otitis externa).

(b) *Middle Ear Disease.* The ossicles are prevented from functioning properly, a condition which frequently follows a nasal catarrh, and starts as an inflammation of the middle ear (otitis media), the infection entering via the Eustachian tube. Later, a pathological condition of the bone round the inner ear may develop (*otosclerosis*). This mainly results in the formation of new bone in the neighbourhood of the oval window which causes fixation of the stapes footplate to the bony capsule, with subsequent loss of hearing. In the later stages, the organ of Corti often shows degeneration.

(c) *Inner Ear Disease.* This usually involves loss of function of the organ of Corti or of the cochlear nerve, and is thus sometimes referred to as "nerve deafness." It may be due to:

(1) *Injuries to the Inner Ear,* such as boilermakers' deafness (Chronic Labyrinthine Concussion);

(2) *Diseases of the Inner Ear and Auditory Nerve,* due to local haemorrhages or inflammation or to general disease (e.g. syphilis, malaria, theumatism). The commonest cause of inner ear disease, however, is middle ear disease.

External and middle ear deafness may often be distinguished from inner ear (nerve) deafness by making use of the phenomenon of "bone-conduction." If the auditory meatus be carefully plugged, a tuning fork will be heard without difficulty if its stem is placed on the bones of the head (e.g. the mastoid bone). The vibrations from the fork set up similar vibrations in the cochlea, transmission taking place through the bones of the skull. It is clear, therefore, that if air-conducted sound is not heard, whilst bone conducted vibrations are readily audible, loss of middle ear function must be suspected. This diagnosis may often be strengthened by inspection of the tympanic membrane, which, in most cases of middle ear disease, presents an abnormal appearance.

Deaf Aids take many forms, but all depend for their action upon raising the intensity of the received sound above normal. This is done electrically by means of a microphone, amplifier, and headphone. With such an instrument the relative intensity of high and low tones may be altered at will, thus compensating for losses over a specific range of frequency. It is difficult, however, to avoid some unwanted distortion, and for this, and other reasons, they are not always entirely satisfactory.

Mechanics of the Ear

There are three stages in the transmission of the mechanical energy from the air to the receptors. The first is concerned with the transmission of the energy in the form of sound waves in air. This part is anatomically the external ear and ends with a diaphragm, the tympanic membrane (Fig. 26.5). In the second stage the energy is transmitted by a lever

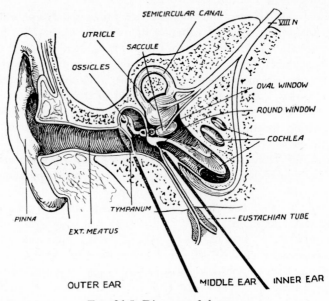

FIG. 26.5. Diagram of the ear.

system and this occurs anatomically in the middle ear. In the last stage the energy is transmitted predominantly through water and this takes place in the cochlea; this is anatomically part of the inner ear, the other parts of which are not concerned with hearing but are concerned with orientation and acceleration and are dealt with in Chap. 24.

Transmission in air, the External Ear. In many mammals the *pinnae* collect sound waves and can be moved so as to be in the optimum position. This not only increases the collecting power of the ear, but may also serve as a means of localizing the source of the sound. In man the pinnae serve little purpose and sounds can be heard almost as well without them. The *external meatus* is, in man, 25 mm long and conducts the waves to a diaphragm, the *tympanic membrane*, which can move in and out as the pressure just outside it goes up and down; remember that a sound wave consists of a succession of increases and decreases of pressure. The *external meatus* is protected against foreign bodies by hairs projecting outwards and from insects by a secretion of bitter wax.

Transmission by Lever, the Middle Ear. The *tympanic membrane* is conical in shape, with its concave surface facing outwards and downwards. Attached to the apex of the cone on its inner side is one of the small bony ossicles of the middle ear. There are three of these called the *malleus, incus* and *stapes*, but they function as a single unit and will be treated as such. Fig. 26.6 shows how this lever system links the inner side of the *tympanic membrane* to the liquid filled inner ear at the *oval window*; a bony "piston" lies in the window and is "sealed" in by means of a membrane. The position of the joint and the bearing on the system are such

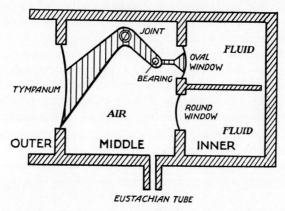

FIG. 26.6. Model illustrating the method of transmission of vibrations from the outer to the inner ear. (Modified from Beatty.)

that displacements at the *oval window* are about one-third of the displacements at the *tympanic membrane*. The force of the thrust at the *oval window* is consequently three times that at the *tympanic membrane*. The force at the *oval window* is spread over an area of 3.2 mm² whereas that at the tympanic membrane is spread over 65 mm². The pressure changes on the liquid just inside the *oval window* are therefore considerably greater than the air pressure changes outside the *tympanic membrane*. The increase in pressure and decrease in displacement is an example of "impedance matching", of which the matching of a loudspeaker to an amplifier is a familiar example. The purpose of this matching is to obtain the maximum transfer of power from one system to another; in this example a maximum transfer is required from air which is light and compliant to liquid which is heavy and stiff. In man the "Transformer ratio" is 18 to 1; in the cat it is 60 to 1.

The lever system has two small muscles associated with it. One called the *tensor tympani* keeps the *tympanic membrane* taut; if its tendon is divided the cochlear microphonic potentials (see below p. 458) fall by about one-fifth. The other muscle the *stapedius* may perform the same function for the membrane of the *oval window*. In both dogs and rabbits reflex contractions of both muscles have been observed in response to high intensity sound waves. Contraction of these muscles would reduce the displacements resulting from given sound pressure changes; this reflex may therefore perform a protective rôle.

One subsidiary matter requires mention and this concerns external pressure changes other than sound pressure waves. Changes of air pressure as when diving or going up in an aeroplane could cause considerable stresses in the tympanic membrane if the pressure in the middle ear were not equalized with the outside pressure. This equalization normally takes place through the *Eustachian tube* (auditory tube) which connects the middle ear to the naso-pharynx. There is a valve at the mouth end of the tube and this is opened by a muscle of the palate which contracts during swallowing. As outside pressure is increased, as during a dive, it is necessary to open the valve by swallowing; as pressure decreases outside, the excess pressure in the middle ear is released through the valve without any need to contract the muscle. Failure to open the tube or blockage because of infection can lead to considerable pain. If the valve is not active on the other hand the individual's own voice can be heard unduly loudly and this is an unpleasant phenomenon.

Transmission in Liquid, the Cochlea. This represents the crucial stage which determines the pattern of activation of the receptors and hence the way in which the information is transmitted in the form of nerve impulses. Although in mammals the cochlea is arranged in a spiral, it can, for functional purposes be regarded as a straight tube divided down its length by a membranous partition (see right side of Fig. 26.6). The receptors are arranged along the length of this partition. At the end of the tube there is a small open connection between the two compartments as indicated in Fig. 26.6. This opening allows slow changes of pressure to equalize on both sides of the partition, but has no effect on the rapid changes of pressure resulting from sound waves. Displacements due to sound pressure changes pass through the partition itself and end at the *round window* (Fig. 26.6). The liquid in the cochlea has mass and hence, by its inertia, opposes the displacements, which the pressure changes tend to produce. The higher the frequency of the pressure change the greater will be the opposition to displacement exerted by the mass of the liquid (i.e. the greater its reactance). One might therefore expect that high frequency waves would spread along the cochlea for shorter distances than low frequency ones. In general this is what happens, but since the distribution of displacement along the partition is of fundamental importance and its mechanical basis is complex, some space must now be given to describing certain experiments.

Von Békésy has made direct observations on the cochlear partitions of fresh human cadavers after grinding away the bone over the apex of the cochlea. He looked at the displacements of the partition and his results are summarized in Fig. 26.7. The lines in each of these diagrams represents the maximum displacement occurring at different distances from the *oval window* (stapes). The actual movements of the partition are in the form of waves which travel from the *oval window* along the partition. The plotted lines can be thought of as joining the peaks of the wave on one side.

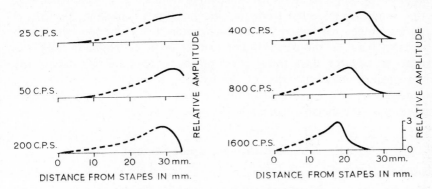

FIG. 26.7. The Displacement of the basilar membrane in response to vibrations of different frequency.

> Vibrations of constant amplitude but with different frequencies were impressed on the fluid within the cochlea, and the amplitude of the oscillatory displacement of the basilar membrane was measured at different distances from the stapes (basal end of the cochlea). At low frequencies, the amplitude is greatest at the apical end of the membrane; as the frequency is increased, the position of maximum amplitude shifts towards the basal end.
>
> In order to observe the more basal parts of the membrane, the uppermost turns of the cochlear spiral had to be removed. This may be expected to affect the displacement of the parts observed at those frequencies at which the parts removed would themselves have undergone displacement; these observations are represented by the broken lines. Control observations showed, however, that in the conditions of measurement the error was quite small (v. Békésy, *J. Acoust. Soc. Amer.* 1949.)

It can be seen that at 25 c/sec the wave travels along the whole length of the partition increasing in amplitude as it goes. As the frequency of the sound wave increases the position on the partition at which the displacement is at a maximum moves towards the *oval window*. Furthermore it can be seen in all parts of the figure that the amplitude increases relatively gradually from the *oval window* to the peak, but that beyond the peak there is an abrupt decline. This means that with frequencies of 200 c/sec or more, the end of the partition far from the window does not move at all; at a frequency of 3,000 c/sec it was found that only a short length of partition was in motion. It will be shown below that the impulse activity in the receptor units, which are spread out along the partition, follows closely the pattern of the mechanical disturbances just described. These mechanical disturbances may therefore be compared with certain properties of the sensation of hearing. If reference is made to Fig. 26.4 it will be seen that the best discrimination between neighbouring frequencies occurs when the maximum disturbance is somewhere in the middle of the partition. It will also be noticed that these results are in accordance with what might be expected from the phenomenon of masking (p. 451). A masking tone, particularly if of high intensity, will cause the whole partition between the oval window and its point of maximum displacement to vibrate: thus those parts of the membrane associated with frequencies higher than that of the masking tone will be activated and masked. Frequencies lower than the masking tone are able to displace the partition in the inactive regions beyond the peak.

The Auditory Receptor System

The results discussed in the last section have shown how the mechanical disturbance of an airborne sound wave reaching the external ear is transmitted and distributed as a displacement of the cochlear partition. The next stage is for these displacements to be converted into electrical changes which can set up the appropriate impulse patterns. This is considered in two sub-sections. The first deals with electrical changes in the cochlea, which are closely related to the mechanical changes; these are the *cochlear microphonic potentials*. The second is concerned with the impulse patterns, which transmit all the required information to the central nervous system.

The Cochlear Microphonic Potentials. The cochlear partition is illustrated in Fig. 26.8 and the various parts can be marked on this. One or two points may be noted. *Reissner's membrane* bounds a liquid filled space the *Scala media*; this boundary separates solutions which have different compositions and which are at different electrical potentials (the solution in scala media is called endolymph while that in the other compartments is called perilymph); the membrane does not, however, form any mechanical boundary so that the spaces marked *scala vestibuli* and *scala media* together form the column of liquid on the side of the partition connected to the *oval window*. The space marked scala tympani forms the column of liquid connected with the *round window*. The cells in the region marked *organ of Corti* are hair cells with their hairs pointing upward in the diagram, their ends being embedded in the *tectorial membrane*. Movement of the partition in the up and down direction of the diagram causes shearing between the tops of the hairy cells and the tectorial membrane, so causing bending of the hairs. The receptor nerve fibres are closely associated with the lower ends of the hair cells, that is the opposite end to the hair.

The displacement of the cochlear partition is a precursor of the initiation of nerve impulses, but is not the immediate cause of the excitation. In Chapter 24 it was pointed out that in most receptors a change of electrical potential, which is graded in amplitude according to the strength of the physical or chemical stimulus, is the immediate cause of the initiation of the nerve impulses. In single receptors the relationship between the stimulus and this receptor potential, and between the receptor potential and the nerve impulse, is fairly clear; but in the cochlea the situation is in some respects both more complex and more difficult to analyse. This is

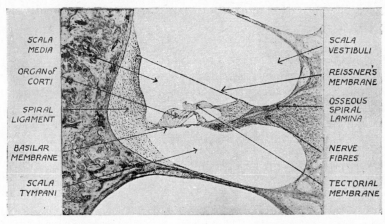

SCALA MEDIA		SCALA VESTIBULI
ORGAN of CORTI		REISSNER'S MEMBRANE
		OSSEOUS SPIRAL LAMINA
SPIRAL LIGAMENT		
BASILAR MEMBRANE		NERVE FIBRES
SCALA TYMPANI		TECTORIAL MEMBRANE

FIG. 26.8. Section through the cochlea of a dog showing the organ of Corti; magnification × 75. (From a photograph kindly supplied by Dr. C. S. Hallpike.)

because it is not easy to investigate the behaviour of single receptors, although potentials developed across the whole organ have been thoroughly investigated. Potential changes are developed between the scala tympani and the scala media when sound enters the ear, and these changes are of the same frequency and phase as the sound stimulus, and are proportional to it in amplitude. These potentials are distributed along the cochlea in a way that is consistent with the pattern of displacement that has already been mentioned; that is to say, they can be found in response to high frequencies mainly near the oval window, and in response to low frequencies mainly at the opposite end. But since the potential changes themselves spread along the cochlea, owing to its electrical properties, it is not easy to locate the sources accurately. These graded changes of electrical potential were first described by Wever and Bray and are termed *microphonic potentials*.

The reason for the name and also an indication of the accuracy with which the microphonic potentials follow the sound waves, can easily be demonstrated in the following way. If an electrode is placed on the round window of an experimental animal and another on, say, the neck, microphonic potentials of all frequencies can be picked up. If this output is amplified and put into a loud speaker, it is found that the system will reproduce voice and other sounds quite accurately. In other words, the cochlea used in this way acts as a microphone.

The cochlear partition lies between the scala tympani containing perilymph and the scala media which contains endolymph. Now the composition of perilymph, as remarked in Chapter 2, is that of the extracellular fluid in general, the sodium ion concentration being large compared with the potassium ion concentration. In the endolymph, however, the potassium ion concentration is greater than the sodium ion concentration, so that its composition is more like that of the intracellular fluid. There is an electrical potential difference between the endolymph and the perilymph and, on the arrival of sound stimuli, this *endolymphatic potential* varies about its "resting" value in accordance with the variations in sound pressure. The microphonic potentials, therefore, are modulations of the endolymphatic potential; power for this activity is derived from the metabolic reactions which create and maintain the endolymphatic potential. This is a good example of the process of "power amplification" which is common, if not universal, in receptor systems, as pointed out in Chapter 24.

The basis of the endolymphatic potential is not completely known. It is opposite in sign to the resting potential between the interior of a cell and the extracellular fluid, the endolymph being electrically *positive* to the perilymph by about 80 mV.

Impulses. At any particular level in the cochlea, the greatest potential field (or gradient) due to the microphonic potential has been found to be in the region of the hair cells and of the associated nerve fibres. Furthermore, it has been found that nerve impulses are set up on each cycle of the microphonic potential, provided that the frequency is not too high. At low frequencies, with sufficiently large stimuli, there may be a burst of impulses during each cycle; but as the frequency gets higher, there is time for one impulse only on each wave. When the interval between successive cycles becomes comparable with the refractory period of the nerve fibres (both relative and absolute), which may range from 3 msec down to 0·5 msec—i.e. when the incoming frequency reaches 300 to 2,000 c/sec—impulses will not appear on every cycle of the microphonic potential, the number missing depending on the stimulus strength. These observations are important for two reasons: first, they suggest strongly that the microphonic potential is associated with the initiation of nerve impulses, even if it is not the immediate cause; and secondly, that the timing of the impulses is closely related, at certain frequencies at least, to the intervals between the peaks of the sound wave. If recordings are made of action potentials in the auditory nerve, it is found that the discharge is intermittent, and related to the phase of the sound wave, up to frequencies of about 4,000 c/sec. No single fibre can be activated at these frequencies. But since the triggering of an impulse in any given fibre is related to the phase of the microphonic potential, any fibre which is ready to fire (after recovering from the refractory state) will not do so until the appropriate moment in the next cycle: in a whole population of fibres there will always be some which fire at each cycle, although any individual fibre will fire on every second, third or fourth cycle, as the case may be. There is thus a temporal pattern of nerve activity, as well as a spatial pattern, which is related to the frequency of the sound wave.

If the displacement of the cochlear partition and the associated microphonic potentials are direct precursors of the excitation of the receptors, one would expect the pattern of varying amplitude with distance from the oval window to be reflected in the behaviour of the primary receptor units. It is very difficult to record from such units, but it has been done by Tasaki. When he recorded from a primary unit, selected at random, he obtained a result such as that shown in Fig. 26.9. With a stimulus of very low intensity, he obtained a response only at one frequency, presumably that which caused the largest displacement at that particular point at which the receptors were located. With larger stimuli, he obtained responses from greater and greater ranges of frequency, the extension of the range being mainly towards the lower frequencies. This is what would be expected from the mechanical evidence, since every lower frequency would displace the basilar membrane from the oval window up to some point beyond the receptor from which the recording was made; higher frequencies, which displace only a short length of the membrane would, on the other hand, leave the receptor in a quiescent part of the membrane. (Compare in Fig. 26.7, for example, the displacement at different frequencies of a point on the membrane 25 mm from the stapes). The shape of the curve in Fig. 26.9 is, in fact, entirely in accordance with the direct observations on the displacement of different parts of the membrane at different frequencies. Thus we see that the greater the intensity of a sound, the greater the length of the membrane in which receptors will be excited; but that the distribution of these excited receptors along the length of the membrane will be different according to the frequency of the sound.

The auditory system can detect differences in frequency of an incoming sound of less than 0·5 per cent over much of the middle range (Fig. 26.4), and simultaneously it can detect differences in intensity of about 10 per cent. These observations imply that there must be a considerable number of distinct impulse patterns in the auditory nerve. Clearly no single receptor unit can transmit all this information; in fact a single unit can only supply a small amount. It has just been pointed out that the timing of impulses, particularly at certain frequencies, is tied to the phases of the microphonic potential; when this is at its most striking, with one impulse to each cycle at frequencies from say 300 to 1,500 c/sec there can be little or no change in the discharge as the intensity of the sound is changed. Furthermore a unit will tend to respond in a similar way to a low intensity at its optimum frequency and to a higher intensity at some other frequency. The same problem is found in the skin, where a single receptor unit will respond in the same way to a small force

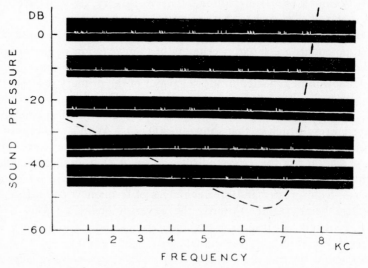

Fig. 26.9. Action potentials from a single fibre in the auditory nerve of a guinea-pig.

> Each line, from left to right, gives the responses to tones of short duration (tone pips) in an ascending series of frequencies, as given in the scale at the bottom, at a constant value of the intensity. The intensity is greatest in the top line, and becomes progressively smaller in the lower lines. The broken line shows the relation between the threshold intensity and the frequency, for this particular receptor unit. The sensitivity is greatest between 6,000 and 7,000 c/sec, falls off gradually as the frequency is reduced and rapidly as the frequency is increased. (Tasaki, 1954, *J. Neurophysiol.*)

in the centre of its receptive field as to a large force further away. The required amount of information to make all the necessary distinctions is provided in both situations by the use of large numbers of units each placed in a slightly different position.

In general, it can be deduced from the experiments described above, that as the intensity increases the number of units active increases. With a change of frequency certain characteristics of the whole pattern, probably in particular the maximum density of active units, moves in relation to the whole population of units. It has been possible to demonstrate this in rather more detail in a situation with skin. It is the task of the central nervous system to analyse these factors and those of timing referred to before. Impulse patterns from receptor systems are the input to the central nervous system. It is a major function of a nervous system to analyse step by step these inputs and to extract from them information required either for storage or to determine immediate action. Such information as we have on this is the subject for another chapter; in order to form a link, however, it can be mentioned here that an early step in analysis may be to reduce the range of sound frequencies which are capable of exciting a single cell and further that inhibition between units is a factor in producing this result.

The idea that the cochlea played an essential part in frequency discrimination by causing different receptors to fire at different frequencies of vibration is much older than the evidence given here. The first of these *place theories*, as they are called, was put forward by Helmholtz: this was his *resonance theory*. He postulated that the partition behaved as a set of strings, each of which was set to resonate at a different frequency. The theory as he proposed it is not consistent with modern findings, but the important point in his idea is that the displacements of different parts of the basilar membrane are different at different frequencies.

There is an entirely different type of evidence which has long suggested a *place theory*. High intensity sounds can, in experimental animals and through industrial injury in man (as in "boilermakers' disease," for example) cause damage to a localized part of the basilar membrane. That such damage can be seen *post mortem* is merely confirmation of what is known of the mechanical behaviour of the cochlea. It does not tell us whether or not the brain finds the analysis so made essential. There is, however, some evidence that such injuries are accompanied by an inability to appreciate sounds that have a frequency which would cause a maximum displacement in the injured region of the basilar membrane.

SPEECH

The sounds of speech are produced, first, by the movement of air exhaled from the lungs past the vocal cords in the larynx, which behave like the reeds of wind instruments and are set into vibration, the frequency depending on the amount to which they are stretched, and put under tension, by the action of the laryngeal muscles. The resulting sound contains many different frequencies besides the fundamental, and certain of these are reinforced by resonance in the cavities of the throat, mouth and nose; adjustment of the size and shape of these cavities, individually, controls the nature of the speech sound, particularly of the vowels, which is emitted. Secondly, the movements of air over sharp edges such as the teeth, and through narrow gaps formed between the tongue and the soft palate and between the lips, produce "hissing" sounds which give rise to some of the consonants, those known as "fricative," such as s, f, v and th. In addition, the way in which the sounds are started and stopped, by the action of the tongue and the lips, gives rise to the "stop" consonants,

such as b, p, g and k. Adjustment of the vocal cords alters the general
pitch of the speech but the distinction between one kind of speech
sound and another depends on the action of the muscles of the throat,
cheeks, tongue and lips. The accurate control of these various muscles is,
to a large extent, reflex. We listen to our own speech as we make it, and
adjust the sound so as to imitate that desired. If a person's speech is
presented to his ears, not instantaneously as ordinarily occurs, but after
a delay of a few tenths of a second, he becomes so confused that further
speech becomes almost impossible.

This may be done by recording his speech on a tape from which it is picked
up again after a short delay and played loudly into his ears through telephone
receivers; the direct and immediate transmission from his mouth to his ears is
thus overpowered by the delayed transmission.

Deaf children do not hear other persons' speech, or their own, and do not
ordinarily learn to speak spontaneously. They will do so if they can be given
adequate hearing aids, and can be taught by special methods. Their speech,
however, though comprehensible, usually has a peculiar quality.

Speech sounds have extremely complex wave-forms—that illustrated in
Fig. 26.2 being a relatively simple example—and may contain components
with frequencies up to 8,000 c/sec. Most of the power (about 1/3) is in
frequencines between 250 and 500 c/sec, and these, therefore, largely
determine the loudness of the speech. But the distinction between one
kind of speech and another, and thus the intelligibility of the speech,
is determined by the higher frequency components, chiefly those between
500 and 5,000 c/sec. Provided that these are all present in their proper
amplitudes in the speech sounds, and are adequately heard by the listener,
there is no serious difficulty in recognizing all the various speech sounds
that may occur. Ordinary speech, in a familiar language, can be understood even when the only frequencies heard are those between 1,000
and 3,000 c/sec; but this is largely because in these circumstances we do
not need to hear and identify every speech sound, or even every word;
those missed can be supplied from the context. Since the higher frequencies are more readily masked than the lower frequencies, as discussed
on p. 451, above, speech may be audible in a room with much background
noise, and yet not intelligible.

Section 9
DIGESTION, METABOLISM AND NUTRITION

***

CHAPTER 27

DIGESTION IN THE MOUTH AND STOMACH

MOST of the food we eat is unsuitable for direct use by the cells of the body, either because it is solid or colloidal and therefore cannot pass through the wall of the intestine into the blood, or because, although diffusible, it is in some form which the cells cannot at once assimilate.

The effect of digestion is to resolve the different foodstuffs into simple components which will pass easily through the intestinal mucosa into the circulation and from there, into the cells which are to make use of them. Polysaccharides must be broken down into monosaccharides, fats into fatty acids and glycerol, and proteins into their constituent amino-acids. A few substances, such as the fat-soluble vitamins which have no value as a source of energy but are of vital importance to the body, may have to be rendered soluble in water before they can be absorbed.

This necessary and radical transformation of the food is effected by the enzymes contained in the digestive juices which are poured into the gut by the various glands situated in or near it, whenever food is eaten. It is noteworthy that all these enzymes are *hydrolytic* in their action, and the minimum of energy is wasted during the process of digestion. Absorption of the products of digestion, which proceeds coincidently with their liberation throughout the small intestine, is also a highly efficient process; the material which is finally collected in the colon for excretion has little food value and consists largely of cellulose, bacteria and débris from the intestinal mucosa.

Besides the products of digestion, the water, salts and organic constituents of the juices themselves must be absorbed. The total volume of digestive juices secreted daily is not accurately known, but it is estimated to be some 4 to 9 litres in man, i.e. of the same order as the volume of circulating blood. There is thus a very large daily "turnover" of water and salts between the blood and intestinal lumen, and if re-absorption of the fluid is prevented (e.g. loss through vomiting or diarrhoea) *dehydration* of the body tissues quickly ensues, fluid being withdrawn from these into the blood to maintain its volume.

The Secretory Work of the Digestive Glands

Vasodilatation occurs in all the digestive glands when they are active, as shown in Fig. 27.1, and again in Fig. 27.3, so that during the digestion of a meal there is a great increase in the blood-flow through the portal circula-

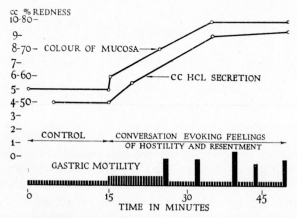

FIG. 27.1. Contractions of the human stomach (gastric motility) and changes in acid secretion and vascularity (colour) of the mucosa accompanying feelings of hostility and resentment aroused by conversation. The subject was a man ("Tom") who had a large gastric fistula. The intensity of the red colour of the mucosa was expressed in arbitrary units. The strength of the contractions of the stomach is indicated by the height of the black bars. (Wolf and Wolff, "Human Gastric Function".)

tion. A ready supply of water and salts is thus assured for the production of secretions; but the enzymes and other organic constituents, e.g. mucin, are probably prepared from "raw materials" in the blood by the gland-cells themselves. Many of the cells in the digestive glands contain granules or droplets which are apparently antecedents of organic constituents of the juice. These accumulate during inactivity and are discharged during secretion, particularly if this is prolonged; these cellular changes can be correlated to some extent with the amounts of enzyme, mucin or other organic material found in the juice (Fig. 27.2).

The act of secretion is not merely a washing-out of preformed constituents from the cell by fluid filtered off from the blood; the submaxillary gland can produce saliva against a pressure much higher than that in the

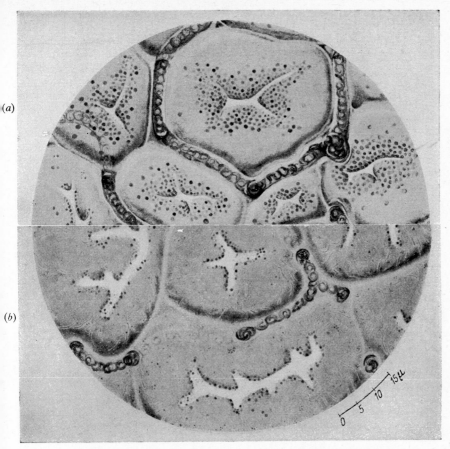

Fig. 27.2. Portions of the unstained living pancreas of a white mouse (a) after twenty-four hours' fast; the cells contain plenty of zymogen granules, and (b) after three hours' stimulation of secretion. Most of the intracellular material has been discharged. (Hirsch.)

arteries (Ludwig) and during secretion its usage of oxygen and sugar is increased (Barcroft).

Apart from the synthesis of organic materials by gland-cells *osmotic* work may be done during secretion; for instance, the parietal cells of the gastric glands concentrate hydrogen ions about three million times in preparing the acid of the gastric juice from blood.

Innervation of the Digestive Glands and Alimentary Tract. The existence of "secretory" nerves was discovered by Carl Ludwig (1851) who stimulated the lingual nerve, a branch of which (the *chorda tympani*) supplies the sub-maxillary gland, and found that it caused the secretion of saliva. It has since become abundantly clear that all the digestive glands receive a dual innervation from the autonomic nervous system (Chapters 22 & 23), namely, vasodilator and "secretory" fibres from the parasympathetic division, and vasoconstrictor and (possibly) inhibitory fibres from the sympathetic division. The former are distributed to the abdomen in the vagus and pelvic visceral nerves; the latter for the most part run from the autonomic ganglia to the viscera along the walls of the large arteries.

There is a similar dual nerve supply to the smooth muscle of the alimentary tract, the parasympathetic fibres increasing the motor activity, and the sympathetic fibres depressing it, so that in general the state of activity of an organ may be said to represent the resultant of the influence of the two systems. However, the extent to which the motor and secretory functions of the digestive tract are normally controlled by these nerves remains problematical; for instance, complete denervation of an intestinal loop produces a striking increase in tone, motility and spontaneous secretion, but a rapid recovery occurs and in a few days the behaviour of this denervated loop is almost indistinguishable from normal.

In addition to the motor or efferent autonomic fibres mentioned, *afferent* fibres carry sensory impulses from all parts of the tract to the central nervous system; the reflex arcs formed by these with the autonomic nerves play an important part in the activities of the gut. Sensations from the normally functioning digestive tract are almost entirely absent, apart from fullness of the stomach after a meal and of the rectum before defaecation, which are readily appreciated. Excessive distension or strong contractions of the intestines, particularly in the presence of inflammation or poor blood-supply, gives rise to *pain* which is griping or colicky in character, is poorly localized and may be "referred" to areas supplied by somatic nerves entering the spinal cord in the same segment as the visceral afferents.

The ultimate "centre" in the brain for visceral afferents and efferents appears to be the *hypothalamus* which thus exerts a general influence over the motor, secretory and vascular reactions of the entire alimentary tract; damage to or experimental interference with this region of the brain produces changes in secretion and motility of the stomach and intestines.

The hypothalamus has connections with the thalamus and cerebral cortex; and stimulation or destruction of certain areas of the cerebral cortex causes changes in motility and secretion of the alimentary tract. Furthermore, the thalamus is well known to be concerned with the perception of the painful or pleasurable quality of sensations. Means thus exist by which disagreeable or pleasant emotions may influence the working of the digestive tract. A good example of this is afforded by the experiment depicted in Fig. 27.1, which is taken from the study by Wolf and Wolff of the daily variations in gastric function of a laboratory technician ("Tom"). This man had had from childhood a large gastric fistula, permitting inspection of the interior, withdrawal of contents, etc. It is common everyday experience that pain, fear, anger, resentment or worry are potent causes of "indigestion," and similar upsets of the gastro-intestinal tract.

Saliva

The prompt response of the salivary glands to the sight, smell, or even the anticipation of appetising food, is familiar to everyone as "watering of the mouth." This is a "conditioned" reflex, i.e. one which has become established by training and experience and in which the cerebral centres play an important part. The stimuli received by the special sense organs are conveyed to the cerebral cortex; from there they are relayed to cells in the medulla which form the "salivatory nuclei" (they lie in the reticular formation in the floor of the fourth ventricle, and from these cells fibres run to the various glands. Salivation is also brought about when food is actually eaten, by direct stimulation of sensory end-organs in the mucosa of the mouth, tongue and pharynx, from which impulses are transmitted to the salivatory nuclei. This reflex is "unconditioned"; it is present from birth and does not involve the higher cerebral centres. Thus, reflex saliva-tion is readily produced in a decerebrate cat by introducing acid, alcohol, etc., into the mouth.

Saliva has a pH of about 6·8, is fairly well buffered and contains a lubricant *mucin* and (in man) the enzyme *ptyalin* which breaks down starch into a mixture of dextrins and maltose. The main functions of saliva are to moisten and lubricate the food, thus preparing it for swallow-ing, and to dissolve its soluble constituents so that the flavour is appre-ciated and the secretion of saliva itself and of other digestive glands thereby stimulated.

Swallowing

Each mouthful of food is chewed and mixed with saliva until it forms a pulpy mass or "bolus" suitable for swallowing, and is collected from time to time on the surface of the tongue for this purpose. Swallowing begins with a quick contraction of the tongue muscles which propels the bolus past the faucial pillars into the pharynx; from then onwards, its progress is beyond voluntary control and is accomplished by a rapid and complicated series of movements which constitute the "swallowing reflex" and are co-ordinated by a "centre" in the medulla.

As the bolus enters the pharynx, the soft palate is approximated to the posterior pharyngeal wall by contraction of its muscles, so as to prevent entry of food into the nasal passages. At the same time the larynx is brought upwards and forwards under the shelter of the base of the tongue, raising and opening the upper end of the relaxed oesophagus, which the bolus now enters. The epiglottis may turn backwards to guard the entrance of the larynx; and the risk of food entering the air-passages is lessened by a reflex approximation of the vocal cords and momentary inhibition of respiration, which also form part of the reflex.

The passage of the bolus from the mouth to the upper part of the oesophagus is so rapid, and the reflex movements so easily disturbed by experimental pro-cedures, that it has proved very difficult so far to elucidate many of the details of the act, and in particular the nature of the forces which transport the bolus so rapidly. X-ray cinematography in subjects swallowing radio-opaque material is proving a most valuable technique for studying the mechanism of swallowing.

The swallowing reflex is touched off by contact of the food with areas on the fauces, pharynx and tonsils which are very sensitive to tactile stimulation and from which impulses travel to the medullary centre; if these areas are anaesthetised by painting them with cocaine, swallowing is impossible.

Having travelled through the upper third of the oesophagus in a fraction of a second, the bolus is now carried the rest of the way much more slowly by an advancing ring-like contraction of the smooth muscle of the oesophagus. If the bolus is soft and well-lubricated, it reaches the cardiac sphincter at the entrance to the stomach in a few seconds; but if dry, it may take a minute or so and *secondary waves* (which give rise to a painful sensation in the chest) may arise in the oesophagus and force it along.

Liquids, owing to the impetus given them by the act of swallowing and the effect of gravity, outstrip the oesophageal wave and arrive at the cardiac sphincter in a second or two, where they wait for the arrival of the oesophageal wave. When this approaches the cardiac sphincter the latter relaxes before it and the food enters the stomach.

Gastric Digestion

X-ray examination of the human stomach after eating meals made radio-opaque by the addition of barium sulphate, shows that there are wide variations among apparently normal persons in the position, shape and motility of the stomach. An ordinary meal begins to leave the stomach less than thirty minutes after it is eaten, and although the rate of gastric emptying varies with the size of the meal and its consistency and composition, gastric emptying is usually completed in four to five hours.

While the food remains in the stomach it becomes mixed with the gastric juice, the secretion of which from the millions of tubular glands buried in the mucosa starts within a few minutes of eating.

Composition of Gastric Juice. The juice is really a mixture in variable proportions of the individual secretions of the various types of cell present in the glands. Heidenhain (1878) first recognised the *chief cells*, which contain pepsinogen, and the *parietal cells*, which secrete HCl. Both are absent from the pyloric region of the stomach; the glands there contain *mucous cells*, which produce mucus, and between the pyloric region and the rest of the stomach there is a transitional zone where pyloric mucoid cells are mingled with chief and parietal cells. Besides the pyloric glands, mucus is secreted by cells in the necks of the glands elsewhere and also by the cells of the surface columnar epithelium.

The parietal cells are believed to secrete a fluid which is isotonic with blood, contains most of the water of the gastric juice and is a practically pure solution of hydrochloric acid, the strength of which as secreted (160 milli-equivalents per litre) is constant whatever the rate of its formation. However, the acidity of the gastric juice is generally much lower than this maximal value, owing to neutralisation by the bicarbonate of the mucous secretion and buffering by the proteins, peptones and polypeptides of the gastric contents.

There is good evidence that the hydrogen ions of the gastric juice are derived by splitting water molecules, the hydroxyl ions remaining being neutralized by

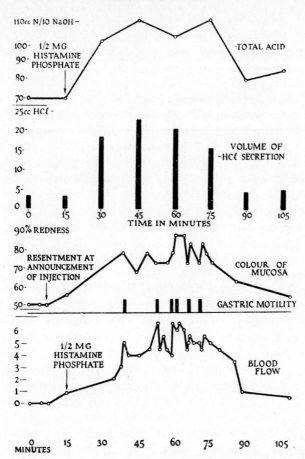

Fig. 27.3. The effect of a hypodermic injection of histamine on gastric
secretion, vascularity, motility and blood-flow in a human subject.

The vascularity was estimated as the redness, in arbitrary units, of
the mucosa. The presence of large gastric contractions only is
recorded. The blood-flow was measured by a thermal method, and
is expressed in arbitrary units from an arbitrary zero. (Wolf and
Wolff, "Human Gastric Function".)

carbonic acid, with the formation of bicarbonate ions. The chloride ions of the
gastric juice probably pass in from the blood passively, so as to preserve electrical
neutrality. The carbonic acid is formed by the hydration of carbon dioxide,
catalysed by the enzyme *carbonic anhydrase*, a large amount of which is found in
the parietal cells.

The chief cells probably contribute a scanty non-acid secretion; it
contains *pepsinogen*, which is activated by acid, forming the proteolytic
enzyme *pepsin*. The mucous cells produce a jelly-like fluid which contains
much mucus and is faintly alkaline owing to the presence of bicarbonate,

Although stimulation of the vagus causes the secretion of a juice containing acid, enzyme and mucus indicating that the cells concerned all have a secretory innervation from the vagus, they can respond to some extent independently of one another to other forms of stimulation (mechanical or chemical) so that the final composition of the gastric juice may show wide variations. Thus the drug *histamine* is a powerful stimulant of the parietal cells, providing a juice of high acidity and containing little pepsin or mucus (its effect on the stomach of the subject "Tom" referred to in Fig. 27.1, is shown in Fig. 27.3); while mechanical or chemical irritation of the mucous membrane causes a profuse flow of mucus, with comparative little acid or pepsin. No selective stimulus for the chief cells is yet known.

Pepsin in acid solution breaks down proteins into peptones and proteoses, which are fairly large fractions of the original molecule; some amino-acids are liberated, but the further breakdown of proteins and the above derivatives is accomplished later by the enzymes of the pancreatic and intestinal juices.

Stimulation of Gastric Secretion. Pavlov (1902) and his pupils were the first to show clearly that the secretion of gastric juice which starts within a few minutes of eating a meal occurs whether the food actually enters the stomach or not, and is due to a combination of "conditioned" and "unconditioned" reflexes similar to those causing the flow of saliva under the same conditions. A dog was provided by a previous surgical operation with a gastric fistula for the collection of gastric juice and an oesophageal fistula, so that the food which was swallowed never entered the stomach but fell out of the opening in the neck (Fig. 27.4). A few minutes after the animal was thus "sham-fed" there began a flow of gastric juice, which could be stopped by cutting the gastric branches of the vagus, or paralysing them by the injection of the drug atropine. Sham-feeding was not always necessary to elicit secretion; in intelligent animals, the mere sight, smell, or sounds associated with the arrival of food were sufficient.

These findings have been confirmed and extended by experiments on human subjects who have become accustomed by training to swallow and retain without discomfort a stomach-tube for withdrawal of the gastric juice; and occasional opportunities have also arisen of making similar and more extensive experiments on patients who, usually on account of an oesophageal stricture, have been provided by means of an operation with a gastric fistula for feeding. The classical example is that of Alexis St. Martin, an Indian "runner" at a trading station in Michigan, U.S.A., who was left as the result of a gunshot wound with a large gastric fistula. The observations and experiments made upon him (1825–33) by his physician, William Beaumont, have become famous. More elaborate studies of a similar kind have since been made by Carlson (1916) and by Wolf and Wolff (1943).

The reflex response to a "sham" meal gradually ceases in about an hour; but if the swallowed food is allowed to enter the stomach in the usual way, to be digested by this juice (and later by the pancreatic and intestinal enzymes), gastric secretion is augmented and prolonged for three hours or more, in fact, long after the meal has been forgotten.

The cause of this continued secretion resulting from digestion of the food was first investigated by Pavlov by means of the famous "Pavlov pouch" (Fig. 27.5). The secretion from this "miniature stomach" always runs closely parallel with that of the remainder, so that it becomes possible to follow the course of secretion in the main stomach during digestion, without interfering with it in any way.

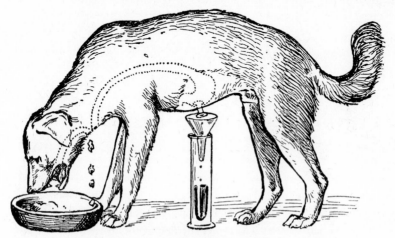

FIG. 27.4. A dog with oesophageal and gastric fistulae

The food consumed is seen dropping out of the open end of the anterior portion of the oesophagus; the animal is fed through the opening in the posterior portion. The gastric fistula consists simply of a tube flanged at each end, stitched into the wall of the stomach at one end, and into the abdominal wall at the other. (Höber.)

Using dogs with such a pouch, and also a gastric fistula, Pavlov showed that placing meat in the animal's stomach without its knowledge (no reflex stimulation) caused little or no secretion, and digestion of the food took many hours; but if the meat was first partly digested with "reflex" juice (obtained by sham-feeding another dog) the mixture stimulated gastric secretion strongly when introduced and digestion was rapidly completed. Not only does this experiment illustrate the importance of the "reflex" juice in gastric digestion, but it also indicates that digestion products are responsible for the later stimulation of gastric secretion.

Similarly, the introduction of food or its digestion products directly into the small intestine stimulates gastric secretion. The existence of this "intestinal phase" of gastric stimulation has been proved in dogs, by Ivy, by making the entire stomach into a pouch at an aseptic operation, joining the oesophagus directly to the duodenum. After recovery from the operation, when the animal eats a meal, this passes straight into the small intestine and is there digested; a considerable secretion of gastric juice from the pouch occurs.

Gastrin. There is present in the mucosal cells of the antral region of the stomach a hormone named *gastrin* (Edkins, 1906) which is liberated into the circulation by the presence of food in the stomach; it stimulates the parietal cells to secrete acid. The release of this hormone can be demonstrated by providing a dog with two gastric pouches, one of the antrum and the other of the acid-secreting (fundic) region, and dividing

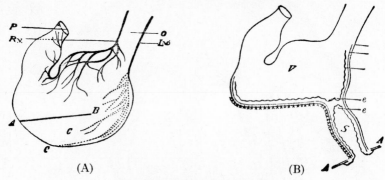

(A)   (B)

FIG. 27.5. The Pavlov pouch.

The left diagram (A) shows the line of the incision, *A—B*, into the gastric wall. *O*, oesophagus; *R. v. L. v.*, right and left vagus nerves; *P*, pylorus; *C*, cardiac portion of stomach.

The right diagram (B) shows the operation completed (part sectional). *V*, main portions of stomach; *S*, cardiac *cul-de-sac* (pouch); *A—A*, abdominal wall; *e, e*, mucous membrane reflected to form a diaphragm between the two cavities.

all nervous connections between them. When the antral pouch is stimulated by distending it with a balloon or irrigating it with meat extract, the fundic pouch secretes. Gastrin has been isolated from the pyloric antral mucosa of human and other species in the form of a peptide containing 17 aminoacid residues. It is an extremely potent stimulant of gastric acid secretion in the human subject (Fig. 27.6).

Experiments on conscious dogs have shown: (1) that the accumulation of acid in the antral contents during gastric digestion inhibits the release of gastrin, so that further secretion of acid is restrained; and (2) that both the release of gastrin from the antrum by appropriate stimulation of this region, and the action of the hormone on the parietal cells, is potentiated by the concurrent reflex vagal excitation to both the antral and fundic regions of the stomach which occurs when a meal is eaten.

The stimulation of acid secretion following a meal thus results from a combination of direct vagal excitation and the action of gastrin, on the parietal cells.

Histamine, a potent stimulus of parietal cell secretion, is present in all parts of the gastric and intestinal mucosa, particularly in the vicinity of the parietal cells; it is also found in the gastric juice. The function of this histamine remains unknown; it has been suggested that it plays some rôle in the activity of the parietal cells, but there is as yet no proof of this.

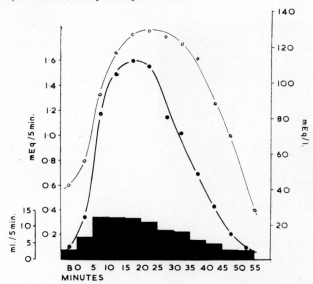

FIG. 27.6. Output in mEq./5 min, secretory rate in ml./5 min, and H^+ ion concentrations following an intravenous injection of gastrin (4 μg) in a human subject. ○ – – ○ mEq./litre, ● – – ● mEq./5 min. (Makhlouf, McManus and Card, 1965.)

Gastric Inhibition. Besides the stimulation of gastric secretion from the intestine, inhibition may be brought about by the presence there of fats, fatty acids and other substances. Since the last century, physicians have employed fat in the form of olive oil or cream, to depress gastric secretion in the condition of peptic ulcer, in order to promote healing. These substances are believed to liberate from the duodenal mucosa into the circulation a hormone *Enterogastrone*, which inhibits gastric secretion and motility. This is the physiological basis for the view that fatty meat such as pork is "indigestible"; it takes a longer time to be digested and leave the stomach.

Movements of the Stomach

Some hours after a meal the normal human stomach is empty apart from a small and variable quantity of gastric juice, saliva, mucus, etc., and its walls are in a state of tonic contraction. When the swallowed food enters it, a *receptive relaxation* occurs as the result of a nervous reflex and the food slides down into the most dependent portion. Soon, as indicated in Fig. 27.7, ring-like contractions appear in the body of the stomach and slowly move towards the pyloric sphincter, becoming deeper as they pass into this region where the muscle is stronger (W. B. Cannon, 1898). As digestion and emptying proceed, the strength and frequency of the contractions increase to a maximum which varies with the size and

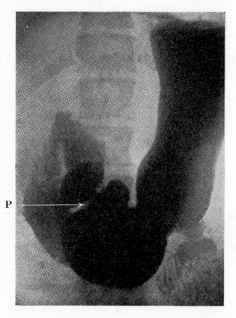

Fig. 27.7. Radiograph of a human stomach after a "barium meal" showing peristaltic waves. P, pyloric sphincter. (F. Haenisch in A. E. Barclay, "The Digestive Tract".)

nature of the meal, and then gradually decline. Each wave occupies the stomach for about half a minute, and as many as four may be seen at the same time during the height of digestion. These contractions serve to mix the food with the gastric juice and, particularly in the pyloric antrum, provide the propulsive force for the passage of gastric contents at intervals into the duodenum.

Although the stomach relaxes when food enters, the tone is gradually regained, so that by the time most of the food has left the stomach a high tone is again present, with small regular fluctuations, termed a "tonus rhythm". This continues for a few hours after the stomach has emptied and then, if the next meal is not forthcoming, gives place to contractions similar in type to those normally seen in the filled stomach, but much more powerful. These occur in groups, lasting for about half an hour, and at intervals of two to three hours. Their incidence coincides with a sensation of hunger; as they become stronger, definite pain—"pangs of hunger"—is felt with each contraction (Carlson, 1919).

Emptying of the Stomach. For many years it was believed that gastric emptying was chiefly controlled by the pyloric sphincter, which was supposed to remain closed for most of the time in the face of the gastric contractions, opening briefly at intervals to allow exit of some gastric contents. However, direct observations of the behaviour of the stomach and pyloric sphincter in human subjects by means of X-rays

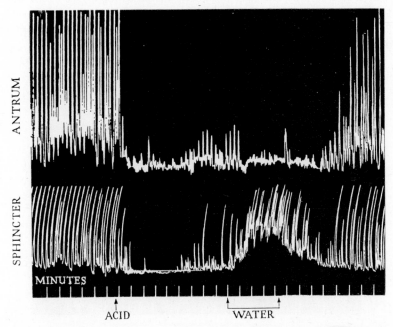

FIG. 27.8. Record showing the effect on the pyloric antrum and sphincter in a conscious dog of: (a) injecting acid into the duodenum (20 ml N/10 HCl); and (b) distending the duodenum with water (30 cm pressure). Acid relaxes both the antrum and sphincter; distension of the duodenum beyond the physiological range of pressure caused contractions and spasm (rise of baseline).

Gastric peristalsis was recorded by a balloon in the antrum, and contractions of the sphincter by a second balloon in the sphincter. (Thomas, Crider and Mogan.)

and the gastroscope, and experiments on trained conscious animals in which the regions concerned have been made accessible by the surgical preparation of fistulae, show that the sphincter has no such independent rôle, but behaves like the pyloric antrum of which it is anatomically a part. In fact, the three regions, pyloric antrum, sphincter, and duodenal cap act as a single co-ordinated physiological unit. As a gastric wave passes over each in turn, the antral contraction expels food through the still relaxed sphincter into the duodenal cap; but this is brought to an end by the closely following contraction of the sphincter, and before the antrum and sphincter have relaxed, the contraction of the duodenal cap occurs, expelling the food down the duodenum. The effect is that of a "gastric pump" (Quigley, 1943), regurgitation from duodenum to stomach being prevented by the slightly persistent contraction of antrum and sphincter; not every gastric wave results in this complete cycle of contractions so that only a proportion of the waves which arrive at the pyloric antrum cause the exit of gastric contents.

Gastric emptying thus depends fundamentally upon the propulsive activity of the gastric muscle and the co-ordination of the three regions

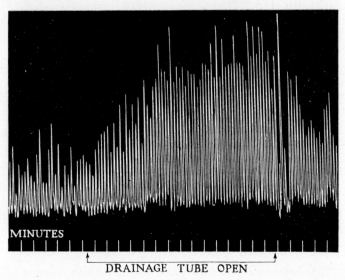

FIG 27.9. Record showing the effect of duodenal drainage on gastric peristalsis in a conscious dog provided with a high duodenal fistula (exclusion of enterogastric reflex). (Thomas, Crider and Mogan.)

mainly concerned; both these factors are controlled to a large extent from the duodenum. There are many substances besides fat, such as acid, hypertonic solutions and protein digestion-products, which retard gastric emptying when they are introduced into the duodenum; this they do by causing reflex inhibition of the gastric musculature including the pyloric sphincter (*the enterogastric reflex*) as shown in Fig. 27.8. In fact, by means of this reflex a constant restraining influence is normally exercised from the duodenum on gastric tone and motility; if the reflex is prevented from operating during gastric emptying, gastric motility is greatly increased and the stomach empties abnormally rapidly (Fig. 27.9).

Towards the end of gastric emptying, particularly of a fatty meal, the contraction cycles are weak, the pressures in antrum, sphincter and duodenum are nearly equal, and the sphincter is open most of the time; such conditions are favourable for the regurgitation of intestinal juices and bile into the stomach, and evidence of this is afforded by the presence of these in samples of the gastric contents withdrawn by a stomach-tube.

Vomiting. This is a reflex act involving the muscles of the diaphragm and abdominal wall and those of the stomach and oesophagus It is coordinated by a "centre" in the medulla, which may be stimulated by irritation of any part of the digestive tract, by impulses from the semicircular canals (sea-sickness) or by disturbance of the centre itself (e.g. by cerebral tumours or the action of drugs such as apomorphine). A more or less prolonged sensation of *nausea* usually precedes retching and vomiting; it is marked by pallor, sweating, salivation and partial or complete inhibition of the gastric musculature; anti-peristalsis in the small intestine has been observed radiographically in human subjects. Nausea may culminate in *retching*, which consists of a series of inspiratory-like efforts accompanied by closure of the glottis, the stomach becoming compressed between the diaphragm and the contracted abdominal muscles; the gastric contents are finally ejected through the relaxed cardiac sphincter and oesophagus. The larynx is drawn up as in swallowing and elevation of the soft palate also occurs; this largely prevents egress of the vomitus by the nose.

CHAPTER 28

INTESTINAL DIGESTION

As the stomach contents pass at intervals into the duodenum, they meet and mix with secretions from the pancreas, liver and intestinal glands, which complete the digestion of proteins, fats and carbohydrates, as the food passes down the intestine. The products are absorbed simultaneously into the portal and lymphatic circulations.

Secretion of Pancreatic Juice. The collection of pancreatic juice from a conscious dog by means of a cannula tied into the pancreatic duct, was first carried out by Regnier de Graaf (1664) and the method was revived nearly 200 years later by Claude Bernard, who gave the first description of the properties of the juice. Animals provided by a previous surgical operation with such pancreatic fistulae remain in excellent health indefinitely, provided the juice is returned to the intestine daily, and not lost to the animal. For some purposes, however, collection of the juice for a few hours after cannulation of the duct in an anaesthetised animal is more suitable.

The acinar cells, which secrete the pancreatic juice, are apparently all of the same type; they produce a secretion containing a number of enzymes and having a pH of 8–8·4 with a bicarbonate content which is approximately 1–5 times that in the blood, increasing with the rate of secretion. The amount of chloride present is approximately inversely proportional to the rate of secretion, so that the sum of the concentrations of the two ions HCO_3^- and Cl^- remains about the same (Fig. 28.3). The pancreas contains the enzyme *carbonic anhydrase* which is presumably concerned in the formation of the bicarbonate in the juice.

As in the case of the saliva and gastric juice, a reflex mechanism exists for the provision of pancreatic juice when a meal is eaten, and again it is the vagus which carries the secretory fibres to the gland (Fig. 28.1); the secretion is scanty, but rich in enzymes. A much greater flow of juice occurs, however, as the gastric contents are passed on into the duodenum (Fig. 28.2), and cause the liberation from the intestinal mucosa into the circulation of a hormone *secretin*, which excites a copious and watery secretion from the pancreas. A second hormone *pancreozymin* is also released with secretin, and this, like excitation of the vagus, causes the secretion of pancreatic enzymes, with little or no effect on the volume rate of flow. These two hormones thus ensure the continued secretion of a copious flow of pancreatic juice, containing enzymes, during the intestinal digestion of a meal. The flow of hepatic bile and of juice from Brunner's glands in the duodenum is also excited to a small extent. The agent chiefly

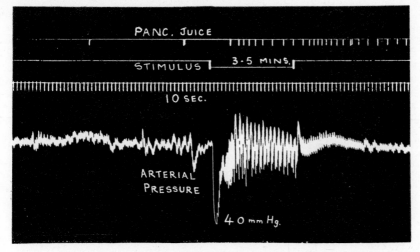

FIG. 28.1. Pancreatic secretion produced in an anaesthetized dog by stimulation of the vagus nerves in the neck.

Note the effect on the heart-rate (cardio-inhibitory fibres in the vagus), the long latent period before secretion commences (forty seconds) and the scanty response. (Gregory, unpublished.)

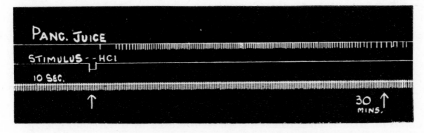

FIG. 28.2. Pancreatic secretion produced in an anaesthetized dog by the injection of acid (50 ml of N/10 HCl) into the duodenum.

Note the copious and persistent secretion, compared with that given by vagus stimulation (Fig. 28.1) in similar circumstances. (Gregory, unpublished.)

responsible for their liberation is the *acid* in the gastric contents, although fats, bile and protein digestion products (e.g. peptones) are also effective; acid is a much more powerful stimulus for the release of secretin than for that of pancreozymin.

Fig. 28.3 shows the effect of an injection of secretin on the flow of pancreatic juice in a human subject; the juice was withdrawn by means of a stomach tube which was swallowed and allowed to pass into the duodenum.

Secretin was the first hormone to be discovered. The fact that the entry of the acid gastric contents into the duodenum excited pancreatic secretion was well known to Pavlov and his contemporaries, but was ascribed to a reflex. However, in 1902, Bayliss and Starling showed that dilute acid still excited pancreatic secretion when placed in a *denervated* loop of small intestine, so that the effect must be mediated by way of the circulation. Intravenous injection of acid was without result; but the injection of an acid extract of the intestinal mucosa caused a copious secretion of pancreatic juice; and the active principle, secretin, has been isolated and identified as a peptide containing 27 aminoacid residues. Pure secretin does not excite the secretion of enzymes, although cruder concentrates of the hormone do so. In 1943, Harper and Raper showed that such secretin extracts contain pancreozymin, now known to be a hormone, which stimulates the output of enzymes but has little action on that of bicarbonate, or on the volume rate of secretion. Preparations of both secretin and pancreozymin suitable for use in human subjects are now available commercially.

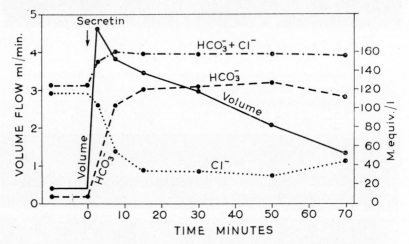

Fig. 28.3. Human pancreatic secretion evoked by intravenous administration of secretin at time 0. The volume-rate and bicarbonate concentration are increased; the chloride concentration is decreased. (Lagerlöf, 1942.)

Actions of Pancreatic Juice. The pure juice is almost without action on most varieties of protein, the powerful proteolytic enzyme it contains being present in an inactive form *trypsinogen*. This is rapidly converted into the enzyme *trypsin* when the juice mixes with the intestinal juice which contains an enzyme-like activator *enterokinase*. Thus formed, trypsin acts upon all proteins and their digestion products, converting them finally into amino-acids and polypeptides. Pancreatic *diastase* breaks down starch into maltose, while the *lipase* also present hydrolyses the fats into fatty acids and glycerol.

The Bile. The entry of the gastric contents into the duodenum provides the stimulus for the appearance there of the bile, whose importance for digestion lies chiefly in the fact that the bile salts and lecithin it contains are valuable aids in the emulsification, digestion and absorption of the fats of a meal. It is also necessary for the efficient absorption of iron and of the fat-soluble vitamins.

Hepatic bile, a neutral golden-yellow slightly syrupy fluid, is secreted by the hepatic cells, and there is little evidence that its production is normally under nervous control. Between meals, the tone of the sphincter-like muscle around the duodenal end of the common bile duct is relatively high, and the bile flows into the relaxed gall-bladder where it is rapidly

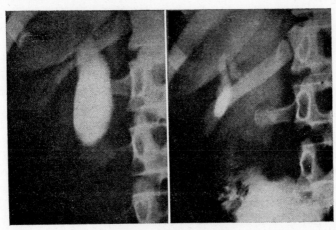

FIG. 28.4. X-ray photographs of the Gall-Bladder of a Man before and after a meal of fat.

Tetra-iodo-phenolphthalein was injected intravenously fourteen hours before the first photograph was taken (Graham-Cole test). The second photograph was taken twenty minutes after the meal of fat. The discharge of the contents of the gall-bladder in response to the presence of fat in the duodenum has filled the cystic and common ducts with dye, and they can be seen, in the second photograph, forming a loop above the gall-bladder; in some cases the hepatic duct becomes filled also. (Ivy.)

concentrated by the activity of the mucosa, becoming more viscid, very dark and slightly acid. When a meal is eaten, a little bile is sometimes reflexly expelled from the gall-bladder into the duodenum; but the main emptying occurs later when contact with the duodenal mucosa of the gastric contents excites the liberation into the circulation of the hormone *Cholecystokinin* (Ivy), which causes slow contractions and emptying of the gall-bladder. Fat is particularly effective in liberating the hormone and hence in stimulating the emptying of the gall-bladder (Fig. 28.4).

After the gall-bladder has emptied, hepatic bile may flow directly into the duodenum for a time until digestion there is over; gradually the tone of the sphincter increases and the bile is once more diverted into the gall-bladder until the next meal.

Cholecystography. This clinical test of gall-bladder function depends on the fact that tetrabromphenolphthalein and similar compounds are opaque to X-rays and are excreted in the bile after oral or intravenous administration. They are concentrated in the gall-bladder and so enable it to be visualized by X-rays. If a meal rich in fat is then fed, the emptying of the gall-bladder may be recorded by serial radiographs (Fig. 28.4).

The increase in the rate of flow of bile from the liver, which occurs during the digestion of a meal, is to some extent due to the passage through the liver of the products of digestion, but the chief stimulus is supplied by the bile-salts themselves. Returning to the liver after absorption from the small intestine they stimulate the secretion of more bile, in which they are themselves incorporated. The total amount of bile salts thus circulating between liver, gall-bladder and intestine (*entero-hepatic circulation*), appears to be maintained at an approximately constant level by the liver; if extra bile salts are administered to an animal, they are destroyed in a few days and the original circulating total is soon restored. If all the bile is drained from an animal having a biliary fistula and not returned to it, the rate of bile salt secretion falls to a low "basal" level; it represents the rate of new bile salt formation by the liver, presumably in response to a maximal stimulus (the fall to zero of the quantity in circulation). When the return of bile is once more instituted, the quantity circulating rises in a few days to the original value.

The bile salts are derivatives of the steroid cholic acid, and are thus allied structurally to cholesterol and the sex and adrenal-cortical hormones (see Chapter 32). A number of different bile acids exist, but only a few are present in the bile of a particular species. A small amount only is present as the acid itself; the rest is in the form of a compound of the bile acid with the base taurine or the amino-acid glycine. Taurocholic and glycocholic acids are present in human and ox bile: the dog, sheep and goat have only the former, the hog only the latter. How the liver synthesises the bile acids is still unknown.

The bile pigments. The haemoglobin of worn-out red blood corpuscles is broken down by the cells of the reticulo-endothelial system, notably those of the liver (Kupffer cells), spleen and bone marrow, through the stages of haemochromogens which still contain the iron and globin of the original haemoglobin molecule, to the *bile pigment biliverdin*, and its reduction product *bilirubin*, which are iron- and protein- free.The latter is set free into the blood, contributing to the yellow colour of normal plasma, and taken up from it by the liver, to be excreted in the bile. In some circumstances, e.g. in starving dogs, biliverdin is excreted by the liver in place of bilirubin.

The Intestinal Juices. The digestive juices contributed by the glands present in the wall of the small intestine come from *Brunner's glands* in the first inch or so of the duodenum, and *Lieberkuhn's glands*, which are found throughout the small and large intestines. Both secretions are alkaline and contain a good deal of mucus; the stimulus for their appearance seems to be local mechanical and chemical excitation of the mucosa by digesting food.

The juice as ordinarily obtained—e.g. by distension with a balloon of an isolated loop of intestine (Thiry-Vella loop, Fig. 28.5), contains small amounts of a variety of enzymes; but similar enzyme activity is also demonstable in extracts of the intestinal mucous membrane, and the invariable presence, in such samples of juice, of cast-off mucosal cells, leucocytes, etc., has given rise to the suspicion that most of its varied digestive properties may be due to *intracellular* enzymes liberated from the debris. If this material is rapidly removed from cat's intestinal juice by centrifuging it immediately after collection, the only enzymes found in appreciable amounts are lipase, amylase, and enterokinase. (Florey.)

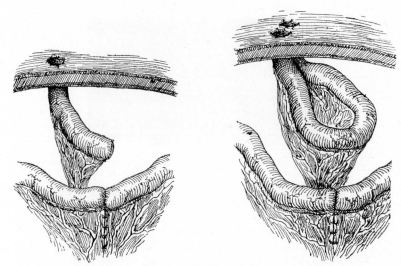

FIG. 28.5. The Thiry and Thiry-Vella intestinal loops.
(From Markowitz, "Text-book of Experimental Surgery".)

The Movements of the Intestines

The mixing of the food with the intestinal secretions, and its passage through the alimentary canal, is accomplished by the intestinal movements; these are nicely co-ordinated with the progress of digestion and absorption so that both are virtually completed by the time the colon is reached.

A good way to gain some idea of the normal pattern of the intestinal movements (and incidentally, to study them experimentally), is to open under warm saline the abdomen of a decerebrate or lightly anaesthetised animal at the height of digestion. The inhibition caused by cold and drying is thus avoided; and the movements of the coils of intestine, as they float outside the abdominal cavity, may be recorded by attaching them to levers writing on a smoked drum (enterograph), or by taking moving pictures which are analysed later; or balloons may be inserted into the intestine and connected to volume or pressure recorders.

Many other methods have been used for study of the intestinal movements; the more fruitful are probably those which utilize as a subject a conscious trained animal previously operated upon to render accessible the required region of the intestine (e.g. the Thiry-Vella loop).

Three types of movement can often be distinguished. The "pendular movements" are a rhythmical lengthening and shortening of a segment of intestine and are probably caused by gentle waves of contraction which travel down the intestine for a short distance at about 2 to 5 cm per second

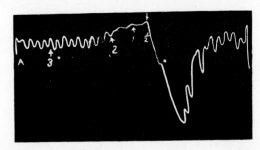

Fig. 28.6. The passage of a bolus along the Small Intestine. Contractions of the longitudinal coat as recorded by an enterograph.

The bolus (of soap and cotton wool) was inserted into the intestine 4 in above the recorded spot at the moment indicated by A. At subsequent moments it was 3 in., 2 in., 1 in. and $\frac{1}{2}$ in. from the recorded spot as indicated below the tracing. As the bolus arrives 2 in. above the levers, there is cessation of the rhythmic contractions and inhibition of the tone of the muscle. This is followed, as the bolus is forced past, by a strong contraction on the rear of the bolus. (Bayliss and Starling.)

and occur about ten to twelve times a minute. Besides these, one occasionally sees a portion of the gut which is the seat of a much stronger contraction of the circular muscle. This contraction obliterates the vessels and the lumen of the gut, blanching the intestine. It travels very slowly down the gut, about 0·1 to 0·5 cm per minute, preceded by a less obvious but equally circumscribed region of inhibition. The double wave is known as a *peristaltic wave* (Bayliss and Starling, 1899), and is elicited by distending or stimulating the intestine strongly at any point. Such a response of the intestine (contraction above, inhibition below, as shown in Fig. 28.6), is probably due to a local reflex in the nerve-plexuses of the intestine, and has for this reason been termed the "Myenteric Reflex" (Cannon).

A third type of movement often seen is "segmentation"; a portion of intestine, frequently the jejunum, becomes occupied by several simul-

taneous localised contractions. After a few seconds these disappear and
are replaced by similar contractions in the intervening regions, so that the
intestine is divided into a fresh set of segments (Fig. 28.7). By this means
the food is mixed with the digestive juices and brought into intimate
contact with the mucous membrane.

The movements just described, and variations of them, are the ground-
work from which is built up the normal complicated pattern of intestinal
activity. But we do not yet understand very well how they are co-ordinated;
for instance, what determines the appearance of a given type of movement
in some region of the gut, its intensity and range of influence, why it
gives place to some other movement after a time, and finally how the

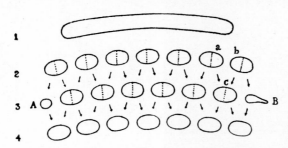

FIG. 28.7. Segmentation in small intestine.

1. Loop of intestine before segmentation begins.

2. The loop is cut into little ovoid pieces by contraction of the circular muscle.

3. A moment later, each segment is divided into two parts, as
shown by the dotted lines, and neighbouring parts, as a and b in
line 2, run rapidly together and merge to form new segments, as c
in line 3. The end pieces A and B are left small and move to and fro.

4. The process is repeated, with a return to the condition shown
in line 2. (Cannon.)

movements as a whole are kept in step with the progress of digestion, so
that the food moves along neither too quickly nor too slowly.

The intestine as a whole shows a descending gradient of activity throughout its length. After a meal, the duodenum and jejunum show great and
varied activity; but as the ileum is approached, the bowel becomes more
and more quiescent, the terminal ileum making only occasional movements
as it gradually fills with the residue of digestion.

Filling and Emptying of the Colon. As the stomach empties, the
ileum is stimulated reflexly (*gastro-ileal reflex* of Hurst), to pass on its
semi-fluid contents into the caecum by sustained "stripping" contractions
which occur every few minutes and persist while food remains in the
stomach. All movement of the caecum is inhibited and it relaxes to receive
the ileal contents. Gradually the caecum, ascending and transverse colons
are filled, without obvious peristalsis or other movement, the general

appearance being one of "impressive immobility" (Hardy). There is a wide range of variation among normal persons in the time taken for different regions of the colon to become filled; but as soon as caecum and ascending colon are well filled, the saccular folds known as haustra appear (Fig. 28.8A), and by their slow filling and emptying knead the contents and aid the absorption of salts and water.

This slow and irregular process of filling is interrupted two or three times a day by a "mass movement" (Fig. 28.8B). Starting usually about

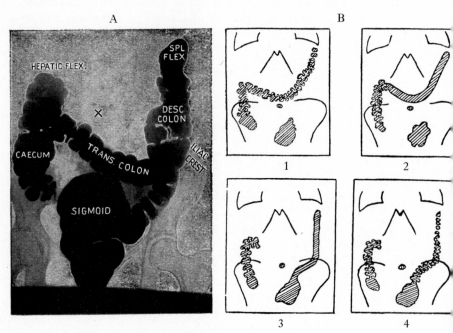

Fig. 28.8. (A) Radiograph of the human colon after a barium enema, showing haustra, and (B) a diagram (Holzknecht) of a "mass movement." (From A. E. Barclay, "The Digestive Tract".)

the middle of the colon, the haustra disappear and the colon becomes shortened and flattened by a rapidly advancing powerful contraction, and its contents are moved on bodily into the descending and pelvic colons in a few seconds usually without any subjective sensations whatever.

In most people the rectum is almost empty until just before the urge to defaecate or "call to stool" comes (commonly after breakfast) which is caused by a mass movement distending the rectum with faeces. The attainment in this way of a certain degree of distension initiates afferent impulses which are sent to a "defaecation centre" in the sacral region of the spinal cord. In newborn animals and infants, or after complete transection of the spinal cord, efferent impulses then return from this centre, and produce contractions of the terminal colon, relaxation of the sphincters, and involuntary or "automatic" defaecation. In normal adults, filling of the rectum is appreciated in consciousness; if circumstances are suitable the sacral centre is "permitted" and even "encouraged" by the cerebral cortex to operate as described above. Expulsion of the faeces is assisted by "straining," i.e. raising the intra-abdominal pressure by expiring against a closed glottis and contracting the abdominal muscles; emptying of the anal canal is completed by contracting the levator ani muscles, which also restores the everted mucous membrane. If on the other hand defaecation would be inconvenient, activity of the sacral centre is inhibited by the cerebral cortex. The tone of the anal sphincters increases and that of the colon decreases; the faeces in the rectum move back into the colon and the desire to defaecate disappears.

Colonic Secretion. The colonic mucosa contains very large numbers of mucous cells; and Florey has shown that a secretion of mucus, accompanied by vasodilatation and contractions of the muscle, is produced by stimulation of the parasympathetic nerve supply, the pelvic visceral nerves. Stimulation of the sympathetic supply causes vasoconstriction and inhibition of movements without secretion.

Absorption of the Digestion Products

The Villi. The columnar epithelium of the small intestine is specially adapted for absorption of the products of digestion by the presence of the villi. These are finger-like projections of the surface, about 0·5 mm long, containing a strand of muscle from the muscularis mucosae, blood-vessels, nerves, and a central lymph vessel termed a lacteal; the surface available for absorption is thus greatly increased. Between the villi open the mouths of the intestinal glands.

During fasting, the villi are shrunken and motionless; but during digestion they swell up, due to the increased blood and lymph-flow through them, and contract rhythmically and independently of each other (Fig. 28.9). These movements are probably of value in maintaining a good circulation through each villus and ensuring that this is constantly brought into contact with fresh portions of the intestinal contents. The water-soluble products of digestion, such as the amino-acids and sugars, are absorbed into the portal venous blood-stream and so pass through the liver before gaining the general circulation.

The pressure in the portal vein is about 20 mm Hg, which is higher than the hydrostatic pressure of the intestinal contents. The intestinal wall, however, is impermeable to colloids, so that unless there is an appreciable colloid osmotic pressure within the intestine, water may well be absorbed as a result of the colloid osmotic pressure of the plasma proteins. The end result of the digestive processes is the breakdown of all colloidal material into crystalloidal; finally, therefore, the intestinal contents exert no colloid osmotic pressure. But in the intermediate stages there may well be a substantial colloid concentration, and water may be drawn in from the blood. Similarly, any substances which can diffuse through the intestinal wall will do so if their concentrations within the intestine are greater than those in the blood; if there is no such concentration gradient in either direction, they will be carried through with the water. There is reason to believe that some substances of relatively small molecular weight normally leave the intestine in this way. On the other hand, other substances are transferred from the intestine to the blood proportionately more rapidly when in low concentration than in high by a "facilitated" process; or they may be absorbed even when the intestinal concentration is less than the blood concentration, i.e. "up" the concentration gradient. Some secretory process, or "active transport," must be involved and metabolic energy, oxidative or glycolytic, is needed. As examples, we may mention urea, xylose and erythritol, which appear to be absorbed by diffusion only, while glucose and most amino-acids are absorbed, at least partly, by active transport.

FIG. 28.9. Portion of a cinematograph film following the movements of the villi in the living intestine of the dog.

The interval between each frame is approximately one second. Note that the villus indicated by the arrow in the right-hand frame becomes progressively shorter until it can only just be seen in the third and fourth frames from the right; it then becomes longer again, and is only a little shorter in the last frame than it is in the first. (Kokas and Ludany.)

Sodium and chloride ions are absorbed rapidly, active transport (the "sodium pump") being involved, but calcium, magnesium and sulphate ions are absorbed very slowly.

Such feats on the part of the intestinal epithelium are reminiscent of those performed by the kidney tubule cells in producing urine from the glomerular filtrate and the intracellular mechanisms involved are no doubt similar.

Absorption of Fat. During the absorption of a fatty meal, the lymphatics draining the intestine can be seen to be filled with a creamy fluid *chyle* which consists of lymph loaded with globules of neutral fat. This very early observation (Asellius, 1622) gave rise to the natural assumption that the emulsified fat in the intestines was absorbed unchanged, much as oil soaks through paper; but Claude Bernard's discovery (1846) of the powerful lipase present in the pancreatic juice originated the view which is generally accepted today, that the greater part of the fat is hydrolysed in the small intestine before absorption; the liberated fatty acids enter the mucosal cells and are there resynthesised

FIG. 28.10. A photomicrograph of the small intestine of a rat, illuminated
with ultra-violet light, during the absorption of fat containing vitamin
A. This is fluorescent, and is visible in the epithelium, central lacteal
of the villus and submucosal lymphatics. (Popper and Greenberg.)

into neutral fat, which passes into the central lacteal of the villus (Fig. 28.10)
and is ultimately discharged into the systemic venous blood via the
thoracic duct. Most of the fat in the blood after a meal is in the form of
minute droplets 0·5 to 1·0 μ in diameter, the *chylomicrons*, which are
believed to consist of neutral fat covered with a thin film of phospholipid
(Fig. 28.11).

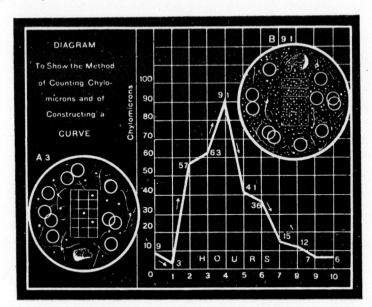

FIG. 28.11. Curve showing the Number of Chylomicrons in a standard
field at various times after a meal of fat.

Two illustrative fields are also shown: A (on left) before absorption has begun, with 3 chylomicrons in the standard area; and B
(on right) with 91 chylomicrons. (From S. H. Gage and P. A. Fish.)

Bernard also showed that the presence of the bile was necessary for the absorption of fat, as indicated by the appearance of chyle in the intestinal lymphatics; the fatty acids liberated by lipolysis in the small intestine do not form soaps, the solution not being sufficiently alkaline, but are kept in solution and rendered absorbable by the bile salts.

Besides the lymphatic pathway for the absorption of fat, there is an alternative pathway—the portal venous blood. The fatty acids of shorter chain length, which are more readily soluble in water, take this pathway to the liver. Thus, although almost all of the stearic (C_{18}) and palmitic (C_{16}) acids are found in the intestinal lymph after feeding, only about one-half of lauric (C_{12}) and one-fifth of decanoic (C_{10}) acids take this route, the remainder entering the portal blood chiefly as free fatty acids.

CHAPTER 29

GENERAL METABOLISM

THE tissues forming the animal body are composed of chemical substances all of which are derived from its environment, and during the
animal's life these substances are returned to that environment many
times over. In spite of this dynamic equilibrium the living animal maintains
its individuality and indeed life is the continuity of this individuality. After
death the continuity is broken, and the elements which composed the
animal body become once more part of the environment. This maintenance
of the individual depends on an elaborate series of chemical processes and
the combination of all these reactions is called metabolism. These chemical
reactions can be regarded mainly as of two kinds. The first is concerned
with the building up of the complex substances of the body tissues out of
simpler substances. These processes are responsible for the maintenance
of the tissues by replacement of the loss due to wear and tear and in addition
to this, in the young animal, they are responsible for growth and development. These synthesizing reactions (sometimes grouped together under
the term *anabolism*) do not supply the energy which the body needs for
carrying out its functions; indeed, they themselves require a certain
amount of energy from some other source. The source of this energy, and
also of the energy which the body needs for its other activities, is provided
by a second set of chemical reactions which are grouped together under the
term *catabolism*. In these reactions more complex chemical substances are
broken down into simpler ones and this disintegration which is mostly of
an oxidative nature, is accompanied by liberation of energy. The complex
substances, capable of yielding energy on oxidation, are taken into the
body as food and it has already been seen how the breaking-down process
begins in the intestine. Digestion, however, is not an oxidative process,
and is accompanied by liberation of only a very small fraction of the energy
of the food substances. The main liberation of energy takes place after the
food has been absorbed into the blood stream and it is to those changes
subsequent to absorption that the term metabolism is generally applied.

The general aim of metabolic studies is to determine how the chemical
energy of the food substances is utilized in contraction of muscles, secretion
of glands, transmission of impulses along nerves, growth of tissues and
the other activities characteristic of the living animal. The present position
of the problem is that a very great deal is known about the chemical reactions which occur and the amount of energy made available, but relatively

little is known about how this energy is used by the tissues for their purposes. Consequently most of this chapter is devoted to an account of the chemical processes occurring in metabolism the methods used for their study, the end products produced and the energy relations involved in these processes.

GENERAL METHODS OF METABOLIC STUDIES

The actual oxidative processes take place in the separate cells which compose the body, but the provision of the metabolic fuel, and the utilization of the energy liberated, is only possible when the cells are organized into tissues, organs, whole animals and indeed societies of animals. On the other hand many of the chemical reactions cannot easily be studied in the whole animal, but only in isolated organs or tissues. Hence it is necessary to study metabolic problems at a series of different levels of biological organization, i.e. to study the metabolism of individual cells, of isolated tissues, of organs and of whole animals. From the disconnected pieces of information obtained from these different sources we try to form a composite picture of the whole process of metabolism. Each type of metabolic experiment has its own special use. In the case of the whole animal we can administer substances by mouth, intravenously, intraperitoneally or subcutaneously, collect the waste products in the urine, estimate chemically the changes in the blood, measure the gaseous metabolism and thus study the energy relationships under physiological conditions. In particular, studies on the whole animal are essential for investigation of the effect of hormones on metabolism and the total nutritional requirement of the individual. Under this heading must also be placed the mass of clinical observation which has contributed greatly to our knowledge of physiological processes in the field of metabolism. Experiments with various organs make possible a rather fuller study of the chemical changes undergone by the food substances and also bring the oxidative processes into relationship with the special activity of each particular organ. The use of isolated tissues has made possible a very detailed study of the enzyme systems of the body and of the chemical changes brought about by these, even although the tissues in the experiments are not working under physiological conditions. The study of the individual cells has shown that at least some of the enzymes can be located in definite cells and in some cases in definite positions in the cell.

The Respiratory Quotient

Whatever method we use to investigate metabolism we consider the amount of oxygen used, the amount of carbon dioxide formed, the nature and amount of the foodstuff oxidized and the energy liberated, and all these must bear a strict relationship to each other. Since of these quantities, the amounts of carbon dioxide and of oxygen are often the simplest to measure, and also because they give easily obtainable quantitative information about metabolism, it is of great importance to understand their full significance.

If the food substance being oxidized is glucose, the reaction (or rather the sum total of a large number of intermediate reactions) is as follows:

$$C_6H_{12}O_6 + 6O_2 = 6CO_2 + 6H_2O$$

Since the volumes of gases are proportional to the numbers of molecules present, the volume of carbon dioxide formed will be exactly equal to the volume of oxygen used. The ratio of carbon dioxide produced to oxygen used, the respiratory quotient, in this case is equal to one. In a similar way if equations for the oxidation of fats are written down the respiratory quotient can be calculated for each case; thus for triolein

$$C_{57}H_{104}O_6 + 80\,O_2 \rightarrow 57\,CO_2 + 52\,H_2O$$

The respiratory quotient in this case is 57/80 or 0·71. In the case of proteins, it is not possible to work out the respiratory quotient in this simple way, but from a knowledge of the percentage composition of the protein, and the products of oxidation in the body, it is possible to calculate that the respiratory quotient is about 0·8.

The respiratory quotient for all forms of carbohydrate is 1·0. The exact value of the respiratory quotient will vary for different fats and proteins, but by taking a mean value for those normally present in the food it can be determined that the respiratory quotient for a diet consisting of fat would be 0·71 and for protein 0·81. A knowledge of the respiratory quotient therefore gives us information about the type of food which is actually being oxidized, and since the energy liberated by a certain amount of oxygen depends on the nature of the substance oxidized, it is evident that, from the amount of oxygen used and from the respiratory quotient, much information can be obtained about metabolic activities. The significance of the respiratory quotient will be considered more fully later in connection with the metabolism of the whole animal.

Metabolism of the Cells

The study of the metabolism of the living cell in relation to its structure is called histochemistry or cytochemistry, and the methods used are largely a combination of histological and biochemical techniques. By disintegration of cells and subsequent centrifuging it has been possible to divide the cell contents into different fractions, and to determine the content of enzymes and other substances in these fractions. As a result of this work, information is gradually being built up on the metabolic activities of the various subcellular particles and the relation of these to each other. For example, it is known that the enzymes concerned with the oxidative processes in the cells are located in the mitochondria.

Metabolism of Isolated Tissues

In the higher animals respiration is often divided into external respiration and internal respiration. External respiration includes all the processes which result in oxygen being brought to the tissues and carbon dioxide being removed. In contrast to this, internal respiration includes the processes which take place inside the cells of the body resulting in the oxidation of the food substances and the formation of the waste products. The study of internal respiration is largely carried out by investigating the chemical changes which take place in isolated tissues. The remarkable thing is that most living tissues, disintegrated to a greater or lesser degree by mincing or slicing and deprived of their blood supply, can still, under suitable conditions, take up oxygen, carry out chemical reactions and produce carbon dioxide. The requisites for respiration in isolated tissues are a supply of available oxygen, the maintenance of normal body temperature, and the provision of a suitable fluid medium in which the tissue is suspended. The media usually employed are balanced salt solutions (see Chapter 4) and the other essential conditions are achieved by the use of microrespirometers, the usual type being that developed by Warburg.

The tissue, either minced or sliced, is put into a glass vessel which can be attached to a manometer. The manometer is fixed on a stand so that it, together with the attached cup, can be shaken continuously with the cup immersed in a water bath at constant temperature. A centre compartment in the cup contains a small piece of filter paper soaked in caustic soda, and this absorbs the carbon dioxide produced. After introducing the tissue suspended in a suitable saline medium, the whole apparatus is filled with oxygen, and the shaking apparatus is then set in motion. Readings are taken at regular intervals and the consumption of oxygen is indicated by the change of pressure in the manometer. The manometer cups are usually provided with one or two side arms into which reagents can be put which are to be added during the course of the experiment. Analysis of the contents of the cups can also be made at the end of the experiment and the products of metabolism estimated. There are many modifications of the manometers and cups and it is possible by various techniques to measure the respiratory quotient or the changes taking place anaerobically.

It is important to appreciate both the possibilities and the limitations of experiments with minced and sliced tissues. There is no doubt that the conditions are highly unphysiological, the tissue is deprived of its blood supply and its normal relations with other tissues. The chemical reactions which can be demonstrated by these techniques do not necessarily take place in the tissues under more physiological conditions and furthermore, we derive no information about how the tissues utilize the energy liberated by the reactions which occur. At the same time the method is invaluable for studying the various enzyme systems present in the cells, and for finding out what substances actually take part in the chemical reactions in the tissues. It is not too much to say that the enormous advances in many fields of biochemistry have been due in great part to experiments of this kind.

From the study of minced and sliced tissues it has been found that the food substances oxidized do not combine directly with oxygen to form the final products of oxidation, but pass through a number of intermediary stages. One of the methods of studying these intermediary stages is to interfere with the normal process of metabolism by blocking the series of reactions at some point so that intermediary substances, which would normally be further oxidized, accumulate in sufficient amounts to allow their detection and estimation. A number of such blocking agents or inhibitors is known, which will specifically put out of action certain enzymes in the tissues, while allowing others to function normally, and by the use of these many of the intermediate products of metabolism have been identified. A few of the outstanding results of this kind of work are referred to in later sections, but for a more complete account of the chemical changes undergone by the food substances, the reader is referred to textbooks of biochemistry.

Metabolism of Isolated Organs

It is often useful to study the metabolism of some particular organ in relation to its functional activity, e.g. to study kidney metabolism in relation to the formation of urine or cardiac metabolism in relation to the pumping activity of the heart. For such purposes it is necessary to use whole organs instead of isolated tissues, but it is also necessary to separate in some way the metabolism of the organ being investigated from the metabolism of the animal as a whole.

Perfusion Experiments. One method of attacking such a problem is to supply the organ with nutrient material and oxygen by an artificial perfusing system instead of by its own circulation. Defibrinated blood or heparinized blood is usually employed for the purpose and this is saturated with oxygen, either by passing it through the lungs or through an oxygenator, and is then pumped through the vessels of the organ to be studied. By such a system organs can be kept "alive" for a number of hours after complete isolation from the rest of the body. The metabolism of heart, lungs, liver, kidney, brain and limbs have all been studied in this way. The gaseous metabolism is measured by estimating the volume of oxygen taken up by the blood and the volume of carbon dioxide given off, or alternatively it may be measured by estimating the content of oxygen and carbon dioxide in the blood supplying and leaving the organ and also the rate of blood-flow. In some cases, e.g. heart and voluntary muscle, the physical work done can be measured and compared with the rate of metabolism; in other cases, e.g. the kidney, the osmotic work can be studied. In some organs, however, such as the brain, we know very little about the quantitative relation between functional activity and metabolism.

Metabolism of Organs in situ. Another method of studying the metabolism of individual organs is to leave the organ *in situ*, and measure the oxygen and carbon dioxide content of the arterial and venous blood together with the rate of blood-flow. For this purpose it is very useful to have an apparatus which will register continuously the amount of oxygen in the arterial and venous blood.

This can be done by means of two *oximeters* in which the degree of oxygenation of the blood is measured by means of photo-electric cells, in terms of the optical transmittance at certain appropriate wave-lengths of the light. A continuous graphic record may thus be obtained of the oxygen content of the arterial and of the venous blood.

The Metabolism of the Intact Animal

When the metabolism of the whole animal is considered it is usually not in terms of the intermediate products of metabolism but rather of the sum total of the metabolic reactions, i.e. the amount of food and of oxygen used and the amount of carbon dioxide and waste products formed. It is also possible to measure the total heat production of the animal and the amount of physical work carried out, so that balance sheets can be prepared of the total intake and output of energy in all its various forms, thermal, chemical, mechanical, etc. Very careful measurements of these energy relations have shown that the animal body behaves exactly like all other chemical or mechanical systems as regards the law of the conservation of energy, in that the total energy produced is equal to the total energy supplied. The vital activities of the body are in no way a creation of energy but simply a transference of energy from one form to another. The particularly "vital" part of the process is that some of these energy transformations can only take place in living tissues and so far have not been imitated in non-biological systems.

The Energy Value of the Foods. In order to prepare our complete balance sheet we require to know the energy values of the foods taken. For this purpose we assume that oxygen is freely available and therefore consider the amount of energy capable of being liberated by oxidation of the food. This can be determined outside the body by means of the bomb calorimeter.

This consists of a strong steel chamber which can be sealed by a tightly fitting lid. Into the chamber a measured quantity of the food substance is introduced and the whole apparatus filled with oxygen at high pressure. The bomb calorimeter is now placed in a known volume of water at a certain temperature. Combustion of the contained substance is initiated electrically and the amount of heat produced is estimated from measurement of the rise in temperature of the surrounding water.

By means of the bomb calorimeter it is found that 1 g of carbohydrate produces 4·1 kilocalories, 1 g of fat 9·2 kilocalories and 1 g of protein 5·3 kilocalories. These are the energy values when combustion is complete. In the body complete combustion of carbohydrate and fat takes place, but in the case of protein the end product, urea, is still capable of further oxidation, though not inside the body, and hence the energy value of the urea must be subtracted from that of the protein. Making these corrections the values for the three types of food are: carbohydrate and protein each 4·1 kilocalories per g and fat 9·2 kilocalories per g. Knowing these values and also the amount of each food substance in the diet we can calculate the total energy provided by the food. This knowledge of the energy content of food is essential in making up diets for people under various conditions.

Energy Production from Oxygen Intake. The food taken into the body gives the total energy intake but it does not tell us the rate of metabolism at any one time, since the food is not all used immediately but may in part be stored. The rate of metabolism is derived from the oxygen intake, for we know the oxygen intake only keeps pace with the immediate metabolic needs. If we wish to know the metabolic rate approximately, we can calculate it from the oxygen consumption by assuming that each litre of oxygen used in the body yields 4·8 kilocalories. Thus in the human subject where there is an oxygen consumption of 300 ml/min, the energy production would be 87 kilocalories per hour. This degree of accuracy is in fact sufficient for many purposes.

If we require to know the metabolic rate more accurately, we must consider the fact that the energy liberated by the consumption of 1 litre of oxygen in the body is not a constant figure of 4·8 kilocalories, but varies with the kind of food being oxidized. The food taken is a mixture of protein, fat and carbohydrate, so that in addition to determining the oxygen consumption we have to determine what proportions of these three kinds of food are present in the diet. This can be done in the following way.

The total nitrogen in the urine is estimated over a known time. By multiplying this value by 6·25 one can calculate the total amount of protein metabolized during that period. (The average amount of nitrogen in dietary proteins is 16 per cent.) We can further calculate the amount of oxygen needed to oxidize this protein in the body and the amount of carbon dioxide produced. These amounts of oxygen and carbon dioxide are now subtracted from the total amounts of the oxygen and carbon dioxide involved in metabolism, and the resultant figures give the oxygen used and the carbon dioxide produced in non-protein metabolism. Since there are now only two substances to be dealt with, fat and carbohydrate, and since we know the respiratory quotient corresponding to each, we can calculate the proportions of each necessary to give the respiratory quotient of the non-protein metabolism. In practice one gets the result from tables already worked out for each possible respiratory quotient (Table 29.1). Such tables also give the energy production per litre of oxygen for each respiratory quotient so that the total energy production can readily be calculated once the total oxygen consumption and the non-protein respiratory quotient are known.

TABLE 29.1

The relation between the Respiratory Quotient, the relative amounts of fat and carbohydrate oxidized, and the energy production of the non-protein metabolism

Non-protein Respiratory Quotient	1·00	0·95	0·90	0·85	0·80	0·75	0·718
Per cent total O_2 consumed by carbohydrate	100	82	65	47	29	11	0
Grams Foodstuff per litre O_2 { Carbohydrate	1·23	1·01	0·80	0·58	0·36	0·14	0
Fat	0	0·09	0·18	0·27	0·36	0·45	0·50
Total	1·23	1·10	0·98	0·83	0·72	0·59	0·50
Kilocalories per litre O_2	5·05	4·99	4·94	4·88	4·83	4·77	4·74

Since the respiratory quotient for protein is intermediate between that for fat and for carbohydrate it is often considered sufficiently accurate to neglect altogether protein metabolism, and treating the whole metabolism of the animal as non-protein metabolism, to make the calculations accordingly.

It is also possible to make the necessary calculations about the gaseous exchanges and the type of food being oxidized from the following equations.

$$\text{Carbohydrate (g)} = 4\cdot12\ CO_{2m} - 2\cdot91\ O_{2m} - 2\cdot54\ U_n.$$
$$\text{Fat (g)} = 1\cdot69\ O_{2m} - 1\cdot69\ CO_{2m} - 1\cdot94\ U_n.$$
$$\text{Protein (g)} = 6\cdot25\ U_n.$$
$$\text{Energy (Cal)} = 3\cdot78\ O_{2m} + 1\cdot16\ CO_{2m} - 2\cdot98\ U_n.$$

where CO_{2m} is the number of litres of carbon dioxide produced, O_{2m} is the litres of oxygen used, and U_n is the urinary nitrogen expressed in grams.

In making calculations from the respiratory quotient it is assumed that the amount of carbon dioxide given out in the expired air is the same as that being produced by the tissues. While this is true if the carbon dioxide output is considered over long periods, it is not necessarily so over short periods. During strenuous exercise lactic acid accumulates in the blood and this results in liberation of some of the carbon dioxide stored in the blood as bicarbonate, so that the amount of carbon dioxide expired by the lungs is greater than the amount which is being formed by the tissues. In such conditions, the respiratory quotient can in fact exceed 1·0. Similarly, in the period of recovery after exercise when lactic acid is being removed from the blood, the amount of carbon dioxide expired may be less than the amount formed by the tissues, as some is being retained by the blood to form bicarbonate. Another factor which can contribute to changes in the respiratory quotient is interconversion in the body of the various food substances.

Methods of Determining Metabolic Rate in the Intact Animal

Two different principles are used for this purpose—direct calorimetry and indirect calorimetry. In the former the object is to measure the heat production directly, while in the latter the heat production is calculated from the gaseous exchange.

Direct Calorimetry This involves very elaborate and expensive apparatus and is therefore little used in routine measurement. For some purposes, however, it gives information not obtainable in any other way, e.g. if we wish to draw up a complete balance sheet of the energy exchanges

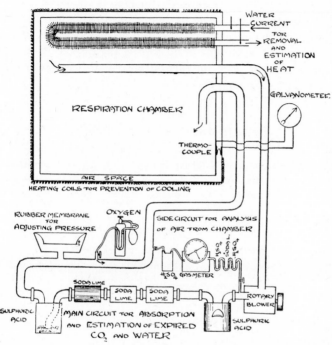

FIG. 29.1. Diagram to illustrated the principle of the Atwater-Benedict Respiration Calorimeter.

The upper part represents the calorimeter, in which the subject is placed, and his heat production measured in terms of the rise in temperature and rate of flow of the cooling water (in practice the cooling pipes are carried right round the chamber).

The lower part represents the Benedict Respiration Apparatus, in which the carbon dioxide produced by the subject is absorbed by the soda-lime, and the oxygen used is replaced from the cylinder through a meter (not shown) at such a rate as to keep the rubber membrane of the pressure equalizer in a constant position. The gas is dried in the sulphuric acid bottles before entering the carbon dioxide absorbers, since soda-lime absorbs water as well as carbon dioxide. Any water that may be evolved from the soda-lime in its reaction with carbon dioxide is absorbed in the second sulphuric acid bottle.

When the respiration apparatus is used for indirect calorimetry only, the tubes leading to the calorimeter are connected to a mouth-piece, which is held between the subject's teeth, his nose being closed by a clip. (Parson's "Fundamentals of Biochemistry".)

in the body. The subject is placed inside a large calorimeter, which in the case of the human subject is a small thermally-insulated room known as the Atwater-Benedict Respiration Calorimeter (Fig. 29.1). The calorimeter is in fact constructed so that the measurement of heat production is combined with the indirect method of measuring metabolism, i.e. by the gaseous exchanges; and these accessories are shown in the diagram. An energy balance drawn up from procedures of this kind is shown in Table 29.2.

Indirect Calorimetry The principle of calculating the metabolic rate from the oxygen consumption has been discussed above. The problem at the moment is the technique of measuring the gaseous exchanges. Two different principles are used for this purpose and these are distinguished as closed methods and open methods.

TABLE 29.2

Energy Balance Sheet for Human Subject

I.—Indirect Calorimetry

Food Ingested[1]		Class of food	Food Oxidized[2]	
Weight, g	Energy, kcal		Weight, g	Energy, kcal
79·2	448	Protein	64·8	366
59·6	569	Fat	117·8	1,124
201·0	842	Carbohydrate	226·3	948
339·8	1,859	Total	408·9	2,438
69·1	579	From body stores (i.e. excess of food oxidized over food ingested)		
408·9	2,438	Total	408·9	2,438

II.—Direct Calorimetry

Heat produced, as measured	2,334 kcal
Potential energy of urine	90 ,,
Total heat produced	2,424 ,,

III.—Test of Law of Conservation of Energy

Heat production as calculated from results of indirect calorimetry	2,438 kcal
Heat production as observed by direct calorimetry . . .	2,424 ,,
Difference . .	14 ,,
	i.e. 0·6 per cent

[1] Corrected for losses in digestion and absorption.
[2] Calculated from respiratory exchange.

Closed Methods. These in general require a less mobile equipment and hence are limited in their use. In the simpler types of apparatus for the human subject the expired air, collected from a mouthpiece supplied with valves, passes over soda lime which absorbs the carbon dioxide. The soda lime is usually contained in a recording spirometer, and from this the subject rebreathes his own expired air freed from carbon dioxide. During this process the volume of the air in the circuit diminishes at a rate equal to the consumption of oxygen and by recording the volume change by means of the spirometer the rate of oxygen consumption can be measured. It will be noted that in such a method no account is taken of the respiratory quotient and the metabolism is calculated by assuming an average for the respiratory quotient.

By means of more elaborate circuits it is possible to measure the carbon dioxide production as well. In such cases the air is circulated by a pump and passes through containers with sulphuric acid to absorb moisture, and with soda lime to absorb carbon dioxide. These can be weighed periodically and hence the production of water and carbon dioxide measured. In these systems, the oxygen consumption is measured by adding oxygen at a known rate so as to replace the amount used. This is most conveniently done by having in the circuit, at some point, a sensitive rubber membrane, which will indicate alterations in the total pressure and hence in the volume of the system. Such circuits are often used for small animals. For application to man, Benedict's apparatus is employed. For more complete metabolic estimations in man, this system may be combined with the Atwater-Benedict Respiration Calorimeter.

By means of such apparatus a complete balance sheet of the energy exchanges in man can be made, and since much can be learned from the study of this, the results of one such experiment are given in Table 29.2.

Open Methods. In these the subject breathes in from the atmosphere, but by means of a mouthpiece containing valves the expired air is collected in a Douglas bag. The volume of air expired in a given time is measured and a sample is taken for determination of the percentage of oxygen, nitrogen and CO_2 present. The oxygen utilization is obtained by calculating the amount of oxygen in the expired air in a given time and subtracting this from the amount of oxygen in the inspired air in the same time. Similarly, the CO_2 produced is the amount of CO_2 in the expired air from which has been subtracted the amount of CO_2 in the inspired air (an almost negligible quantity). In making these calculations, particularly for oxygen, it must be remembered that the volume of inspired air is not the same as the volume of expired air, owing to the fact that the volume of oxygen taken in is greater than the volume of CO_2 given out, unless the R.Q. is exactly 1. It is the volume of expired air which is measured, but since the *amount*, although not the percentage of N_2 in the inspired and expired air, is the same, the volume of inspired air can be calculated as follows:

$$\text{Vol. of inspired air} = \text{Vol. of expired air} \times \frac{\text{Percent. } N_2 \text{ in expired air}}{\text{Percent. } N_2 \text{ in inspired air}}$$

The open methods of measuring gaseous exchanges have the merit of great mobility, and this enables metabolic rate to be measured in a great

variety of conditions. In recent years much improved forms of the open
method have been devised, in which the whole apparatus is more portable
and very little resistance is applied to the flow of expired air, and one of the
best of these is Wolff's Integrating Motor Pneumotachograph (the IMP).

The Basal Metabolic Rate

The rate of metabolism depends on the amount of physical work which
the body does and, therefore, can be reduced if the subject remains
completely at rest. But even when all unnecessary movements are stopped
a certain amount of energy is used in maintaining the body temperature
and in providing for the needs of circulation, respiration and other
vegetative processes, and this cannot be further reduced without damage
to the tissues. This amount of metabolism is considered the basal level,
on which extra metabolic activities are superimposed when the body
undertakes more work. It is called the basal metabolic rate, or more
usually the B.M.R.

Although the term B.M.R. is very firmly fixed, there is a case for replacing this by the term "resting metabolism". This is what is actually
measured and makes no assumptions about what activities are basal. One
of the functions of this resting metabolism in warm blooded animals is to
keep the body temperature above that of its surroundings and, since the
loss of heat from the body takes place from the surface exposed to the
atmosphere, it is not surprising to find that the BMR is more closely
related to the body surface than to the body weight. This is well illustrated
in Table 29.3, which gives the B.M.R. for animals of different sizes
expressed per unit weight and per unit body surface.

TABLE 29.3

The Basal Metabolic Rates of Various Animals

Animal	Weight in kg	Kilocalories produced per day per kg of weight	per sq m of surface
Horse . . .	441	11·3	948
Pig	128	19·1	1,078
Man . . .	64·3	32·1	1,042
Dog	15·2	51·5	1,039
Mouse . . .	0·018	212	1,188

The area of the body surface is not an easy quantity to measure directly.
In man it is usually obtained from the height and weight by means of the
following formula of Du Bois,

$$S = 0{\cdot}007184 \times W^{0{\cdot}425} \times H^{0{\cdot}725}$$

where S is the body surface in sq. metres, W the weight in kilograms and
H the height in centimetres. It can be obtained more easily from nomo-
grams based on this formula (Fig. 29.2).

In a well-nourished man the B.M.R. has been found to be about 1,700 kilocalories per day. This is equivalent to about 40 kilocalories per sq. metre body surface per hour or to about 1 kilocalorie per kg body weight per hour. It varies with sex and with age, being higher in males and young people. It is usual to express the B.M.R. of an individual as a percentage

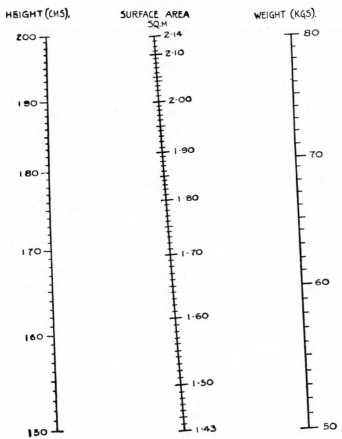

FIG. 29.2. Alignment Chart for calculation of the area of the human body surface from the height and weight. (W. A. M. Smart.)

increase or decrease above or below these standard values. In normal individuals, the values lie within about 15 per cent of the standard values.

Since the metabolic activities of the body can be increased by taking food or by performance of work, it is very important in measuring the B.M.R. that the subject should be at complete mental and physical rest and should be in a condition of fasting for about twelve hours. Extremes of temperature, previous diet, previous exercise, emotion or menstruation may all have some effect on the result.

The Thyroid Gland and the Basal Metabolic Rate. Of the pathological causes of alteration in the B.M.R. the commonest is abnormal activity of the thyroid gland discussed in Chapter 32. In diseases where there is thyroid deficiency, as in cretinism and myxoedema, there is a low B.M.R. and this can be increased by administration of thyroid extract. In exophthalmic goitre there is hyperthyroidism and here the B.M.R. is considerably increased. Surgical removal of part of the thyroid gland leads to a fall in the B.M.R. along with alleviation of the other symptoms. The active principle in thyroid extract which is responsible for the effect on metabolism is thyroxine. The stimulating effect of this and related compounds on metabolism has been used for their biological assay. Since pure thyroxine is administered in quantities of the order of milligrams, which may increase the metabolic rate by some 200 kilocalories per day its action is clearly independent of any specific dynamic action it may have as an amino-acid. This could not amount to more than a small fraction of a calorie.

Specific Dynamic Action

Under basal conditions a certain amount of metabolism is going on at the expense of the body tissues and stores, resulting in a certain rate of energy production. If food is given to a fasting animal it is used to replace the body tissues as metabolic fuel, but in addition it causes an increase in the metabolism. For example, if sufficient protein is given to cover the calorie needs of basal metabolism, it is found that the metabolic rate rises by about 30 kcal and the protein intake must therefore be increased, if it is to cover metabolic requirements. This effect is called the *specific dynamic action*. It is shown by fat and carbohydrate also, but to a lesser extent. The exact cause of the specific dynamic action is uncertain, but is thought to be due to chemical changes carried out by the body on the food substances preparatory to oxidation. The specific dynamic action of protein has been most studied on account of its greater magnitude. If certain amino-acids are injected into the blood stream, they produce a specific dynamic action equal to that of the corresponding amount of protein, so that the effect cannot be due to digestion. The specific dynamic action of protein is prevented by previous removal of the liver, and this would suggest that the effect is probably concerned with deamination of the amino-acids or formation of urea rather than with stimulation of cellular metabolism generally.

The Use of Isotopes in Metabolic Studies

A new phase in the study of metabolism began with the introduction of isotopes as a means of following the chemical changes which take place in the body. Many elements can exist in more than one form and these forms are known as isotopes. The isotopes vary in atomic weight, but are chemically indistinguishable from each other, and if metabolizable compounds are prepared containing the isotopes, many experiments have shown that the animal body does not treat these in any way differently from the corresponding compounds containing the ordinary form of the element. For example, amino-acids containing nitrogen of atomic weight 15 (^{15}N) follow the same course of chemical changes as do those containing ordinary nitrogen of atomic weight 14. Two kinds of isotope are available for metabolic studies. There are first, the stable isotopes which are distinguished by the mass spectrograph and secondly, the radioactive isotopes, recognized by the radiations which they emit. Both kinds of isotope are extensively used, but in general, the radioactive ones are preferred, when possible, on account of the simpler techniques for their estimation. The use of isotopes enables certain substances, or even parts of the molecule of the substance, to be "labelled", so that they can be again recognized after passing through various chemical transformations. Sometimes two isotopes are introduced into one molecule, e.g. the carbon chain of an amino-acid may be labelled with the radioactive ^{14}C, while the amino group may be labelled with the stable ^{15}N or one of the hydrogen atoms replaced by deuterium. One of the great advantages of isotope studies is that chemical reactions can be investigated in whole animals under natural physiological conditions. These reactions could previously be investigated only on isolated tissues or organs, or under abnormal conditions where substances not normally metabolized by the body were used, or where inhibitors had to be used to stop metabolic processes at some particular stage.

CHAPTER 30

THE METABOLIC HISTORY OF THE FOOD SUBSTANCES

IN the preceding chapter the general methods of metabolic studies have been discussed and we can now turn to the special problems of the various substances in the food. The energy-liberating substances are proteins, fats and carbohydrates. These are broken down in the alimentary tract, and from them are formed the substances which can be regarded as primarily available for metabolism, i.e. amino-acids, fatty acids and glucose. All these undergo a series of chemical transformations which result ultimately in the formation of carbon dioxide and water. (In the case of protein some other end products are also formed, e.g. urea.) These chemical transformations can be divided into two stages, and one of these stages—the citric acid cycle—is common to all the different types of food substances. The pre-citric acid cycle stage is quite different for different food substances; it is therefore convenient to consider the pre-citric acid cycle stage for fats, proteins and carbohydrates, and then to consider subsequently the citric acid cycle which is common to them all (Fig. 30.3). The important connecting link between the two stages is a substance called coenzyme A, which therefore occupies a very special place in metabolism.

Coenzyme A. This is a complex substance containing adenosine and pantotheine (a substance related to one of the B vitamins) joined by two molecules of phosphoric acid. It exists in two forms, coenzyme A and acetyl coenzyme A, and its function can be regarded as a carrier of acetyl groups (CH_3CO—), which it is able to accept from one compound and transfer to another. Coenzyme A contains an —SH group, and since this is the part which combines with the acetyl radical, the free and combined forms of coenzyme A are often abbreviated to H—S—CoA, and $CH_3COS.CoA$. In general the final reaction in the pre-citric acid cycle stage of metabolism is the formation of acetyl-coenzyme A. This transfers the acetyl group to the citric acid cycle and coenzyme A is re-formed, to take part in the further formation of acetyl coenzyme A.

Protein Metabolism

The protein taken in the food is absorbed from the intestine after breakdown to amino-acids. Some of these amino-acids are subsequently resynthesized to protein to help to replace the worn tissues of the body, or to produce hormones or enzymes. The remaining amino-acids are used to supply energy. The replacement of the worn tissues can be carried out only by protein supplied in the food, whereas the energy supplying function of the protein can be replaced by fat or carbohydrate. Since protein is the most expensive part of the diet, and under many conditions the part most likely to be scarce, it is important to determine precisely how far it can be replaced by the other food substances, and what is the minimum protein intake. This can be discovered by studying the nitrogen balance of the body.

Nitrogen Equilibrium. When an animal is living on an adequate diet and maintaining its weight at a constant level, it takes in a certain amount of nitrogen in the protein of the food, and loses the same amount of nitrogen in the excreta. Such an animal is said to be in nitrogen equilibrium. The nitrogen in the excreta comes partly from the nitrogen of the food, and partly from the breakdown of protein in the animal's own tissues, this being replaced again from the food. If now the animal be given a diet with ample fat and carbohydrate, but completely lacking in protein, it continues to excrete some nitrogen from its own tissues, and since this is not replaced it loses weight and ultimately dies. If after a short period of nitrogen starvation protein be added to the food in known amounts and at the same time the nitrogen loss estimated, it can readily be determined how much nitrogen must be given in the food to bring the animal back to nitrogen equilibrium. The result of such an experiment is given in Table 30.1.

TABLE 30.1

Establishment of Nitrogen Equilibrium in a Dog after Starvation

Food	Nitrogen in Food	Nitrogen in Excreta	Difference
	g	g	g
Starvation	0	4·00	− 4·00
100 g Meat	4·10	5·56	− 1·46
140 g Meat	5·74	6·50	− 0·76
165 g Meat	6·77	7·22	− 0·45
185 g Meat	7·59	7·80	− 0·21
200 g Meat	8·20	8·73	− 0·53
230 g Meat	10·24	10·58	− 0·34
360 g Meat	11·99	12·05	− 0·06
410 g Meat	15·58	14·31	+ 1·27
360 g Meat	13·68	13·62	+ 0·06
Starvation 3rd day	0	4·03	− 4·03

From such an experiment two important conclusions can be drawn. First, the minimum protein requirement for the particular animal can be seen. In the example given, an intake of about 360 g of meat is required to make the intake of protein balance the loss. But another important result appears. The amount of nitrogen which a starving animal excretes is not the amount which is needed to maintain it in nitrogen equilibrium, for it can be seen that by the time it has reached nitrogen equilibrium it is taking in and excreting about three times the amount excreted in the starvation state. The principal reason for this is the following. The protein given in the food does not supply the amino-acids in the proportion required by the body, so that food containing a considerable excess of some may have to be given to supply a sufficient quantity of others. The amount of protein needed to maintain nitrogen equilibrium depends, therefore, on the type of proteins supplied; and the value of proteins is estimated from the amounts they contain of certain of the amino-acids, which the body cannot manufacture for itself, and which are, therefore, regarded as essential in the diet. If an animal be fed on a protein deficient in any one of these, it cannot be kept in nitrogen equilibrium no matter how much of the protein is supplied. An essential amino-acid has been defined as one which cannot be synthesized by the organism out of materials ordinarily available at a speed commensurable with the normal requirements. The essential amino-acids as determined for the rat are: lysine, valine, tryptophan, methionine, histidine, phenylalanine, leucine, isoleucine, threonine and arginine. In the human subject arginine and histidine are not essential in the adult; while in some species glycine is essential at a certain stage of growth. From the practical aspect, the important point is that proteins can be divided into those of high biological value (first-class proteins) and low biological value (second-class proteins), the first group containing the essential amino-acids in proportions approaching those required by the body. The term "first-class protein" usually means protein of animal origin (proteins of milk, cheese, meat, eggs, etc.).

The Break-down of Protein. The amino-acids not used for synthesis of body tissues are oxidized with liberation of energy. The first stage in the process is deamination, i.e. the removal of the nitrogen-containing group from the rest of the molecule. If amino-acids are injected into the blood stream they are rapidly removed and can be partly recovered from various tissues. Of these the liver has been found to take up the largest quantity. It can further be shown that the amino-acids taken up by the liver gradually disappear, suggesting that they undergo some transformation. At the same time as the amino-acids disappear from the blood there is a rise in the concentration of blood urea. It is possible to keep an animal alive for some time after removal of the liver and, if in such a preparation amino-acids be injected, they are only removed slowly from the blood and there is no increased formation of urea. These experiments together with much other evidence show that the liver plays a very important part in the formation of urea from amino-acids. Urea is one of the end products of protein metabolism. It does not undergo further change and is excreted in the urine. A small fraction of the amino groups is not excreted in this form, but as ammonia which is formed largely in the kidney itself, the amount being related to the acidity of the urine.

Formation of Urea. If ammonium salts containing ^{15}N be fed to animals the isotope appears in the urea, so that formation of ammonia is probably a preliminary process in the formation of urea. The method of formation of urea from ammonia is still a matter of discussion, but it seems very likely that it depends on a cyclical series of reactions involving ornithine, citrulline and arginine. Ornithine combining with carbon dioxide and ammonia forms first citrulline and then arginine, which is hydrolyzed by the enzyme arginase to form urea and ornithine.

Fate of the Non-nitrogenous Residues. The non-nitrogenous part of the amino-acid left after deamination undergoes oxidation, the ultimate products being carbon dioxide and water. In carnivorous animals much of the energy needed by the body is obtained from this source, but in man the amount obtained is relatively small, depending on the excess protein in the diet over the protein minimum. The immediate product of deamination is a keto-acid but the type of keto-acid will vary according to the amino-acid from which it is derived. All of them are ultimately oxidized by the citric acid cycle, but before they reach that stage, the metabolism proceeds by two different routes. Some of the keto-acids, e.g. pyruvic acid, are known to be intermediaries in carbohydrate breakdown and could thus provide a route by which the further breakdown of protein might follow the line of carbohydrate metabolism, or by which proteins could cause formation of carbohydrates. It can be shown that this does actually happen under certain conditions. In a diabetic animal, or in an animal poisoned with *phlorrhizin*, there is a great loss of sugar from the body. (Phlorrhizin is a drug which causes elimination of sugar through the kidneys without any increase in the blood sugar concentration.) In such an animal, the carbohydrate stores are rapidly depleted. If now carbohydrates be withheld from the diet but protein be given it is found that the excretion of glucose continues, and this must have been derived from protein.

The amino-acids which can give rise to glucose during metabolism are glycine, alanine, valine, serine, cystine, cysteine, ornithine, proline, hydroxyproline, aspartic acid, glutamic acid and hydroxyglutamic acid. Some amino-acids, e.g. leucine, phenylalanine and tyrosine, do not give rise to glucose, but to acetoacetic acid. This is a product of fat metabolism, which under certain conditions accumulates in large quantities in the blood, and leads to a condition called ketosis. (See sections on fat and carbohydrate metabolism.) For this reason, leucine, phenylalanine and tyrosine are said to be ketogenic, while those amino-acids which give rise to glucose are said to be anti-ketogenic. A few amino-acids, lysine, histidine and tryptophan form neither glucose nor acetoacetic acid.

Creatinine. This is another end product of protein metabolism. It is formed from creatine (methyl guanidine acetic acid) of which it is the anhydride. Creatine is present in the tissues in the form of creatine phosphate and, in this form, it plays a part in the chemical processes responsible for muscular contraction. Creatinine is regarded as a waste product of muscle metabolism and is always a normal constituent of the urine. Creatine is not normally present in the urine but in some cases, for reasons not understood, it may be a urinary constituent. It often appears in the urine of women, but its relation to the menstrual cycle is uncertain.

Nucleo-proteins. These are proteins found especially in the nuclei of cells, and they form a small part of the dietary protein. They consist of a protein conjugated with nucleic acid, this latter substance being a combination of a purine or pyrimidine base with phosphoric acid and a pentose. The purines present are adenine and guanine, the pyrimidines, thymine and cytosine. The nucleoproteins are broken down during digestion, and among the products are the purine and pyrimidine bases. The latter after absorption are completely oxidized. The purine bases undergo deamination and partial oxidation to uric acid. In man, this is an end product of nucleoprotein metabolism and is excreted in the urine, but in most mammals it undergoes a further stage of oxidation to allantoin.

Exogenous and Endogenous Metabolism. The main end products of protein metabolism differ considerably in different states of nutrition. The urea output of the body is fairly closely dependent on the amount of protein in the diet. On the other hand the amount of creatinine excreted is almost constant, even during large fluctuations of dietary protein. Uric acid occupies an intermediate position as regards the relation between the amount excreted and the protein intake. The different behaviour of these substances suggests that protein metabolism can be divided into the metabolism of the protein fuel supplied by the diet, and the metabolism of that supplied by the tissues. Since the amount of creatinine does not vary with the diet it is thought to be an index of tissue metabolism, or "endogenous" metabolism, while urea is thought to be an index of "exogenous" metabolism. Experiments with isotopes have shown, however, that protein metabolism cannot be divided in this way. Animals were fed with leucine and glycine containing deuterium attached to the carbon chain and ^{15}N in the amino group of the molecule. When the excreta were collected and examined, it was found that only a small amount, about one-third, of the isotope had been eliminated from the body. An examination of the different tissues showed that the proteins of the blood, and the proteins of most of the organs, contained isotopic leucine and glycine. Since deuterium as well as ^{15}N was present in the tissue proteins it proved that not only the amino-group but the whole molecule of the amino-acid given in the food had been incorporated in the tissue proteins. The animals had not gained weight during the process, so that it was not a question of retention of amino-acids to build up extra body tissues. The only possible conclusion was that the amino-acids given had replaced some of the leucine and glycine previously present in the body proteins. This showed that there is a constant synthesis and breakdown of body protein with replacement of the amino-acid molecules by new ones derived from the dietary protein. It is thus not possible to separate the exogenous and the endogenous metabolism, as there is a dynamic equilibrium between the amino-acids in the body tissues and those in the blood stream. Further investigation showed that there was not only replacement of amino-acids in the tissue proteins, but also replacement of the nitrogen in the amino-acids. When isotopic leucine or glycine was fed, other amino-acids isolated from the tissues contained the ^{15}N. This indicated that the ^{15}N supplied in the leucine and glycine had been used for the synthesis of other amino-acids to supply new units for the tissue protein. Even when abundant quantities of some particular amino-acid are supplied in the diet synthesis of this amino-acid still occurs.

Metabolic Acidosis and Alkalosis. Most kinds of protein contain sulphur and phosphorus atoms in organic (un-ionized) combination, and some also contain chlorine atoms. When these molecules are completely oxidized, sulphate and phosphate ions (and perhaps chloride ions) are released into the body fluids, the negative charges being derived from hydrogen atoms which are oxidized to hydrogen ions. These hydrogen ions combine with bicarbonate ions, and form carbon dioxide which is eliminated in the lungs. The net result, therefore, is the replacement of bicarbonate ions in the body fluids by sulphate and phosphate ions, so that according to the Henderson-Hasselbalch equation (Chapter 10, p. 151), if the alveolar carbon dioxide pressure were constant, the acidity of the blood would rise (the pH would fall). Actually, since the respiratory centre is activated by an increase in acidity of the blood (Chapter 14, p. 206), there would be an increase in the respiratory minute volume, the alveolar carbon dioxide pressure would fall, and the increase in acidity would be diminished. The essential point, however, is the *reduction* in the bicarbonate concentration of the body fluids (the "alkali reserve"), and it is this that is called *acidosis*.

For experimental purposes, this type of acidosis may be produced to almost any desired extent, by ingesting ammonium sulphate or ammonium chloride. The ammonia is converted into urea in the liver, and hydrogen ions, together with sulphate ions or chloride ions, are released into the body fluids.

Many kinds of vegetable food, on the other hand, notably fruits, contain substantial quantities of salts of organic acids. The acids undergo oxidative metabolism, with the formation of bicarbonate ions, so that the alkali reserve is increased and an *alkalosis* results. On a mixed diet, of course, the reduction in bicarbonate consequent on eating protein will be compensated by an increase on eating fruit and vegetables; but in man, the former usually preponderates, and there is a net gain of hydrogen ions, which are excreted in the urine.

Lipid Metabolism

The term "lipid" is applied to a number of different classes of substance which occur in the animal body and in the diet. These are: (1) the simple triglycerides of fatty acids (the fats proper); (2) the sterols and their esters with fatty acids, and (3) the more complex phospholipids and cerebrosides. Of these the fats proper form the greatest bulk of the tissue and dietary lipids and most of this section will be devoted to them.

Fats. The fatty acids present in the body fat are restricted to those with even numbers of carbon atoms in the molecule. Of these all members of the series from acetic acid (2 carbon atoms) to stearic acid (18 carbon atoms) have been found, but by far the most important quantitatively are the 16 and 18 carbon atom fatty acids, palmitic ($C_{15}H_{31}COOH$) and stearic ($C_{17}H_{35}COOH$), together with the unsaturated oleic acid ($C_{17}H_{33}COOH$). These three in the form of their glycerol esters make up most of the body fats.

Unsaturated Fatty Acids. More highly unsaturated fatty acids, linoleic, linolenic and arachidonic, occur in the body and play an important though unknown part in metabolism. They cannot be synthesized in the body and, if not supplied in the diet of rats, symptoms of deficiency appear in the form of skin disturbances.

The physical properties of the body fat depend on the varying proportions of the constituent fatty acids and are more or less characteristic for each species. This constancy of body fat is, however, dependent on dietary habit and if an animal be starved so as to reduce its fat stores and then fed with an unusual type of fat, it is quite easy to alter the nature of its body fat as regards physical and chemical properties, e.g. melting point, iodine number, saponification value, etc.

The Storage of Fat. There are certain parts of the body where the fat content can be greatly altered and such parts like the omentum and the subcutaneous tissues can act as fat depots. When an animal is putting on weight, fat is laid down in these stores and, when it is living on its reserves, the fat in these parts diminishes before other parts of the body are called on to contribute their share of metabolic fuel. The source of this depot fat we have just seen is the dietary fat, of which a part is used directly for oxidation and part is laid down as storage in the fat depots. If fat containing deuterium is fed to animals, it can be shown that the depots do not consist of a static deposit of storage fat, but that the fat laid down is constantly being used and replaced.

It has also been well established that the non-fat part of the diet can contribute to the fat stores. This was demonstrated by the classical experiments of Lawes and Gilbert in 1852. Young pigs were fed on a diet of barley containing very little fat, and it was found that the amount of body fat present when the animals were killed was greater than could have been obtained from the fat supplied or even the fat and protein together, thus proving that carbohydrate can be converted into fat. Whether or not fat can be derived in the body from protein is uncertain.

Interconversion of Fat and Carbohydrate. Glycerol is known to be produced in small quantities during fermentation of glucose by yeast, and it is possible that a similar production can occur in the body. The formation of fatty acids from carbohydrates takes place by addition of 2-carbon units and the substance involved in this addition is acetyl coenzyme A, which is produced from pyruvic acid. The fatty acid thus formed combines with glycerol to form neutral fat. The process of fat production from carbohydrate requires the participation of certain vitamins of the B group, and aneurin, riboflavin and pantothenic acid are all probably involved.

One important aspect of the interconversion of fat and carbohydrate in the body is the effect on the gaseous exchanges. While the respiratory quotient usually depends only on the type of food being oxidized, It will also be affected by the interconversion of fat and carbohydrate. Inspection of the formula of glucose and a typical fat shows that the latter contains fewer atoms of oxygen per carbon atom than the former and hence, when fat is being formed from carbohydrate, oxygen will be freed for use in general metabolism and so less will be taken into the body from the lungs. Since the carbon dioxide production and excretion remains unchanged the respiratory quotient will be abnormally high. An example of this process is seen in the behaviour of those animals which hibernate. At the end of summer when they are building up large reserves of fat from carbohydrate to last over the winter, the respiratory quotient is abnormally high, and may reach a value of 1·5.

The Oxidation of Fat. The fats utilized by the body normally undergo complete oxidation with formation of carbon dioxide and water. Evidence as to how oxidation proceeds was obtained by Knoop's method of feeding to animals fatty acids containing a benzene ring attached to the carbon chain.

If benzoic acid is fed to animals it is found to be conjugated with glycine to form hippuric acid, and this is excreted in the urine.

$$C_6H_5.COOH + NH_2.CH_2.COOH = C_6H_5.CONH.CH_2.COOH$$

If phenylacetic acid is fed, the excretory product is phenaceturic acid, which again represents a conjugation with glycine.

$$C_6H_5.CH_2.COOH + NH_2.CH_2.COOH =$$
$$C_6H_5.CH_2.CONH.CH_2.COOH$$

If phenyl derivatives of higher fatty acids are fed, it is found that the product of excretion is always either hippuric acid or phenaceturic acid, depending on whether there is an even or odd number of carbon atoms in the side chain. Thus hippuric acid was produced from $C_6H_5.COOH$, $C_6H_5.CH_2.CH_2.COOH$ and $C_6H_5.CH_2.CH_2.CH_2.CH_2.COOH$, while phenaceturic acid was given by $C_6H_5.CH_2.COOH$, $C_6H_5.CH_2.CH_2.CH_2.COOH.$, and $C_6H_5.CH_2.CH_2.CH_2.CH_2.CH_2COOH$. These findings suggested that during the course of oxidation of the fatty acid chain the carbon atoms are split off in pairs, or in other words, oxidation takes place at the β-carbon atom. Hence this suggested method of fat oxidation was called β-oxidation.

The details of the reactions of β-oxidation cannot be discussed here, but coenzyme A plays a very important rôle. In general the process can be summarized by saying that one molecule of fatty acid combines with a molecule of coenzyme A thus:—

$$R.CH_2CH_2CH_2COOH + HS.CoA \rightarrow R.CH_2CH_2CH_2COS.CoA$$

where R represents the rest of the molecule. After various intermediate stages this is oxidized to form a keto acid $R.CH_2CO.CH_2COS.CoA$.

This reacts with another molecule of coenzyme A thus:

$$R.CH_2CO.CH_2COS.CoA + HS.CoA \rightarrow$$
$$R.CH_2COS.CoA + CH_3COS.CoA.$$

The result is that two C atoms are split off, with formation of acetyl coenzyme A. This process proceeds until only a four-carbon compound is left, which is $CH_3CO.CH_2COS.CoA$, i.e. acetoacetyl coenzyme A. The end products are thus a number of molecules of acetyl coenzyme A, together with one molecule of acetoacetyl coenzyme A, and these products are normally oxidized by the citric acid cycle.

Ketosis. In certain conditions the oxidation of fat is incomplete and certain products appear in the urine, β-hydroxybutyric acid, acetoacetic acid and acetone. These substances are called "ketone bodies", and the condition in which they appear is called ketosis. It occurs typically in diabetes mellitus, but it also occurs in less serious disturbances such as fasting, and severe vomiting. Of these ketone bodies it is known that acetone is formed from acetoacetic acid, and that the primary substances are the four-carbon atom substances, β-hydroxybutyric acid and acetoacetic acid. Probably acetoacetic acid is formed first, but the two substances are known to be interconvertible in the liver. The appearance of ketone bodies in fat metabolism is always related to a lowered oxidation of carbohydrate by the tissues, and this may be brought about either by lack of carbohydrate as in fasting, or by inability of the tissues to oxidize carbohydrate as in diabetes. When the formation of ketone bodies is very great it may be sufficient to lower the alkali reserve of the blood and produce a condition of acidaemia (movement of pH of blood towards the acid side).

Theories of Ketone Body Formation. The acetyl coenzyme A is metabolized by various different routes, the two most important of which are by the citric acid cycle and by formation of acetoacetic acid. The acetoacetic acid formed is metabolized by the tissues so that the concentration of ketone bodies is maintained at a very low level. If there is a reduction in the amount of acetyl coenzyme A entering the citric acid cycle then more acetoacetic acid is formed than can easily be used up by metabolism and ketosis results. Since oxaloacetate is necessary for incorporation of acetyl coenzyme A in the citric acid cycle the availability of oxaloacetate is an important factor in ketosis. Oxaloacetate is a product of carbohydrate metabolism and hence a certain minimum rate of carbohydrate metabolism is essential to prevent ketosis. Ketosis is thus seen to result from excessive utilization of fat relative to utilization of carbohydrate.

Carbohydrate Metabolism

The greater part of the carbohydrate in the body consists of the glycogen stored in the tissues, principally in the liver and in the muscles, and of the glucose in the blood and tissue fluids. The total amount of carbohydrate present in a well-nourished human body, of which about one-half is present in the liver as glycogen, is equivalent to less than one day's supply at the normal rate of consumption. It must be remembered, however, that carbohydrate taken into the body can be stored as fat, and also that carbohydrate can be formed in the body from non-carbohydrate sources.

The carbohydrate absorbed from the small intestine from a normal diet consists largely of three monosaccharides—glucose, fructose and galactose. They are all convertible to glycogen in the liver, and the glycogen so formed breaks down, either by acid hydrolysis *in vitro* or under the influence of the enzyme systems present in liver, to give glucose which may therefore be considered as the form in which carbohydrate is available to the tissues.

The Equilibrium between Glycogen and Glucose. Many years ago Claude Bernard showed that the glycogen of the liver, but not that of the muscles, could break down in the body to give glucose, and that, except after a recent meal containing carbohydrate, the blood leaving the liver contained more sugar than that entering the organ. The process of formation of glucose from glycogen is called glycogenolysis. Other organs of the body, and in particular the muscular tissues, appeared to be continuously absorbing glucose from the blood flowing through them. These important observations established the fact that although the concentration of the sugar in the blood falls only slightly during post-absorptive conditions or even during a long fast, this was not because the tissues ceased to absorb glucose from the blood under these conditions. The relative constancy of the blood glucose concentration was to be ascribed to the fact that the amount of glucose withdrawn from the blood by the tissues in general was counterbalanced by the amount of glucose liberated into the circulation by the liver under these conditions. The importance of this power of the liver to secrete glucose is dramatically emphasized by the fact that if the liver is removed from a dog the blood sugar concentration falls rapidly and death ensues within a few hours unless glucose is administered in large amounts. Undoubtedly some part of the glucose secreted by the liver comes from the glycogen present in it, but the stored liver glycogen is quite insufficient to supply the body's needs for very long and, as will be discussed below, glucose can be formed in the liver from non-carbohydrate sources, a process called gluconeogenesis.

After the ingestion of carbohydrate food the blood glucose concentration rises from its normal post-absorptive value of 0·08 to 0·1 per cent to a value in the neighbourhood of 0·15 per cent. As the blood glucose concentration rises the liver secretes less and less glucose until, when the concentration reaches about 0·12 per cent, the liberation of glucose by the liver ceases altogether. At blood glucose concentrations above this, the liver begins to absorb glucose from the blood stream and the liver glycogen content begins to rise. It is clear, therefore, that the glycogen in the liver represents, in part at least, a storehouse for carbohydrate coming from the food. The glucose which is thus stored during the temporary period of plenty is liberated by the liver during the lean period of post-absorptive conditions. The ability of the liver to adjust its output of glucose to the requirements of the body is sometimes described as its homeostatic function.

Although the skeletal muscles also absorb more glucose when the blood glucose concentration rises after carbohydrate food, the glycogen which accumulates in these tissues is not reconverted to blood glucose during post-absorptive conditions. The glycogen of muscle may be oxidized or it may be converted to lactic acid, a process called glycolysis, but it never forms glucose in the body; this contrast with events in the liver is to be ascribed to differences between the enzyme systems of liver and muscle tissues.

The process of the formation of lactic acid from glycogen in skeletal muscle is one which does not involve the addition of oxygen nor the elimination of hydrogen from the system. It is accordingly not an oxidation process and can take place under the largely anaerobic conditions which exist in skeletal muscles during exercise. If the exercise is light, any lactic acid formed may be in part reconverted to glycogen in the muscles themselves, but if the exercise is severe most of the lactic acid may escape into the blood stream and be then converted to glycogen in the liver. Therefore, in the presence of the liver, muscle glycogen can give rise to blood glucose indirectly. These relationships will be clear from the diagram.

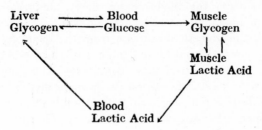

It should be noted that just as the formation of lactic acid from glycogen in the muscles liberates energy, the reformation of glycogen from lactic acid requires the addition of energy to the system. In the muscles any energy thus required can be provided, under aerobic conditions, by oxidation of part of the lactic acid formed or equivalent glucose or glycogen. In the liver the source of the energy required for the formation of glycogen from lactic acid is not known with certainty.

Investigations with radioactive carbon dioxide suggest that the formation of glycogen in the liver from lactic acid, and even from glucose, may involve the linking up of carbon dioxide with intermediate substances formed, so that the carbon skeleton of the glycogen which accumulates contains a significant proportion of carbon atoms originating from carbon dioxide.

Gluconeogenesis. The amount of glycogen stored in the liver is insufficient to maintain the normal level of blood sugar for more than a short time, and glucose is in fact formed by the liver from various non-carbohydrate sources, a process called gluconeogenesis. These sources are alcohols such as glycerol, many amino-acids, and a number of organic acids, e.g. fumaric, malic, succinic, etc, formed in metabolism. Of these the amino-acids are the most important and, hence, the dietary protein can be considered an important source of blood glucose. The process of gluconeogenesis is inhibited by insulin, and stimulated by the hormones of the anterior pituitary gland (see below).

During starvation or deprivation of carbohydrate, the utilization of carbohydrate by the muscles and other tissues is diminished and some part of their energy requirements is met by oxidation of fats. It seems probable, however, that nervous tissue is peculiarly dependent on a constant supply of carbohydrate or similar substances and that hepatic gluconeogenesis is of particular importance in providing the nervous system with one of its requisite metabolites. It should be mentioned that the brain (and the heart also) can oxidize lactic acid as well as glucose and thus can utilize the lactic acid formed anaerobically in skeletal muscle during vigorous exercise.

The Regulation of the Blood Sugar Concentration. The accurate control of the blood sugar concentration is of the utmost importance in the economy of the human body. If the concentration rises above about 0·18 per cent—the renal threshold—the re-absorption of sugar from the renal tubules is incomplete and glucose is lost to the body in the urine. If, on the other hand, the concentration falls below about 0·04 per cent, the central nervous system becomes disturbed. In man there is at first extreme hunger and fatigue, with general sweating; later, delirium and profound coma are produced. In rabbits and certain other mammals, severe convulsions occur in addition just before the coma and death from respiratory failure; these are known as *"hypoglycaemic convulsions"*. If the condition is not relieved by the administration of glucose, death may ensue. Even if death does not occur as the result of a temporary lowering of the blood sugar concentration, lesions may appear in the brain which cause permanent functional damage.

The mechanism which ensures that the blood sugar concentration normally varies only within the relatively narrow range of 0·08 per cent to 0·16 per cent, is largely hormonal in character, adrenaline, insulin and the growth hormone of the anterior pituitary being concerned.

(a) *Adrenaline*. When the blood sugar concentration falls below about 0·07 per cent, the excitation of nervous centres in the lower part of the brain causes sympathetic stimulation and a release of adrenaline from the adrenal glands. The adrenaline so released stimulates a breakdown of liver glycogen to glucose, the liberation of which tends to arrest the fall of blood sugar concentration. The general sympathetic stimulation may assist this process. Under the influence of adrenaline, muscle glycogen breaks down to lactic acid which may be carried to the liver for reconversion to glycogen and glucose. These several processes tend to prevent a fall in the blood sugar concentration by rapidly mobilizing the glycogen stores of the body.

During muscular exercise there is a general stimulation of all the sympathico-adrenal system, so that the rate of breakdown of glycogen in the liver is accelerated on just those occasions when glucose is being used most rapidly by the muscles. As far as we know, however, adrenaline does not directly affect gluconeogenesis in the liver, but can only bring about the breakdown of glycogen which has been stored in that organ.

It was shown many years ago by Claude Bernard that puncture of the floor of the fourth ventricle in the rabbit results in hyperglycaemia and glycosuria; this is known as *"diabetic puncture"*. The hyperglycaemia is due to the excitation of fibres that run into the sympathetic system, with a consequent outpouring of adrenaline.

(b) *Hormones of the Adrenal Cortex*. The adrenal cortex plays a part in carbohydrate metabolism as is shown by the fact that if it is removed, or diseased, the blood sugar concentration falls, and there is muscular weakness, in addition to other abnormalities to be discussed in Chapter 32. Administration of the "gluco-corticoid" hormones, extracted from the adrenal cortex, abolishes the hypoglycaemia and increases the rate of glycogen formation by the liver.

(c) *Hormones of the Pancreas*. The two hormones taking part in the regulation of blood sugar are insulin, produced by the beta cells of the islets of Langerhans, and glucagon, produced by the alpha cells. When the blood sugar concentration rises as a result of the ingestion of carbohydrate the liver responds by first diminishing and then abolishing the blood sugar of the blood stream and then proceeds to absorb part of the excess into the blood stream. The ability of the liver to suspend the production of sugar and inhibit gluconeogenesis, and to promote glycogen storage at the expense of the excess glucose in the blood, is dependent on the presence of insulin.

When the blood sugar concentration rises after a carbohydrate meal the excess glucose is stored as glycogen in the muscles as well as in the liver, while in the muscles the rate at which sugar is oxidized may increase under these conditions. All these processes for the storage and utilization of glucose depend on the availability of insulin, and there is good evidence that the secretion of insulin by the pancreas is stimulated by a rise in the concentration of sugar in the blood; the controlling action appears to be the direct effect of the excess sugar concentration on the cells of the pancreas, although it is possible that a nervous reflex is also involved. Apart from the formation of glycogen a further process for the storage of energy from the excess ingested carbohydrate is the conversion of glucose to fat (glycerides) which are then stored in the fat depots. In general, therefore, insulin may be said to promote those metabolic processes which cause glucose to leave the blood stream (conversion to glycogen or fat, or promotion of carbohydrate oxidation) and to inhibit gluconeogenesis. All these processes tend to lead to a fall of the blood sugar concentration and if a large dose of insulin is given to a normal person in a post-absorptive state, fatal hypoglycaemia may develop.

The other hormone from the pancreas, *glucagon*, plays a rôle which appears to be identical with adrenaline.

(*d*) *Anterior Pituitary Hormones.* An animal from which the anterior pituitary gland has been removed becomes abnormally sensitive to the hypoglycaemic action of insulin. Conversely, a normal animal to which anterior pituitary extract is administered becomes highly insensitive to the action of a small dose of insulin in lowering the blood sugar concentration. These observations show that in some respects anterior-pituitary secretion and insulin act antagonistically.

It seems possible that anterior pituitary secretions exert two separate actions on carbohydrate metabolism. The first, attributed to the action of pituitary adrenocorticotrophin (A.C.T.H.), stimulates the liberation of adrenal-cortical hormones from the adrenal gland and thus promotes gluconeogenesis, with consequent accumulation of glycogen in the liver. The second action, possibly associated with the growth-promoting principle of anterior-pituitary extracts, depresses carbohydrate oxidation in the skeletal muscles with the accumulation of muscle glycogen stores.

Diabetes in Man If a normal man takes 50 g of glucose by mouth and the blood sugar concentration is determined at intervals afterwards, the type of curve shown in Fig. 30.1 is obtained. The rise of the blood sugar concentration stimulates the secretion of insulin and the mechanism which we have considered in the previous section comes into play, with the result that much of the glucose is stored as glycogen; the blood sugar concentration thus falls again without having reached so high a value that glucose is excreted by the kidneys, i.e. the renal threshold is not exceeded and glycosuria is absent. Such a test is called a **"glucose tolerance"** test and is of much value clinically in the diagnosis of *diabetes mellitus*. Occasionally glycosuria may follow the ingestion of a large amount (150 to 200 g) of glucose by a normal person, but this is not considered to be necessarily indicative of diabetes mellitus; it is described as *alimentary glycosuria*.

When a glucose tolerance test is performed on a diabetic person, the

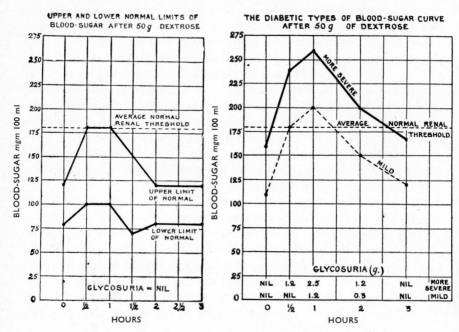

FIG. 30.1. The effect of the ingestion of 50 g glucose on the concentration of sugar in the blood.

(*Left*) *Normal Subjects.* The concentration is not increased excessively and returns to the initial value within 2 hr. No sugar is excreted in the urine.

(*Right*) *Diabetic Subjects.* The concentration rises to a considerably higher value and takes 3 hr to return to the initial value. Considerable quantities of sugar are excreted in the urine.

The figures under "glycosuria" indicate the total quantity of sugar excreted in the sample of urine collected at that time. (Harrison's "Chemical Methods in Clinical Medicine".)

blood sugar concentration may be very high initially and may rise excessively after glucose administration, failing to fall again to the original value for many hours. The mechanism for the storage of glycogen in the liver and muscles is defective, while glucose oxidation is also subnormal; much of the carbohydrate taken in with the food is therefore lost in the urine as glucose. The depression of carbohydrate utilization causes the production of excess ketone bodies in the liver with the development of ketosis and ketonuria. The appearance of ketone bodies in the urine is an indication of the gravity of the disease, a slight glycosuria being of no great importance. If the ketone bodies continue to accumulate, the patient ultimately dies in a coma, if he has not already succumbed to infection, to which he becomes very liable. Daily subcutaneous injections of insulin, however, can relieve most of the symptoms and the patient can lead a normal life; omission of the insulin is rapidly followed by a reversion to the diabetic condition. Excess insulin, as we have seen, leads to hypoglycaemia and serious consequences, so that doses must be carefully controlled; immediate subcutaneous injection of glucose, or a large quantity given by mouth, quickly alleviates the symptoms should an overdose be given accidentally.

In recent years considerable advances have been made in the production of slowly-absorbed insulin preparations. These have the great advantage that fewer and larger injections can be given, and these more nearly simulate the physiological secretion of insulin by the pancreas.

The Aetiology of Diabetes Mellitus. It is extremely probable that *diabetes mellitus* is not a single syndrome with one origin; it must consist of a number of different conditions arising from various causes but with the majority of symptoms in common. Accordingly, it is most unlikely that one causative agent can be assigned to this disease.

Experimentally a condition resembling human *diabetes mellitus* in some important respects can be induced in certain animals by surgical removal of the pancreas. The fact that degenerative lesions in the cells of the islets of Langerhans of the pancreas are sometimes found in human diabetes, together with the presence of subnormal amounts of insulin in the pancreas, suggests that pancreatic islet lesions are to be regarded as one direct cause of *diabetes mellitus*. Nevertheless, in a substantial proportion of human diabetics no obvious pancreatic islet lesions are demonstrable and, even where these exist, we still have to seek the reason for their development. Abnormally high secretory activity of the anterior pituitary gland can obviously be regarded as one possible extra-pancreatic cause of clinical *diabetes mellitus*. Experimentally, a diabetic condition can be induced in intact cats and dogs by repeated injections of anterior pituitary extract, and such treatment may cause the appearance of lesions of the pancreatic islets of such severity that they remain after the pituitary treatment ceases, so that a persistently diabetic condition is seen. After the daily injections of anterior pituitary extract have ceased the persistent diabetes is easily controlled by the administration of insulin, but during the period of pituitary treatment the diabetic condition shows a remarkable insensitivity to control by insulin. It seems possible that continued over-activity of the anterior pituitary lobe may account in part for the "insulin insensitive" type of diabetes that is met with clinically, while a short period of pituitary overaction might be responsible for permanent islet lesions associated with a persistent clinical diabetes which is not abnormally unresponsive to control by insulin.

Overactivity of the secretory function of the adrenal cortex, either primary or secondary to pituitary overaction, can initiate or exacerbate clinical diabetes if adrenal steroids of the corticosterone type are produced in excessive amount, while abnormally high thyroid activity might also contribute to the development or maintenance of a diabetic condition. Thus a number of endocrine glands may be considered as possible extra-pancreatic factors concerned in the appearance of the symptoms of human *diabetes mellitus*, though dysfunction of the islets of Langerhans is, in a substantial proportion of cases, the direct, though perhaps only the secondary, cause of the condition.

The Chemistry of Carbohydrate Metabolism

The details of the chemical reactions involved in breakdown of glucose and glycogen must be sought in textbooks of biochemistry and only some general outlines will be discussed here. Like the other food substances the metabolism of glucose can be divided into two stages, the pre-citric acid cycle stage and the citric acid cycle, the connecting link being acetyl coenzyme A.

Glycolysis. The pre-citric acid cycle stage of carbohydrate metabolism is a series of reactions often included under the term glycolysis,

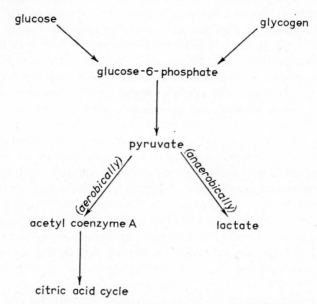

Fig. 30.2. Carbohydrate metabolism in tissues. The intermediate stages between glycogen and glucose-6-phosphate, and between glucose-6-phosphate and pyruvate are omitted.

although this term strictly applies to the production of lactic acid from glucose and glycogen. The relation between the oxidative pathway for glucose metabolism and the glycolytic pathway is seen in Fig. 30.2. The reactions can start either from glucose taken in from the blood stream or from glycogen stored in the tissue. Both are converted to glucose-6-phosphate and this undergoes a series of changes which result in formation of pyruvate. In aerobic conditions the pyruvate forms acetyl coenzyme A, which goes into the citric acid cycle, while in anaerobic conditions pyruvate is reduced to lactate. This formation of lactate provides an important source of energy in muscle, when work is taking place at a faster rate than can be covered by current oxygen intake.

The Citric Acid Cycle

The citric acid cycle, or Krebs' cycle, is the final common pathway for oxidation of proteins, fats and carbohydrates. The preliminary reactions result in formation of acetyl coenzyme A, and this is the substance which enters the citric acid cycle. The details of the reactions of the cycle must be sought in textbooks of biochemistry, and only a very bare outline is given here, which is shown schematically in Fig. 30.3. Acetyl coenzyme A (two-carbon unit) reacts with oxaloacetate (four-carbon unit) to form citrate (six carbon unit). Citrate undergoes a series of reactions with formation and breakdown of a large number of substances and ultimate formation of oxaloacetate again. During the course of the cycle carbon dioxide appears twice as an end product, so that the six-carbon skeleton of citric acid is reduced first to a five-carbon skeleton and then to the four-carbon skeleton of oxaloacetate. The re-entry of another molecule of acetyl coenzyme A starts the cycle off again. The carbon dioxide produced by the cycle is excreted by the lungs. The other end product is hydrogen and, as seen in Fig. 30.3, each complete operation of the cycle results in the formation of four pairs of hydrogen atoms, which are ultimately oxidized to water by the oxygen taken into the body by respiration. This final oxidation of the hydrogen is, however, in itself a complex process involving a number of different stages. The hydrogen is not able to react with molecular oxygen but is "accepted" by substances called coenzyme 1 and coenzyme 2, which are pyridine nucleotides. These substances can exist in either oxidized or reduced forms and the oxidized form can accept hydrogen and hence become reduced. The reduced forms of the coenzymes can in turn pass on their hydrogen to substances called cytochromes, which can in their turn exist in oxidized or reduced forms. The reduction of the cytochromes re-oxidizes the coenzymes which are thus available to accept more hydrogen from the substances of the cycle. Finally, the cytochromes are re-oxidized by passing on their hydrogen to cytochrome oxidase and this substance is able to pass on hydrogen to molecular oxygen. The final products of the cycle are thus water and carbon dioxide.

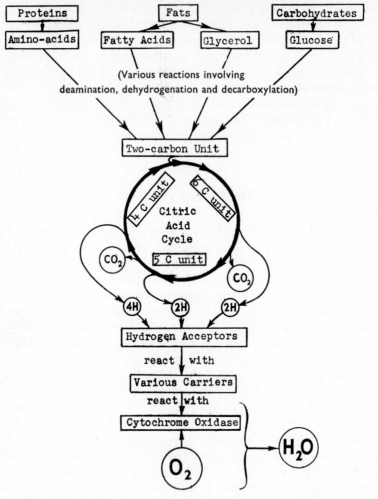

Fig. 30.3. Schematic representation of the probable course of
breakdown of the food substances.

The citric acid cycle is shown diagrammatically in a much abbreviated form. The various six-, five- and four-carbon compounds
actually taking part form at least nine stages in the cyclical process.

Metabolism and Energy Liberation

The oxidation of food substances results in the production of water and
carbon dioxide and the release of energy, which is partly utilized by the
various tissues in the processes of growth, secretion, muscular contraction,
etc., while the rest appears as heat. The way in which the energy becomes
available is one of the fundamental problems of metabolism and it is only in
recent years that a tentative answer has been formulated. It now seems

fairly certain that the "useful" part of the energy is very largely derived from one chemical reaction, the dephosphorylation of adenosine triphosphate (usually referred to as ATP). The removal of one phosphate radical from ATP results in the formation of adenosine diphosphate (ADP). The ADP formed can, in suitable conditions, combine again with a phosphate radical to form ATP. The phosphorylation process requires energy and the dephosphorylation process makes energy available. The amount of energy associated with this type of reaction is relatively large and hence, the term "active (or energy-rich) phosphate" has been used in connection with it. Since the dephosphorylation of ATP is the primary reaction which makes energy available to the tissues, the function of the other reactions of the food substances can be regarded as supplying the energy necessary for ATP synthesis; a considerable fraction of the energy liberated by oxidative breakdown of the food substances thus becomes available. Not all oxidative reactions, even though they yield energy, can take part in ATP synthesis, and, furthermore, if the process is to be carried out efficiently, the amount of energy liberated by a particular oxidative reaction should not be too large, in relation to the amount of energy needed for ATP synthesis. This makes more understandable the apparently complicated pathway of metabolism of the food substances. The large number of reactions which occur ensures that the energy is liberated in small amounts, which are suitable for an efficient synthesis of ATP, and some of the reactions are directly "coupled" with ATP synthesis.

From the biological point of view the "efficiency" of metabolism can be measured in terms of the ATP produced; in fact, much more ATP is generated at the citric acid stage than in the preliminary stages. Some of the ATP generated is required to maintain the metabolic reactions and, if this is subtracted from the ATP generated, the amount available for biological work is obtained, which can be called the net yield of ATP. In the case of glucose, for each molecule metabolized under aerobic conditions, the net yield in the glycolytic reactions is six ATP compared with thirty ATP in association with the citric acid cycle. Most of the ATP is generated in the oxidation of hydrogen by the pyridine nucleotide—cytochrome system. In anaerobic conditions where the pyruvate is reduced to lactate the glycolytic reactions yield only two moles of ATP.

Chapter 31

NUTRITION

The natural stimuli that lead to the choice of appropriate foods are hunger, thirst and appetite, guided by the sensations of sight, taste and smell. Under the conditions of twentieth-century civilization where food is, in general, not produced in the place where it is consumed, and where for one reason or another adequate supplies of food are likely to be periodically restricted, it is necessary to replace to some extent the operation of natural desires by carefully calculated allocation of the different food constituents. Nutrition is the science on which such attempts are based and embraces a very wide field of study. In deciding a nutritional policy for a population the following factors would have to be considered: (1) the amounts of the different food constituents required by the human body in different working and climatic conditions; (2) the amounts of these food constituents in the different food materials used; (3) the availability of food in terms of labour and space required for production, bulk and value of food in relation to transport, cost of food in relation to wages level, ability to import and export, etc.; (4) the storage and preparation of food so that the highest nutritive value is maintained and (5) general propaganda and education in regard to the preparation and use of foods. Of these aspects of nutrition, only the first two belong to the province of physiology, and accordingly only these will be considered here.

The six essential classes of substance required in the diet are proteins, fats, carbohydrates, vitamins, mineral salts and water. The first problem is to know the amounts of each of these required by the body under different conditions, and the second to know the amounts of each of these in the food materials, or more accurately to know the amounts of these absorbed from the intestine. Substances originally present in the food but destroyed by cooking or not absorbed from the intestine will have no food value. In thinking of the food requirements we can divide these into foods supplying energy for bodily activity, and foods necessary for some other purpose. In the first case we are concerned with making up a certain number of calories which are required for metabolism and, in this respect, the different calorie-providing foods are within certain limits interchangeable. In the second case we have to think of specific functions of food constituents which cannot be replaced by giving other types of food. To the energy-providing foods belong proteins, fats and carbohydrates and the only other dietary constituent likely to be a source of energy is alcohol. The

mineral salts, the vitamins, and water belong to the group of food substances with specific functions, but to these we must also add the proteins
and fats, as these in addition to supplying energy have other rôles, which
cannot be taken over by any other food constituent.

THE CALORIE REQUIREMENTS

When the body is at rest it requires an energy production of about
40 kcal m²/hr, which for an average adult amounts to about 1,700
kilocalories in twenty-four hours. When any physical activity is undertaken
the energy consumption increases and the greater the physical work
carried out the greater will be the need for calories. While mental work
can cause a feeling of great fatigue and even hunger, it does not cause an
increase in energy consumption apart from any physical movements
accompanying it. Calorie requirements are, therefore, dictated by physical
effort. There are two main ways in which the calorie needs can be assessed,
(1) calorimetry or measurement of the metabolic rate of the body in the
appropriate conditions, and (2) the dietary survey, or measurement of the
amount of food consumed.

The techniques for calorimetry have already been discussed in Chapter 29
and, in general, indirect calorimetry, i.e. measurement of the oxygen
consumption, is employed. Modern techniques have enabled oxygen
consumption to be determined by subjects at work or play of many
kinds, and as a result, fairly accurate figures are now available for calorie
requirements in these conditions.

Dietary Survey

The dietary survey is an important approach to nutritional problems
because it expresses calorie needs in terms of actual food used, and also
gives information about wastage in preparation, storage and distribution.
The survey can be carried out at different levels. There is the detailed
survey on one individual, and this is the most accurate as regards actual
calorie intake, provided the subject is intelligent and co-operative. Then
there is the family survey, in which a trained observer attempts to assess
the food intake of a normal family living under their usual conditions. In
addition there is the survey at national level, where the total food production, imports, exports and consumption are assessed. These dietary
surveys will give information of a rather different kind from that given by
calorimetry, but this kind of information is equally important in assessing
nutritional problems as a whole.

As a result of techniques of these kinds the requirements of individuals
for calories can be drawn up, and in doing so it is usual to divide the day
into three periods of eight hours each, i.e. a period of rest in bed, a period
of work, and a period of non-occupational activities, and to assess the calorie
needs for each of these. This can be expressed in relation to the "reference

man" or "reference woman", and these terms apply to an average individual in standard conditions. The needs of these individuals are shown in Tables 31.1 and 31.2 (from Food and Agriculture Organization of the United Nations, 1957); corrections are then made for deviations from the standard age, weight and environmental temperature. In correcting for age in adults the following percentages of the allowances for the reference man and woman are taken: 97 per cent for age 30–40; 94 per cent for age 40–50; 86 per cent for 50–60; 79 per cent for 60–70; and 69 per cent for ages over 70.

TABLE 31.1

The Energy Expenditure of a "Reference Man"

(Weight, 65 kg. Age, 25 years. Mean annual environmental temperature, 10°C)

	kcal/day
A. 8 hr. Working activities: mostly standing (overall rate, 2·5 kcal/min)	1,200

B. 8 hr. Non-occupational activities:

	kcal/day
1 hr washing, dressing, etc, at 3 kcal/min . . .	180
1½ hr walking at about 6 km/hr at 5·3 kcal/min . .	480
4 hr sitting activities at 1·54 kcal/min	370
1½ hr active recreations and/or domestic work at 5·2 kcal/min	470
	——
	1,500

	kcal/day
C. 8 hr. Rest in bed at basal metabolic rate	500

Total 3,200

TABLE 31.2

The Energy Expenditure of a "Reference Woman"

(Weight, 55 kg. Age, 25 years. Mean annual environmental temperature, 10°C)

	kcal/day
A. 8 hr. Working activities in the home or in industry: mostly standing (overall rate, 1·83 kcal/min)	880

B. 8 hr. Non-occupational activities:

	kcal/day
1 hr washing, dressing, etc, at 2·5 kcal/min . . .	150
1 hr walking at about 5 km/hr at 3·6 kcal/min . .	220
5 hr sitting activities at 1·41 kcal/min	420
1 hr active recreation and/or heavier domestic work at 3·5 kcal/min	210
	——
	1,000

	kcal/day
C. 8 hr. Rest in bed at basal metabolic rate	420

Total 2,300

For adjusting for different weights the following formulæ can be used:

$$\text{For man} \quad E = 815 + 36 \cdot 6 \, W$$
$$\text{For woman} \quad E = 580 + 31 \cdot 1 \, W$$

where E is the number of kcal and W the weight in kg. To correct for temperature the calorie requirement is increased by 8 per cent for each 10° fall in environmental temperature from the standard, 10°, and decreased by 5 per cent for each 10° rise. This is based on the fact that man is better able to protect himself from the effects of cold than of heat. Occupation naturally is one of the most important factors in providing for the individual and in some heavy occupations the daily calorie requirement may amount to more than 5,000 kcal. For an excellent discussion of the energy expenditure of the human subject in many conditions, the reader is referred to "Energy, Work and Leisure" (Durnin & Passmore).

The requirements of children have to be considered separately and it must be remembered in children particularly that the range of activities vary enormously in individuals. Table 31.3 gives figures for the calorie requirements based on recommendations from various sources.

TABLE 31.3

Calorie Requirements of Children

Recommendation of Davidson & Passmore (1966)

		Age (in years)	kcal/day
Children	. . .	1–3	1,300
Children	. . .	4–6	1,700
Children	. . .	7–9	2,100
Children	. . .	10–12	2,500
Boys	. . .	13–15	3,100
Girls	. . .	13–15	2,600
Males	. . .	16–19	3,600
Females	. . .	16–19	2,400

Calorie Content of Food

The determination of the calorie content of food by the bomb calorimeter has been discussed on p. 498, and the figures usually taken are carbohydrate and protein 4·1 kcal/g, and fat 9·2 kcal/g. Most foods eaten are in fact mixtures of these and when calorie need has to be translated in terms of actual food, reference is made to food tables which give the required values for the actual food material eaten. It is usual to find that by far the greatest part of the calorie supply in the human diet is provided by carbohydrate, as this is usually the cheapest and most plentiful source. When food is scarce, the aim is to supply sufficient protein and fat dictated by other needs (see following sections), to calculate the calories provided by these and to make up the rest of the calories with carbohydrate. A good average peace-time diet, e.g. as recommended by the British Medical Association Report in 1933, might make up the calories as follows:—

100 g protein .	. .	410 kcal
100 g fat	. . .	920 kcal
500 g carbohydrate .	.	2,050 kcal

There is no doubt that many people live reasonably healthy lives making up a greater proportion of the calories with carbohydrate, and the general rule is that the cheaper the diet, the more carbohydrate it contains.

SPECIFIC REQUIREMENTS

In the following paragraphs are discussed the specific requirements for different food substances. Figures are given in Table 31.4 of the amounts of the various constituents which are regarded as desirable in the diet. In considering these figures it must be borne in mind that they are somewhat arbitrary and often more in the nature of a generous guess rather than an accurate knowledge of the amounts which are required. Since the effects of deprivation of certain food constituents, particularly the vitamins, may not become apparent for a long time, it is obvious that the difficulties of assessing accurately the minimum requirements of the human subject for any one food factor are very great. It is easier to be sure that a certain intake is adequate than to know what is the threshold requirement for health, and probably for this reason figures tend to be somewhat too high. They must be interpreted as something to be aimed at, rather than as a carefully determined minimum need.

Protein in the Diet

In addition to supplying energy, protein is necessary for the building up of new tissues and replacing of used ones. It has been seen in Chapter 30 (p. 509) that a minimum amount of protein must be supplied and also, that this must contain certain essential amino-acids. If even one of these is not present the body proteins will be broken down to supply it and hence it will not be possible to keep the animal in nitrogen equilibrium. From the dietary point of view it is important to assess the nutritional value of different kinds of proteins and this has been done in various ways. One way is to give a certain protein in the diet and make calculations about the fraction of the nitrogen retained by the body. This fraction is called the biological value of the protein and varies widely with different dietary proteins, e.g. egg albumen has a value 94 per cent, milk protein 85 per cent, gluten in wheat is as low as 40 per cent. Another method of expressing quantitatively the value of a protein is the chemical score. The amino-acid content of a protein is determined and expressed as a percentage of that of an ideal protein, i.e. one which contains all the essential amino-acids in the correct proportions. The lowest value found for any essential amino-acid is taken as the chemical score. There is a reasonable correlation between the biological value and the chemical score measured in these ways. A simpler approach to the problem is to classify proteins as first class (animal protein) and second class (vegetable protein) as generally, although there are exceptions, vegetable protein is of less biological value.

Recommendations have been made in various forms about dietary protein. The League of Nations (1936) suggested a minimum of 1 g/kg body wt/day, with part of this comprising animal protein. The British Medical Association (1950) recommended that 11 per cent of the calories of the food should come from protein (14 per cent in the case of pregnancy, lactation, children and adolescents). The recommendations of the U.S. National Research Council are included in Table 31.4.

Fat in the Diet

The fat of the diet is used like the carbohydrate and part of the protein to supply energy by oxidation, but in this respect it has certain advantages over the other types of food. One gram of fat on oxidation will yield more than twice as much energy as the same amount of carbohydrate or protein and furthermore the fat is taken in a concentrated form in the food, whereas in the case of protein and carbohydrate foods, a large part of the bulk of the food is composed of water. Fat has another important rôle in metabolism in that it is the only form of food which can be stored in large amounts as such. This stored fat is valuable in the protection of the body against cold since it is stored partly below the skin where it forms an insulating layer. The food fat has an irreplaceable function in acting as a solvent for the fat-soluble vitamins and also for providing the body with the indispensable unsaturated fatty acids. It has been seen (on p. 475) that fat inhibits the movements of the stomach and, on account of this property, fat taken in the diet prevents the onset of hunger for a longer time. It is rather striking that in spite of these important and definite rôles of fat in the body economy, few figures are available to suggest what are the minimum fat requirements. The usual aim is to supply 100 g daily.

In recent years in the more highly developed countries the possibility has been widely considered of the possible harmful effects of excessive fat in the diet. Fat adds greatly to the palatability of the diet, and even apart from possible specific harmful effects, fat is often a great temptation to excessive calorie intake.

Carbohydrate

As this usually forms the bulk of the human diet and is the cheapest form of calories, it is never likely to form too small a fraction of the total calorie requirement. The idea that it has no specific function is, however, erroneous. The functioning of the citric acid cycle depends on a constant supply of oxaloacetate (Chapter 30, p. 525); this is derived from dietary carbohydrate, and to a lesser extent from some amino-acids. These can be grouped together as the antiketogenic substances and, in order that ketosis should be avoided, the antiketogenic substances being metabolized should amount to at least half the ketogenic substances, which are comprised mainly of fats.

TABLE

Recommended Dietary Allowance
(Food and Nutrition Board,

	Kilocalories	Protein g	Calcium g	Iron mg
Man (70 kg):				
Sedentary	2,500		0·80	12
Moderately Active	3,000	70	(0·56)	(8·5)
Very Active	4,500			
Woman (56 kg):				
Sedentary	2,100		0·80	12
Moderately Active	2,500	60	(0·56)	(8·5)
Very Active	3,000			
Pregnancy (latter half)	2,500	85	1·5	15
Lactation	3,000	100	2·0	15
Children up to 12 years				
Under 1 year[4]	100/kg	3 to 4/kg	1·0	6
1–3 years[5]	1,200	40	1·0	7
4–6 years	1,600	50	1·0	8
7–9 years	2,000	60	1·0	10
10–12 years	2,500	70	1·2	12
Children over 12 years				
Girls, 13–15 years	2,800	80	1·3	15
16–20 years	2,400	75	1·0	15
Boys, 13–15 years	3,200	85	1·4	15
16–20 years	3,800	100	1·4	15

[1] Tentative goal towards which to aim in planning practical dietaries; can be met by a good diet of natural foods. Such a diet will also provide other minerals and vitamins, the requirements for which are less well known. The restricted allowances are probably adequate for adults other than nursing or expectant mothers.

[2] Requirements may be less if provided as vitamin A; greater if provided chiefly as the pro-vitamin, carotene.

[3] 1 mg thiamin equals 333 I.U.; 1 mg ascorbic acid equals 20 I.U.

[4] Needs of infants increase from month to month. The amounts given are for approximately 6–8 months. The amounts of protein and calcium needed are less if derived from milk.

[5] Allowances are based on needs for the middle year in each group (as 2, 5, 8 etc), and for moderate activity.

Mineral Salts

The important inorganic substances which are essential in the diet are calcium, sodium, potassium, magnesium, iron, phosphorus, iodine and chlorine. In addition, smaller amounts of many other elements are required, copper, bromine, cobalt, zinc, etc. These do not liberate any energy on oxidation, but they are responsible for the maintenance of the normal function of many parts of the body. The concentration of these substances necessary in the body fluids is usually small, but on the other hand there is a constant loss of small amounts in the urine and other body secretions,

31.4

(Restricted Allowances in Brackets)
National Research Council)

Vitamin A[2] I.U.		Thiamin[3] (B[1]) mg	Riboflavin mg	Nicotinic Acid mg	Ascorbic Acid[2] mg	Vitamin D I.U.
5,000	⎫	1·5 (1·1)	2·2 (1·5)	15 (10·5)	75 (52)	[6]
(3,500)	⎬	1·8 (1·3)	2·7 (1·9)	23 (13)		
		2·3 (1·6)	3·3 (2·3)	23 (16)		
5,000	⎫	1·2 (0·8)	1·8 (1·3)	12 (8)		
(3,500)	⎬	1·5 (1·1)	2·2 (1·5)	15 (10)	70 (49)	[6]
		1·8 (1·3)	2·7 (1·9)	18 (13)		
6,000		1·8	2·5	18	100	400 to 800
8,000		2·3	3·0	23	150	400 to 800
1,500		0·4	0·6	4	30	400 to 800
2,000		0·6	0·9	6	35	[6]
2,500		0·8	1·2	8	50	
3,500		1·0	1·5	10	60	
4,500		1·2	1·8	12	75	
5,000		1·4	2·0	14	80	[6]
5,000		1·2	1·8	12	80	[6]
5,000		1·6	2·4	16	90	[6]
6,000		2·0	3·0	20	100	

[6] Vitamin D is undoubtedly necessary for older children and adults. When not available from sunshine, it should be provided probably up to the minimum amounts recommended for infants.

Further Recommendations. The requirement for iodine is small; probably about 0·002 to 0·004 mg/day for each kg of body weight. This amounts to about 0·15 to 0·30 mg daily for the adult, which is easily met by the regular use of iodized salt; the use of this salt is especially important in adolescence and pregnancy.

The requirement for copper for adults is in the neighbourhood of 1·0 to 2·0 mg/day. Infants and children require about 0·05 mg/kg body weight. The requirement for copper is approximately one-tenth of that for iron.

The requirement for vitamin K is usually satisfied by any good diet. Special consideration needs to be given to new-born infants. Physicians commonly give vitamin K either to the mother before delivery or to the infant immediately after birth.

and this loss must be replaced. The minerals present in highest concentration in the body fluids are sodium and chloride. In the case of most of the mineral requirements, the amounts likely to be in the diet will be more than adequate for the body's needs and there will be excretion of the excess in the urine. The substances which demand special attention are sodium chloride, iodine, calcium and iron. Sodium chloride is only likely to become deficient when there is a great loss of sweat from the body, as in conditions of working in very hot atmospheres, or in certain abnormal conditions, when there is a repeated loss of gastric juice or of intestinal secretions by persistent vomiting or diarrhoea. Iodine deficiency only occurs regionally and may cause abnormal thyroid metabolism; this will be considered in Chapter 32. The two minerals to be considered in ordinary nutritional problems are calcium and iron.

Calcium

The recommended calcium intake can be seen from Table 31.4. Calcium is most abundant in milk and cheese, and is contained only in very small quantities in bread and meat. It is, however, a common practice to fortify bread with increased amounts of calcium. There is a considerable loss of calcium in the intestine as part of the calcium of the food is not absorbed. For this reason the calcium required in the diet is much greater than that actually needed by the tissues. Calcium has a great diversity of functions in the body, and reference to other chapters will show its relation to heart beat, clotting of blood, clotting of milk, permeability of membranes, neuro-muscular excitability and bone formation. Pregnancy and lactation make specially heavy demands, and the dietary calcium should be specially considered in these conditions.

Iron

The chief function of iron is in connection with the haemoglobin and the cytochrome in the tissues. In women there is a periodic loss of iron with menstruation, but in man the loss of iron from the body is extremely small. It will be recalled that disintegration of the red cells is followed by excretion of the iron-free bile pigment, while the iron is used again for haemoglobin production. The daily amount recommended, 10 to 15 mg, certainly does not represent the amount lost from the body. It seems that most of the iron taken in the food is not absorbed, but a certain surplus is necessary in order that a small fraction should be available. Deficiency of iron is associated with anaemia.

THE VITAMINS

It is well known that animals cannot be maintained in good health on diets which will supply the necessary calories together with protein, fat and mineral requirements, if certain accessory food factors, the vitamins, are absent from the diet. There are, at present, a great many different substances which have been recognized as vitamins. The usual conception of a vitamin is an organic substance which is necessary for health, including growth in young animals, and which does not act by supplying energy. Most of the vitamins have a known composition and chemical formula and many of them can be synthesized. Several of the vitamins, especially of the B group, are known to take part in the oxidative processes of the body, either as coenzymes or carriers (aneurin, nicotinic acid, riboflavin).

The vitamins can be classified according to their solubility in fats or in water. The following shows the different members of each of these groups:

Fat soluble:—
Vitamin A
Vitamin D_2 (calciferol)
Vitamin D_3
Vitamin E (alpha-tocopherol)
Vitamin K

Water soluble:—
Vitamin B group
Thiamine (aneurin)
Riboflavin
Pantothenic acid
Nicotinic acid amide
Pyridoxine
B_{12} (cobalamin)
Biotin
Choline
Folic acid
Vitamin C (ascorbic acid)
Vitamin P (citrin)

The human dietary requirement of the more important vitamins is given in Table 31.4.

Vitamin A

Deficiency of vitamin A in the diet leads to cessation of growth, loss of weight and decreased resistance to infection. There is keratinization of the epithelium in the eye, respiratory tract and genito-urinary tract. In the human subject there is xerophthalmia and night-blindness. The vitamin is related to β-carotene, and represents half the molecule of this with addition of an alcoholic group. β-carotene can be regarded as a forerunner of the vitamin and can replace it in the diet, if large quantities are given. Neither β-carotene nor vitamin A can be synthesized in the animal body, but they are ingested with green plants and are found in the fatty tissues, especially the liver. There is a chemical relation between vitamin A and rhodopsin (visual purple) which probably explains the connection between vitamin A and night-blindness.

Sources: Butter, egg yolk, carrots, spinach, and particularly fish liver oils.

Thiamine (Aneurin)

This is the anti-neuritic part of the B complex, and its absence leads to polyneuritis in the pigeon and rat, and to beri-beri in man. Lesser degrees of deficiency cause fatigue, loss of appetite, dyspnoea on exertion, and neuritis. In the pigeon and rat, bradycardia (slowing of the heart) is characteristic. Experimentally and clinically, symptoms of deficiency occur on a diet composed mainly of polished rice, as the vitamin is present in the outer part of the grain. The pyrophosphoric acid ester of thiamine is co-carboxylase, which forms part of the enzyme system for metabolizing pyruvate, and in deficiency of the vitamin the pyruvate concentration of the blood is raised. Thiamine is also essential for the conversion of carbo-hydrate into fat.

Sources: Yeast, wheat germ, pulses, meat.

Riboflavin

Deficiency of riboflavin in the diet causes disturbances in the mouth and tongue, in the cornea and in the skin. In combination with a protein and phosphoric acid it forms flavo-proteins, enzymes concerned with tissue respiration.

Sources: Yeast, liver, meat, eggs.

Nicotinic acid (P.P. factor)

This is the pellagra-preventing factor of the B group. Pellagra is a disease characterized by diarrhoea and skin disturbances in the human subject. In dogs, deficiency of the vitamin causes black-tongue. Either nicotinic acid or its amide will prevent these disturbances. Chemically nicotinic acid amide forms part of the molecule of the phospho-pyridine nucleotides, known as Coenzymes I and II, or as DPN and TPN, sub-stances which are known to take part in the oxidative processes in the body.

Sources: Yeast, meat, fish, wheat flour, liver.

Pyridoxine

Deficiency of this substance has been found to produce a disturbance in young rats, which resembles pellagra, but which cannot be cured with nicotinic acid: it can be obtained from rice bran. Pyridoxine forms part of the enzyme systems necessary for protein metabolism.

Pantothenic Acid

When rats are fed on diets deficient in the B complex with added aneurin, nicotinic acid, riboflavin and pyridoxine they develop a greying of the skin, which can be prevented by addition of pantothenic acid to the diet. Deficiency of pantothenic acid also leads to a pellagra-like dermatitis in chickens. The function of pantothenic acid in human nutrition is not known, but it is thought to be essential. Pantothenic acid enters into the constitution of Coenzyme A which plays a major rôle in metabolism (Chapter 30).

Vitamin B_{12}

This is the anti-pernicious anaemia factor, present in liver, and is identi-cal with the "extrinsic factor". The molecule contains about 4 per cent of cobalt. Its relation to the other factors concerned in the maturation of the erythrocytes is not fully known.

Other Vitamins of the B Group

Other substances which have been found to be effective in replacing deficiencies in experimental diets are choline, folic acid, biotin, p-amino-benzoic acid and inositol. Choline is one of the constituents of the phospholipid, lecithin. If it is not present in the diet, changes occur in the liver which are chiefly characterized by excessive fat deposition. The addition of choline to the diet prevents this, and choline is thus said to exert a "lipotropic action". Little is known about the human requirements of the other substances.

Vitamin C (Ascorbic acid, Antiscorbutic Vitamin)

It has been known for several hundred years that scurvy could be prevented by including fresh fruits in the diet and it was found in 1932 that the anti-scorbutic substance in fresh fruits was ascorbic acid. In the animal body ascorbic acid is found in the adrenal cortex. On oxidation it readily forms dehydro-ascorbic acid, and can be easily reformed from this by reduction, but the biological significance of this is unknown. Vitamin C deficiency is associated with disturbance in the formation of the enamel in the teeth, and with the process of calcification of bone.

Sources: Fresh fruits and vegetables, especially the citrus fruits, oranges and lemons.

Vitamin D (Antirachitic Vitamin)

Absence of vitamin D in the diet gives rise to the characteristic appearance of rickets, a disease of children associated with softening of the bones and hence giving rise to abnormal shapes of the parts of the skeleton which have to bear the weight of the body. Rickets is associated with an abnormal metabolism of calcium and phosphorus, and it can be prevented by giving vitamin D. The antirachitic property is possessed by a number of substances, but of these the most important are called vitamin D_2 and vitamin D_3. Vitamin D_3 (cholecalciferol) is the naturally occurring vitamin, while vitamin D_2 (ergocalciferol) is produced from ultra-violet irradiation of ergosterol. Vitamin D_3 can also be produced by ultra-violet irradiation, the precursor in this case being 7-dehydrocholesterol. This substance is present in the skin and the beneficial effect of sunlight in preventing rickets is due to formation of the vitamin. The mode of action of these substances in preventing rickets is not known. Vitamin D is the vitamin which is most likely to be inadequate in the diet and hence the widespread habit of giving to children cod liver oil or other vitamin D source.

Sources: Butter, cream eggs, but especially fish liver oils.

Vitamin E (Alpha-tocopherol)

Deficiency of vitamin E in rats gives rise to failure of the reproductive organs. In male rats there is deterioration of the testis and in the female, death of the foetus. In other animals deficiency may be accompanied by muscular disturbances. Little is known definitely about the requirements of the human subject, and the value of treatment with vitamin E for prevention of abortion is still a matter of some dispute.

Sources: Cereals, especially oats and wheat, liver and eggs.

Vitamin K (Anti-haemorrhagic Vitamin)

Deficiency of vitamin K in the diet of chickens produces a haemorrhagic disturbance associated with a lowering of the amount of prothrombin in the blood (Chapter 44). In the human subject a vitamin K deficiency can be produced when there is an absence of bile in the intestine, e.g. in case of a biliary fistula. The vitamin does not have any effect on such haemorrhagic diseases as haemophilia or purpura and, as far as is known, is only related to formation of prothrombin.

Sources: It occurs more abundantly in plants than in animals. Cabbage, spinach, cauliflower are good sources, while milk is very poor.

ALCOHOL

Alcohol is capable of oxidation by the animal body, but it is usually taken not so much for the purpose of providing energy as for the effect it produces on the higher centres of the central nervous system. The relaxation of rigid self-control and discrimination which it produces in suitable doses is found by many people to increase the enjoyment of congenial company, and its widespread use lends interest to a consideration of its metabolism by the tissues of the body.

Alcohol differs from other energy-providing foods in that it can be absorbed from the stomach, although the rate of gastric absorption is much less than that from the intestine. After absorption most of it is metabolized, the remainder being excreted either in the urine or in the expired air. When taken in small doses so that the concentration in the blood does not rise above a certain level, most of the alcohol is oxidized without any accompanying pharmacological action.

The concentrations of alcohol in the blood, expired air and urine has considerable practical interest in relation to tests for drunkenness. In Britain it is now a legal offence to drive a vehicle while the proportion of alcohol in the blood is in excess of 80 mg/100 ml. An instrument called the *breathalyser* operates on the principle that the concentration of alcohol in expired air is proportional to the blood concentration, and when expired air containing alcohol comes into contact with potassium dichromate, the dichromate is reduced by the alcohol and changes colour. The concentration in the urine is also proportional to the amount in the blood, and urine tests are also used for determining the amount of alcohol in the blood.

The oxidation of 1 g of alcohol in the body yields 7 kilocalories of energy. Alcohol metabolism proceeds at a practically constant rate for any one individual, varying usually from 6 to 10 g of absolute alcohol per hour. The food value of alcohol is, however, limited in spite of the fact that it is quickly absorbed and requires no digestion, partly because there is no storage mechanism and partly because of the inconvenient effects of alcohol on the central nervous system.

If alcohol is taken in larger doses it acts on various parts of the body, chiefly on the central nervous system. The effect is mainly dependent on the concentration in the blood, although it is also influenced by the rate

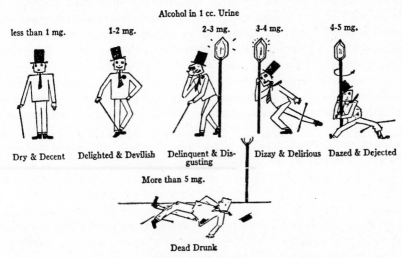

Alcohol in 1 cc. Urine

less than 1 mg.   1-2 mg.   2-3 mg.   3-4 mg.   4-5 mg.

Dry & Decent   Delighted & Devilish   Delinquent & Dis-   Dizzy & Delirious   Dazed & Dejected
                                             gusting

More than 5 mg.

Dead Drunk

FIG. 31.1. The relation of the degree of intoxication to the concentration of alcohol in the urine.

The concentration of alcohol in the urine is approximately the same as that in the blood and tissues, except during absorption from the alimentary canal, when the concentrations are changing rapidly. (From Emil Boger Emerson's "Alcohol and Man", by permission of The Macmillan Co.)

at which the concentration is attained. Hence the effects of a large dose of alcohol will be reduced if it is taken with food and particularly with fatty foods which delay the emptying time of the stomach. Thus cocktails before a meal are more potent than liqueurs containing a similar quantity of alcohol after the meal and the practice of starting a meal with hors d'oeuvres with a high content of fat and oils is conducive to the retention of a discriminating palate throughout the course of that meal. The relation between blood concentration and pharmacological action is of considerable medicolegal interest, as the symptoms of alcoholism can be roughly related to the concentration of alcohol in the blood at the particular time (Fig. 31.1).

Alcohol has a definite diuretic action. If 50 g ethyl alcohol are taken in

250 ml of water it is followed by an output of urine of 600 to 1000 ml in two to three hours. The mechanism of the diuresis may be depression of the hypothalamic centre with consequent decrease in the secretion of the anti-diuretic hormone of the pituitary gland (Chapters 32 and 38). Alcohol is neither concentrated nor diluted by the kidney and the concentration in the urine may therefore be used as a rough measure of the concentration in the blood plasma.

HUNGER AND APPETITE

The sensations of hunger and appetite are ill-defined feelings of "emptiness" in the one case and pleasant anticipation of food in the other. Although usually related, they are more or less distinct sensations. The hunger feeling is referred to the epigastrium and may be accompanied by contractions of the stomach. Attempts have been made to relate hunger to some measurable change in the blood, e.g. to the blood sugar concentration. That there is no simple relationship is shown by the observations that injection of insulin produces a fall in blood sugar which is accompanied by a sensation of hunger, while on the other hand hunger is a common symptom of diabetes where the blood sugar is raised. Appetite is still more difficult to relate to any physiological or biochemical basis. It is more susceptible than hunger to other influences such as emotion, habit or artificial stimulation by attractively prepared food. Under conditions of modern life other factors besides hunger and appetite take part in the selection of food (e.g. children training and example, and in adults advertising and propaganda). Fashions, fads and the cultivation of a discriminating palate also play a part in the choice of diet.

It is now recognized that the hypothalamus (see Chapter 32) plays an important part in the regulation of food intake. Experimental lesions in the hypothalamus in rats may produce a voracious appetite, and such animals rapidly increase in weight; other lesions may abolish appetite. Electrical stimulation of the hypothalamus (in unanaesthetized goats) has led to excessive feeding. The most probable basis for hypothalamic control of appetite is that the hypothalamus responds in some way to the total amount of fat in the body, with increase in fat content depressing food intake. How this mechanism functions is quite unknown.

How far the sense of taste is a reliable nutritional guide is a problem of considerable interest. A good deal of experimental work in this field has been done on animals suffering from deprivation of some body constituent, and given the opportunity to select a diet from a large choice of substances with a view to testing their ability to make good the deficiency. Removal of the adrenal gland causes a fatal loss of sodium from the body, and it was found that adrenalectomized rats chose sodium salts out of a number of substances available and by this process outlived a control group of adrenalectomized rats to which sodium was not given. Sodium-deficient sheep, also, choose to drink salt solutions rather than water. In another set of experiments, rats from which the parathyroid glands had been removed increased their intake of calcium lactate, and thereby prevented the fall in blood calcium which, accompanied by tetany, usually supervenes in parathyroidectomized animals.

One of the important principles of animal physiology is the maintenance of the "internal environment" of the body cells and many reflex processes contribute to this end. It has been suggested that the ability to select diets suitable to physiological need is an example of the behaviour regulators acting towards the common goal of stabilizing the composition of the body fluids, so essential for the continued activity of the cells (physiological "homeostasis").

WATER

Water is an essential constituent of a man's diet; he can live longer without food than without water. The amount that he must take each day, as such, by drinking, depends on the amount which is lost from the body and on the amount which is gained in other less obvious ways.

A continuous loss of water is unavoidable, for the following reasons.

(1) The non-volatile end-products of metabolism—chiefly those of nitrogenous metabolism—and any excess of salts taken in with the food, are eliminated in the urine dissolved in water. Normally, a man loses about 2 litres of water a day in the urine: but this may be reduced to less than 1 litre a day when the loss of water has been greater than the intake, as in hot, dry environments; or increased many-fold if excess water has been taken.

(2) About 0·1 l/day is lost in the faeces. This small quantity is the residue of the much larger quantity of water which enters the alimentary canal—2·1 l with the food and drink (see below) and possibly up to 9 l with the digestive juices—most of it being absorbed; it may vary considerably according to the condition of the large intestine.

(3) About 0·4 l/day is lost by evaporation in the lungs, the expired air being saturated with water vapour at 37°C, while the inspired air is only partially saturated at a much lower temperature; this loss will be greater when the air is very dry, and will be many times as great when the ventilation of the lungs is increased, as for example during muscular activity.

(4) About 0·9 l/day is lost by evaporation from the skin by "insensible perspiration", the skin usually being warmer than the air and not completely "water-tight". Some loss of water is necessary in order to get rid of the heat produced by the combustion of the food. Normally, in temperate climates about one-quarter to one-third of the total heat produced is lost by evaporation, but in hot surroundings nearly all of it is lost in this way, and there is manifest sweating (Chapter 39). During muscular exercise,

when the metabolic rate is greatly increased, some 10 or 15 litres of water per day may be lost from the skin.

A gain of water, on the other hand, is also unavoidable, even if none is drunk. (1) The molecules of all food substances contain hydrogen atoms, and these on oxidation give rise to water molecules: an ordinary diet, yielding, say, 3,000 kilocalories a day, produces about 0·36 l of water in this way.

(2) Water is concealed in apparently "dry" food substances: the ordinary diet provides in this way some 1 to 2 l of water a day. (This includes the water added to the food when preparing it for the table.)

These losses and gains of water are summarized in Table 31.6.

Some calculations of the gain and loss of water in the metabolism of various food substances, in ordinary conditions in temperate climates are given in Table 31.5.

TABLE 31.5

Quantity of water lost or gained when 100 kilocalories are released in the complete metabolism of certain food substances

Food Substance	Gain of Water (g)		Minimum Loss of Water (g)		
	Pre-formed	By oxidation	In dissipating heat (1/4 of total)	In excreting end-products	Net Loss (g)
Protein . . .	0	10·5	43	212	245
Starch . . .	0	13·5	43	0	30
Fat	0	11·5	43	0	32
Meat (lean) (average) .	52	11	43	150	130
Fish (lean) (e.g. cod) .	100	10·5	43	230	143
Fish (fatty) (e.g. herring)	33	11	43	85	84
Eggs (whole) . .	48	12	43	80	63
Bread (white) . .	18	13	43	40	52
Milk (cow's) . .	130	12	43	70	— 29
Bananas . . .	67	14	43	37	— 1
Apples (fresh) . .	225	13·5	43	65	— 130

In constructing this Table, it has been assumed, to begin with, that the quantity of each foodstuff eaten is such as to provide 100 kilocalories of energy in its metabolism. We then know, from its average composition, how much water is "concealed" within it and how much water is formed when it is oxidized. It is then assumed that one-quarter of the total quantity of heat produced—i.e. 25 kcal—is lost by evaporating water, so that, knowing its latent heat, we know the amount of water evaporated. Lastly, in order to estimate the minimum quantity of water necessarily lost in excreting the end-products of metabolism and the mineral constituents of the food, the following assumptions are made: (*a*) the urine contains 4 per cent of urea, provided that the salt concentration is less than 0·5 per cent; (*b*) the urine may contain up to 2 per cent of salts; (*c*) as the salt concentration rises, the urea concentration falls progressively and is only 2 per cent when the salt concentration is also 2 per cent. These assumptions are based on experimental observations, but are somewhat arbitrary, and the values calculated can be only approximate.

The figures emphasize the need for fluid water in the diet, as it is seen that of the substances listed only fresh apples and, in the conditions assumed, cow's milk, provide any extra water over and above that which must be lost from the body as a result of taking the food. In drier and warmer climates (indoors as well as outdoors) than those of the British Isles, such as those of the U.S.A., a larger quantity of water is lost by evaporation, up to 60 g for each 100 kilocalories of heat produced; cow's milk may then fail to provide any appreciable excess of water. In human milk, however, there is a smaller concentration of protein and a greater concentration of carbohydrates. Except perhaps in tropical conditions, human milk will always provide an excess of water, even to an infant whose kidneys cannot produce so concentrated a urine as can those of an adult.

Water Balance

As first stressed by Claude Bernard in 1879, the concentration of the fluid surrounding the living cells of all vertebrates and most invertebrates (the "internal environment") remains constant, within quite narrow limits.

TABLE 31.6

Water balance; representative values for 24 hr in a temperate climate

Loss (litre)			Gain (litre)		
Urine .	.	. 1·5	Food—		
Faeces .	.	. 0·1	preformed	.	1·0
Lungs .	.	. 0·4	oxidative	.	1·4
Skin	.	. 0·9	Drink	.	. 1·5
Total	.	. 2·9	Total .	.	2·9

Water can move freely into and out of the cells, so that the concentration of the fluid inside them is also constant. The concentration of the body fluids is determined, of course, by the amount of dissolved substances (chiefly salts) present in them, as well as by the amount of water. The two fluids, inside and outside the cells, contain different kinds of solute, although salt balance and water balance are interrelated, it is important that the amount of water in the body should not fluctuate very greatly in spite of the unavoidable losses and gains already discussed. In fact, as brought out in Table 31.6, the gains are adjusted so as to equal the losses.

A man weighing 70 kg contains about 14 l of water outside the cells (in the internal environment), so that about one-fifth of this is ordinarily lost and replaced each day. In exceptional conditions, the daily "turnover" may amount to almost the whole of this extracellular volume. An infant, of

7 kg weight, will have an extracellular fluid volume of about 1·6 l, but the daily intake and loss of fluid will be about 0·7 l even in normal circumstances. One-half of the extra-cellular fluid is thus "turned over" each day. It is clear that the intake must be accurately controlled if water balance is to be preserved, and that in the infant the margin of reserve is much smaller than in the adult; any variation in the water intake and water loss will cause proportionately greater disturbances in the volume of its body fluids. The relative values of the volume of the extracellular fluid and of the volumes of water gained and lost per day are summarized in Fig. 31.2.

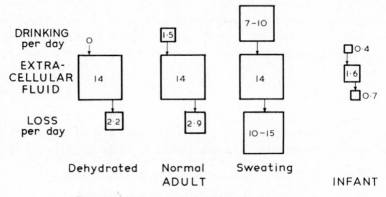

FIG. 31.2. Diagram illustrating water balance.

The volume of water taken in by drinking is the difference between the total volume lost and the volume derived from the food. The dehydrated adult would not be in water balance, the net loss of water being about 0·8 l/day, even though the urine is as concentrated as possible.

Water balance must ordinarily be maintained by drinking an appropriate amount of water and the need to do this is indicated by the sensation of thirst. There is no special sensation for indicating that too much water has been drunk, but any excess "spills over" rapidly through the kidneys. This "water diuresis" is brought about by an entirely involuntary reflex initiated by "osmoreceptors" sensitive to the concentration of the body fluids, and controlling the release of the "antidiuretic hormone" by the neurohypophysis.

Disturbances of the Water Balance

Loss of water from the body may be affected by several kinds of disorder, notably in the activities of certain ductless glands, as discussed more fully in Chapter 32. Deficiency in the secretion of the neurohypophysis (post-pituitary gland) leads to an excessive excretion of dilute urine (*diabetes insipidus*) and thus to dehydration of the body. Deficiency in the secretion of the adrenal cortex leads to an excessive excretion of sodium chloride and secondarily to a loss of water. Depletion of the body fluids may also result from: (1) loss of fluid from the alimentary tract by persistent vomiting or diarrhoea; and (2) metabolic disturbances such as *diabetes mellitus* (Chapter 30), when there is an unavoidable loss of water and salts accompanying the glucose and ketone bodies excreted by the kidneys. Disorder of the kidneys or of the heart, on the other hand, may so reduce the rate of elimination of water and salts that the volume of the body fluids becomes excessive, as described in Chapter 2.

In abnormal external conditions, the water balance may become disturbed even in normal men. Sustained and profuse sweating, for example, involves large losses of both water and salts both of which must be replaced. If only water is taken, the body fluids become diluted, leading to water diuresis and loss of much of the water. Correspondingly, many people find that thirst is quenched most effectively after copious sweating if they take enough salt along with the water. If a normal man drinks too much water, and for some reason the excess is not adequately eliminated, "water intoxication" may follow, as in "miners' cramp". On the other hand, if he drinks only sea water, in which salts are more concentrated than they are in the most concentrated urine that can be formed, the body fluids inevitably become excessively concentrated; as they may do in people surviving from shipwreck after the fresh water is exhausted.

Most of the experimental investigations on the control of water and salt balance must be performed on conscious animals or human subjects, because most general anaesthetics put the controlling systems out of action. The experimental procedures that can be used are correspondingly limited, and interpretation of the results made more difficult.

Thirst

It is generally agreed that water intake is largely governed by thirst, indeed it is difficult to define or measure thirst except in terms of the volume of water required to assuage it. Nevertheless, there is no good agreement about the physiological basis of the sensation of thirst except to the extent that several factors must be involved.

Dehydration of the body tissues becomes manifest most conspicuously as dryness of the mouth and throat, and it has been thought that sensations from this region give rise to a drinking reflex. There is now substantial doubt about this simple explanation of thirst partly because dehydrated animals with oesophageal fistulae in whom no water reaches the stomach, drink more than they need to rehydrate the body. It seems that some sensation of fullness in the stomach is concerned in inhibiting drinking. Indeed, dilatation of a balloon in the stomach will put a stop to the drinking of such experimental animals. Moreover, a fairly high proportion of normal people claim to feel thirsty when the mouths are not dry, and quite a few fail to feel thirsty when their mouths are dried by drugs such as hyoscine, employed to prevent travel sickness but which unfortunately also inhibit salivary secretion.

An altogether different approach to the problem of thirst has been the search for a *drinking centre* in the brain, activated by dehydration of its cells which therefore act as osmoreceptors. (These appear to be different from those which are concerned in the onset of water diuresis.) Injection into a confined region of the hypothalamus of a goat of a few microlitres of a solution of sodium chloride more concentrated than the body fluids, induces excessive drinking; while similar injection of a solution of the same concentration as the body fluids, or less concentrated, does not. Moreover, electrical stimulation of the appropriate region induces drinking which begins 20 to 30 sec after the stimulus starts and lasts until a few seconds after it stops. Over-hydration up to 40 per cent has been produced in goats in this way. Furthermore, destruction of the appropriate region by electrocoagulation has abolished drinking in dehydrated dogs and rats. Clearly, therefore, a region in the hypothalamus is concerned with drinking behaviour and may incorporate the essential osmoreceptors which signal dehydration.

If such a centre were accepted as the primary control of drinking the usual association of drinking with sensation of dryness in the mouth and throat could well be interpreted as a conditioned reflex, as could the inhibition of drinking by the sensation of fullness in the stomach. On the other hand, these and other receptors which respond to tissue dehydration and the volume of water drunk may give rise to primary reflexes starting and stopping drinking independently of the central receptors associated with the "centre" in the brain.

Profound haemorrhage makes most people thirsty and this has been attributed to reduction of the volume of fluid in the body, exciting some unidentified volume receptors. After haemorrhage, or reduction of the fluid volume by other means, rats have been found to drink more: but no consistent change in drinking pattern has followed substantial haemor-rhage in horses or dogs, nor in human donors who have yielded from 5 per cent to 10 per cent of their blood volume to the blood banks. Pre-sumably, therefore, the traditional belief that thirst follows profound haemorrhage from wounds or disease such as gastric ulcer, is to be explained largely in terms of some other shock-like effect of the injury, and not only as a consequence of the reduction in blood volume.

Section 10

ENDOCRINOLOGY AND REPRODUCTION

CHAPTER 32

THE ENDOCRINE GLANDS

ENDOCRINE glands secrete substances into the blood stream. These substances travel to, and control the activities of, other tissues which are usually remote from the secreting gland and sometimes widely distributed in the body. Such chemical messengers are called *internal secretions* to distinguish them from secretions which, like bile or the digestive juice from the pancreas, are transmitted through ducts. More commonly they are called *hormones* (from a Greek word meaning "I arouse to activity"). the name suggested by W. M. Bayliss and E. H. Starling after their studies in 1902 on how secretin excites pancreatic secretion. The endocrine glands discussed in this chapter and in that on Reproduction are often called the endocrine organs and their study is the rapidly developing branch of physiology known as endocrinology.

Hormones may be extracted from most of the endocrine glands by crushing or boiling them in water. The study of the action of tissue extracts, however, is in the first place a branch of pharmacology, for it must not be supposed that the action observed, however specific or potent, necessarily represents the normal function of the gland. One might as well imagine that the effect of digitalis on the vertebrate heart was a normal function of the glucoside in the foxglove from which it had been extracted. The assertion that a particular action is a normal function of an endocrine gland depends on the correspondence between the consequences of excision of the organ, and replacement by injection of extracts, or of implantation of gland tissue.

To avoid confusion, it is essential to distinguish between the specific and the non-specific actions of tissue extracts. All crude tissue extracts contain histamine and produce capillary dilatation and a fall of blood

549

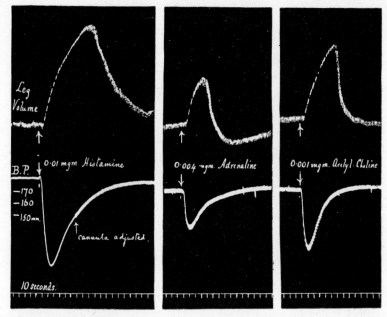

FIG. 32.1. The action of histamine, adrenaline (in minute concentration) and acetylcholine on the arterial pressure and the volume of the denervated limb of a cat.

A larger dose of adrenaline (say, 0·05 mg) would have given the more characteristic vasoconstrictor effect, *i.e.* rise in arterial pressure and diminution in limb volume. (Dale and Richards.)

pressure when injected intravenously (Fig. 32.1); in exceptional circumstances, this depressor effect may be masked by the action of a sufficiently potent pressor substance. A specific depressor effect can, therefore, only be distinguished from the non-specific action of histamine, if the effective substance in a tissue extract can be isolated and purified. The actions of acetylcholine and of very small doses of adrenaline, shown in Fig. 32.1, are instances of this kind. A pressor action, on the contrary, is readily recognized as a specific effect of the extract which induces it, as exemplified by extracts of the posterior lobe of the pituitary gland (Fig. 32.12), and of the adrenal medulla in all but minute doses (Fig. 6.6, p. 57).

CRITERIA OF AN ENDOCRINE GLAND

Before an organ can be classified as an endocrine gland it must be shown to fulfil most of the following criteria.

(1) *Histological Structure.* On microscopic examination the endocrine glands reveal the presence of glandular cells, no ducts, but a copious blood supply. The cells frequently possess granules (anterior pituitary cells) or

lipoid-filled vacuoles (adrenal cortex, corpora lutea, interstitial cells of the ovaries or testes). The size and cytological appearances of the cells may be related to the state of activity of the gland.

(2) *Hypofunction.* Removal of the gland in an experimental animal or man, or disease of the gland in man, produces a state of "hormonal deficiency".

(3) *Replacement Therapy.* The state of hormonal deficiency may be corrected by administration of extracts of the gland.

(4) *Transplantation.* Endocrine glands usually function normally if transplanted to a distant site in the body. Successful transplantation demonstrates that any factors maintaining and regulating the activity of the gland do so *via* the blood stream, and that the gland exerts its action by secretion into the blood stream. The first demonstration of endocrine activity was made by Berthold in 1849 when he showed that a transplanted testis in the cock could maintain the comb of the bird.

(5) *Hyperfunction.* Administration of large amounts of extracts of a gland or some types of tumour of the gland result in a condition of "hormonal excess".

(6) *Assay of Venous Blood from the Gland.* Hormone activity has not yet been detected in the venous blood from all the endocrine glands (e.g. anterior pituitary gland); when it can be detected, however, it shows clearly that endocrine activity is occurring in the particular structure, especially if it can be shown that the amount of hormone in the blood varies in a regular manner in varied physiological states.

General Control of the Endocrine System

The endocrine organs co-operate with the nervous system in co-ordinating the activities of the various parts of the body; and accordingly they are influenced by changes in the external and internal environments and react appropriately. For example, the secretion of insulin by the pancreas depends on the concentration of sugar in the blood; seasonal changes of light, temperature and food supply may profoundly modify the activity of the ovary or testis (Chapter 32); changes in environmental temperature affect the activity of the thyroid gland (Chapter 29); stressful or noxious procedures excite the activity of the adrenal cortex and medulla, but inhibit the thyroid and gonads; and changes in the osmotic pressure of the blood, tactile stimuli to the mammary glands, and coitus activate the posterior pituitary gland.

The endocrine system is unsuited to effect changes with the speed of nervous reflexes. Some endocrine glands, particularly those which are controlled by a secretomotor nerve supply (e.g. adrenal medulla, posterior pituitary gland), secrete hormones which exert their actions within seconds after liberation into the blood stream, and are then quickly destroyed in the blood or tissues, or rapidly excreted. Other glands are themselves controlled by hormones (e.g. thyroid, gonads). These react more slowly to any appropriate stimulus and secrete hormones which are more stable in the blood stream and exert their effects slowly and over a more prolonged period. The secretomotor nerve supply to the posterior pituitary gland, and that to the adrenal medulla are derived ultimately from the hypothalamus. This part of the brain also controls the anterior pituitary gland, and since the trophic hormones from this gland maintain and regulate the activity of the thyroid, adrenal cortex, ovary and testis, it is clear that this region of the brain determines, either directly or indirectly, the activity of the major part of the endocrine system. The hypothalamus may be affected both by afferent nervous stimuli and by changes in the composition of the blood. The effects of these factors are probably integrated in the hypothalamus, which thereby co-ordinates and regulates the activity of both the autonomic nervous system (Chapters 22 and 23) and the endocrine glands. It may be said that this part of the central nervous system is intimately concerned with the maintenance of a constant internal environment.

Many hormonal actions have been considered in previous chapters under their appropriate systems: the secretions of the gastro-intestinal mucosa (gastrin and secretin, for example) in Chapter 27; of the pancreas (insulin) in Chapter 28; of the gonads (androgens and oestrogens, for example) and of the pituitary body (gonadotrophins) in Chapter 32. This chapter will deal with some of these in rather more detail, and with some hormonal actions which have not yet been considered. Various organs have been numbered among the endocrine glands in the hope that a suitable function would be found for them; some, like the carotid body, are now known to have quite a different kind of function, while others, like the pineal body, can as yet have no function confidently assigned to them.

THE ADRENAL GLANDS

The paired adrenal glands are situated immediately above the upper poles of the kidneys. Each consists of two histologically distinguishable parts: the cortex, which in fresh specimens is yellow and stains darkly with silver nitrate or fat soluble dyes, and the medulla which represents a small mass of the gland and stains brown with chromates. It is for this reason that it is referred to as the "chromaffine" or "chromaphile" tissue. Embryologically the cortex arises from the mesodermal tissue of the genital ridge of the coelomic epithelium, whilst the medulla is ectodermal in origin and is derived from cells of the neural crest. Why these two entirely different tissues come to be so intimately associated during development of the embryo is unknown.

As the two portions of the gland are distinct in structure and function it will be convenient to discuss them separately.

Structure of the Adrenal Medulla

Unlike the adrenal cortex, the cells of the medulla in man are not arranged in an orderly manner, nor are they of any specific shape. Many small sinusoids provide a profuse blood supply to this region of the adrenals, and indeed the venous drainage of the cortex is through the medullary sinusoids. Early histochemical studies suggested the presence of granules in chromaffine cells, and with the electron microscope each cell can be seen to contain many dense granules (circa 250 mμ in diameter) sometimes in contact with the cell membrane. These granules can be depleted of their electron dense material by repeated stimulation of the splanchnic nerve.

The Hormones of the Medulla

Two hormones have been isolated from the adrenal medulla, adrenaline and noradrenaline. Both are ultimately derived from the dietary amino-acids tyrosine and phenylalanine. The biosynthetic pathways of the two hormones are set out below, and it can be seen that noradrenaline is converted to adrenaline by a process of N-methylation. The naturally occurring form of both adrenaline and noradrenaline is the laevo-rotatory isomer which has, in both instances, much greater biological activity than the dextrorotatory form. The proportion of adrenaline to noradrenaline that is present in the adrenal medulla varies with the species. Rabbit adrenals contain little noradrenaline, human and cattle about 20 per cent, and those of the cat about 50 per cent of the total content of both hormones. The cellular localization of these hormones was the subject of controversy for a while but it now seems that adrenaline and noradrenaline are stored in separate cells in adult adrenals, and that the hormones are contained in the electron dense granules (chromaffine granules) described above. The chromaffine granules also contain ATP in large quantities and the binding of the hormones in these granules may depend upon its presence as well as on the presence of water-soluble proteins. Recently it has been found that stimulation of the gland results in the secretion not only of the hormones but also of the ATP and soluble proteins from the chromaffine granules.

Rapid destruction of adrenaline and noradrenaline occurs in solution at pH 7 when exposed to air. In body fluids this rapid destruction is, to some extent, prevented because the hormones may be protected by an unknown mechanism. It has recently been found that the nerve terminals of adrenergic neurones may actively accumulate the catechol amines.

The Function of the Adrenal Medulla

Complete removal of the adrenal medulla whilst leaving behind functional cortical tissue can be achieved with no untoward symptoms occurring. This may seem surprising, but it must be remembered that the medulla is derived from cells of the neural crest which also give rise to the sympathetic nervous system. The elements of the sympathetic system contain predominantly noradrenaline which is synthesized and stored in a similar manner to the noradrenaline of the adrenal medulla. There are also isolated chromaffine cell groups distributed in various parts of the body.

In general it may be said that adrenaline and noradrenaline act on the organs of the body innervated by the sympathetic nervous system and that noradrenaline has the same action upon them as does stimulation of the sympathetic nerves (with the exception of the sweat glands). The functions of the sympathetic nervous system have been discussed further in Chapter 22.

The sympathetic actions of adrenaline and noradrenaline on the cardio-vascular system were discussed in Chapter 6. Both produce a rise in arterial pressure, which is greater after section of the vagi. Adrenaline has an augmentor and accelerator action on the heart, a constrictor action on the arterioles of the skin and kidneys and a dilator action on those of the skeletal muscles (in man) and the coronary system of the heart. The vaso-dilator effect is often more easily evoked than the vasoconstrictor effect by a very minute concentration of adrenaline, so that in suitable animals an overall vasodilatation may be produced by injection of minimal doses of adrenaline with a consequent fall in blood pressure (see Fig. 32.1). Nor-adrenaline has little or no vasodilator action and has little direct action on the heart, but is more potent than adrenaline in producing vasoconstriction. The musculature of the alimentary canal and of its outgrowths, such as the bronchi, is relaxed by both adrenaline and noradrenaline, though the sphincters may contract; the pupil is dilated. Administration of adrenaline produces a breakdown of glycogen to give glucose in the liver, with conse-quent hyperglycaemia and possibly glycosuria (Chapter 30), and may produce an increase in the rate of discharge of the adrenocorticotrophic hormone from the anterior pituitary gland. Noradrenaline is less potent than adrenaline in both these respects. The action of adrenaline persists after section of the sympathetic nerves, even if time has been allowed for complete degeneration of their peripheral ramifications; the heart and the pupil are, in fact, more sensitive to adrenaline when this has been done; therefore, it does not act on the nerve endings (Chapter 23). The action of adrenaline may be prevented by drugs, such as ergotoxine and apo-codeine, which also interrupt the influence of the sympathetic system, but which do not abolish the contractile response of the muscle to direct electrical stimulation, or to the application of certain other drugs, such as barium chloride. These facts are usually summarized by the statement that adrenaline acts on an excitatory mechanism in the tissue, whereas certain abnormal stimuli (e.g. an electric shock and barium chloride) can act more directly on the contractile mechanism.

Small quantities of adrenaline in tissue extracts or body fluids can be estimated by matching their effects with those of a known concentration of the pure substance on isolated muscles suspended in Ringer's solution. The contraction of the rabbit's uterus, or relaxation of its intestine, are convenient indicators for this purpose and are sensitive to concentrations varying from 1 in 10^{10} to 1 in 10^6, the latter producing a nearly maximal effect (Fig. 32.2). Even more sensitive tests are available which will detect a few micrograms. Such a quantity of adrenaline antagonizes, for example, a contraction of the rat's isolated uterus due to the action of acetylcholine; a similar dose of noradrenaline raises the arterial pressure of an anaesthetized rat which has previously been treated with hexamethonium. These

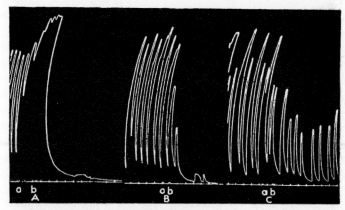

FIG. 32.2. Estimation of the adrenaline content of blood. Adrenaline inhibits the rhythmic contractions of the intestinal muscles of a cat.

The muscle had been undergoing spontaneous contractions in Ringer's Solution (upstroke of the lever indicates contraction). At *a*, in each case, this solution was removed and at *b* was replaced by cat's blood containing: A, 1:1,000,000 adrenaline, B, 1:2,000,000 adrenaline, and C, 1:3,000,000 adrenaline. After a preliminary contraction, due to the action of the blood, inhibition of the spontaneous activity was produced, which was complete in the first two cases, and well marked in the last. (Cannon.)

responses serve to emphasize the extreme physiological potency of these substances. Recently spectrophotofluorometric methods have been developed which allow adrenaline and noradrenaline to be estimated separately in amounts as low as 10 nanograms.

Control of the Adrenal Medulla

That control of the release of medullary hormones is mediated via the nervous system is well established; however, the factors controlling synthesis of adrenaline and noradrenaline are less well understood. It has been stated, in the past, that the adrenal medulla is not under the control of the pituitary gland, but recent evidence suggests that the adrenocorticotrophic hormone (ACTH) of the anterior pituitary may indirectly influence the production of adrenaline. In hypophysectomized animals the activity of the enzyme responsible for the formation of adrenaline from noradrenaline is markedly reduced. Enzyme activity is restored after administration of ACTH and also after treatment with dexamethasone, which has similar actions to the adrenal cortical hormones. It has already been noted that the venous drainage of the adrenal cortex is through the vessels of the medulla, and the pituitary may exercise control over adrenaline synthesis by regulating the availability of the glucocorticoid hormones.

As far as release of the medullary hormones is concerned, stimulation of the splanchnic nerve is followed by changes in the organism which are due in part to the direct stimulation of the sympathetic system and in part to the discharge of adrenaline which reinforces and prolongs the immediate effects of nervous stimulation. It has been estimated that the normal concentration of adrenaline in the blood leaving the adrenal glands is equivalent to a few hundredths of a microgram per minute per kilogram body weight under ordinary resting conditions. This is reduced to a negligible quantity after section of the splanchnic nerves and may be increased forty-fold by electrical stimulation of these nerves. Electrical stimulation of various parts of the hypothalamus may cause the release of a medullary secretion which is either preponderantly adrenaline or noradrenaline. This makes it likely that in normal circumstances these substances are liberated independently. Indeed, it has been suggested that emotional excitement liberates largely noradrenaline in *aggressive* forms, and adrenaline in *passive* forms.

Reflex stimulation of the sympathetic system is produced under a variety of conditions, such as (1) physical exercise, (2) emotional states of fear and rage, (3) pain produced by stimulation of a sensory nerve, (4) asphyxia, (5) exposure to cold and (6) general anaesthesia. The effects on the organs of the body are similar to those described above as resulting from injection of adrenaline or noradrenaline, and they may be summarized as a mobilization of those resources of the body concerned in the response to an emergency and an inhibition of those functions which are not of immediate importance under such conditions. This is the foundation of the *emergency theory* of the function of the adrenal medulla. It asserts that many of the physical changes which accompany intense emotion are due to the activity of the sympathetic and adrenal systems. Such activity results in a rapid pulse and rise in blood pressure, hair "standing on end", dilatation of the pupil and inhibition of the digestive processes, which are among the well-known signs of emotional excitement. The output of the heart is increased and the flow of blood directed primarily to the skeletal muscles, at the expense of that to the skin and abdominal organs. The crucial test of the emergency theory depends upon direct observation of the rate of discharge of adrenaline in the adrenal veins of an animal suitably stimulated. Exposing a cat to a barking dog, for example, increases the secretion of adrenaline, as shown in Fig. 32.3. The emergency theory seems the more likely because it fits in happily with the conception of an organism well adapted to changes in its environment.

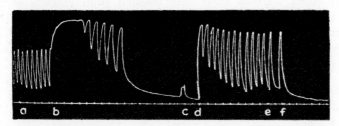

FIG. 32.3. The secretion of adrenaline during excitement. Record of rhythmically contracting intestinal muscle.

The muscle was intially beating in Ringer's solution. At *a*, this solution was removed, and at *b*, was replaced by blood taken from the inferior vena cava of a cat which had been excited by being "barked at by a dog for 15 minutes." After a preliminary contraction complete inhibition was produced. At *c*, this blood was removed, and at *d*, was replaced by blood obtained in a similar manner from a quiet cat; the muscle immediately began to contract rhythmically. This blood was removed at *e*, and "excited" blood again added at *f*: the contractions ceased. Compare this with Fig. 32.2, which shows the effect of blood containing known amounts of adrenaline on an intestinal muscle under similar conditions. (Cannon.)

Clinical Aspects

Because the adrenal medulla is not essential for the normal working of the body there is no clinical picture associated with medullary insufficiency. Tumours of chromaffine tissue do arise (phaeochromocytomata) and result in a rare but characteristic clinical picture. Such tumours, associated with attacks of high blood pressure and tachycardia, have been shown to contain noradrenaline as well as adrenaline.

Structure of the Adrenal Cortex

The embryological derivation of this part of the gland from the genital ridge has already been mentioned. With this knowledge it is not difficult to visualize that certain metabolic properties may be shared by the gonads and adrenal cortex. Both tissues are concerned with the production of steroid hormones. The cortex can be divided into three distinct zones in the adult. There is an outermost zona glomerulosa followed by a zona fasciculata and an internal zona reticularis surrounding the medullary tissue. A fourth zone is distinguishable in the young of certain mammals enclosing the medulla; this is the so-called X- or foetal zone. In man the foetal zone undergoes involution in the first year of ante-natal life but in mice, for example, this zone degenerates at puberty in the male and during the first pregnancy in the female. Its function remains enigmatic.

The Hormones of the Adrenal Cortex

Nearly thirty steroids have been isolated from extracts of adrenal cortical tissue and of these, some seven have been found to be active in maintaining the life of an animal lacking adrenal cortical tissue.

The physiologically active adrenal steroids may be divided into three groups. (See Fig. 32.4).

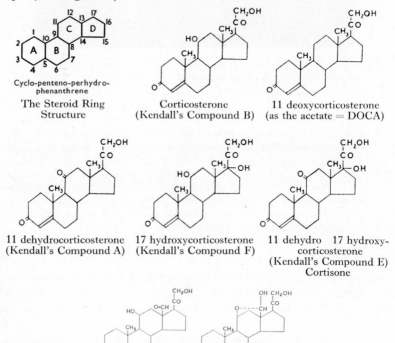

Aldosterone (exists in two forms).

Fig. 32.4. Structural formulae of some compounds related to the adrenal cortical hormones.

(1) Steroids with an oxygen or hydroxyl group at the C-11 position. These compounds correct the abnormalities of carbohydrate metabolism, of the performance of muscular work, of the thymus and lymphoid tissue and of the blood cells of adrenalectomized animals. They may be referred to as the gluco-corticoids.

(2) Steroids lacking an oxygen or hydroxyl group at the C-11 position, such as deoxycorticosterone. These compounds are particularly active in

maintaining the life and growth of adrenalectomized animals and in correcting the disturbances of water and electrolyte metabolism, and are therefore referred to as the mineralo-corticoids.

(3) Steroids related to the sex hormones, including progesterone.

Studies of the steroids present in the blood of the adrenal vein have demonstrated the presence of compound B (mainly) in the rabbit, and compound F (mainly) in the monkey and man. Other forms examined were found to have varying ratios of compound B to compound F present. However, the hormone pattern present in adrenal vein blood was found to remain constant in any one species under varying degrees of activity of the adrenal cortex. Deoxycorticosterone has not been found present in significant amounts in either adrenal cortical extracts or in adrenal vein blood. A steroid which is relatively unstable but highly active in affecting the electrolytic balance of the body has, however, been detected in adrenal vein blood; it has been crystallized, and its chemical structure is known. It has been given the name "*aldosterone*" since it possesses an aldehyde group at C-18. Studies of the above type have also shown that the rate of secretion of adrenal cortical hormone is normally very high if compared with the amount of hormone stored in the gland at any one time. The adrenal cortex has, therefore, a high rate of turnover but a low capacity for storage.

The hormones mentioned above are formed in the different parts of the adrenal cortex, aldosterone being formed in the glomerulosa, and the glucocorticoids largely in the fasciculata. Cytological differences are apparent between the cells of these two zones; the enzymatic complement also differs.

Functions of the Adrenal Cortex

Removal of both adrenal glands is fatal within a period of one or two weeks. That this is due to a loss of the adrenal cortex has already been made evident, for removal of medullary tissue alone is not followed by any severe abnormality. Adrenalectomy and replacement therapy of adrenocortical hormones provide the best ways in which to study the function of the adrenal cortex. The completely adrenalectomized animal, however, after recovery from the shock of the operation, may appear normal for a few days. Then loss of appetite, muscular weakness, reduced temperature and blood pressure, diarrhoea, vomiting and anuria supervene. Loss of weight occurs and death follows usually within a few days of the first sign of illness.

In both experimental animals and man, loss of adrenal cortical tissue results in an increased excretion of sodium, and thus of water, by the kidney and a diminished excretion of potassium. As a result of this change in urinary excretion, concentration of the blood occurs which is probably responsible for the low blood pressure and renal failure and therefore for the raised concentrations of urea, phosphate and creatinine in the blood.

It is found that administration of large quantities of sodium chloride causes a dramatic improvement in the condition of adrenal deficiency in men and animals. The concentrations of sodium and potassium in the blood are restored to normal with corresponding improvement in the blood volume, blood pressure and renal function. Such treatment may prolong life indefinitely. Certain abnormalities due to adrenal cortical deficiency are, however, not relieved by sodium chloride administration. These are: (1) disturbances in carbohydrate metabolism resulting in a tendency to hypoglycaemia; (2) muscular weakness as demonstrated experimentally by the rapid onset of fatigue to repeated electrical stimulation of the muscle; (3) disturbances in lymphoid tissue; and (4) a very low resistance to conditions of stress.

Administration of adrenal cortical steroids to adrenalectomized animals will maintain the life and growth of such animals. The carbohydrate metabolism is restored to normal by depression of the glucose utilization by the tissues, an increased formation of glucose from protein and an increased glycogen storage. The electrolyte and water balance of the body is also restored to normal since the sodium and water excretion is reduced and the potassium excretion increased. The rapid onset of fatigue in the muscles is abolished. A striking effect of the glucocorticoids is the atrophy of the thymus and lymphoid tissue and the lymphopenia and eosinopenia which they produce. As mentioned above, the adrenalectomized animal is extremely sensitive to stress. Exposure of the normal animal to relatively mild stress stimuli (the prick of a hypodermic needle or emotional excitement), as well as to more severe stresses (extremes of environmental temperature, radiations, starvation, hypoxia, hypoglycaemia, infections, surgical trauma, muscular exercise, or administration of drugs, toxins or anaesthetics and so on), will result in greatly increased activity of the adrenal cortex. The adrenalectomized animal, however, does not adapt normally to stress and will succumb to degrees of stress that may be well tolerated by the normal animal. It is worth emphasizing that both the adrenal medulla and adrenal cortex are involved in the reaction of the body to conditions of emergency or stress, but that the severe and often fatal nature of stresses in the adrenalectomized animal is due to the loss of the adrenal cortex. Administration of relatively large doses of glucocorticoids to the adrenalectomized animal will restore nearly normal resistance to stress. The mineralocorticoids are ineffective in this respect.

Not all the steroid hormones present in the blood stream circulate as the free hormones. As much as 80 per cent of the corticosteroids present in the blood may be bound to a specific binding globulin known as transcortin. In some circumstances in which an increased plasma corticosteroid level is found, e.g. during pregnancy, it is not the level of the free hormone which necessarily rises, but rather the concentration of transcortin which is increased, and with it the level of the bound hormones.

Control of the Adrenal Cortex

It is likely that the mineralo-corticoid, aldosterone, is secreted by the zona glomerulosa of the adrenal cortex, and that the glucocorticoids, corticosterone and 17-hydroxycorticosterone, are secreted by the zona fasciculata. The main factor regulating the release of the glucocorticoids is the secretion of the adrenocorticotrophic hormone by the anterior pituitary gland. Following hypophysectomy, or disease of the pituitary gland, the adrenal cortex atrophies and the production of glucocorticoids largely ceases. Following injurious stimuli or stresses of an emotional or physical type, the secretion of the adrenocorticotrophic hormone is rapidly and markedly increased with a corresponding rise in discharge of the glucocorticoids from the adrenal gland. On the other hand the secretion of aldersterone seems largely, though not completely, independent of pituitary control. It is now believed that aldosterone secretion is at least in part regulated by the renin : angiotensin system. Renin is formed by the cells of the juxtaglomerular apparatus in the kidney and in turn causes a rise in angiotensin in the blood stream. Under conditions of reduced blood volume, renin secretion increases and the resulting increase in angiotensin acts directly on the adrenal cortex to stimulate aldosterone release (see also p. 663).

Clinical Aspects

Chronic adrenal insufficiency may result from two main causes: a primary insufficiency due to disease of the adrenal cortex itself, and a secondary insufficiency due to hypopituitarism. One of the commonest causes of primary adrenocortical failure is infection of the glands with *B. tuberculosis*. The clinical condition, known as Addison's disease, is characterized by muscular weakness, loss of weight, low blood pressure, low body temperature and vomiting. An additional feature of the disease is the increased pigmentation observable in certain areas of the skin. This pigmentation may be due to an increased ACTH secretion by the pituitary gland in its attempt to stimulate the failing adrenal tissue.

In secondary chronic adrenal insufficiency due to panhypopituitarism there is less disturbance of the electrolyte balance, because aldosterone production is little affected, and an absence of pigmentary disturbance since an increase in ACTH secretion does not occur.

Hyperfunctional states of the adrenal cortex exist and again may be of primary origin, or secondarily produced by an overproduction of pituitary ACTH.

Cushing's syndrome is the name applied to the clinical picture observed in hyperfunctional states of the adrenal cortex due to the overproduction of 11, 17 oxygenated corticosteroids. Among the more common clinical signs are adiposity confined to the face, neck and trunk; kyphosis, possibly accompanied by rarefaction of the vertebrae; sexual dystrophy, which may start in females with precocious development but which ends with amenorrhoea (and impotence in males); a tendency to masculine distribution of the hair; a high coloured or swarthy skin; purple abdominal striae; high blood pressure and polycythemia. The oedema commonly observed, and giving rise to the typical "moon-faced" appearance of the patient, may be due to an increased aldosterone production but is more probably caused by the mineralocorticoid properties of excessive amounts of glucocorticoids. Cushing's syndrome, as originally described, was thought to be caused by a basophile adenoma of the pituitary gland. Although increased pituitary activity is the cause in some cases, overactivity of the adrenal cortex may also arise from a tumour of the adrenal itself or as a result of the production of ACTH by an extrapituitary tumour. For example, in certain cases of carcinoma of the lung the tumour appears to be capable of producing an ACTH-like substance and may give rise to adrenal hyperfunction.

Since the adrenal cortex has a similar embryonic origin to the gonads it is not surprising that certain errors of hormonal synthesis in the adrenal cortex give rise to an overproduction of sex hormones. In the adrenogenital syndrome a deficiency in some of the enzymes leading to adrenocorticoid synthesis results in an overproduction of androgens. This results in masculinization in females and precocious sexual development in males.

A condition known as primary aldosteronism (Conn's syndrome) has been described. It is due to an adrenal cortical tumour producing excess amounts of aldosterone.

THE THYROID GLAND

Structure

The thyroid gland arises from the endodermal lining of the floor of the pharynx and in the adult consists of two lobes connected by an isthmus. It is situated anterior and lateral to the upper part of the trachea and larynx. Histologically the thyroid gland is composed of numerous follicles each formed by a wall consisting of a single layer of epithelium surrounding a lumen filled with colloid. There is an abundant blood supply to the follicles and most of the secretions of the gland are transported via the blood stream. Some may find their way into the lymphatics.

Hormones of the Thyroid

The thyroid gland has a remarkable ability to extract inorganic iodine from the plasma, even though the concentration of such iodine is many hundreds of times less in the plasma than in the gland. Inorganic iodide is rapidly oxidized in the cells of the thyroid giving rise to molecular iodine which in turn combines with the amino-acid tyrosine to give rise to monoiodotyrosine (MIT), and di-iodotyrosine (DIT). Two molecules of DIT or one of DIT and one of MIT may then be condensed in the presence of a coupling enzyme to give either $3:5:3':5'$ tetraiodothyronine (thyroxine, T_4) or $3:5:3':$ tri-iodothyronine (T_3) respectively. This trapping of iodine and the formation of various iodotyrosines and iodo-thyronines is effected much more readily with tyrosine residues of the protein thyroglobulin which is a specific product of the cells of the thyroid. Thyroglobulin is a glycoprotein with a molecular weight of 670,000 which is made in the thyroid cells and transported into the colloid of the follicles. It is probably here that the iodination occurs, for studies with radioactive ^{131}I have shown extremely rapid incorporation into the follicular protein rather than into the cells.

The large size of the thyroglobulin molecule precludes its release into the blood stream from the intact, healthy thyroid and it is clear that thyroglobulin is not the hormone secreted into the blood. T_4 and T_3 have been detected in the plasma and it is likely that thyroglobulin is hydro-lysed enzymatically releasing its iodothyronines and iodotyrosines. The latter are probably de-iodinated in the gland and the iodine re-utilized, whilst the former are the only products of the thyroid which show any hormonal activity. Both T_3 and T_4 are loosely bound to the thyroxine binding globulin (TBG) of the plasma proteins. T_3 appears to have less affinity for the globulin than does T_4, and it may be for this reason that T_4 acts much more slowly and over a much longer period than T_3. It has also been surmised, in the past, that because T_3 appears to have a more pronounced metabolic effect than T_4 it is derived from T_4 at the site of activity.

Function of the Thyroid Gland

The functions of the thyroid gland are best studied in experiments involving removal of the organ or replacement therapy with thyroidal hormones, or desiccated thyroid tissue. Administration of excessive amounts of thyroid hormone results in a much increased metabolic rate, increased nitrogen excretion, loss of weight, rapid pulse, raised body temperature, sweating and flushing, a heightened sensitivity of the autonomic nervous system, fine muscular tremors and, in man, marked anxiety. Experimental removal of the gland results in a marked diminution in the metabolic rate, slow pulse, lowered body temperature, and disturbances in general bodily, sexual, and mental development. The effects of the thyroid on bodily development is striking in amphibians. In these forms, removal of the thyroid in the tadpole results in a lack of, or greatly delayed, metamorphosis so that enlarged tadpoles are produced instead of the normal sized young frogs.

The mechanisms whereby the thyroid hormones exert their numerous effects are largely unknown.

Thyroid Activity and its Control

Since the introduction of radioactive isotopes it has become possible to measure thyroid activity quickly and directly by making use of radioactive iodine ^{131}I. Injection of a chemically minute, and metabolically negligible, amount of ^{131}I into an animal makes it possible to follow the rate of uptake of this radioiodine by the thyroid, and also to follow it as it passes through the various phases in the gland to be incorporated as part of the molecule of thyroglobulin or thyroid hormone. A large proportion of injected ^{131}I is excreted through the kidneys, which is a factor that must be remembered when using the thyroid uptake of radio-iodine as a measure of thyroid activity. An alternative method of measuring thyroid activity in laboratory animals is to measure the rate of release of radioactive hormone from the gland. Forty-eight hours after the administration of a small dose of ^{131}I the radio-iodine left in the body is nearly all in the form of radioactive hormone in the thyroid gland. Measurement of the rate at which the radio-activity in the gland declines gives values which are, under standardized conditions, proportional to the rate of discharge of thyroid hormone. It is important to emphasize that the thyroid metabolises radioactive iodine in the same way as non-radioactive iodine, and that the methods available for detecting and measuring ^{131}I are so sensitive that the amounts administered to perform the above tests do not in any way disturb iodine metabolism.

Thyroid activity is regulated by the secretion of the thyrotrophic hormone (TSH) by the anterior pituitary gland. Hypophysectomy greatly reduces thyroid activity although such activity is not entirely abolished. The changes in the external environment which lead to alterations in the rate of secretion of thyroid hormone appear to do so by affecting the rate of secretion of TSH. Exposure to a cold environment exerts a pronounced stimulating effect on the thyroid. Other environmental stimuli, which may be interpreted as emotional or physical stresses (restraint, painful stimuli, operative procedures, haemorrhage and so on) have been reported as exerting pronounced inhibitory effects on the thyroid gland. The thyroid gland of the female shows increased activity at various stages of the reproductive cycle, but the mechanism of these changes is uncertain, although they can probably be correlated with changes in ovarian activity.

Autoradiographic studies of sections of the thyroid gland after administration of ^{131}I and ^{125}I have shown that the iodine is rapidly incorporated into the colloid of the follicles. After treatment with TSH it has been shown that labelled colloid droplets are to be found in the cytoplasm of the thyroid cells and that these droplets lose their radioactive content. It has been suggested that in moments of synthesis iodine is transported from the circulation into the thyroid cells and into the colloid, and that the release of thyroid hormones follows the reverse pattern. Thyroid cells contain a large number of lysosomes, sub-cellular particles which contain autolytic enzymes, and perhaps it is the stimulated activity of these lysosomes which is involved in the splitting of T_3 and T_4 from the thyroglubulin molecule and their release into the general circulation.

Antithyroid Substances

Many substances are known to inhibit the uptake of iodine by the thyroid, or to inhibit the organic-binding of iodine and so prevent the formation of di-iodotyrosine and thyroxine.

(a) Iodine uptake from the blood may be reduced by administration of *excess* iodine (the reason for this is not known), of thiocyanates and by various common foodstuffs, such as cabbage.

(b) Incorporation of iodine in the gland into organic combination may be blocked by the aminobenzene derivatives including the sulphonamides, and by the thioureas and thiouracils. One of the most potent of these substances is propylthiouracil. Experimentally it has been found that administration of these compounds is particularly effective in producing a goitrous enlargement of the thyroid. The probable sequence of events is that the antithyroid compound inhibits the synthesis of thyroid hormone, the concentration of the hormone in the blood falls, and this results in increased secretion of thyrotrophic hormone and thereby hyperplasia of the thyroid.

Clinical Aspects

Clinical conditions associated with thyroid disorders may be classified into those caused by increased function of the gland and those caused by a reduced activity.

The term *goitre* refers to any visible swelling of the thyroid gland. A goitrous gland may be associated with a state of hypo-, eu- or hyperthyroidism. One common form of goitre, endemic goitre, is mainly due to a lack of iodine in the diet and tends to occur in various geographical areas in which iodine content of the water or of the soil (and therefore in the vegetable food of the region) is low. This type of goitre used to occur, for example, in the British Isles in a belt running roughly from Somerset through Derbyshire to Durham, but is not restricted to this area. A goitrous population of this kind shows also a high incidence of cretinism and goitre in the children. Addition of small quantities of iodine to the diet, usually by iodizing the table salt consumed, leads to a reduction in the size of goitrous glands and tends to reduce to negligible proportions the incidence of goitre and cretinism in children.

Disorders caused by a deficiency of thyroid hormone are manifested clinically in different ways dependent upon the age of the patient. *Cretinism* is caused by a severe lack of thyroid hormones during infancy and may be correlated with those geographic regions where goitre is endemic, or with a genetic deficiency affecting iodine metabolism. In its most severe form it begins to be apparent at the age of three months. The child, even should he grow up, never achieves a mental capacity greater than that of a normal child of about three years, and may actually lack initiative to feed himself at the age of twelve years. The long bones fail to grow at the epiphyses, leading to much loss of stature, but the skull does enlarge, giving a characteristic deformity. The fontanelles are late in closing. The visceral organs also grow, so the individual becomes pot-bellied. The muscles become disproportionately large (without achieving any great strength) with the consequence that the tongue is too big for the mouth, from which it protrudes, causing a dribble of saliva. To these grotesque abnormalities may be added pads of fat, deposited on the shoulders and buttocks.

Adult hypothyroidism is manifested in the condition known as *myxoedema*. This is characterized by a thickening of the subcutaneous tissue, coarsening of the features, dryness and pallor of the skin and falling out of the hair. The patient is mentally dull, sluggish in action, with a slow pulse and perhaps a subnormal temperature. A history of constipation and, in women, amenorrhoea may be obtained. A striking feature is the reduction in basal metabolic rate, which may be 30 or 40 per cent below the normal (Fig. 32.5). Nitrogen excretion is diminished and the serum contains abnormally large quantities of cholesterol. Typical changes occur in the facial expression with puffiness of the eyelids and flabbiness of the cheeks. The nose tends to be thickened. The metabolic effects of hypothyroidism are similar in cretinism and myxoedema.

Administration of thyroxine or thyroid extracts by mouth will, if begun early enough, prevent development of the abnormalities of the hypothyroid state. It is especially important that thyroid therapy should begin early in cases of cretinism, for after several years, irreversible changes will have occurred and improvement is all that can be hoped for. Cessation of treatment in either myxoedema or cretinism leads to a prompt relapse into thyroid deficiency.

It was mentioned earlier that thyroglobulin was too large to diffuse into the general circulation. In some individuals this does happen and antibodies may be made to this colloid protein. The end result is an autoimmune response with destruction of the thyroid. The disease is known as Hashimoto's disease.

Of the hyperthyroid states met with the most common is *exophthalmic goitre* or Graves' disease. This condition of hyperthyroidism, first described by Parry in 1825, is associated with a diffuse hyperplasia of the thyroid gland. *The basal metabolic rate is greatly increased* and the skin is flushed and moist. There is a loss of weight and tachycardia, the apex beat being diffuse, and its position suggests an enlargement of the heart which is not, however, apparent post-mortem. Mental activity is accelerated, with exaggerated responses to sensory and emotional stimuli. Just as the increased frequency of the heart beat may cause cardiac failure, so the heightened excitability of the nervous system may lead to insanity.

The cause of the exophthalmos in patients suffering from Graves' disease is unknown. It has been claimed that an exophthalmos producing substance (EPS) can be isolated from the serum of such patients, but

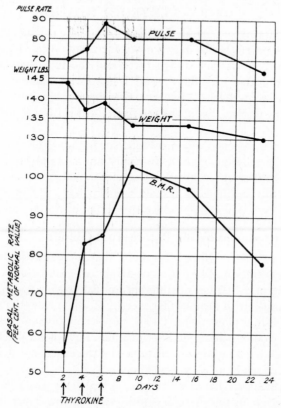

FIG. 32.5. The action of thyroxine on the basal metabolic rate, the weight and the pulse frequency of a patient with myxoedema.

5 mg of synthetic thyroxine was injected intravenously on the second day, 4 mg on the fourth day, and 5 mg on the sixth day; in addition to the increase in basal metabolic rate, fall in weight and rise in pulse frequency shown on the chart, the injections produced a rise in temperature, diuresis and diarrhoea. (After Lyon.)

TSH has also been implicated in this respect. The aetiology of the disease itself is unknown. In many cases of Graves' disease there is no detectable increase in plasma TSH and it is uncertain whether the overactivity of the thyroid cells is primary or secondary. Recently an abnormal thyroid stimulating substance has been found in the plasma of patients with Graves' disease. This substance has a much more protracted action upon the thyroid than TSH and has been named "long acting thyroid stimulator" (LATS). LATS is of extra-pituitary origin and appears to be one of the gamma globulins. How it acts upon the thyroid has yet to be elucidated, but it has been suggested that some form of autoimmune response to TSH receptors may be involved.

THE PARATHYROID GLANDS

That the parathyroid glands function to regulate calcium and inorganic phosphate homeostasis has been known for many years. In the adult the glands are present as paired structures and the four glands are usually intimately associated with the thyroid, a fact which delayed the discovery of their separate existence. However, they have a separate embryological origin from the thyroid, being derived from the third and fourth pharyngeal pouches.

Histologically, species differences are to be found in the cellular composition of the parathyroid glands. In many animals only one cell type is evident, the principal, or *chief cell*. Another cell type, the *oxyphil cell*, is present in the parathyroids of man, monkey, horse and cow. Whether or not these two types of cells produce two different hormones is uncertain.

Hormones Produced by the Parathyroid Glands

The parathyroids produce a hormone that increases the blood plasma calcium concentration. The active principle has been isolated from parathyroid tissue of a number of different animal species and has proved to be a polypeptide with a molecular weight of about 9,000. The hormone, called the parathyroid hormone (PTH), can be split into smaller peptides by treatment with dilute acids, and yet maintain its biological activity. There appears to be an active core to the molecule the exact size and amino-acid composition of which is, as yet, unknown.

Recently, evidence has been produced which suggests that there is a hormone present in the thyroid-parathyroid system, which acts to lower blood calcium. Two opposite views have been put forward, one suggesting that the thyroid is the site of synthesis of this hormone, and the other which suggests that both a thyroid and parathyroid calcium lowering hormone exist. The former has been named thyrocalcitonin and the latter calcitonin. Calcitonin has yet to be isolated but the presence, in the thyroid tissue, of a hypocalcemic hormone of molecular weight around 5,000–6,000 seems reasonably well established. It has been claimed that this hormone is manufactured in the mitochondrion rich cells of the thyroid which occupy parafollicular and interfollicular sites.

Functions of the Parathyroids

The parathyroid glands are necessary for life. After extirpation of all parathyroid tissue, there are no untoward effects for the first three or four days; but then follow periodic spasms of the musculature, high fever, increased irritability of the peripheral nerves and death due to asphyxia during one of the "tetanic" convulsions. This condition of *tetany* is associated with an abnormally low concentration of calcium salts in the blood; it can be alleviated by administration (oral or intravenous) of calcium salts, and more completely controlled by periodic injections of parathyroid extract. Such injections result in an increased concentration

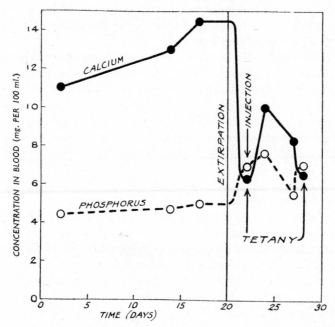

Fig. 32.6. The effect of extirpation of the parathyroid glands and subsequent injections of parathormone on the concentrations of calcium and inorganic phosphorus in the blood, showing their actions in inducing and preventing tetany in a dog.

Tetany occurred whenever the calcium concentration fell below about 7 mg per 100 ml. (After Weaver and Reed.)

of calcium in the blood, the extra calcium being derived from the bones. These relations are illustrated in Fig. 32.6, which also indicates the characteristic variations in concentration of inorganic phosphate in the blood; the phosphate and the calcium concentrations vary in opposite directions.

How PTH causes the transfer of calcium from bones to blood remains conjectural. Injections of the hormone, or local grafts of parathyroid tissue, have been shown to cause an increase in the activity of the osteoclasts which cause dissolution of the bone. The removal of calcium from bone occurs in acid media, and it has been suggested that the effects of PTH on glycolysis with the production of lactic and citric acids by the osteoclasts may be responsible for calcium transfer.

PTH also promotes the tubular reabsorption of Ca by the kidneys, and decreases the reabsorption of inorganic phosphate from the tubular fluid. As a consequence the concentration of inorganic phosphate in the blood falls, calcium phosphate is mobilized from bone and the blood calcium concentration therefore rises further. If this were the only action of parathyroid hormone, then it would lose activity if the kidneys were removed. However, experiments designed to test this possibility indicate that PTH is still active in the nephrectomized animal, and that it also exerts a direct action on bone in mobilizing calcium.

That the hormone also increases intestinal absorption of calcium has been demonstrated in isolated loops of intestine. Very large doses of vitamin D have been found to increase the concentration of calcium in the plasma. This is apparently due to a direct action of the vitamin upon bone, and also in promoting absorption from the gut. It now seems that vitamin D and PTH act synergistically but without interaction, although it has been suggested that trace doses of the vitamin are necessary for a full realization of PTH activity.

Control of Parathyroid Secretion

Since parathyroid transplants appear capable of maintaining normal function it is unlikely that the glands are regulated *via* a secretomotor nerve supply. There is also little reason to believe that the parathyroids are controlled by an anterior pituitary hormone. Rather the evidence indicates that the activity of the gland is influenced directly by the calcium concentration of the blood, for hyperplasia of the parathyroids appears to be associated with conditions in which the blood calcium concentration is low (rickets, chronic nephritis), and conversely the parathyroids are reduced in size if the blood calcium concentration is raised by varying the diet. Exactly how blood calcium exerts its effect is unknown, but suggestions have been made that calcium ions may affect the rate of passage of amino acids into the cells of the parathyroids, and thereby control the rate of PTH production.

As PTH acts to maintain, as far as possible, a steady blood calcium level of about 10 mg Ca/100 ml plasma, it might be imagined that the hormone is secreted more or less continuously. This appears to be the case. Since the biological half life of the PTH molecule is short, the secretion rate is relatively rapid. How calcitonin and thyrocalcitonin fit into any picture of calcium homeostasis remains problematical.

Clinical Aspects

The fact that there are two pairs of parathyroid glands makes it rare to encounter hypoparathyroidism. If one or more gland is destroyed, there is compensatory hypertrophy of the remaining tissue and only in cases of surgical removal of the glands is parathyroid insufficiency commonly met with. Autoimmune conditions may possibly exist in which antibodies to parathyroid tissue are produced with consequent hypoparathyroidism.

The tetany observed after parathyroidectomy has received attention above, and is one of the cardinal signs of hypoparathyroidism. Central nervous effects of depression, headache and anxiety may occur and cataracts of the eye may appear later in life. Treatment of hypoparathyroidism involves increasing the plasma levels of Ca^{++}. This may be done by administration of PTH, by careful dietary arrangements, by injection of calcium salts or by administration of vitamin D. It has been found also that a substance known as tachysterol, which is an intermediate product in the formation of ergo calciferol (vitamin D_2) by irradiation of ergosterol, is also effective in a similar way, and that di-hydroxy-tachysterol is even more effective. This substance, known as "A.T.10", may be used to raise the serum calcium concentration, and to counteract the effects of chronic hypoparathyroidism.

Hyperparathyroidism is usually associated with an adenoma of the glands resulting in an excessive production of PTH. The onset of the disease is gradual, many of the symptoms are due to the hypercalcemia produced. There may be deposits of calcium in the lungs, myocardium and gastric mucosa. There is a high correlation between the incidence of hyperparathyroidism and the occurrence of kidney stones. Peptic ulcers are also common in hyperparathyroid patients. Since PTH acts to release Ca^{++} from bones it is obvious that skeletal abnormalities may be expected in patients with overactive parathyroid glands. As the disease is now diagnosed earlier the skeletal deformities observed in the past are no longer met with. At one time, devastating deformities used to be observed in a condition known as Von Recklinghausen's disease of bones.

PTH injections have been given to man in cases of lead poisoning to remove the lead which has accumulated in the bones. Calcium comes away with the lead and produces a hypercalcaemia, and cases are recorded in which the blood calcium rose to nearly 20 mg/100 ml without producing severe symptoms.

THE PINEAL GLAND

The pineal gland arises in all vertebrates as an outpushing of the roof of the third ventricle. In man the pineal is attached to the ventricular roof by a hollow stalk and the epithelial cells of the roof of the third ventricle, which give rise to the main mass of the organ, form the parenchymal and glial elements. Histologically the pineal has a glandular appearance in early foetal life, with a tubular arrangement of its cells. This picture is superseded in the adult by which time the tubules have disappeared and the gland has the appearance of a solid mass of parenchymal cells with glial elements interdigitating amongst them. That there are nervous elements present in the pineal cannot be doubted, but the innervation seems to be entirely derived from the cervical sympathetic chain with no efferent fibres from diencephalic structures supplying the organ.

Hormones Produced by the Pineal

For a long time it was considered that the pineal was a vestigial organ with no apparent endocrine function. However, the high oxygen uptake of the gland (higher than that of the pituitary), its high rate of phosphorus turnover and its abundant blood supply argued that the pineal was, in some way, physiologically active.

Pineal tumours have been correlated with either precocious puberty or delayed puberty in the past, and a variety of experimental data has accumulated suggesting that the gland somehow acts to inhibit gonadal activity. However, so few of these early experiments are amenable to statistical analysis that they cannot be used in arguments assessing pineal function.

That pineal tissue is capable of causing pallor when fed to young frog tadpoles has been noted since the beginning of this century. This fact prompted an attempt to isolate a skin lightening agent from mammalian pineal tissue. A most potent lightening agent has been isolated and named *melatonin*. As well as containing melatonin the pineal is exceedingly rich in 5-hydroxytryptamine and several other biogenic amines.

In mammals melatonin has no effect upon skin colour. Recent experiments in mammals have centred around its possible rôle as an antigonadal hormone. Certain laboratories have claimed that melatonin is a hormone and on injection causes a decrease in the size of the gonads of rats. However, this result has not been confirmed by other workers and the endocrine rôle of melatonin, and the pineal, in the control of gonadal, and possibly pituitary and hypothalamic functions, remains far from proven.

Control of Pineal Function

At the moment it is very difficult to assess what factors might be controlling pineal function. There may be some hormonal control of the gland, or there may be a nervous control via the cervical sympathetic chain. Removal of this chain has been claimed to upset the normal diurnal rhythm in pineal 5HT content, and also the close correlation between light and dark and melatonin production. The same operation has also caused loss of fluorescent amines from pineal parenchymal cells. It has even been claimed that there is a pathway from the eyes to the pineal passing via the superior cervical ganglia. Although little can be deduced from the enormously increased literature upon the pineal, this organ can no longer be dismissed lightly as vestigial.

Clinical Aspects

Tumours of the pineal may be caused by hyperplasia of the parenchymal, or glial elements. In those cases where the tumour is of parenchymal origin a correlation with delayed puberty has been claimed and in one recent case a high level of melatonin production has been observed. A tumour of the glial elements is said to give rise to precocious puberty and hypertrophy of the gonads (macrogenitosoma praecox). Exactly how such a tumour exerts its effects is uncertain; those who claim an endocrine rôle for the pineal argue that destruction of parenchymal tissue could be the causative factor, while others claim that pressure effects on hypothalamic areas are the basis for the physiological disturbances observed.

THE PITUITARY GLAND

The pituitary gland weighs about 0·5 g in man, and is attached to a region of the base of the brain, the hypothalamus, by the *pituitary stalk*. It is a well-protected structure lying in a fossa in the sphenoid bone known as the *sella turcica*. The gland is composed of two parts, the neurohypophysis which is embryologically an outgrowth from the hypothalamus, and the adenohypophysis, derived from an evagination from the roof of the embryonic mouth, Rathke's pouch. This pouch loses all connection with the mouth, but still retains its original lumen as a cleft in the fully developed

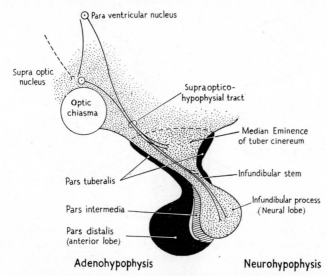

FIG. 32.7. Diagram of a sagittal section through the hypothalamus and pituitary gland to show the various subdivisions of the adenohypophysis and neurohypophysis. The supraoptico-hypophysial tract is shown arising in the hypothalamus and terminating in all three parts of the neurohypophysis.

organ. Since the adult gland is easily split by tearing into two portions, and since the line of cleavage occurs through this cleft, the two parts so obtained are commonly referred to as the *anterior* and *posterior* lobes. It should be remembered, however, that the term posterior lobe also includes the pars intermedia and therefore is not a clear definition of a functional region of the gland. Nevertheless the term *posterior lobe extract* is still in common use. The generally accepted terminology of the various parts of the pituitary is shown in Fig. 32.7. The adenohypophysis is subdivided into the pars distalis (the main secretory part), the pars tuberalis which is a leaf like extension forming a collar around the upper end of the pituitary stalk, and the pars intermedia. The neurohypophysis is subdivided into the median eminence, the infundibular stem and the infundibular process.

Nerve Supply and Blood Supply of the Pituitary

The main nerve supply of the pituitary is derived from the hypothalamus. The supraoptic and paraventricular nuclei send a very rich bundle of unmyelinated nerve fibres, the supraoptico-hypophysial tract, to end in all three parts of the neurohypophysis (Fig. 32.7). In contrast to this rich innervation of the neurohypophysis, the anterior lobe receives a very scanty nerve supply, which probably consists of sympathetic vasomotor nerves.

The blood supply of the pituitary gland (Fig. 32.8) is derived directly from the internal carotid artery and the circle of Willis. The venous drainage passes into nearby dural venous sinuses. The pars distalis possesses

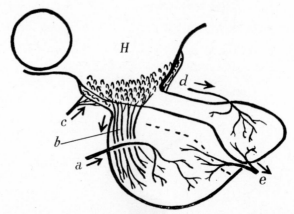

FIG. 32.8. Diagram of a sagittal section through the hypothalamus (H) and pituitary gland of a rabbit to illustrate the vascular supply of the pituitary gland. The anterior lobe receives a systemic arterial supply (*a*) from the internal carotid artery, and a portal supply (*b*). The portal vessels originate in the primary plexus in the tuber cinereum which is itself fed by arterial twigs (*c*) from the carotid artery and the posterior communicating artery. The posterior lobe or infundibular process acquires a separate blood supply (*d*). The venous drainage (*e*) is into surrounding venous sinuses in the dura.

in addition a second blood supply in the form of a portal circulation, which is arranged as follows. Arterial twigs supply a rich vascular plexus in the pars tuberalis, and from this plexus spring a wealth of capillary loops and sinusoids (the primary plexus) that penetrate the neural tissue of the median eminence. From the primary plexus the blood is collected into the trunks of the portal vessels, which pass down the pituitary stalk, and are distributed into the sinusoids of the anterior lobe.

Hypophysectomy

Removal of the pituitary gland is a relatively simple operative procedure in most laboratory animals (rats, rabbits, ferrets, cats and others) when the parapharyngeal route is used and the gland is removed through a drill hole in the base of the skull. The operation is not fatal. Under favourable conditions the life span of the hypophysectomized animal is about half that of the normal. However, the operation is followed by dramatic changes that are due mainly to the loss of the anterior lobe. Posterior lobe function may not be greatly disturbed since the median eminence and the infundibular stem, which form part of the neurohypophysis, are left *in situ*. It might be argued that the pars tuberalis of the adenohypophysis is also left intact, but it is doubtful whether this part of the gland has any secretory function.

The effects of hypophysectomy may be summarized as follows. Growth (in the young animal) is greatly slowed. The ovaries and reproductive tract fail to mature or undergo atrophy. The thyroid and adrenal cortex atrophy, though the adrenal medulla is unaffected. Increased sensitivity to insulin occurs, and hypoglycaemic convulsions may follow and result in early post-operative death. If the operation is performed in the lactating female, lactation promptly ceases. Since the anterior pituitary is of such importance in maintaining the activity of the ovary, testes, thyroid and adrenal cortex, these latter glands are sometimes referred to as pituitary "target organs". Although these target organs undergo marked atrophy in the absence of the pituitary, it is to be noted that some slight basal level of activity is maintained. For example, the adrenal cortex secretes sufficient hormone to maintain life, the thyroid secretes a small (about one-twentieth of the normal) amount of thyroid hormone, the testis may still contain spermatogonia dividing into primary spermatocytes and the ovary shows the presence of primordial follicles developing to the stage of beginning antrum formation. This minimal level of activity seems to be inherent in the target glands themselves and independent of external control.

ADENOHYPOPHYSIS

Hormones of Anterior Pituitary

Current views hold that at least six hormones are secreted by the anterior lobe—the gameto-kinetic or follicle-stimulating hormone (FSH); luteinizing or interstitial-cell-stimulating hormone (LH or ICSH); lactogenic or luteotrophic hormone (prolactin, LTH); growth or somatotrophic hormone (STH); thyrotrophic hormone (TSH) and adrenocorticotrophic hormone (ACTH). The ill effects of hypophysectomy are due to hormonal deficiency as may be shown by grafting anterior pituitary tissue from another animal beneath the hypothalamus of the completely hypophysectomized animal. Normal anterior pituitary function is re-established after a successful graft has "taken". A pituitary transplant placed elsewhere in the body, however, is not capable of maintaining normal function. This fact does not reflect on the endocrine status of the anterior pituitary, but rather indicates that the normal stimulus to activity of the gland is derived, in some way (see below), from the hypothalamus.

The hormones of the anterior pituitary are all protein or peptide in nature. It is not yet possible to measure the quantities present in pituitary venous blood or to give figures representing their rate of secretion under different physiological states.

Gonadotrophic Hormones

(Follicle-stimulating hormone, FSH; luteinizing or interstitial-cell-stimulating hormone, LH or ICSH; and luteotrophic or lactogenic hormone, LTH or prolactin.) FSH and LH (or ICSH) are glycoproteins, the molecular weight of the former being around 30,000 and of the latter being variously estimated at 26,000 (man) up to 100,000 (pig). LTH is a simple protein with a molecular weight of about 30,000 and has been obtained in a crystalline form. The double actions of these hormones on the gonads will be discussed in Chapter 34, p. 602: FSH and LH maintain the production of sperm and ova, and all three maintain the various secretions of androgens, oestrogens and progesterone. LTH is necessary, also, for the *formation* of milk by the mammary glands (Chapter 35, p. 620).

Growth Hormone (Somatotrophic hormone, STH)

The growth hormone is a simple protein the molecular weight of which varies from species to species. It has been obtained in a pure crystalline form. In the pig and the whale molecular weights of 40,000 have been determined as against 46,000 in the ox and sheep and 27,000 in man. The molecular weight of monkey growth hormone has been estimated at 25,000.

Growth hormone will correct the arrested growth of the hypophysectomized young animal, and, if given in excess, will lead to experimental gigantism (Fig. 32.9). The hypoglycaemia and increased sensitivity to insulin of the hypophysectomized animal are due in part to loss of the growth hormone. Repeated injections of large amounts of growth hormone into adult dogs result in hyperglycaemia and glycosuria, and may lead to a state of permanent diabetes; while in younger animals, in which the islet tissue of the pancreas is able to compensate with increased insulin secretion, protein is laid down and increased growth ensues. What used to be called the diabetogenic hormone is now known to be identical with the growth hormone. The activity of the pituitary gland in carbohydrate metabolism has been discussed in Chapter 30.

Growth hormone preparations are species specific. Extracts derived from ox and pig tissue were known to be disappointing in their effects on the primate. It has now been established that extracts of primate pituitary

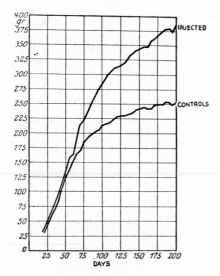

FIG. 32.9. The effect of injection of extracts of the anterior lobe of the pituitary gland on the growth of rats.

 Two groups of thirty-eight rats each were selected; the rats in one group served as controls, while those in the other were injected daily, and the average weight of the animals in each group was plotted against the time. Note the "gigantism" produced in the injected group. (Trendelenburg, after Evans and Long.)

tissue are active in causing nitrogen retention, growth and typical effects on carbohydrate metabolism in primates.

Primate growth hormone is different in molecular size from STH of the lower mammals. Sheep prolactin and human growth hormone have similar chemical properties and, as primate STH is of the same molecular size as sheep prolactin, it has been suggested that primate growth hormone has evolved from a sheep type prolactin, and that in man LTH and STH are the same molecule. However, a full analysis of this problem suggests that the two hormones, in man and monkey, are separate entities but with certain similarities in their molecular structure.

Thyrotrophic Hormone (TSH)

This hormone has not been completely purified, but appears to be a glycoprotein with a molecular weight of about 30,000. Extirpation of the pars anterior of the pituitary body results in a reduction of the basal metabolic rate by some 30 per cent, and diminished nitrogen excretion. Conversely, if the thyrotrophic hormone is injected daily into hypophysectomized rats the basal metabolic rate is raised to normal in three or four days. That it acts through the thyroid may be shown by the discharge of colloid, and hyperplasia of the epithelial cells (a direct action of TSH on peripheral tissues may be the exophthalmos which follows TSH, though not thyroxine, administration). When TSH is injected into the normal animal, the metabolic rate is raised, but in spite of continued injection this returns to normal in two or three weeks and indeed falls to 20 or 30 per cent below normal if the injection is long continued. This is due to the gradual production of a substance which is antagonistic to the hormone. In view of the action of the thyroid extract on growth and development already described, it is necessary to state here that the lack of growth following hypophysectomy is not corrected by administration of thyroid gland, i.e. it is not attributable wholly to absence of the thyrotrophic hormone, though this deficiency plays its part.

Adrenocorticotrophic Hormone (ACTH)

ACTH is a peptide of molecular weight of 4,500. Its molecular structure has now been determined in various species. It consists of a chain of 39 amino-acids of which the first 24 amino-acids are common in the different species studied. It is in this part of the chain that the biological activity of ACTH resides. The atrophy of the adrenal cortex which follows hypophysectomy may be corrected by ACTH administration and excessive amounts of this hormone may lead to hypertrophy of the adrenal cortex. The action of ACTH on the adrenal cortex may also be observed by measuring the fall in cholesterol or ascorbic acid content of the adrenal gland which follows administration of this hormone. The ascorbic acid depletion test has been developed as a highly sensitive method of assay for ACTH. Injection of ACTH in the normal animal causes increased release of the gluco-corticoids, with their corresponding actions on carbohydrate metabolism, lymphoid tissue, blood cells and response to stress. ACTH has, therefore, been used therapeutically, instead of cortisone, in the treatment of rheumatoid arthritis.

The Control of Anterior Pituitary Secretion

Endocrine activity in general is regulated mainly by the hypothalamus. This controls the neurohypophysis and adrenal medulla by a secretomotor nerve supply, and through its control on the secretion of the anterior pituitary trophic hormones also regulates, indirectly, the activity of the gonads, thyroid and adrenal cortex (Fig. 32.10).

Under quiescent optimal conditions the resting rate of secretion of the pituitary trophic hormones seems to be set by the concentration in the circulating blood of the target-organ hormones. The gonadal, thyroid and adrenal cortical hormones exert an inhibitory influence over the secretion

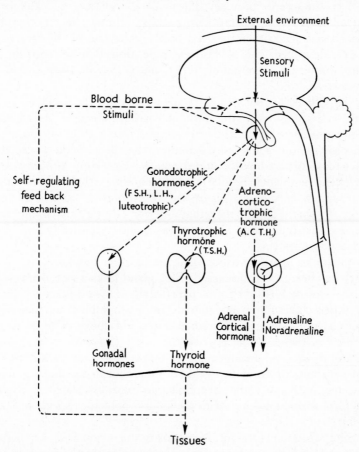

FIG. 32.10. Diagram to illustrate neuro-endocrine inter-relations.

of their respective pituitary trophic hormone. It is uncertain whether this action is a direct one on the cells of the anterior pituitary; it seems possible that the target-organ hormones affect some neural mechanism in the hypothalamus which in turn adjusts pituitary secretion. This feed-back mechanism is clearly of importance in setting a constant "base-line" activity of the glands.

Exteroceptive stimuli exert a profound influence on anterior pituitary secretion. Changing conditions of environmental light are particularly potent in many kinds of animal in varying the rate of FSH secretion; coitus in a number of mammals acts as a trigger stimulus to LH release. The tactile stimulus to the nipple of suckling appears to augment lactogenic secretion, whilst stressful or noxious stimuli will markedly increase ACTH, and decrease TSH secretion. These and other environmental stimuli probably act *via* nervous reflex paths to the hypothalamus which, in turn, affects the anterior pituitary. The evidence indicates that exteroceptive stimuli are over-riding factors in regulating pituitary secretion and that they take precedence over the feed-back mechanism of the target organ hormones described above. For example, injection of cortisone will normally inhibit the secretion of ACTH but fails to do so in the presence of severe stress.

The hypothalamus seems to regulate not only the level of anterior pituitary activity, but also the hormonal pattern secreted. As mentioned above the pituitary gland of the male secretes little LH, but if a male gland is transplanted into a hypophysectomized female in such a way that it becomes revascularized by the portal vessels it may support normal female sex cycles and pregnancy. Similarly it has been shown that anterior pituitary tissue from new-born animals is capable of supporting adult female sexual functions. It would appear then that anterior pituitary tissue is plastic in nature, and that the mosaic of hormones secreted is normally "set" by the central nervous system.

The anatomical path by which the hypothalamus influences the anterior pituitary has been much discussed. This gland lacks a rich nerve supply, but it has been established that the pars distalis of the pituitary is connected to the tuber cinereum in all animals from amphibians to man by the hypophysial portal vessels, described on p. 574 above. The direction of blood flow in these vessels is *from* the tuber cinereum *to* the pituitary gland, and the general arrangement would seem well suited for the transport of substances formed in the tuber cinereum to the anterior lobe. It now seems likely that the hypothalamus and associated hypophysial vessels form a functional unit with the anterior lobe for reasons such as the following:

(*a*) Simple section of the pituitary stalk in the region of the trunks of the portal vessels is followed by variable results so far as the function of the anterior pituitary is concerned. In those animals in which normal anterior pituitary activity is regained, regeneration of the vascular connections across the site of the cut can be shown to have taken place. In those animals in which regeneration does not occur, or is prevented by the insertion of a plate, anterior pituitary function is very much reduced or abolished after operation, and remains so.

(*b*) A pituitary graft placed beneath the median eminence of the hypophysectomized animal obtains a blood supply from the primary plexus of the portal vessels and will maintain normal anterior pituitary function, whereas grafts placed beneath the temporal lobe or in other sites remote from the sella turcica may obtain an equally good blood supply but show very little, if any, sign of functional activity.

(*c*) Lesions of the hypothalamus may interfere with the release of gonadotrophic, thyrotrophic and adrenocorticotrophic hormones. Stimulation of the hypothalamus electrically has been shown to result in liberation of gonadotrophic, thyrotrophic and adrenocorticotrophic hormone. Similar stimuli applied directly to the anterior pituitary gland are ineffective in causing hormone release. This latter finding has been taken to indicate humoral (vascular), rather than direct nervous, control of the anterior lobe.

There can be little doubt that the hypothalamus and hypophysial portal vessels are intimately concerned with maintaining and regulating anterior pituitary activity. On the present data it is likely that hypothalamic nerve fibres liberate chemical transmitter (releasing factors) into the portal vessels, and that these are carried to excite or inhibit the activity of the anterior pituitary gland.

The releasing factors have been much studied in the last few years. It is now established that extracts of the median eminence of the tuber cinereum (see Figs. 32.7 and 32.8), that is of the tissue in which the hypothalamic nerve terminals end on the endothelium of the primary plexus of the portal vessels, have marked effect on anterior pituitary activity. Corresponding to the six trophic hormones of this gland there seem to be six releasing factors. Five of these exert a stimulating effect on the secretion of the hormones (FSH, LH, ACTH, TSH and STH), and one an inhibiting effect (prolactin). Although real progress has been made in the last few years in the purification of these substances, their chemical structure has not been fully established. It is likely that they are peptides with molecular weights somewhat higher than those of the posterior pituitary peptides.

Clinical Aspects

At least three types of cells in the anterior pituitary gland may be differentiated by simple staining techniques. These are the chromaphobe (non-secreting mother cells), acidophile or α-cells and basophile or β-cells. Three types of tumour, or overgrowth (adenomata), are known corresponding to these cells.

Chromaphobe Adenoma. This is the commonest type of anterior pituitary lesion. Since the cells forming the tumour are non-secreting no signs of hyperpituitarism appear. The pressure of the tumour on surrounding normal secreting cells may, however, give rise to signs of hypopituitarism, and may also involve the hypothalamus.

Acidophile Adenoma. Since the acidophile cells are associated with secretion of the growth hormone, a secreting tumour of this cell type gives rise to *gigantism* if it arises before growth ceases, or *acromegaly* if it arises later in life. This latter condition is associated with overgrowth of the extremities and head, kyphosis, weakness, sexual hypofunction, and there may be visual disturbances from pressure of the tumour on the optic chiasma. There is frequently a decreased sugar tolerance and even hyper-glycaemia or diabetes.

Basophile Adenoma. This tumour is associated with Cushing's disease which has already been described.

Simmond's disease is the term applied to loss of anterior pituitary function which can arise from necrosis of the gland after interruption of its blood supply, infection with tuberculosis and other causes. The disease is characterized by a drop in the BMR to nearly half normal values, repro-ductive activity is abolished with atrophy of the gonads, and hypoglycaemia is common. The disorder is most commonly met with in females who have suffered post-partum haemorrhage.

Some types of dwarfism may be due to a deficiency of growth hormone, probably caused by a genetical defect in the cells producing the hormone. A hereditary lack of acidophile cells, for example, has been demonstrated in the pituitary gland of a strain of dwarf mice.

NEUROHYPOPHYSIS

Extracts of the neurohypophysis, commonly called posterior pituitary extracts, possess a variety of pharmacological activities, but only some of these represent normal physiological functions of the gland. Some of the actions are produced only by doses much larger than the gland could secrete during normal life.

Crude posterior pituitary extracts were first separated into two active fractions, called vasopressin and oxytocin, in 1923. The chemical structures of the active compounds were established some twenty-five years later, both being polypeptides containing 8 amino-acids. In 1953, du Vigneaud and his colleagues succeeded in synthesizing both oxytocin and vasopressin, a remarkable achievement which constituted the first synthesis of a poly-peptide hormone. Both oxytocin and vasopressin have very similar amino-acid constitutions. Oxytocin contains cystine joining tyrosine, isoleucine, glutamine and asparagine as a closed ring and proline, leucine and glycine as a side chain. Vasopressin is constructed in a similar pattern except that the isoleucine and leucine are replaced by phenylalanine and arginine (or lysine) (Fig. 32.11).

During the last few years a most interesting story has become apparent concerning the biochemical evolution of the posterior pituitary hormones in the vertebrates. The most primitive vertebrates (the cyclostomes) contain an 8 amino-acid peptide called vasotocin. As the vertebrate scale is ascended new octapeptides are formed by changes in one amino-acid at a time. These changes are localized to positions 3, 4 or 8 in the molecule and are in all probability genetically determined. Thus a series of peptide hormones may be traced up the evolutionary scale from the cyclostomes to man. Vasotocin is found in all vertebrates except mammals. Oxytocin and vasotocin are found in the birds, whereas oxytocin and vasopressin occur in mammals. It is of interest that the great majority of mammals possess (8-arginine) vasopressin, whilst the pig family (pigs, peccaries and the hippopotamus) possess (8-lysine) vasopressin.

Destruction of the neurohypophysis, or interruption of the supra-optico-hypophysial tract (its nerve supply) which leads to atrophy of the gland, is associated in man with the disease *diabetes insipidus*. The characteristic feature of this is a marked polyuria, in which 15 litres or more of

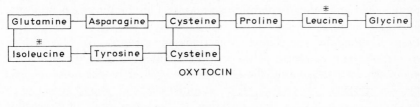

OXYTOCIN

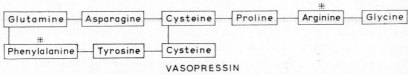

VASOPRESSIN

Fig. 32.11. Composition of oxytocin and vasopressin. The nature and arrangement of the constituent amino-acids is identical in the two hormones except that oxytocin contains isoleucine and leucine, whereas vasopressin contains phenylalanine and arginine, as is indicated by the asterisks. The two molecules of cysteine are united by the S-S bond, which closes the ring; they thus form a single molecule of cystine, and there are only eight amino-acids in the molecule.

urine may be secreted in 24 hr; there is a corresponding increase in thirst (polydipsia). In addition, there may be constipation; and difficulties in parturition have been described in female patients. All these conditions may be relieved by injection of posterior pituitary extracts, though unfortunately the relief is of short duration (a few hours).

The adequacy of such replacement therapy, together with the results of surgical and other studies in experimental animals, provide evidence as to which of the pharmacological actions of pituitary extracts are to be regarded as true hormonal actions in the normal animal.

(1) **Vasopressin**

This is so called because it constricts blood vessels and raises the arterial pressure when injected in large doses. Its antidiuretic action is exerted by much smaller doses and constitutes its most important physiological action. This action of vasopressin in reducing urine flow and increasing the concentration of urine will be referred to in Chapter 38. Experimental removal of the posterior lobe, or denervation of the gland, leads to persistent polyuria in mammals similar to that of the disease diabetes insipidus. Application of acetylcholine to, or electrical stimulation of, the supraoptico-hypophysial tract in the conscious animal inhibits water diuresis. It is presumed therefore that the polyuria and water diuresis are due to a lack of vasopressin, and that normally both are prevented by a steady secretion of vasopressin by the neurohypophysis. This view is largely the outcome of extensive studies of Verney and his colleagues. They have injected into the carotid artery of unanaesthetized dogs hypertonic saline and other hypertonic solutions. This produced an inhibition of water diuresis which could be accurately matched in amount and time relations by intravenous injections of vasopressin. The changes in osmolar concentration of the carotid blood passing to the head were about the same in amount (though opposite in direction) as those involved in the systemic circulation after administration of water sufficient to produce diuresis. Moreover, injection of the same dose of hypertonic solution elsewhere into the circulation produced little or no effect since this produced a very much smaller change in concentration of the blood going to the head. It is consequently believed that the antidiuretic secretion of the gland is controlled in part by "osmoreceptors" probably in the neighbourhood of the supraoptic nuclei.

Vasopressin is probably one of the factors concerned in the control of intestinal peristalsis. Electrical stimulation of the supraoptico-hypophysial tract in rabbits produces increased peristalsis and, as pointed out above, cases of diabetes insipidus may suffer from constipation.

(2) Oxytocin

(i) *Uterine Contraction.* The action of posterior pituitary extracts in increasing the contractions of an isolated mammalian uterus gave rise to the term "oxytocic action" and hence"oxytocin". Lesions of the supraoptico-hypophysial tract interfere with normal birth of the young in cats and guinea-pigs. Electrical stimulation of this tract increases uterine motility in oestrous rabbits and in post-parturient rabbits and cats. Dilatation of the uterine cervix, as occurs during parturition, evokes a reflex secretion of oxytocin and an increased contraction of the uterus. Coitus, also, appears to evoke a nervous reflex release of oxytocin, and the consequent increase in uterine motility may play a part in the transport of seminal fluid up the female reproductive tract. In these experimental animals, therefore, oxytocin appears to be a true hormone.

(ii) *Milk Ejection.* The nervous reflex secretion of oxytocin, produced by the tactile stimulus of suckling the young, and the consequent excitation of myo-epithelial cells in the mammary gland and *ejection* of milk already present, will be discussed in Chapter 35, p. 620.

Injections of posterior pituitary extracts produce two further effects; neither of these is of physiological importance in mammals.

(*a*) *Vasoconstriction.* When injected into anaesthetized animals, vasopressin produces a marked rise in blood pressure. The action is more prolonged than that of adrenaline, and has the curious property of rendering the blood vessels insensitive for some time (e.g. about half an hour) to a second injection (Fig. 32.12). The dose of vasopressin required to raise the

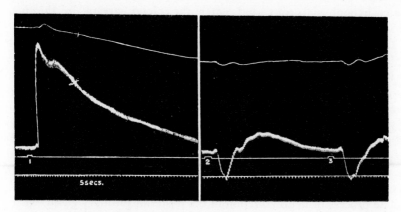

FIG. 32.12. The action of extracts of the posterior lobe of the pituitary gland on the blood pressure of a cat.

From above downwards: intestinal volume; arterial pressure; injection signal; time in five second intervals. Note that the second and third injections had practically no vaso-motor action; the fall in pressure actually produced was due to the presence of histamine as an impurity in the extract. Note also the prolonged constriction of the intestinal vessels. (Schafer and Swale Vincent.)

blood pressure is so much greater than that which arrests water diuresis, that it is unlikely that the neurohypophysis is normally related to the control of blood pressure.

(*b*) *Melanophore Dilatation.* This leads to a darkening of the skin, which is easily observed in amphibians. It is due to contamination of post-pituitary extracts by the melanocyte stimulating hormones (α and β MSH) from the pars intermedia. α and β MSH are polypeptides sharing a common core of amino acids with ACTH. Their function in mammals is uncertain.

The Site of Formation of the Posterior Pituitary Hormones—Neurosecretion

Microscopic examination of the neurohypophysis reveals a structure composed of nerve fibres, connective tissue, neuroglial elements and, contrary to most accounts, a rich supply of blood vessels. No cells are present which have the appearance of gland cells. For this reason, it was thought at one time that the posterior pituitary hormones might be formed in the anterior lobe and transported back into the posterior lobe. Some kinds of animal, however—whales, for example—have a thick dural septum between the two lobes; but substances with the usual activities can, nevertheless, be extracted from the neurohypophysis. There is now good evidence that the hormones are formed in the nerve cells of the supraoptic and paraventricular nuclei in the hypothalamus by a process called "neurosecretion", and that they migrate down the nerve fibres of the supra-optico-hypophysial tract and enter the blood stream in the neuro-hypophysis.

The hormones, whilst in the nerve fibres, are bound to a large protein molecule called neurophysin, and the whole complex contitutes the van Dyke protein, once thought to be the active principle of the posterior pituitary. Experiments with radioactive tracers have shown that during migration down the nerve fibres of the pituitary stalk the amount of neurophysin remains constant, but the proportion of bound neurohypophysial hormones increases. This has led to the concept that oxytocin and vasopressin are manufactured throughout the length of the neurosecretory nerve fibres and that only "immature" granules leave the hypothalamic nuclei.

The process of neurosecretion in the posterior pituitary gland, whereby the peptide hormones are transferred from the nerve terminals in the gland directly into the blood vessels, forms a similar picture to that seen in the median eminence. In this latter structure hypothalamic nerve terminals liberate (probably) peptide releasing factors directly into the blood vessels of the hypophysial portal system. In this connection it may be remembered that the median eminence is composed of neurohypophysial tissue which is in many of its characters different from the tissue of the central nervous system including the hypothalamus.

CHAPTER 33

REPRODUCTIVE PHYSIOLOGY

ONE of the major attributes of all living matter is its ability to reproduce. In the higher forms the simple process of reproduction has become inextricably mixed with the complications of sex, to form a mechanism for the intermingling of genes in new individuals.

In mammals, the developing young pass the early part of their lives within the actual body cavity of the mother, protected in this way from the physical and chemical vicissitudes of the external environment and provided, from her blood stream, with a supply of food and oxygen. The developing embryo, formed from the union of the ovum and sperm lies in the uterus, a thick-walled, muscular organ situated in the lower abdomen. The embryo has a blood circulatory system which comes into intimate relationship with the circulation of the mother, the maternal and embryonic blood vessels producing a structure called the placenta. It is through this organ that food, oxygen and other substances diffuse from the mother to the foetus and through which carbon dioxide and waste products pass in the opposite direction. During pregnancy, the foetus and the placenta associated with it, continue to grow and during this growth process the uterus itself enlarges to accommodate its expanding contents. Pregnancy, which in the human lasts for about forty weeks, is terminated by a series of contractions of the muscular wall of the uterus, a process which ultimately leads to the expulsion of the foetus and the placenta. For a time after birth, the young are fed wholly or partly by means of milk secreted by the mother's mammary glands.

The nervous system co-ordinates body function, a fact known before the time of Hippocrates, but the details of other co-ordinating and regulating mechanisms have been elucidated since. Among the first of these mechanisms known, was the influence exerted by the primary reproductive organs, or gonads, on various aspects of sexual function. Subsequent investigations indicated that a relatively complex system of circulating chemical substances, hormones, acted as controlling agents in the activity of the reproductive system. The pituitary gland was found to have the primary controlling function in the series of physiological processes which occur in reproduction. A number of these hormones are now known to exist, some having been isolated chemically, yet in many cases detailed explanations for the observed phenomena are still lacking or imperfectly understood.

During early embryonic life, the reproductive system develops identically in the male and female, although the genetic make-up of the embryo has already determined its sex. The genital ridge, which later is to give rise to either the male or female primary reproductive organs, is differentiated by the fifth week of intra-uterine life. The germinal epithelium which forms the germ-cells, is the top layer of this ridge and between the eighth and tenth week differentiates into either ovarian tissue of the female or testicular tissue of the male.

The influence of hormones which originate in the gonads, even at this early developmental stage, can be shown by removing the gonads. If this is done, in either male or female embryos, a female type of internal and external genital system develops. Thus the conclusion may be drawn that the testis secretes a hormone, the presence of which is necessary for differentiation into the male pattern.

After a period of growth, in man eleven to fifteen years, puberty occurs. At this time, in the female the ovaries begin to produce and release ova, and in the male the testes form spermatozoa. Physical and psychological changes take place resulting in the development of the secondary sexual characteristics. Girls become an interesting and attractive shape (to boys) as a result of enlargement of the breasts, deposition of subcutaneous fat and changes in the bony structure of the pelvis. Pubic and axillary hair appear in both sexes although the distribution is slightly different. In boys, the beard grows, the voice breaks, and typically male skeletal and muscular growth takes place. These changes occur in response to the presence in the body of increased amounts of the sex hormones—androgens in the male; oestrogens in the female—secreted by the testes and ovaries respectively.

PHYSIOLOGY OF THE FEMALE REPRODUCTIVE SYSTEM

The female organs of reproduction consist of the *ovaries* and their accessory organs: the *uterus* in which the fertilized ovum is retained during pregnancy, the *Fallopian tubes* (or oviducts) which convey the shed ova to the uterus and the *vagina* and *genitalia*. The *mammary glands* develop partially at puberty, increase their growth during pregnancy and become functional during the first part of the extra-uterine life of the offspring.

THE OVARIES

The two ovaries, each the size and shape of a walnut in the human female, puzzled the early Anatomists who could not believe that mammals had eggs. Regner de Graaf, in 1672, described follicles (the Graafian follicles) in the ovaries of sheep, rabbits, cows, cats and women; de Graaf, in fact, mistakenly thought that these follicles were the eggs and it was not until 1827 that von Baer discovered the smaller ova within the ovarian follicles.

At birth, the ovary consists of a stroma of spindle-shaped cells covered by a layer of cuboidal epithelial cells, the *geminal epithelium*. Embedded in the stroma are many *primordial follicles*, which arise as downgrowths of germinal epithelial cells occurring during foetal life. Each of these primordial follicles is about 200–300µ in diameter, has a large central single cell 45µ in diameter with a pale, vesicular nucleus, mitochondria and Golgi apparatus. An external cell membrane is replaced by 10 to 20 follicular cells arranged round its periphery (Figs. 33.1, 33.2, 33.3, 33.4).

In the two ovaries of a young woman aged 22 years, Haggström was able to count as many as 420,000 primordial follicles. Normally, during the reproductive life of a woman, about 400 of these follicles ripen and ultimately discharge their ova. The remainder, in varying stages of their

FIG. 33.1. Section of cortex of an infantile ovary with primordial ova. G = germinal epithelium; O = ovum with nucleus; S = stroma of ovary.

development wither, to become the so-called *"atretic follicles"*—simply small masses of fibrous tissue laid down as a physiological response to dead cells. It is not known why the ovum dies in this way or what factors are involved in differentiating between those which die and those which survive.

Maturation of Follicles

Maturation of the follicles is a process beginning at puberty. A mass of cells formed by mitotic division of follicular cells now surrounds the ovum, to form a cavity filled with a fluid called the *liquor folliculi*. The epithelium surrounding the ovum is separated into two parts—the *membrana granulosa* which is a thin layer of syncytium composed of finely granular, polyhedral cells, surrounding the whole follicle and a solid mass of follicular cells in which the ovum is embedded—the *discus proligerus*—projecting into the liquor folliculi. Outside the granulosa cells the stroma of the ovary forms a capsule of two layers. The outer layer, or *theca externa* is of tough fibrous tissue while the *theca interna* is a thin layer of secretory cells having a rich blood supply. The cells of the *theca interna* are very important as we shall see later.

When completely ripened, the ovum itself is well over 100μ in diameter, and is contained within a distinct membrane, the *zona pellucida*, through which pass small canals, while the whole follicle may reach 5 or 6 mm across.

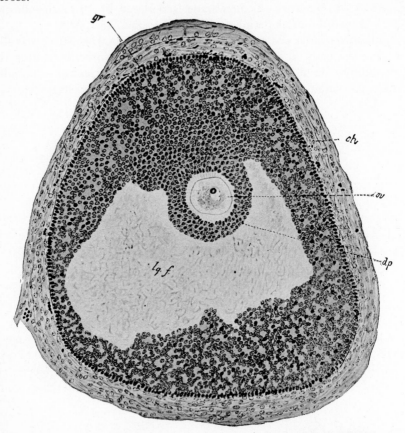

Fig. 33.2. Graafian follicle of mammalian ovary. (Prenant and Bouin.)

Ov. Ovum. *dp.* Cumulus. *ch.* Theca. *gr.* Membrana granulosa. *lq. f.* Liquor folliculi.

Ovulation

The mature follicle enlarges and moves near to the external surface of the ovary, bulging it outwards and as the intra-follicular pressure rises, the surface layers get thinner and thinner until eventually the blood vessels are compressed. A small region at the apex ruptures and liquor folliculi, cell debris, together with the ovum are discharged into the peritoneal cavity. This sequence of events is termed ovulation. In some animals this process

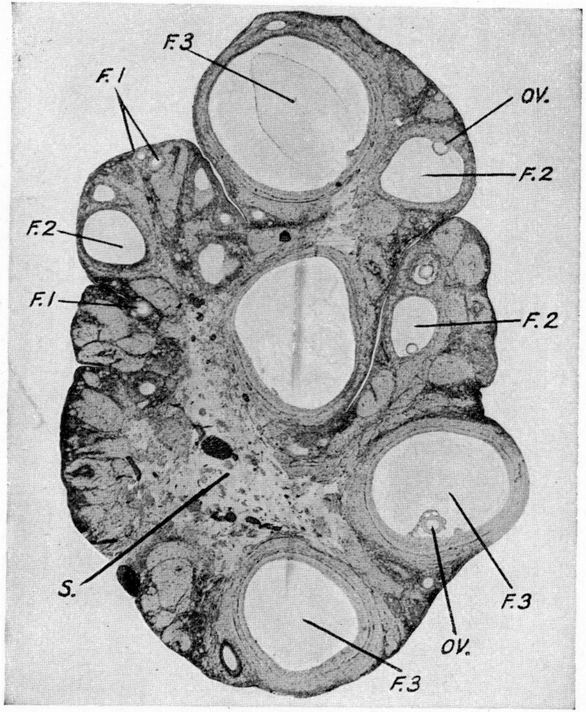

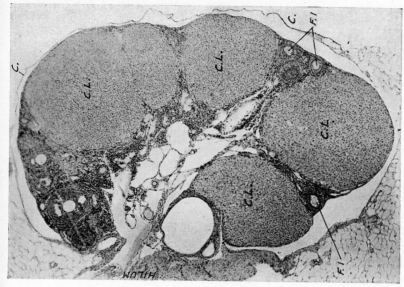

Fig. 33.4. Section through the ovary of a mouse during di-oestrus.

F.1, immature follicles; *C.L.*, corpora lutea; *C.*, capsule of ovary. (From a photograph supplied by Dr. Parkes.)

Fig. 33.3. Section through the ovary of a ferret just before ovulation.

F.1, very immature follicles; *F*.2, developing follicles; *F*.3, mature follicles; *OV*, ovum; *S*, stroma tissue. (From a photograph supplied by Dr. Parkes.)

of ovulation takes place at definite seasons (bitch); in others ovulation only occurs after coitus (rabbit); in the human female ovulation usually occurs alternately from each ovary, every month or so. Unless ovulation does occur in this way, the follicle—even if apparently fully mature—degenerates and is turned into a fibrous atretic follicle.

Corpus Luteum Formation

Once the ovum has been discharged, the remaining portions of the ruptured follicle turn into a structure known as the *corpus luteum*, which in addition to the *theca interna* has an important controlling function.

The mammal, unlike the frog or the fish, is still responsible for the developing egg which must be given nourishment and protection within the mother's uterus. The uterine wall must be adapted to house the ovum; also the mammary gland has to be stimulated to give milk after the foetus has been born. One of the main mechanisms involved in this complex chain of responses to the developing foetus, is brought about by the secretion of a hormone called *progesterone*. At first, the main source of this hormone is to be found in the *corpus luteum*, formed in the cavity left in the ovary after ovulation by rapid proliferation of the remaining membrana granulosa cells. These quickly increase, both in size and number so that a dense mass completely fills the original follicle. At first these cells are grey in colour; if fertilization has occurred they continue to grow, reaching a maximum size about 10 to 12 weeks later (Fig. 33.4).

The developing cells soon have a yellow colouration (orange in humans) due to the presence in them of a *lipochrome* (lutein). There also develops a rich blood supply. In the absence of fertilization, the *corpus luteum* undergoes degenerative changes about three weeks after it was first formed. Animals which produce a single offspring at a time, naturally have a single *corpus luteum* since only one ovum has been shed into the peritoneum. Others, with multiple litters, have a *corpus luteum* for each ovum.

The function of the *corpora lutea* remained a mystery; even in the early years of this century it was still possible for a thesis to be written which gave as many as twenty-five different, and all quite incorrect, hypotheses regarding their function.

However, they have the usual characteristics of endocrine tissues. They are large cells having a granular cytoplasm, a profuse blood supply and they communicate with the rest of the body via blood vessels only. We will consider the physiology of progesterone later.

THE FALLOPIAN TUBES

The rupture of the follicle leads to the ovum being discharged into the abdominal cavity. This procedure is in fact less hazardous for the ovum than one might imagine. In the first place the open internal end of the oviduct is applied to the surface of the ovary at the instant of ovulation and in addition the abdominal cavity is not a vast open space but is closely packed with intestines and other viscera. A flow of the serous fluid found within the abdominal cavity towards the funnel-shaped extremity of the Fallopian tube has been demonstrated using indian ink particles. Nevertheless, there are unexplained mysteries concerning the mode of transport of ova (they are non-motile of course) because frequently pregnancy has occurred following the removal of one ovary and ligation (tying with surgical thread) of the opposite tube.

The oviducts are called *Fallopian tubes* after Gabriele Fallopio (1523–1562) chiefly because he was *not* the first to describe them, although he put forward a

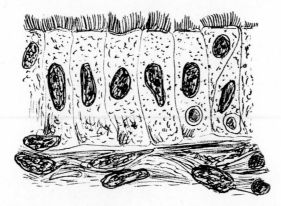

Fig. 33.5. Epithelium of Fallopian tube from human female aet. 25 yr., showing ciliated epithelial cells and submucosa. Specimen obtained at mid-interval (×600)

most attractive theory to explain their function, namely that they acted as ventilators to disperse noxious fumes from the uterus. The structure of the Fallopian tubes is complex and the interior is folded into numerous, high branched ridges of mucous membrane so that in cross-section the appearance is like a honeycomb. The whole length of the tube, about 12 cm, is lined with cilia. In these spaces, the spermatozoa and ovum meet and fertilization occurs. (Figs. 33.5 and 33.6.)

Transport of the Ovum

How are the ova transported from the ruptured follicle to the uterus? There is some difficulty in attributing the passage of the ovum to any single agency. It is known that the lashing of cilia gives rise to a general flow from within outwards; the tube, being muscular, undergoes squirming and peristaltic-type movement. However, some animals have oviducts without cilia.

It has been found that in all mammals, the ova take 3 to 4 days to make the passage of the oviduct. That this might have interesting implications is evident when one considers that the oviduct of the sow is at least forty times as long as that of the mouse! The explanation is now thought to be due to a delay in the ovum's passage through the middle portion of the tube, where the honeycomb-like structure is at its thickest. This is the probable reason why it is that if you cut a large number of cross-sections of tubes, it is only in this middle region that ova are ever found.

We can therefore assume that, in addition to its function of transport, the Fallopian tube acts as a temporary nidus for the ovum. Presumably a short-term retention of this nature would increase the chances of fertilization taking place and also would give the uterus time to respond to the

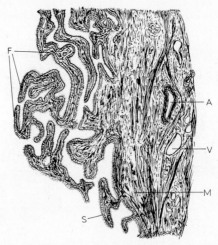

FIG. 33.6. Part of cross-section of Fallopian tube from a 25 yr old woman. s = mucosa; M = muscular layer, showing bundles of smooth muscle cut both longitudinally and lengthwise; A = artery; V = vein. Note the extremely folded processes of mucous membrane covered with ciliated epithelium and containing blood vessels (=F). (×40).

hormonal secretion of the newly-formed *corpus luteum*. It can indeed be shown that progesterone has certain effects on the lining of the uterus, that in the absence of these changes implantation of the ovum cannot occur and, in addition, if the ovum arrives in the uterus 2 or 3 days too early, it is not viable.

THE UTERUS

The uterus is part of the excretory passages; here the ovum develops into the foetus until the time of delivery. In the human, it is a single cavity and, together with the vagina, is the development of the embryonic Müllerian ducts, fused in the mid-line. In other mammals the fusion occurs only at the vagina and the uterus then has two "horns". Developmental abnormalities can lead to this situation occurring in the human. The human uterus is a pear-shaped organ having a small cavity and a thick muscular wall. The body of the uterus consists of a fundus (the larger, rounded upper end), an isthmus and the cervix, the cylindrical lower part with its canal. The wall consists of a great mass of smooth muscle, the *myometrium*, and an inner lining, the *endometrium*.

A great deal is known about the myometrium, in particular its response to drugs, because in virgin small rodents it provides an extremely easily set-up test-organ. When suitably perfused, it will continue to contract and relax for long periods and the action of vast numbers of relevant or irrelevant drugs can be investigated or, if necessary, quantitatively assayed. The adult non-pregnant uterus is continually undergoing cycles of contraction and relaxation. During the pre-ovulatory phase, these become more rapid and are at maximum frequency at about the time of ovulation. Following ovulation they then become slower again and more irregular. Changes in the endometrium will be discussed in the section on menstruation.

The embryo passes into the uterus on the fourth or fifth day following ovulation. It is at the 4-cell stage of development by this time.

Implantation

The developing embryo becomes attached to the uterine wall, and is said to be implanted, by the seventh day after ovulation. The lining endometrium of the uterus is prepared for this by hormonal action— particularly by progesterone—which produces the enlargement and secretion of its tubular glands without which the ovum would be unable to survive or become attached. An unfertilized ovum does not become implanted.

THE OESTROUS CYCLE

The sexual, and indeed most, behaviour of females, shows cyclic changes varying in detail in different species. One complete cycle of such changes is known as an oestrous cycle. These recurrent periods of sexual excitement or "heat" as they are popularly known, were first named *oestrus* by Walter Heape in 1901. The word originates in Virgil's description of the insect "called the gadfly, a brute with a shrill buzz that drives whole herds crazy.. .".

In many species, there is only a single oestrous period in a sexual season. The quiet period between each season is termed *anoestrus*. In other species the oestrous cycles occur more or less continuously; the short interval between two cycles is termed *dioestrus*. The precise arrangement of these sexual activities is timed to ensure that in the wild state, offspring are produced at times when the environment is least inclement. It appears to be subject to fairly rapid adaptation (as is found in the domestic animals) to different environmental conditions. Humans do not show any clear alternation between sexual rest and activity (oestrus and anoestrus); neither are there any marked behavioural changes with each sexual cycle.*

The functional significance of the behavioural changes during the oestrous cycle is that these are patterns which will ensure successful mating. Therefore, just following ovulation, sexual excitement occurs, the female will receive the male, coitus and fertilization will occur. If this course of events is not followed through, the whole cycle is repeated. This is the basic plan. Of course there are many variations on this theme in the animal kingdom (e.g. the guinea-pig female cannot mate, even if it wanted to, other than during oestrus, since a skin grows over the vaginal orifice only breaking down at oestrus). Human females are probably more easily aroused sexually at the time of ovulation.

The Menstrual Cycle

A particular variation of the oestrous cycle occurs in primates. Mating will occur in primates at any stage of the sexual cycle; the common phenomena of heat are suppressed and behavioural changes with the cycle are minimal. In the middle of the cycle a period of breakdown of the uterine wall and bleeding occurs. The relationship between menstruation and oestrus naturally interested early physicians greatly and also proved confusing to them, because mammals have one prominent feature— *oestrus*—while primates have another—*menstruation*. Are these processes comparable ?

The menstrual cycle is the interval between the onset of two periods of uterine breakdown. The modal length (i.e. the most frequently observed duration) is approximately 28 days. The average length is longer, by 2 or 3 days. In order to see the relation between the oestrous cycle and menstruation we need to know whether the menstrual flow is comparable with oestrus, i.e. in other words does it accompany ovulation?

The Time of Ovulation in the Menstrual Cycle

The generally accepted view is that ovulation takes place about the *middle* of the menstrual cycle. At first, this conclusion emerged from observations of the cyclic changes in the histology of the endometrium of the human uterus but now is based on a great deal of evidence obtained both in women and apes.

* Many women show the syndrome of "pre-menstrual tension". This consists in varying degrees of irritability, lassitude, depression and occasionally frankly psychotic changes, lasting for 2 or 3 days just before the commencement of a menstrual period. Statistical surveys show that women are more accident-prone and untidy at these times and even athletic performance or examination results suffer. It is held to be the result of water retention in extracellular spaces, including the brain, because there is a rapid weight gain which is lost with a diuresis at the time of menstruation, and is due to low oestrogen levels. Nowadays, treatment is often efficacious and consists in administering oral diuretic compounds.

Direct evidence was obtained from the inspection of ovaries at *operations* undertaken at various times in the cycle. It is possible to see with the naked eye whether ovulation has occurred recently. *Single matings* at known times, resulting in pregnancy enable the time of ovulation to be dated within a day or two and finally *live ova* have been recovered during abdominal operations in women (Allen, 1930) and also in monkeys.

Indirect evidence includes many observations which indicate that the first half of the menstrual cycle is associated with physiological parameters differing from those occurring in the second half. These suggest that some abrupt change is taking place at about the middle of the cycle. Examples are:

(1) *The endometrium* in both monkeys and humans is subject to cyclic changes. The spontaneous contractile activity of the human uterus varies with the two phases (see p. 598). Hormone levels in the blood and urine of women show characteristic differences during the first and second halves of the cycle.

(2) *The vaginal pH* is usually lower during the first half of the cycle than it is during the second.

(3) *The basal body temperature* is lower in the first part of the cycle. The transition occurs abruptly and there is a sudden rise of about 0·5°C at the presumed time of ovulation.

(4) Some women have a short-lived attack of *pelvic pain* in the "mid-interval", often accompanied by slight "inter-menstrual" bleeding. The evidence that this is due to the process of ovulation comes from a small series of cases whose ovaries have actually been examined (at operation) at the height of the pain and show clearly that ovulation has just occurred.

In view of the evidence that ovulation takes place about the middle of the menstrual cycle, it is clear that the menstrual cycle and the oestrous cycle are not strictly comparable. We may look upon the menstrual cycle as a modified form of the general type of sexual cycle, in which, in addition to the changes leading to ovulation, a phase of uterine bleeding and breakdown occurs.

Phases of the Menstrual Cycle

Although the primary event in the female sexual cycle is ovulation, there is no *easy* method in women of determining when this has occurred, so it is customary to time the menstrual cycle from the first day of the menstrual flow. Ovulation occurs, on this basis, about half-way through the cycle, at about the fourteenth day.

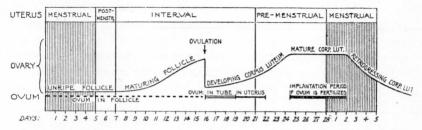

Fig. 33.7. Course of events in the human menstrual cycle. (G. W. Corner.)

The menstrual cycle can therefore be divided into a *pre-ovulatory* and a *post-ovulatory* phase. The pre-ovulatory phase seems to be more variable in length than the post-ovulatory phase so that in those cycles shorter than average it is the pre-ovulatory phase which is curtailed. In fact there is, in women, a fairly constant interval of 14 days between ovulation and the succeeding menstrual period (Fig. 33.7).

Control of Menstrual Periodicity

It is known that menstruation can occur without preceding ovulation. Hence the length of the two phases of the menstrual cycle, and the duration of the menstrual cycle as a whole, is not necessarily related to ovulation or to the processes involved in maturation of the follicle. Such "anovulatory" cycles do not have a different length from those with ovulation so that it is reasonable to assume that ovulation and the formation of a *corpus luteum* are not the primary factors underlying the cyclical rhythm of the uterus.

It is, of course, difficult to determine the precise mode of operation of the factors responsible for the menstrual rhythm, because of the impossibility of predicting the exact duration of a particular cycle. However, emotional disturbances can often alter the menstrual periodicity; in some individuals the onset of the menstrual period is delayed and in others it is accelerated following psychological stresses of various kinds. Presumably, since the length of the post-ovulatory phase is relatively constant, such psychological stress is acting to alter the time of ovulation. There is experimental evidence, obtained in monkeys, that this effect is probably mediated by nervous pathways, because severing the preganglionic fibres to the ovaries does give rise to temporary disturbances of the ovarian and also the uterine cyclical changes.

Other mechanisms also influence uterine periodicity for, in the monkey and in women, it is found that uterine bleeding occurs regularly in the absence of the ovaries provided that a constant threshold dose of oestrogen is given. Experiments suggest that the pituitary gland is not concerned in this although the adrenal cortex definitely plays an important part.

The way in which this effect is brought about is not known but possibilities include:—

(*a*) The adrenal cortex cyclically secretes small amounts of oestrogenic hormone (this would summate with the maintained constant dose given).

(*b*) Similarly, the cyclical secretion by the adrenal of androgens or progesterone would give a regular neutralization of the injected oestrogen.

(*c*) Cyclical activity of the adrenal cortex might give rise to changes in the distribution of intracellular and extracellular water in the endometrium, thus altering its sensitivity to the pre-existing, artificially administered oestrogen.

We will return to this problem of the interaction of hormones and the regulation of cyclical uterine activity in the section on the endocrine control of the sexual cycle.

Composition of Menstrual Fluid

Menstruation has been recorded in all human races and anthropoid apes. The periodic flow of mucus and blood from the uterus begins at about 14 years of age, the time of *puberty*, and continues throughout the female reproductive life until the age of cessation, the *menopause*.

The number of days for which the flow lasts varies, but is usually from 3 to 7 days. The amount of blood and debris lost varies from a total of 50 ml in virgins* to 200 ml in matrons, and in composition it is different from circulating blood as it contains serum, uterine secretions, mucosal cells and occasional tissue fragments. The flow from the external os of the uterus is not continuous but occurs at 3 to 5 min intervals with the uterine contractions. Normal menstrual fluid does not coagulate as does blood; it is partly haemolysed. The presence of clots in the fluid indicates excessive bleeding or "menorrhagia".

Changes in the Endometrium During the Mentrual Cycle

Since, as we have seen, the endometrial lining of the uterus undergoes, at the menstrual period, a structural breakdown with bleeding, it follows that considerable changes must be apparent in the histological structure of the mucosa during the course of the cycle (Fig. 33.8).

In the course of a normal cycle, the thickness of the mucosa increases from about 0·5 mm just after the menstrual period to 5·0 mm at the beginning of the phase of breakdown. The histological changes in the endometrium are well known because it is a common clinical procedure (D & C

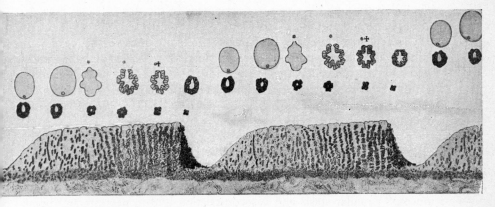

Fig. 33.8. Diagram showing, from left to right, the changes in the human endometrium (below) and ovary (top row, this month's follicle or corpora lutea; lower row, last month's) during two complete menstrual cycles. (After Schröder.)

* The volume of blood lost varies in any one woman, as well as between women, and like the time of onset of the bleeding, is also subject to psychological factors such as stress, emotion etc.

—dilation and curettage) to remove small portions of the mucosa and these may be examined by the usual histological techniques.

The changes involved can be categorized according to the time in the cycle.

(1) **Phase of Repair** (or proliferation)

This lasts from the first to the tenth day (day 1 being the first day of the menstrual period). Immediately after the endometrium has been shed, re-epithelialization begins, even before the bleeding has stopped. The tissues shed comprise the whole thickness of epithelium, sub-mucosa and part of the stratum vasculare, so that after menstruation there is left only a thin layer of endometrial stroma and the basal regions of the uterine glands. The only epithelial cells are those lining the ducts of the glands and it is these cells, at the torn-off mouths, which spread over the endometrial surface to form a new lining, which is complete within the first 4 or 5 days of the cycle. The endometrium increases in thickness as a result of proliferation of stromal cells and growth of endometrial glands and blood vessels. By the time that ovulation occurs, the endometrium is about 3 mm in depth.

(2) **Secretory Phase**

Following ovulation the thickness of the endometrium increases further, due mainly to increases in size and tortuosity of the glands, the development of secretion in them and to the increased size of the stromal cells already laid down. The blood vessels also become more tortuous and the blood flow through the tissue is augmented. In the stromal cells, glycogen and lipids are deposited.

These changes prepare the uterine lining to receive the developing embryo, the blood supply, the stored nutrient materials and the general secretions providing ideal conditions for its survival. At first the embryo simply absorbs the uterine secretions; later, after implantation, the trophoblast cells digest and absorb the endometrium itself to provide nutrition until the placental transfer mechanism is functional.

(3) **Phase of Breakdown** (menstruation)

During the last day of the menstrual cycle there is a rapid involution in the endometrium due to spasm of the small spiral arteries supplying the mucosa. Vascular stasis and vasoconstriction lead to necrosis and breakdown of the blood vessels. Not all blood vessels are affected simultaneously by the constriction and there are transitory periods of local vasodilatation during which bleeding takes place.

The mechanism responsible for the breakdown process has been investigated by an elegant method involving the transplantation of a fragment of endometrium into the anterior chamber of the eye (of a female monkey) where direct microscopical observation is then possible. The commonly held theory is that primarily, dehydration of the mucosa leads to shrinkage and hence the spiral arteries are compressed and necrosis follows. However, it is unlikely that this is the whole explanation, for menstruation occurs in certain South American monkeys in whom there are not any spiral endometrial vessels.

It has been suggested that the uterus produces a "menstrual toxin" which is responsible for the vascular damage leading to menstruation but this remains to be proved.

During menstruation, large number of leucocytes are released from the endometrial surface, as one of the many mechanisms responsible for rendering the uterus resistant to infection, in spite of the large amount of tissue destruction which occurs at this time.

CHAPTER 34

THE HORMONAL CONTROL OF SEXUAL CYCLES

THE oestrous cycle and, of course, the menstrual cycle are controlled and timed by the action of hormones. As we have seen in the last chapter relatively complex feed-back mechanisms control the output levels of various hormones. The pituitary gland constitutes the central controlling system and the inter-relationships between the anterior lobe and the ovaries bring about the cyclical changes in sexual function that we have already discussed.

The anterior pituitary gland secretes three gonadotrophic hormones:

(1) *Follicle Stimulating Hormone or F.S.H.* This hormone stimulates unripe follicles to mature and thus indirectly controls the amount of oestrogen produced by the ovary.

(2) *Luteinizing Hormone or L.H.* This hormone controls the formation of the *corpus luteum* and hence the production of progesterone by the body.

(3) *Luteotrophic Hormone or Lt.H.* This is responsible for control of the mature *corpus luteum* and also has an action on the mammary gland (it is also called Prolactin for this reason).

The Ovarian Hormones

Two female sex hormones are secreted by the ovaries, oestrogen and progesterone. Oestrogenic hormones stimulate growth and cell division in certain tissues and organs and are responsible for the development of the primary sexual organs and the secondary sexual characters in females. Progesterone is responsible for the secretory changes which occur in the endometrium to enable it to receive the fertilized ovum and also for the growth of the secretory cells in the mammary glands prior to lactation.

Oestrogens

The oestrogens are secreted only by the ovaries in normal females. In pregnancy and certain pathological states, however, oestrogenic substances may be secreted in large amounts by other tissues. In the human, six oestrogenic compounds are known to be present in circulating blood but, of these, three are considered to have functional significance. *β-oestradiol* and *oestrone* are found in relatively large amounts in the venous outflow from the ovaries and *oestriol* is their oxidation metabolic end-product. All these substances are steroids and are derived from cholesterol, the primary compound in their synthesis being 17-α-hydroxy-progesterone.

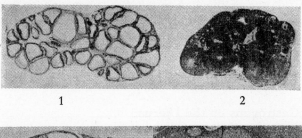

1 2

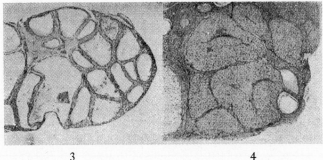

3 4

FIG. 34.1. To illustrate the effect of the follicle-stimulating and luteinising hormones on immature ovaries.

(1) Follicle-stimulating effect on rat, from F.S.H. fraction of 1 g. sheep pituitary. No luteinisation.
(2) Ovary of rat after unfractionated (F.S.H. and L.H.) pituitary of sheep, 0·1 g. Full of corpora lutea.
(3) Rabbit, after F.S.H. fraction of 2·5 g. sheep pituitary.
(4) Rabbit, after 2·5 g. whole sheep pituitary.
(After Hisaw *et al.*)

The ovarian oestrogens combine in the plasma with plasma protein, about 75 per cent being in combination and the remainder in free form.

The liver inactivates oestrogens, as can easily be demonstrated by transplanting the ovaries into the spleen so that their venous outflow all has to pass through the liver. In these circumstances, no oestrogenic activity can be detected in the experimental animal, although the ovaries are active and functional.

Oestrogens are secreted by the *theca interna* cells of the developing follicle and since this development is controlled by the pituitary gonadotrophins, it is clear that the level of oestrogen in the circulating blood is ultimately determined by the action of the anterior pituitary gland.

Function of Oestrogens

As already mentioned, oestrogens are mainly concerned with the regulation of cell division and growth, particularly of the sexual organs. Before puberty, only small amounts are secreted, but after, large amounts are produced under the influence of pituitary gonadotrophins. Their effect is to increase the size of the Fallopian tubes, uterus, vagina and external genitalia until they reach adult dimensions. The breasts and skeletal growth are also affected.

The nature of these widespread bodily effects of oestrogens can be studied by the administration of these substances to ovariectomized animals.

Effects of Oestrogens on the Uterus

The administration of oestrogen gives rise to an increase in size of the uterus as a result of cellular proliferation. Removal of the ovaries, as might be expected, has the opposite effect of decreasing the size of the uterus. The mucosa is also affected by oestrogens. Its thickness and vascularity are increased and its cellular water and electrolyte content rises.

In the absence of oestrogen, uterine muscle is quiescent; when oestrogens are given the myometrium undergoes rhythmical contractions and its sensitivity to oxytocin is enhanced. These effects are, in fact, due to the action of oestrone on the resting membrane potential of uterine muscle which is increased (with resultant changes in threshold and excitability).* The effects of oestrogens on the Fallopian tubes are similar.

Effects on the Vagina

Oestrogen administration, in the ovariectomized animal, results in cell division and cornification in the vaginal mucosa. There is, in addition, deposition of glycogen and increased vascularity. Detailed changes in histological structure of the vaginal mucosa can be detected by taking vaginal smears for microscopical observation and in animals the time in the oestrous cycle can be determined. In the human these changes are less marked but are still useful in determining when ovulation has occurred.

Metabolic Effects

The main action of oestrogens is on the state of hydration of tissues and on the sodium and chloride balance. Retention of sodium and chloride ions occurs in the kidney, urine volume is less and hence water-loading tends to occur. There is also an increase in general anabolic reactions, including protein retention (positive nitrogen balance), calcium and phosphate retention and increased deposition of fat in subcutaneous tissues.

Effects on Bone

Oestrogens give rise to an increase in osteoblast activity and at puberty the female skeleton is affected in a characteristic way. Early epiphyseal

---

* Action potentials only occur in normal uterine muscle or in muscle from an ovariec-tomized female if it is treated with oestrogen. The rise in membrane potential produced by oestrogen only takes place if calcium ions are present. The general effects of oestrogen are to increase excitability in endometrial cells and to give rise to increased spontaneous activity. (See Chapter 42.)

union occurs as a result of oestrogenic activity with the result that female skeletal growth, in general, stops at an age two, or three years earlier than in the male. A female eunuch is, on this account, several inches taller than her normal sister because of the absence of oestrogen production.

Function of Progesterone

Progesterone is mainly concerned with the preparation of the uterine wall for implantation of the fertilized ovum and preparation of the mammary glands for lactation. It is secreted, as we have already seen, by the *theca lutein* cells and as these are controlled both by L.H. and Lt.H. from the anterior pituitary; here again is an example of the overall influence of the pituitary gland on sex hormone levels.

The Effect of Progesterone on the Uterus

Here the effects are "secretory". By this we mean that the uterine glands are stimulated, they become tortuous, the lumen filled with secretion and water accumulates in the tissues. This so-called "progestational response" of the endometrium occurs after it has previously been primed with oestrogen. In the absence of this initial priming the changes brought about by progesterone are much less marked.

An additional effect on the uterus is that the contractions of the myometrium are inhibited by the presence of progesterone. This is a physiological mechanism to prevent premature expulsion of the developing embryo, and is brought about by hyperpolarization of the uterine smooth muscle cell membrane which leads to the expected decreased excitability. A similar effect on motility is to be found in the Fallopian tubes.

Effects on Mammary Glands

The proliferation of alveolar secretory cells is promoted by the action of progesterone. Milk secretion does not actually occur, however, until the additional action of prolactin further stimulates the breast. Swelling of the breasts occurs as a result of increased subcutaneous tissue fluid accumulation.

Effects on Water Balance and Electrolytes

The effects of progesterone are very similar to those of aldosterone (see Chapter 32) and sodium, chloride and water reabsorption from the distal tubules are increased. Progesterone can replace deoxycorticosterone in the therapy of adrenal cortical insufficiency. However, in the normal individual there is competitive inhibition between the actions of progesterone and aldosterone, presumably because both hormones are combining with the same receptor sites in the kidney tubules. Hence in the normal, progesterone has the paradoxical effect of actually reducing sodium and chloride retention because its effects are very much less potent, although it still blocks the action of normally secreted aldosterone.

Progesterone also has a slight stimulating effect on protein breakdown; it has a slight elevating effect on basal body temperature, the mechanism of which is unknown and, as one would expect from its steroid structure, it has effects which mimic androgens and adrenal corticoids in nature.

Cyclic Activity of Hormones

In summary, the events in the oestrous cycle consist of development and maturation of follicles in the ovaries, ovulation (with certain behavioural changes) and the growth of *corpora lutea* to control progestational changes in the endometrium. In the absence of the implantation of a fertilized ovum the cycle is repeated; in primates breakdown and shedding of the endometrium also occurs.

These repeated cyclic changes in reproductive activity in the female are brought about by changes in circulating levels of the two primary sex hormones, oestrone and progesterone. These levels are set by complex interactions between the ovaries, the anterior lobe of the pituitary and its secretion of gonadotrophins, and the nervous system (see Chapter 32 for details of hypothalamic control of hormones).

The exact way in which the pituitary regulates the ovarian hormones is unknown but work in rodents seems to show that there are extensive feed-back mechanisms by which the circulating blood-levels of oestrogens and progesterone affect the pituitary output of F.S.H. and L.H. respectively.

The experimental evidence for this follows the lines we have already discussed in the chapter on endocrinology. This is a simple concept, and consisted of administering either pituitary hormone (or implanting pituitary glands) in immature experimental animals. Ovaries examined later showed that follicles had been stimulated, ovulation had occurred and luteinization taken place. Some of the extracts produced mainly growth of follicles; others gave rise to ovulation and *corpora lutea* in addition. It is, moreover, found that a small dose of L.H. augments the ovarian response to F.S.H., so one can say that it is essentially a synergistic action and that balanced amounts of each hormone are necessary to produce the observed effects. F.S.H. and L.H. are mucoproteins, secreted by distinct cell types in the peripheral and central parts of the pars distalis of the pituitary respectively. Lt.H. (or prolactin) is an unconjugated protein of high molecular weight. (Fig. 34.1 shows the effects of F.S.H. and L.H. on rats' ovaries.)

Pituitary-ovarian Feed-back Mechanisms

Pituitary F.S.H., combined with a small amount of L.H. gives rise to ovarian production of oestrogen. This raises the blood level of oestrogen which in turn has a feed-back action, which results in increased output of L.H. and decreased output of F.S.H. Ovulation and luteinization then occur. As the *corpus luteum* regresses, both progesterone and oestrogen secretion fall off. The pituitary, in consequence, again begins to secrete more F.S.H. and thus the cycle is repeated. These cyclic variations in hormone level have been shown experimentally in the blood and in the urine. (For a summary see Fig. 36.2.)

In the human, it is possible to inhibit ovulation by giving progesterone but it is much more difficult to induce ovulation artificially by the injection of gonadotrophins. One imagines that this is because a finely graded amount of F.S.H. and L.H. is needed for growth of the follicle and that the proportions of the two hormones must be appropriately altered at the correct stage of growth in order to induce ovulation. It is interesting to note that follicles may be stimulated hormonally and fail to rupture. Cysts in the ovary can be produced in this way and a possible cause of the clinical condition of follicular cysts in the ovary, is an endocrine imbalance.

FERTILITY CONTROL

Thomas Malthus, in his famous book "An Essay on Population", published in 1799, pointed out the need for a balance between the numbers of a population and the amount of food required. Cautious estimates made by expert demographers indicate that the present world population of $2\frac{1}{2}$ billion, will become 4 billion by A.D. 2000 and 6 billion by A.D. 2050. The agriculturalists at the 1954 Rome Conference on Population claimed that the food production of the world might be doubled, but not increased more. It is clear, therefore, that the control of population is perhaps the most important social problem at the present time.

Contraceptive Methods*

Contraception is employed (a) to postpone the first pregnancy, (b) to space out children and (c) to prevent conception occurring at all.† Methods in common use depend on one, or a combination, of four different principles:

(1) Occlusive and impermeable barriers to the passage of sperm into the uterus (rubber diaphragms worn by the woman; rubber sheaths worn by the male).

TABLE 34.1

The efficacy of contraceptive methods

Method	Number of Pregnancies per 100 Women–Years of use
Vaginal douche . .	18–36
Jelly or cream . . .	6–49
Withdrawal . . .	3–38
Safe period . . .	14–35
Condom . . .	6–28
Diaphragm . . .	3–34
Intra-uterine device . .	2– 8
Oral tablets . . .	0– 3

* AMA Committee on Human Reproduction, *J. Amer. Med. Ass.* **194,** 462 (1965).

† It must be understood that the *fear* of pregnancy and its consequent disastrous effects on the life and behaviour of women is a very common and potent cause of marital disharmony. One of the major contributions of modern medicine and the discoveries of contraceptive techniques of proven efficacy, is in lightening this psychological burden which had to be borne by previous generations of women.

(2) Chemical spermaticides which immobilize or kill the spermatozoa in the upper part of the vagina or cervical canal (quinine, chinosol or phenyl-mercuric-acetate).

(3) Mechanical irritant devices placed within the uterine cavity which render impossible implantation and embedding of the fertilized ovum.

(4) The oral contraceptive pill.

The relative efficacy of these methods is shown in Table 34.1.

Oral Contraception (general principles)

Since this is illustrative of applied physiological principles, oral methods of fertility control will be considered in more detail. The administration of progesterone was known for many years to inhibit ovulation in experimental animals. When this effect was studied in humans it was found that ovulation could be prevented in a group of normal women by giving them 300 mg of progesterone daily between day 5 and day 24 of the menstrual cycle. However, this represented a large amount of the hormone to administer and there were unpleasant side effects, apart from the fact that it was not completely effective. In 1955 clinical studies were undertaken with orally active progestational substances called 19-nor steroids. Field trials were carried out in Puerto Rico which showed the contraceptive effectiveness of these compounds (nor-ethisterone and nor-ethynodrel) particularly when combined with a small amount of oestrogen. (Twenty-one tablets were given, one each day as a course, at the end of which time progesterone withdrawal bleeding occurred.)

Physiological Action

The precise way in which oral contraceptives work is not known at present. Primarily, they are considered to act by the inhibition of ovulation as a result of depression of the pituitary output of gonadotrophin. Oral progestogens prevent the rise (and peak at the fourteenth day) in concentration of L.H. in the blood. F.S.H. is unaffected. Oestrogens, in small doses, have the opposite effect on L.H. secretion, i.e. it is increased, but in larger amounts oestrogenic compounds suppress ovulation by lowering secretion of both L.H. and F.S.H.

Other effects on the reproductive system are produced by oral contraceptives, which may play an important part in their action. The viscosity of cervical mucus increases at the mid-cycle; the endometrium is thin and hypoplastic, both factors which militate against fertilization and successful implantation of the ovum if it has been fertilized.

There are, in a small minority of women, unpleasant side-effects experienced with oral contraceptives such as nausea, vomiting, tenderness in the breasts, headache and various mild psychiatric disturbances. These are, in the main, the same kind of unpleasant symptoms as occur in the early months of pregnancy. Long-term adverse effects are said to include the possibility of an increase in frequency of cervical cancer in women regularly taking the pill and also an increase in the incidence of thrombosis of peripheral blood vessels due to hypercoagulability of the blood. In fact, studies extending over ten years show a slightly decreased incidence of cervical smears giving cytological evidence of carcinomatous change and there is as yet (1966) no proof that arterial or venous thrombosis is associated with the use of oral contraceptives.

PUBERTY

At the time of puberty, the pituitary begins to secrete gonadotrophins, the ovaries show developing follicles and *corpora lutea*, and the *secondary sexual characteristics* begin to develop. Adult body contour is attained, public and axillary hair growth takes place, and the reproductive organs (uterus, vagina, mammary glands, etc.) become mature.*

The end of the pubertal stage is at the *menarche*, or onset of menstruation which occurs between the ages of 12 to 15 years.

THE MENOPAUSE

Menstruation continues for 30 to 40 years and then ceases, usually gradually. Cessation is termed the *menopause* and the period immediately preceding this, when ovarian sexual function is declining, is termed the *climacteric*. At this time, follicles in the ovary are depleted, the menstrual periods may become profuse (menorrhagia), painful (dysmenorrhea), and irregular; they ultimately cease completely. Blood oestrogen levels fall, urinary excretion therefore falls and in virtue of the interrupted feedback to the pituitary due to lack of ovarian function gonadotrophin secretion (and excretion in the urine) is augmented. This gonadotrophin is mainly F.S.H., and the *rôle* of feed-back in its production is shown by the fact that when oestrone is injected the amount of it in the plasma is reduced.

One must conclude, therefore, that the primary cause of the menopause is exhaustion of the ovaries. The pituitary continues to function and produces more F.S.H. than normally. Unpleasant symptoms often accompany the menopause, presumably as the result of hormonal changes, and include vasomotor effects (hot flushes), sweating and other autonomic disturbances. Psychiatric disturbance is relatively common during the climacteric, also as a result of hormonal imbalance. These symptoms are often treated by small doses of oestrogens.

* Gabriel Chevallier's somewhat Rabelaisian novel "Clochemerle" should be consulted for details of the secondary sexual characteristics of the female and indeed for descriptions of various other aspects of reproductive and renal physiology. One such description is of Judith Toumignon, a local beauty, "whose lovely curves were so designed that your gaze was held fast until you had taken them all in. It seemed as though Pheidias, Raphael and Rubens had worked together to produce it, with such complete mastery had the modelling of the prominent points been carried out, eschewing scantiness in every way, and dexterously insisting upon amplitude and fullness in such manner as to provide the eyes of desire with conspicuous landmarks on which to rest. Her breasts were two lovely promontories...at the sight of which the men of Clochemerle grew hoarse of speech and were overcome by feelings of recklessness and desperation."

CHAPTER 35

PREGNANCY, PARTURITION AND LACTATION

Fertilization

Due to the delayed passage of the ovum in the Fallopian tube, the spermatozoa meet the ovum here and fertilization takes place, normally in the ampulla. The ovum is surrounded by many follicle cells embedded in an intercellular substance which is largely *hyaluronic acid*. Spermatozoa secrete an enzyme called *hyaluronidase*, which breaks down this ground substance and enables them to penetrate the outer layers of cells.

When the fertilizing spermatozoon enters the vitellus, the ovum undergoes cell division with the production of the *female pronucleus*. The *male pronucleus* is the head of the spermatozoon, the two unite and this is followed immediately by the first mitotic division of the embryonic nucleus to give

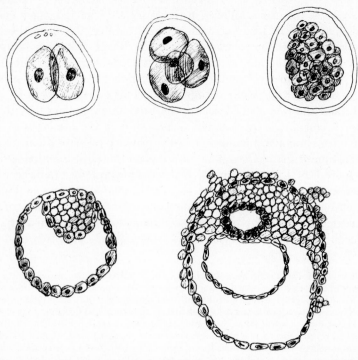

FIG. 35.1. Development of fertilized ovum. *Upper row:* segmentation, 2, 4 and many cell stages. *Lower left:* blastocyst. *Lower right:* developing embryo.

the first two daughter cells. As soon as one spermatozoon penetrates the zona pellucida, a chemical change occurs over the surface of the zona preventing the entry of any other spermatozoa. This block may fail, but if several spermatozoa penetrate the ovum at once, the normal events leading to fusion of the male and female pro-nuclei do not occur, and fertilization fails.

Implantation

The fertilized ovum is transported to the cavity of the uterus where it remains free, on the uterine wall for several days. This time, of course, coincides with the height of the secretory, progestational phase of endometrial development and the uterine glandular secretion provides nutriment and a bland environment for the developing embryo. Not all the cells in the embryo divide at the same rate; those on the outer surface are smaller in size and form the trophoblast.

Embedding in the endometrium occurs in the early blastocyst stage. It does so in virtue of the trophoblast secreting proteolytic enzymes which digest the endometrial tissue with which it comes into contact.* It sinks into the uterine wall like a hot shot into a piece of butter, but as it sinks it is all the time getting larger and hence does not fall out again.

Chorionic Gonadotrophin

The cells of the trophoblast also secrete "chorionic" gonadotrophin, which passes into the maternal circulation and prevents degeneration of the *corpus luteum*. Because of continued hormonal stimulation of the *corpus luteum*, progesterone is produced in gradually increasing amounts and the endometrium develops into a *decidua*. Also menstruation is inhibited for the same reason, a state of affairs termed the "physiological amenorrhoea of pregnancy". Chorionic gonadotrophin passes easily through the kidneys and appears in the urine of the mother.

Pregnancy Tests

Since human chorionic gonadotrophin appears in the urine within 10–12 days after ovulation, some form of bio-assay should enable this fact to be put to applied use as a pregnancy test. The amount of urinary gonadotrophin reaches a peak at about the seventh week of pregnancy and is very largely composed of L.H., so

---

* Chorion-epithelioma

The trophoblast of the developing embryo burrows into the endometrium until a balance is struck between tissue destruction and new growth of the trophoblastic villi. In some circumstances this equilibrium fails and the result is an overgrowth of the chorionic cells. In this way tumours arise ranging from the comparatively benign in the uterus to the overwhelmingly malignant.

These tumours give rise to large amounts of chorionic gonadotrophin and in consequence the ovaries are often filled with *lutein cysts* and the Ascheim-Zondek test may be positive at 1 in 1,000 dilution. Death ensues from haemorrhages or from secondary deposits of the chorionic tumour in the lungs and elsewhere, often within only a few weeks of the onset.

that a possible biological test for it would be whether or not ovaries in experimental animals show *corpus luteum* formation when the urine is injected into them.

The *Ascheim-Zondek* test depends on the fact that chorionic gonadotrophin induces hyperaemia (increased vascularity) in immature mouse ovaries. The *Friedman* test involves the production of ovulation by the intravenous injection of pregnant women's urine into the rabbit, and the *Hogben* test utilizes the Xenopus toad, which ovulates when immersed in urine containing gonadotrophin. A thriving industry centres on testing urine samples for gonadotrophin using these toads. Gonadotrophins can now be detected by chemical analysis.

The Decidual Reaction

While the trophoblast is making living space for the embryo and absorbing food materials, reactive changes are taking place in the endometrium. Initially this occurs in the vicinity of the ovum, but later the whole uterine lining takes part. The *decidua of pregnancy* is the result.

(1) There is proliferation and hyperplasia of the endometrial stromal cells, to form large polygonal cells, closely packed and relatively lacking in intercellular fibrillary material. Thus the endometrium is thicker and softer.

(2) The uterine glands alter. Superficially they are small but in the deeper layers they become tortuous and dilated.

(3) The decidua thus is divided into two layers, a superficial compact layer and a deep, spongy layer.

These changes adapt the endometrium to combine with the foetal tissues of the placenta for the purpose of transfer of oxygen, carbon dioxide and food materials between maternal and foetal circulatory systems.

The Placenta

The embryonic mesoderm sends processes containing foetal blood vessel loops between the inner and outer layers of the trophoblast, to form the primary or *anchoring villi*. Later, by budding and branching from these, *secondary villi* are formed whose ends project into the intervillous blood spaces. These secondary villi are very numerous and comprise most of the villous septum covering the placental area. Hence, over a large area, maternal and foetal blood is separated by very thin connective tissue and a thin layer of trophoblast. The *discrete placenta* is formed by the third months of pregnancy.

Placenta as an Endocrine Organ

The placenta has two major functions:

(*a*) It enables exchange to occur between the maternal and foetal blood although these do not mix.

(*b*) It has endocrine functions directed towards maintaining a suitable environment for the developing foetus.

The placenta secretes oestrogens, progesterone and gonadotrophins and analysis shows that the foetal part, in particular the trophoblast cells, have the highest concentration of them, so it is reasonable to suppose that these cells are secretory. The high hormone levels produced by the placenta may sometimes affect the embryo itself. For instance, it is not usual for human newly-born males to have hypertrophied mammary glands. This may also be one cause of male pseudo-hermaphrodism (see p. 634).

Extra-uterine Changes in Pregnancy

From the fifth or sixth week onwards for a period of weeks or months, many pregnant women often experience frequent episodes of nausea and vomiting, particularly on rising each morning. This *morning sickness* varies from a minor inconvenience to a severe disturbance (*hyperemesis gravidarum*) which may necessitate the termination of pregnancy. The cause is unknown but is probably the result of a hypersensitivity to foreign protein—the chorionic gonadotrophin—which is partly of paternal origin. Other unpleasant symptoms may occur such as pain in, and enlargement of, the breasts, frequency of micturition and digestive upset. Frequently, there are periods of craving for unusual foods and, although it is said by some to represent an attempt by nature to secure supplies of some essential mineral or vitamin, there is no evidence for this view. This condition becomes definitely pathological when materials such as household coke are consumed with relish. Changes occur in the activity of the central nervous system, presumably as a result of hormonal factors operating. Emotional outbursts, irritability and depressive episodes are common, but it must be remembered that pregnancy is essentially a physiological process and in consequence many pregnant women alter for the better in their attitude.

Body weight increases due to water retention as well as the added bulk of the foetus, membranes, amniotic fluid and the uterus. Fat is deposited. The distension of the anterior abdominal wall is accommodated by splitting of the skin which shows up as the so-called *striae gravidarum*. Symptoms and signs of increased intra-abdominal pressure may include oedema of the legs, dyspnoea, palpitations and the dilatation of superficial veins of the legs (due to mechanical obstruction of the femoral veins). Obvious changes also occur in the mammary glands which hypertrophy and which exude a clear (or in multiparae*—a milky) fluid which can be expressed in the latter half of pregnancy. Pigment is deposited in the areola round the nipple, which turns from pink to brown during the first pregnancy, and also in other regions of the skin. Occasionally, unsightly patches of pigmentation occur on the face (chloasma uterinum) but fortunately fade after the child is born.

Nitrogen is retained by the mother in excess of the needs of the foetus; the same applies to calcium. Often the red cell count falls and there is a leucocytosis. Other blood changes are a lipaemia, cholesterolaemia and a

* A "multiparous" woman is one who has borne children previously.

reduction in the alkali reserve. Cardiac output rises progressively in the second half of pregnancy—presumably a physiological mechanism required to maintain adequate oxygen supply to the foetus.

Changes in the Uterus in Pregnancy

The uterus has a number of functions during the course of pregnancy. At first it acts as a suitable site for the fertilized ovum to pass its early developmental stages; later its wall is adapted to implantation and to the reception of the placenta. During pregnancy it enlarges to keep pace with the growing foetus and eventually it plays a large part in the expulsion of the foetus during parturition.

Thus the virgin uterus in the human is about 5 ml in capacity; at the end of the period of gestation it is 5 or 6 litres. The increase in weight likewise is from 50 g to 1 Kg. All structures hypertrophy, particularly the myometrium. Each muscle fibre increases in length 5–10 times and its diameter about 5 times. There is also a hyperplasia (increased number of fibres). These changes are due to:

(*a*) the action of oestrogens. There is a slight hypertrophy during oestrus; also in female castrates treated with oestrogens.

(*b*) Distension of the uterus also causes hypertrophy, even if produced by an inflated balloon within the lumen.

Uterine Contractions

In the first half of pregnancy there are continuous and regular contractions of the myometrium once or twice per minute. These gradually increase in amplitude during pregnancy until, during the last two weeks, the contractions resemble those of parturition but on a smaller scale. The uterus is sensitive to posterior pituitary secretion (A.D.H. in humans; oxytocin in guinea pig) and the response to a given amount of hormone increases throughout pregnancy.

There are three factors causing this increased excitability:

(*a*) there is a steady rise in circulating oestrogen levels throughout pregnancy. These stimulate the myometrium;

(*b*) during the latter months of pregnancy progesterone levels decrease. Progesterone inhibits the stimulating effect of oxytocin;

(*c*) distension stimulates muscle directly.

HORMONAL CONTROL OF PREGNANCY

In the pregnant female the anterior lobe of the pituitary gland is hypertrophied. The thyroid and adrenal cortex also increase in size. The urine contains large quantities of oestrogens, pregnanediol (the excretion product of progesterone) and chorionic gonadotrophins. The *corpus luteum* does not regress in the presence of an implanted fertilized ovum, possibly due to raised oestrogen production by it and its gonadotrophins. The precise way in which this persistence is brought about is unknown but it is clear that this phenomenon is the initial trigger in the sequence of hormonal changes which control pregnancy.

The activity of the *corpus luteum* continues up to the third or fourth month of pregnancy, after which time the glandular cells undergo gradual involution. Progesterone is produced and gives rise to the following effects:

(*a*) It enables pregnancy to continue because menstrual cycles and ovulation are inhibited.

(*b*) It inhibits uterine motility.*

(*c*) It maintains the progestational stage of endometrial development and has a similar action on the formation of the placenta.

(*d*) Alveolar development of the mammary gland is stimulated (see p. 619).

By the third month the placenta takes over the function of producing progesterone and also produces large amounts of chorionic gonadotrophins, oestrogens and ACTH. It is the main source of oestrogens in pregnancy.

The hormonal interactions in pregnancy are complex and not yet fully understood. One of the main reasons for this lies in the fact that there is considerable confusion in the experimental evidence, a state of affairs not helped by the undoubted fact that the various hormones do have different actions in different species.

The Pituitary Gland

A great deal of information on the *rôle* played by the various endocrine glands in pregnancy can be obtained by their removal and observation of the consequent effects.

In some animals the whole pituitary gland is necessary for gestation to continue and it cannot be removed at any stage of pregnancy (e.g. rabbit, dog). In others it can be removed without obvious effect on the pregnancy (cat, mouse, rat).

The posterior lobe is not necessary for normal parturition.

The Ovary

Presence of at least one ovary is necessary for the normal continuance of gestation in all species during the first week because presumably the process of embedding will not occur in the absence of its progesterone secretion. After that, in some species (rat and mouse) removal terminates pregnancy; in others (women, mares) the ovaries can be dispensed with without interfering with the pregnancy.

---

* In cases of habitual abortion it used to be the practice to administer large doses of progesterone on the basis that this would remedy a natural deficiency of it, deemed to be responsible for the premature termination of pregnancy.

The Placenta

In mice, rats and monkeys when the placenta is fully established, the foetus can be removed without disturbing it and the placenta will remain and be delivered at the time for normal parturition. Meanwhile, the extra-uterine signs of pregnancy persist although they disappear if the placenta is removed.

This suggests that pregnancy is a complex maternal syndrome, having a definite duration controlled by the placenta.

Summary

(1) Changes in the uterus are controlled by oestrogens and progesterone.

(2) Activity of the *corpus luteum* is controlled by chorionic gonadotrophin and hence oestrogens (and uterine contents later in pregnancy).

(3) Activity of the ovary is controlled by the anterior pituitary. In pregnancy ovulation is inhibited.

(4) Activity of the anterior pituitary affects uterine contents by an unknown mechanism.

(5) The pituitary gonadotrophin secretion increases until just before parturition.

PARTURITION

We have seen that the uterus is quiescent and not undergoing violent contractions during the first half of pregnancy. From the thirty-sixth week onwards the contractions increase in frequency, strength and duration, having a marked effect. They compress the foetus, particularly downward, and as a result it assumes the correct anatomical position for expulsion. The *internal os* of the uterus begins to dilate and the pregnant woman, at sometime between the thirty-sixth to fortieth week, is amazed to discover that her stomach has apparently become smaller again. This is due to the infant's head "engaging" in the pelvis, i.e. it sinks into the pelvic canal (Fig. 35.2).

Stages of Labour

With the onset of "labour" (midwives' terminology for parturition) uterine contractions now occur strongly and are accompanied by painful sensations presumably due to pressure within the myometrium rising above arterial pressure and so giving rise to ischaemic pain. These "pains" (midwives' term for contractions) occur at first every $\frac{1}{2}$ to 1 hr but then every 3–5 min lasting about $\frac{1}{2}$–1 min each and result in the final length of uterine muscle being a little shorter with each one.

Labour is divided into three stages:

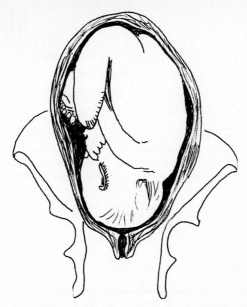

FIG. 35.2. First position of the vertex; left occipito-anterior (LOA). Vertex presentations occur in 96 per cent of all cases. There are four types, according to the position of the back of the foetus or of its occiput. If the vertex is in the uterine fundus, the presentation is abnormal and is said to be a breech presentation.

1st Stage

The cervix is dilated by these continual contractions and usually—but not necessarily—the membranes rupture, allowing escape of amniotic fluid ("breaking of the waters").

2nd Stage

Full dilatation of the cervix marks the beginning of the 2nd stage. This is characterized by longer, stronger contractions which force the infant down through the pelvic canal. Abdominal muscles and diaphragm also contract with the uterus and the infant is finally expelled from its hitherto comfortable nidus to an inclement world (see Fig. 35.3).

3rd Stage

After a rest of 5 to 10 min, the uterus again contracts vigorously and the placenta, with the ruptured membranes, is expelled; the uterus then contracts down and venous sinuses are thus closed up.

Parturition in the human *primigravida* (mother having her first baby) lasts on the average 15 to 20 hr. The next labour lasts a mere 7 to 10 hr and may indeed, to the consternation of all concerned, be very much more

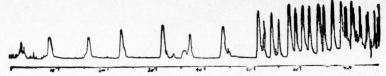

FIG. 35.3. Record of the intra-uterine pressure of a woman in labour.

The contractions are relatively infrequent up to the fifty minutes' mark, when the first stage ends and the second begins; they immediately become more frequent and more violent. The head of the child was born after seventy-five minutes, at the moment indicated by the sudden fall in the pressure below the previous minima, and the body, just after the last rise in pressure. (Bourne and Burn.)

rapid than this. After several children (*multipara*) two or three good contractions only, may do the trick!

The Puerperium

After delivery (a period called the puerperium) the uterus involutes and lactation begins after about 24 to 48 hr. Many authorities hold that menstruation does not begin until lactation has finished or has been terminated. This is undoubtedly not the case, and in many women the periods begin two or three months after birth even though lactation is proceeding normally.

CONTROL OF PARTURITION

Factors determining the end of pregnancy and the onset of parturition are unknown. However there is good evidence that the end of gestation is accompanied by large changes in the hormone balance. The major changes are

(1) Decrease in luteal hormone secretion.

(2) Decrease in circulating oestrogens.

Progesterone

There is direct evidence that parturition is *preceded* by a fall in progesterone production. The pregnanediol excreted in the urine decreases before parturition. In cases of habitual abortion there is often a lower pregnanediol excretion than normal. It is possible to prolong artificially the duration of pregnancy in rabbits if the luteal phase is also prolonged by giving progesterone or by giving gonadotrophin. In fact, in the rabbit near term, gonadotrophins can be given, a new *corpus luteum* is stimulated in the ovary and parturition does not begin until *this corpus luteum* has regressed.

Oestrogens

Circulating oestrone levels reach a peak just before birth of the foetus. There is a sudden increase just before parturition. (Fig 35.4).

It has been suggested that the uterus is sensitized to the action of oxytocin by the presence of oestrogen and that oxytocic activity is inhibited on uterine muscle by the presence of progesterone. This might represent a possible mechanism to account for the onset of labour in view of the hormone changes described above but the difficulty in accepting such an explanation is that by no means all species have these changes nor do the actions of oxytocin occur in all species.

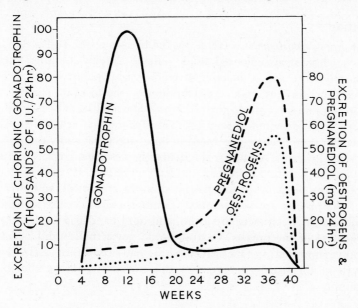

Fig. 35.4. Urinary excretion of chorionic gonadotrophin, pregnanediol and oestrogens during pregnancy.

Distension of the uterus is an obvious stimulus which might, upon reaching a certain level, start labour. However, this is not so because in multiple human pregnancy the uterus and contents are very large; in animals, after removal of the foetus, the placenta is of negligible bulk, but in both instances parturition occurs normally at the right time. Several other mechanisms to account for the onset of parturition have been postulated and it is by no means impossible that a combination of numerous stimuli is in fact responsible. In biological terms, such a system would have a greater safety margin. Parturition can take place after dorsal section of the spinal cord and even after complete destruction of the lumbo-sacral region.

LACTATION AND THE MAMMARY GLANDS

Development of Mammary Glands in Pregnancy

The mammary glands enlarge in pregnancy due to the combined effects of oestrogens and progesterone. In the majority of mammals, oestrogens increase the development of the duct system; progesterone influences the proliferation of alveoli. Since these hormones are ineffective in producing this mammary development in hypophysectomized animals, it is now generally agreed that growth hormone and adrenocortical hormones are essential as well. Prolactin (which is the same as luteotrophic hormone) is required to start of the actual secretion of milk. Although the pituitary is not necessary for the continued secretion of milk in certain species, in the human, necrosis of the pituitary (which may follow severe post-partum haemorrhage: Sheehan's syndrome) abolishes lactation.

Lactation

In women, *colostrum* is secreted by the breasts at the end of pregnancy and is a clear straw-coloured fluid, possibly largely an ultra-filtrate of plasma from the as yet inactive alveoli. It is popularly held to have a laxative function but upon consideration of the fecal proclivities of the new-born infant, any mechanism such as this would seem to be gilding the lily. True milk does not appear until some three days after parturition.

Secretion then occurs; it is rapid in onset and is generally thought to be due to the lowering of maternal circulating oestrogens after parturition acting on the pituitary to release suddenly prolactin. If suckling does not take place the breasts become distended and very painful, and after a few days if the breasts are not emptied, lactation ceases. If breast-feeding is not undertaken, oestrogens are given, and tight bandages used, to prevent engorgement of the breasts. Oestrogens do not actually inhibit lactation, as is often supposed; in fact, if feeding the baby continues, oestrogens can be given in the usual amounts (for this purpose) without affecting the milk supply.

Secretion and Expulsion of Milk

The process of suckling (or emptying the breast in any other way) initiates nervous reflexes which lead to:

(*a*) further milk secretion;

(*b*) expulsion of milk already in the gland.

Milk *secretion* is due to release of prolactin reflexly from the pituitary. *Expulsion* is due to the reflex secretion of oxytocin from the posterior pituitary gland, which stimulates contraction of the myoepithelial cells in the duct system. Children are normally weaned at six to nine months of age; but lactation and suckling can be continued for several years and, indeed, this is often the case in certain Eastern cultures or among famine-stricken populations.

Clinically it is found that failure of lactation may occur and is often due initially to failure of milk ejection. In such cases, an injection of oxytocin at the beginning of breast-feeding may greatly increase the milk yield, at the time and thereafter. Many of these cases have a psychological origin. A cow, for instance, will "hide her milk" if she is frightened or is disturbed by the presence of a different milk-maid. The calf's presence, on the other hand, gives rise to an increase in milk flow. The presence of the child, or hearing its cry, will stimulate a nursing mother's milk flow, and many complex conditioned reflexes are often built up in the process.

Milk

Milk is a white opaque fluid containing lactose and caseinogen in solution and various salts and fats in suspension.

Milk ferments, if allowed to stand, by the action of *bacillus lacticus*, the lactose being hydrolysed to lactic acid. The resultant increase in acidity denatures the caseinogen and it "curdles" or eventually coagulates as in cheese. Cream is formed on the top of milk because the fat droplets rise, a process which can be hastened with a centrifuge (cream separator). Violent agitation of cream (churning) gives a phase reversal. Cream is a suspension of fat globules in a watery medium, while butter is a suspension of watery droplets in fat.

The chemical composition of milk is not the same in all mammals. Cows' milk, for instance, contains less lactose and more caseinogen and salts than does human milk. This difference is largely the reason why it is often difficult to raise babies on cows' milk and why its composition must be altered by dilution and altering curd formation before it can be used in artificial feeding. The caseinogen is the difficult factor. It is not due merely to the difference in *amount* in cows' milk but also to the difference in its nature. On addition of acid, cows' caseinogen gives a solid curd; human milk is flocculent.

CHAPTER 36

THE MALE REPRODUCTIVE SYSTEM

THE male reproductive system produces spermatozoa for fertilization of the ovum. Spermatozoa are produced in the *testes*; the rest of the male genital system consists of the necessary ducts for storage and transport of spermatozoa to the exterior, and glands for producing secretions in which the sperm are suspended. The testes are organs of internal secretion and elaborate male sex hormones under the primary control of the pituitary gland.

Spermatogenesis

Very large numbers of spermatozoa are produced by the testes— several millions daily—although for fertilization to occur very much smaller numbers are needed (e.g. 50–100 reaching the surface of the ovum). Development occurs in the *seminiferous tubules* which form most of the volume of the testis. The seminiferous tubules are formed by a number of layers of cells with a thin connective tissue membrane outside. The cells in the outermost layers are called *spermatogonia*. These divide and give rise to *first order spermatocytes*, and since the progress of development is inwards (towards the lumen of the tubule) these cells are then more superficial. A further division produces *second order spermatocytes*, which on a third division give the *spermatids*. These, without division, mature into spermatozoa. (Fig. 36.1).

Between the developing spermatogonia are masses of columnar cells, extending as far as the lumen, which are called *Sertoli cells* on which the spermatozoa hang until they are ripe for release and ejaculation. Spermatogenesis begins at puberty and, just as might be expected, the control of this process is in large measure brought about by the anterior pituitary, which secretes the gametogenic hormone. This has been shown to be the same hormone as the female F.S.H.

Endocrine Function of the Testis

The *interstitial cells* in the testis are mesodermal in origin, being typically epithelial in nature with mitochondria, granules, rods and pro-secretion granules in their cytoplasm. They have a well-developed, pale-staining nucleus, and occur mainly around the blood vessels. In mammalian species the development of interstitial cells is controlled by the *interstitial cell stimulating hormone*, or ICSH, which is the same as L.H. in the female.

In certain species, including man, the testes are permanently active; spermatogenesis is continuous. In others there are sexual seasons and activity in the testis alternates with periods of rest. In man, spermatogenesis gradually decreases from the age of about 50 years onwards.

The hormone *testosterone* (an androgen) is secreted by the interstitial cells. This fact can be shown by tying the vas deferens, whereupon the seminiferous tubules degenerate, only the Sertoli cells remaining. The

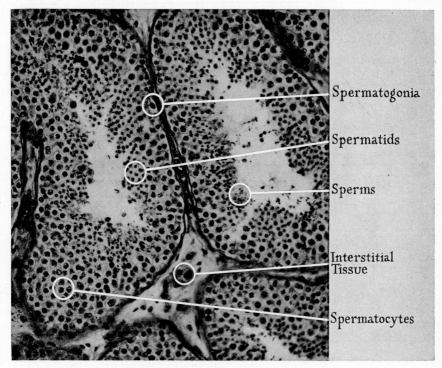

Fig. 36.1. Microscopic section of human testis, showing seminiferous and interstitial tissue. (From a preparation by Mr. K. C. Richardson.)

interstitial cells, on the other hand, undergo hypertrophy and hyperplasia. Hormone levels in blood are unaltered, or even enhanced, and the secondary sexual characters, which are controlled by testosterone, are unaffected. Small doses of X-irradiation have a similar effect; larger doses cause atrophy of the interstitial cells as well and the various phenomena of castration ensue.

Action of Androgens

Androgens stimulate spermatogenesis. If the pituitary is removed in an experimental animal, the testes atrophy; this effect can be prevented by the administration of androgens. A compound is said to be androgenic if it has a "masculinizing" or "virilizing" effect. The main androgens are:

(1) *Androsterone*, which can be synthesized and was first extracted from urine.
(2) *Testosterone*, obtained by testicular extraction. It is about 10 times as active as androsterone.
(3) *Dehydroisoandrosterone*, less active and also found in urine.
(4) Various other androgenic steroids which occur in the adrenal cortex.

All these substances are rapidly inactivated by the liver and hence are not suitable for oral administration. The synthetic derivative, methyltestosterone, however, is active when given by mouth.

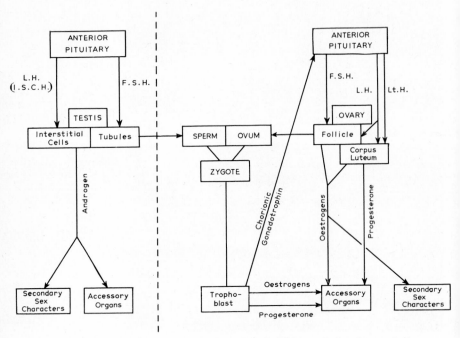

Fig. 36.2. Diagrammatic summary of the inter-relationships of the principal hormones concerned with reproduction.

L.H., luteinising hormone; F.S.H., follicle stimulating hormone; I.C.S.H., interstitial cell stimulating hormone; Lt.H., luteotrophic hormone.

Testicular hormones have specific sexual actions and widespread general effects.

The primary sexual action is on the development of male genital organs and the male secondary sexual characteristics.

The sexual action of androgens can be investigated by (*a*) administration of androgens in the foetus (gives rise to male organs or intersexuality; see p. 634), (*b*) in immature animals (when precocious puberty is induced) and (*c*) in male castrates or females when masculinization is produced.

Androgens, if administered before puberty, at first increase growth but as the ossification of epiphyseal cartilages occurs prematurely, normal height is not exceeded. The penis, prostate and seminal vesicles develop more rapidly. All bodily hair grows to the adult male distribution. There are also changes in the skin, the larynx enlarges, with deepening of the voice, muscles develop and all the psychological changes characterizing maleness appear. Fig. 36.2 gives a summary of the hormonal factors which are concerned in the male and female reproductive systems.

Removal of Testes (castration)

If the testes are removed *before puberty*, the pubertal changes do not occur. In man, the penis remains small, seminal vesicles, prostate and Cowper's glands remain undeveloped and the secondary sexual characters fail to appear.

Castration *after puberty* has less effect. The seminal vesicles regress but the other changes of puberty such as penile enlargement and alterations in the larynx persist. Erection and copulation may continue to be undertaken for years in some post-pubertal castrates, though *libido* (the sex urge) is usually diminished to a greater or lesser extent. Frequently, castrates of this kind tend to be "effeminate" in nature, but intellectual development is not disturbed by castration and it is well-known that many castrates are of outstanding intellectual achievement.

The removal of one testicle and most of the other is not followed by the usual signs of castration. Only 2 to 5 per cent of intact testicular tissue is sufficient to maintain normal hormonal function, a fact due to the remaining interstitial cells undergoing hyperplasia owing to pituitary action. Just as we have seen in the female, in the male there are feed-back mechanisms which ensure adequate secretion of gonadotrophins. Thus in the partial castrate, an excess of ICSH is produced and the cells left are overstimulated.

Testicular Insufficiency

Total castration gives rise to the condition of *eunuchism*; relative testicular insufficiency results in *eunuchoidism*. These conditions, apart from testicular removal or injury, result from various factors:

(a) *Primary disturbances* in the testes; e.g. castration, congenital absence of testicles, and tumours or infections (e.g. mumps). In all these conditions, both endocrine and spermatogenic functions are abolished or diminished. ICSH secretion is increased; testosterone is decreased.

(b) *Seminal insufficiency*; in these conditions (e.g. Klinefelter's syndrome) seminiferous activity is reduced or absent but the interstitial cells are normal. *Cryptorchism* or undescended testicle is accompanied by lack of spermatogenesis because the germinal epithelium degenerates if it is kept at body temperature. In the scrotum, the temperature is from 1 to 8°C lower than in the abdomen. Heating the scrotum beyond its normal temperature quickly injures the germinal cells and prolonged pyrexia may be followed by temporary sterility. For a few months recovery is possible but ultimately the damage is irreversible. Thus, unless cryptorchism is treated before the onset of puberty, sterility ensues and cannot be corrected by surgery later.

(*c*) *Secondary testicular insufficiency* occurs as a result of hypopituitarism; in all cases both interstitial cells and seminiferous tubules are atrophied. Causes are, for example, complete pituitary destruction by tumours, selective insufficiency of gonadotrophin secretion, and inhibition by excess circulating oestrogens.

Treatment of eunuchoidism and eunuchism is by giving methyl-testosterone by mouth, in regular maintenance doses.

Testicular Hyperfunction

Androgens or gonadotrophins when injected produce testicular hyperfunction, although it is interesting to note that contrary to expectation, injections of testosterone soon abolish spermatogenesis. Prolonged treatment in men gave first a reduction, then total abolition, of sperm with marked histological abnormality in the seminiferous tubules. It was surmised that this was due to the testosterone having its action in stopping the anterior pituitary secretion of L.H., a fact confirmed when it was found that urinary excretion of gonadotrophins had ceased. Recovery took 18 months!

There is also a control mechanism for adjusting sperm production to the demand. In the absence of sexual activity (coitus or masturbation), production gradually falls off to a low level. Continuous sexual activity increases the rate of production accordingly. It is likely that this control is mediated via the pituitary ICSH secretion.

Various studies (e.g. Kinsey Report) show that the great majority of male humans have regular and frequent "sexual outlets" (*sic*), a term covering normal heterosexual intercourse, homosexual activity and masturbation. Masturbation (self-stimulation) occurs particularly at puberty and for several years thereafter and appears to be a necessary process (in maintaining spermatogenesis) in the absence of the heterosexual activity prohibited to the adolescent and young adult in modern society. The only morbid results of this practice are likely to be of psychological origin engendered by superstitious fears and by unfortunate propaganda. Sexual behaviour to be regarded as normal in this respect, depends greatly upon age group, social class, general health, etc., but between 14–20 years of age it is claimed that 99 per cent of individuals masturbate. Average rates quoted are 5 to 6 "outlets" (of any kind) per week, with the peak frequency at 18 years of age; a low, but presumably normal rate would be 1 per month, and a high rate 5 per day.

Spermatozoa

Mature spermatozoa of different species show enormous morphological variation. The human spermatozoon (Fig. 36.3) consists of a head 4.6μ long and 2.6μ wide and of a caudal appendage 35μ to 45μ long. The head contains the nucleus at its base. The caudal appendage includes the midpiece, tail and terminal filament. The midpiece is about the same length as the head and is traversed by the axial filament, covered by a sheath. Around this is coiled the helical filament of five or six turns contained within a cylindrical sheath. The tail is 30μ to 40μ long.

The life span of sperm, during which they are capable of fertilizing the ovum is only 24 hours, although they can be frozen ($-169°C$) and stored and still be fertile on rewarming. Sperm concentrations of less than 5×10^6 per ml of ejaculate in the human generally result in sterility. 10^9 sperm are produced in the male for every single ovum produced by the female!

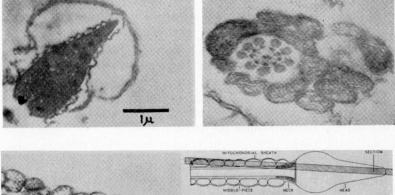

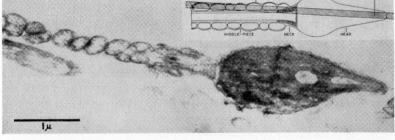

FIG. 36.3. *Human spermatozoa. Top left:* longitudinal section through head of human spermatozoon. Acrosome and enveloping membranes have separated from suface of sperm head (× 20,000). *Top right:* Transverse section through middle-piece of human spermatozoon which may be immature (×80,000). *Bottom:* Longitudinal section through head and middle-piece of human spermatozoon (×27,000). Small inset diagram shows approximate plane of section. (Rothschild; The Human Spermatozoon. *Brit. Med. J.,* 1958, *i.* 301 by permission of the Author, Editor and Publisher.)

Environmental Conditions Influencing Spermatozoa

The most important is hydrogen ion concentration, the optimum pH for preservation being a little over 7·0. Other ions may exert an important but less fully investigated effect. As the pH rises up to 8·5, sperm motility increases but this exhausts the small available supply of energy. It is often said that epididymal spermatozoa are quiescent but this is not true; when, on operation on men with blockage of the tail of the epididymis (caused by gonorrhoea), the distended head of the epididymis is incised and a drop of fluid from it is examined under the microscope, highly active spermatozoa are often found. Prostatic secretion (pH 7–8) increases, vaginal secretion (acid) diminishes and cervical secretion (alkaline) increases motility.

Body temperature is optimal for the motility, a lower temperature for the preservation of spermatozoa. The significance of the natural secretions which they meet is not known for certain, though there is little doubt that these do have some effect on the fertilizing capacity of the sperms. It has clearly been demonstrated that spermatozoa must pass a certain minimal time within the Fallopian tubes, during which they undergo an effect called *capacitation*, before they become capable of fertilizing an egg.

COITUS, OR COPULATION

This is the act of union whereby the male deposits spermatozoa in the genital tract of the female. Coitus is attended by excitement which culminates in the *orgasm*—a paroxysm of sensation largely contributed by sensory elements in the glans penis and accompanied by the ejaculation of semen. The degree of sexual excitement experienced by females varies considerably in different sub-human species but it is doubtful if, in most, orgasm is experienced at all. Among women, great variability of orgastic experience is encountered; in some it is intense, in others totally absent.

The nervous basis for coitus is a spinal reflex and the act can occur after section of the spinal cord in the dorsal region, when there is complete absence of sensation. The two essential parts of the act are erection, which enables the penis to be inserted into the vagina, and ejaculation. *Erection* is the result of distension with blood of the venous sinuses of the *corpus spongeosum* and of the *corpora cavernosa* whose resistant fibrous capsules then render the penis hard and rigid. This is brought about by dilatation of the helicine arteries of the penis, as a result of which inflow of blood into the *corpora cavernosa* increases, while through compression of veins the outflow of blood is hindered. Associated with this is relaxation of the smooth muscles in the trabeculae of the fibrous tissue. Stimulation of the pelvic nerves (second, third and fourth sacral segments) initiates erection and their section abolishes it. Stimulation of sympathetic fibres from the lumbar region is said to constrict the vessels of the penis and make it flaccid. The afferent side of the reflex arc conveys sensory impulses from the penis but superimposed upon the basic reflex arc are the effects of impulses from the higher nervous centres, by means of which many other stimuli, such as sight, smell, sound, as well as the results of purely cortical activity, such as thought, memory and so on, can cause erection. At the same time, many stimuli acting through the association areas of the brain can exert an inhibitory effect on the erection reflex, either preventing its occurrence or abolishing it once it has begun. This inhibitory mechanism is held responsible for most cases of impotence. It also provides the means whereby some control of a voluntary nature can be exercised so that, for example, whereas in some circumstances various stimuli may evoke erection, in others where erection would be undesirable it can be deliberately prevented. Involuntary inhibition of an erection in progress may result from disturbing influences of all sorts occurring at an inopportune moment.

A further important factor affecting erection is the presence of male sex hormones (testosterone). Erections occur in boys long before puberty, in eunuchs (men whose testes have been removed) and in eunuchoids (men whose testes have never developed properly); hence, testosterone is not essential for erection. On the other hand, many eunuchoids complain of infrequent and imperfect erections which are rendered normal by appropriate treatment with male hormone. Moreover, if given in excessive doses, testosterone may induce a state of more or less continuous erection (called priapism). On the other hand, the administration of testosterone to men who are impotent but who secrete normal amounts of male hormone is almost invariably without any effect whatsoever. It would seem, therefore, that testosterone facilitates the normal erection reflex, reducing the threshold of the stimuli necessary to excite it; it is powerless, however, to overcome the effects of inhibition exerted by the higher centres and it is quite clear that these inhibitory stimuli are prepotent since, coming in circumstances which have already excited erection, they can abolish it.

When the stimuli which excite erection are sufficiently intense and sufficiently prolonged, they set in train a remarkable series of nervous and muscular effects, culminating in orgasm and ejaculation. Pulse and respiratory rates increase and blood pressure rises; there is a general development of muscular tension throughout the body and rhythmic movements, especially of the pelvic region, occur and increase in speed. At the climax, or orgasm, tensions are released, ejaculation occurs and the body then rapidly returns to its normal state. Ejaculation, like erection, is brought about primarily by a spinal reflex and once the reflex has been set in motion it is beyond the reach of voluntary inhibitory control. In this it is unlike the subjective accompaniments, since these can be enhanced by influences acting on the higher centres of the brain. Preceding the actual ejaculation, the stimuli, which will eventually produce it, cause reflex increased secretion of the accessory sex glands so that, in some men, clear fluid (mainly derived from the glands of Littré) may escape from the urethral meatus. The discharge of impulses from the spinal centre eventually causes rhythmic contractions of the vasa deferentia, seminal vesicles and prostate, thereby expelling the contained spermatozoa and accessory secretions. The seminal fluid so formed is ejected from the urethral opening in a series of spurts, varying in number from two or three to perhaps a dozen. The first spurt is usually devoid of spermatozoa, being composed chiefly of secretions from the urethral glands and Cowper's glands. An intermediate fraction of the ejaculate is rich in spermatozoa, the remainder consists largely of seminal vesicle and prostatic gland secretions. The smooth muscles involved in ejaculation are supplied by the presacral nerve (sympathetic) and its section will therefore lead to sterility.

In the female, similar events lead to the orgasm. Erectile tissue in the vulva and around the vagina becomes engorged as a result of sexual stimulation and secretions of the various glands provide the necessary lubrication for coitus. As in the male, the nervi erigentes are cholinergic, parasympathetic fibres arising in the first, second and third sacral segments.

SEXUALITY AND HUMAN BEHAVIOUR

It will be apparent that the behavioural, emotional and general psychological aspects of sexual matters in the human species, far exceed in scope and magnitude, the requirements of a purely reproductive process. After all, reproduction as a biological act, proceeds quite satisfactorily in all other species without the elaborate and far-reaching sexuality that accompanies the process in humans. For instance, in no other species is it known that the female has an orgasm on copulation; neither does the male usually experience such prolonged and satisfying sensation as in humans. In particular, the human spends an inordinate proportion of his waking hours in the direct or indirect pursuit of sexual gratification.

The generally held view is that the secondary manifestations of sex in the human have evolved as a mechanism for cementing the family bond, in other words for ensuring that once a male and female form a pair, this pairing is maintained for a long period of time. The necessity for a stable family unit is imposed by the comparatively slow rate at which the human offspring matures. The complex nature of human brain function, and the enormous load of information that the developing brain must absorb, imply a necessarily lengthy process of learning and education. The parents must, in order to play an active rôle in these processes, remain securely bonded together and it is the gratifications and rewards inherent in this heightened sexuality which have a great deal to do with family stability.

CHAPTER 37

SEX DETERMINATION AND DIFFERENTIATION

THE factors determining the sex of an individual are primarily genetic. The nuclei of the ovum and spermatozoon each contain only half the number of chromosomes (the *haploid* number) present in the remaining cells of the body but by their union they form a cell whose nucleus has the normal (*diploid*) sum. Chromosomes in all cells except the gametes are therefore paired and so are the genes which they carry. For every maternal gene which affects, for instance, eye colour, there is in the complementary chromosome a corresponding paternal gene which influences it in the same or a different way. In the latter event, the final eye colour will be decided by the "dominant" gene of the pair and the

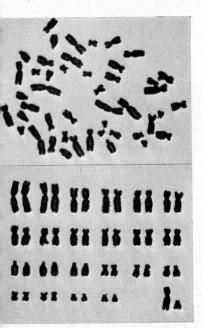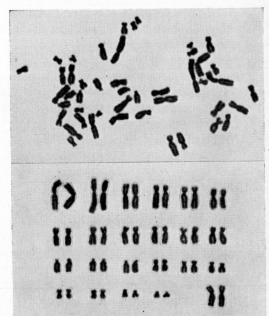

Fig. 37.1. Chromosomes of normal human cells.

Left: male. *Right*: female.

The 44 autosomes of each cell have been selected and arranged in pairs in descending order of size, leaving the two sex chromosomes, XY in the male cell and XX in the female cell, as shown at the bottom right-hand corners. (From photographs kindly provided by Prof. L. S. Penrose.)

"recessive" gene will be powerless until the next generation. Apart from this kind of genic inequality, the half set of chromosomes in an ovum is similar to that in other ova and to that in half the spermatozoa of members of the same species. In the other half of the spermatozoa, one chromosome is modified. This is called the Y chromosome and is smaller than the alternative chromosome, which is called X, X and Y being the "sex chromosomes" (Fig. 37.1). Half the unions between ova and spermatozoa result, therefore (theoretically), in cells having nuclei with two exactly paired sets of chromosomes. These cells divide and differentiate to form individuals bearing ova, i.e. females. The other half of the union yields cells in whose nuclei one member of one pair of chromosomes differs slightly from its fellow. These cells divide and differentiate to form individuals producing spermatozoa, i.e. males. Females are said to be *monogametic* and males *digametic* (in moths and birds the same principle holds good but the female is the digametic member).

Genetic Sex Differentiation

A survey of the animal kingdom shows that *secondary sexual characters* (variations in parts of the body other than in the gonads and accessory organs which characterize animals as male or female) are governed by two agencies, respectively genetic and chemical. The first is found in its purest form in the insect world.

We have seen (Fig. 37.1) that the combination of two similar sex chromosomes (XX) yields a female and of dissimilar sex chromosomes (XY) a male. The accepted explanation is that the X chromosome carries a factor making for femaleness which, when doubled, is sufficiently strong to balance the tendency of the combined remaining chromosomes (*autosomes*) to produce maleness. When single, as in the XY combination, it is not strong enough. In insects, the form of all sex variable parts of the body emerges according to the state of this balance. For example, the shape of a wing is not determined solely by the coincidence of a *single* gene in a paternal chromosome with the corresponding gene in the corresponding maternal chromosome, but by the combined effect of several genes scattered through each complementary half set of chromosomes. The gene, or genes, which can influence wing shape and which reside in the second sex chromosome have the "casting vote" on sex form.

Sometimes in a genetically female zygote (XX) a fault occurs in the first mitosis of the fertilized egg and the X chromosomes of one of the daughter cells are altogether lost. Since each daughter cell gives rise to one-half of the body, all the cells in, say, the left half are, sexually XX and in the right half, OO. The result of this accident is an insect in which the left half of the body in all its sex-variable parts is female and the right half male. Other degrees of genic imbalance which give a range of inter-sexual forms can be produced experimentally in insects.

Chemical Sex Differentiation

The findings of embryologists, many in lower vertebrates and many depending on experiments difficult to perform and to interpret, suggest the following generalization.

In vertebrate embryos, the primitive gonad is bi-potential, the cortical part being capable of developing into an ovary and the medullary part into a testis. The influence of the genetic factor is exerted at a very early stage, causing the suppression of the medullary part with development of the cortex in the case of females and of the reverse situation in the case of males. It will be appreciated that a failure of the normal balance between "femaleness" sponsored by the X chromosomes, and "maleness" by the autosomes, can, in certain circumstances, lead to a disturbance of the above-described process so that either both cortex and medulla develop to form an ovo-testis (as is found in some true hermaphrodites) or a testis may develop on one side and an ovary on the other, or various other possible combinations (as have also been described in human true hermaphrodites) may occur. Moreover, it is possible for an ovary to develop in a genetic male or a testis in a genetic female in the same kind of way and such gonadal anomalies are believed to exist in certain humans. Such gonads are defective to a varying extent.

Further experimental studies, in which the gonads in the "indifferent" stage have been removed from embryos or have been destroyed *in situ* by X-irradiation, have demonstrated that, whereas the removal of the gonads in a genetic female does not disturb the normal development of female assessory sex organs, if those of a genetic male are removed, the individual develops as though it were a female. From this it has been concluded that the embryonic testis secretes a substance which is necessary for the development of the male accessory organs (i.e. Wolffian duct derivatives, penis and scrotum) and for the suppression of the female counterparts, while in its absence the female structures (i.e. Müllerian duct derivatives and vulva) develop and the male structures are suppressed. There is experimental evidence that treating embryos at a sufficiently early stage with sex hormones may modify the development of the primitive gonad. One of nature's best-known experiments of this kind is found in cattle when the circulations of twins of genetically opposite sex communicate with each other during the early indifferent stage of development. The male twin develops normally (possibly because its ovarian rudiment disappears before it can be stimulated) but the "female" twin, a so-called "free-martin", is extensively modified. Sterile testes and male genital ducts are formed, the ovaries and female ducts being suppressed. The external genitalia are indeterminate, usually of a rudimentary female type, though the clitoris may be enlarged.

Although differentiation of mammalian sex characters is thus vested mainly in the sex hormones, the genetic foundation on which these work is often subject to modification. This is well seen in the plumage of some birds but is also apparent in man. Many traits, such as cephalic index, presence or absence of palmaris muscle, and height, about which we say "most men are taller than most women", and so forth, are thought to be fundamentally genetic in origin.

Intersexuality occurs in man in three forms: true hermaphroditism, chromosomal intersexuality and male and female pseudo-hermaphroditism. The first is rare and implies the presence of gonadal tissue of both sexes in the same individual. It has been mentioned above. Chromosomal intersexes are individuals with sex-chromosome aberrations. One group, with XO constitution (45 chromosomes only), consists of hypogonadal "females" with dysgenetic gonads ("chromatin negative Turner's syndrome"). Another, with XXY constitution (47 chromosomes)

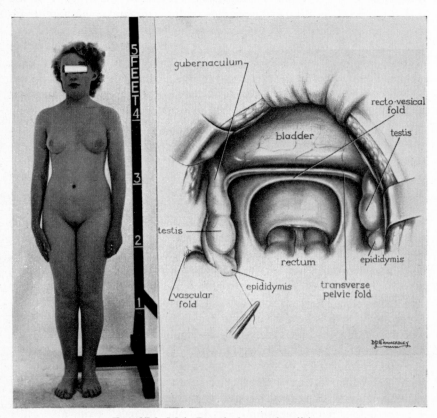

FIG. 37.2. Male Pseudo-hermaphroditism.

A patient, 17 years old, with "testicular feminization". Well developed breasts and external feminine characteristics (in fact, won a beauty competition) but no pubic or axillary hair and infantile vulva. At laparotomy, no internal female genitalia, but undescended testes found. Sex chromatin negative. (Case of Dr. C. N. Armstrong.)

consists of hypogonadal males with abnormal testes ("chromatin positive Kline-felter's syndrome"). Reduplication of sex chromosomes may also give rise to XXX, XXXYY and similar anomalies, most of the individuals so affected being mentally defective as well as showing sexual abnormalities. A further group consists of individuals believed to be "mosaics", some nuclei having one sex chromosome constitution and others another. In the pseudo-hermaphrodites, the sex of the gonad is indicated by the adjective "male" or "female", while the external genitalia and the secondary sex characters partake to a greater or less extent of the nature of those associated with the opposite sex.

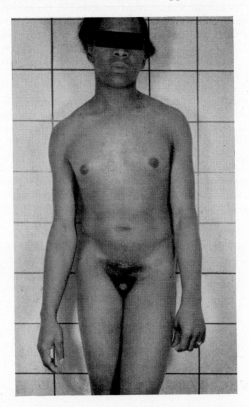

FIG. 37.3. Female Pseudo-hermaphroditism.

A patient aged 24 who complained of genital abnormalities and primary amenorrhoea. Bodily configuration male with fairly well-developed muscles, no breasts and a narrow pelvis. Phallus measured 3 cm and urethra opened at its base. No vaginal orifice. Very high excretion of adrenal steroid metabolites, reduced to normal by prednisone (which suppresses pituitary ACTH secretion). Laparo-tomy revealed ovaries, uterus and tubes and a cervix opening into a vagina, access to which was gained by incising the perineum, so constructing a vaginal orifice. The phallus was amputated. With continued prednisone treatment, menstruation began within a month, has continued normally and the patient has conceived and delivered a normal infant. (Case of Dr. G. I. M. Swyer.)

In *male pseudo-hermaphrodites*, testes are present but are usually undescended, and although they show apparently normal interstitial cells, spermatogenesis does not occur. The external genitalia are mal-developed to a greater or less extent. Thus, the urethral meatus opens under the glans penis or at the base of the penis or several centimeters behind in the perineum (hypospadias). Sometimes the penis is so poorly developed as to resemble merely an enlarged clitoris. The internal genital organs appropriate to the female are sometimes found in a rudimentary form. In some individuals, flat male breasts are found but in others, well-developed breasts of female type are found. Indeed, in one group of these patients (sometimes referred to as the "testicular feminization syndrome"), the individuals appear to be normally developed females except that pubic and axillary hair are usually absent and the vagina is short and ends blindly, no uterus being present (Fig. 37.2). In some intersexual individuals it may be impossible to determine, on clinical grounds, whether they are male or female pseudo-hermaphrodites except on the basis of hormone studies, biopsy of the gonads or nuclear sex studies.

The commonest cause of *female pseudo-hermaphroditism* (Fig. 37.3) is a genetically determined disturbance of adrenal function arising in embryonic life and leading to the production of excessive amounts of androgenic steroids by the adrenal cortex. These, though not interfering with the development of the ovary or of the internal female genital apparatus, cause great enlargement of the clitoris, so that it resembles a hypospadiac penis. They may also produce varying degrees of vaginal mal-development, and cause the early appearance of hirsutism and of masculinization. In a small proportion of these individuals, the adrenal defect leads to excessive sodium loss, so that, unless treated, the infant dies within the first few weeks of life. Very rarely, a non-adrenal form of female pseudo-hermaphroditism is encountered, in which the only defect appears to be enlargement of the clitoris. This has been observed to result from treatment of the mother with male hormone during pregnancy but it is also known to occur occasionally after treatment with progesterone-like substances or even when there has been no treatment at all. In these cases, it is believed that the embryo must have been abnormally sensitive to the slight androgenic action of the maternal or administered progesterone-like bodies.

Section 11

EXCRETION AND
TEMPERATURE REGULATION

CHAPTER 38

URINE

HUNGER and appetite largely control the intake of food; thirst influences the intake of water; taste, to some extent controls the intake of salt. So might the water content and composition of the body be kept fairly steady, were it not that we like to eat different kinds of food, giving rise to different kinds and quantities of metabolic end-product and affecting differently the water balance of the body, and were it not for extraneous influences such as the social habits of drinking partners and the culinary customs of the home. The ample variation possible in urine formation provides for the spill-over of excess water and salts and indeed of most other soluble constitutents of the plasma; so the constituents of the body fluids are kept at the steady levels required for normal physiological working as described in Section 1 on Body Fluids.

The daily output of urine varies widely in amount and composition; 1,500 ml may be taken as representative for a man under average conditions in this country. Over shorter periods of time, the *rate of production* of urine varies between about 0·3 ml/min and about 20 ml/min according to the state of hydration of the body (1 ml/min is equivalent to 1,450 ml per day). Normally, urine contains about 4 per cent solids, many of which are included in Table 38.1; but the concentration varies inversely with the rate of water output, and the *total (osmolar) concentration*, as measured for example by the freezing point, varies from about one-sixth to four times or more that of plasma. The specific gravity, a rough measure of the total concentration, is usually between 1·015 and 1·025, but may fall to 1·002 or rise to 1·030. The *colour* of the urine, due to the presence of urochrome, a pigment of uncertain origin, chemically related to haemoglobin, is also a rough indication of the concentration. Urine is normally somewhat acid, its pH being about 6; this may vary between the limits of 4·7 and 8·2 according to the nature of the food and the amount of acid or alkali being excreted.

Quantitatively, the chief constituents of the urine are urea and the chlorides, sulphates and phosphates of sodium and potassium (Table 38.1). A concentrated urine often deposits amorphous sodium and potassium urates on cooling. The precipitate is coloured pink by uro-erythrin and can be redissolved by warming. Another amorphous deposit may occur in normal urine, namely, phosphates of the alkaline earths; these have a low solubility in alkaline solution, and are precipitated (a) usually as $Ca_3(PO_4)_2$ when the urine is alkaline when voided, or (b) as NH_4MgPO_4—"triple

TABLE 38.1
Typical Concentrations in Man

	Plasma g per 100 ml	Urine g per 100 ml	Urine/Plasma Concentration ratio
Water	90–93	96	1·05
Proteins	7–9	0	0
Urea	0·03	2	60
Creatinine	0·001	0·15	150
Uric Acid	0·002	0·05	25
Glucose	0·10	0	0
Sodium	0·32	0·35	1
Potassium	0·02	0·15	7
Calcium	0·01	0·015	1·5
Magnesium	0·002	0·01	5
Chloride	0·37	0·6	2
Sulphate	0·003	0·18	60
Phosphate	0·003	0·12	40
Ammonia*	0·0001	0·04	400

* Ammonia is synthesized in the kidney.

phosphate" when previously acid or neutral urine becomes alkaline on standing owing to bacterial conversion of the urea into ammonium carbonate. The phosphate is dissolved by the addition of dilute acetic acid. Crystalline deposits are usually associated with abnormal processes. In acid urine, calcium oxalate, cystine, leucine or tyrosine may be found, whereas in alkaline urine, calcium carbonate and phosphates are the commonest.

Urea is the chief nitrogenous end-product of protein metabolism and occurs in large quantities in normal urine. The ability of a kidney to concentrate urea is considered a valuable index of functional activity in disease. It is estimated by administering 15 g of urea in 100 ml of water by mouth and collecting urine at hourly intervals; the first sample may be dilute owing to diuresis, but less than 2 per cent in the second sample would be unusual in normal kidneys.

Other nitrogenous substances in urine occur only in relatively small amounts. Ammonium salts, usually in small concentration, may be increased in acidosis. A large proportion of the ammonia in normal urine is formed in the kidney itself. Uric acid is formed from nucleins, and about one-half persists in starvation and is therefore regarded as of endogenous origin; the other half varies in amount with the diet, and is of exogenous origin. Creatinine in the urine is probably formed mainly from the creatine in muscle.

When urine has been allowed to stand for some time, a faint cloud of mucus from the walls of the bladder and urinary passages can often be seen.

Abnormal constituents appear in urine from normal kidneys when soluble and diffusible foreign substances, including many drugs, have been administered. Or again, they appear when certain normal constituents of plasma are present in excessive concentration. For example, the concentration of glucose, normally around 0·10 per cent in plasma, may rise as a result of swallowing 200 g or more within a short time; if the plasma concentration then exceeds a "threshold value" of about 0·18 per cent, some of the glucose is excreted in the urine, a finding known as "alimentary glycosuria". Likewise in some diseases, normal kidneys will eliminate substances not normally secreted, for example, glucose and ketone bodies in diabetes mellitus or bile salts and bile pigments in jaundice. Diseased kidneys may allow substances which are normally retained in the plasma to pass into the urine, and most characteristically so, plasma protein. Proteinuria is characteristic of nephritis, of failure of adequate blood supply to the kidney and of the action of certain poisons on it. A transient appearance of protein occasionally occurs in the urine of healthy people, especially adolescents, after severe exercise and after prolonged standing; the latter may be due to a rise in pressure in the renal vein. Albuminous casts of the tubules may appear in the urine secreted by diseased kidneys, and cells derived from the blood or from the excretory organs are present in the urine in certain pathological circumstances.

THE STRUCTURE OF THE KIDNEY

Urine formation from plasma cannot be understood without reference to the structure of the kidney. The urine is formed in long unbranched tubules called *nephrons* many of which combine to form a smaller number of collecting ducts from which the urine is discharged into the pelvis and so to the single channelled ureter. Nephrons are very numerous, well over a million have been found in pairs of dog's kidneys and there are probably two million or so in human kidneys.

The glomerulus

Each nephron begins with a wider blind end, the glomerular capsule (Fig. 38.1) into which protrudes a bunch of blood capillaries known as the glomerular tuft or the glomerulus. The capillary walls are covered by a thin membrane forming the blind end of the tubule and called the glomerular membrane. This is continuous with the outer cup-shaped membrane (Bowman's capsule) which forms the wide end of the tubule, the space between the inner glomerular membrane and the outer funnel-like membrane being called the capsular space which contains glomerular fluid. The idea that the function of the glomerulus is ultrafiltration, that is transport of only the non-colloidal elements of blood into the tubule under influence of blood pressure, was first suggested by the microscopic appearance of Bowman's capsule but has since been proved experimentally.

The tubule

Beyond the neck of the funnel, the thin flat cells of the outer capsule change into the columnar or cubical granular cells of the proximal convoluted tubule, resembling in appearance the cells in secretory organs. The glomerulus and proximal convoluted tubule are found in the outer zone, the cortex, of the kidney. The tubule than takes a dip into the medulla before returning to form the distal convoluted tubule near its own glomerulus; the loop formed in this way is known as Henle's loop and the part it plays in concentrating urine by a countercurrent mechanism has been discovered more recently. Beyond the distal tubule, the tubule plunges once more toward the medulla to enter a collecting duct.

The blood supply

The blood supply to these renal elements is arranged in a peculiar manner. The glomerulus receives blood from branches of the renal artery by a short, wide, "afferent" vessel. From the glomerular capillaries the blood is collected into a longer and narrower "efferent" vessel, which, in turn, divides into capillaries distributed over the tubules. From the peri-tubular capillaries the blood collects into venous sinuses, where it reaches the radicles of the renal vein (Fig. 38.1). In the mammalian kidney, nearly all the blood which reaches the peritubular capillaries has previously passed through the glomerular capillaries. There are, however, shunts in this circulation which play a disputed part in normal function. Thus the blood normally approaches the glomeruli through the wide channels of the renal arterioles and vasa afferentia, and emerges through the narrow vasa efferentia to reach the tubular capillaries. Owing to these two anatomical factors—the double capillary system and the difference in diameter of the vasa afferentia and efferentia—the blood pressure in the glomerular capillaries is much higher than in capillaries in other organs. Its pressure in the peri-tubular capillaries, on the other hand, may be even lower than the normal capillary pressure elsewhere in the body. Thus, on histological grounds alone, it appears that blood at high pressure is separated from the lumen of the renal tubule only by the thin walls of the glomerular capillaries and by the single layer of flattened cells composing the inner membrane of Bowman's capsule. This is most aptly arranged to provide hydrostatic pressure for the filtration in the glomerulus mentioned earlier.

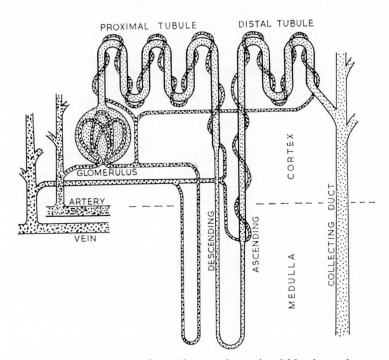

FIG. 38.1. Diagram of a nephron and associated blood vessels.

The proximal and distal tubules have been reduced in length; and the arrangement of these, as well as that of the dual system of capillaries—those within the glomerulus in series with those ramifying over the tubules—has been considerably simplied.

The peri-tubular capillaries, on the other hand, may be at a lower pressure than capillaries in other organs, and this would facilitate the re-absorption of water and other substances which will be shown later to occur there.

SHORT DESCRIPTION OF URINE FORMATION FROM BLOOD

Current views of how urine is derived from the blood flowing through the kidney, depend largely on the results of the chemical analysis of fluids obtained by micropipettes inserted into glomeruli or into various segments along the tubules. This evidence is, of course, confined to observation of superficially visible and accessible structures in the kidney, mainly in immobilized animals such as the frog, rat or dog. Additional indirect evidence in unanaesthetized animals and man confirms the picture so obtained and augments it in many ways.

Arterial pressure drives almost protein-free glomerular fluid across the glomerular capillary membrane by ultrafiltration. In man, about 720 ml per min of blood plasma flows through both kidneys and yields about 125 ml per min of glomerular filtrate to enter the proximal convoluted tubules. Only about 25 ml per min emerges, four-fifths having been re-absorbed into the blood-stream. The reabsorption is primarily due to secretory activity of the tubule cells, which removes sodium ions and transports them to the blood plasma in the peri-tubular capillaries. Chloride ions follow passively impelled by electrical forces, and water is transported by osmosis. Glucose is also actively reabsorbed but most normally occurring substances such as urea and potassium are partially reabsorbed by diffusion.

The modified tubular fluid continues down the loop of Henle and reaches the ascending limb where tubule cells actively secrete more sodium ions out of the tubule into the medullary interstitial space with its comparatively small blood flow. The water largely remains in the tubule fluid which becomes hypotonic, whereas the interstitial tissue fluid becomes hypertonic.

The earliest part of the distal tubule accessible to micropipettes contains hypotonic fluid but further sodium is then transferred out of the tubule, some of it in exchange for potassium and hydrogen ions, so that the fluid entering the collecting duct system is about isotonic. Soon, further reabsorption of sodium dilutes the fluid if the collecting duct wall is relatively impermeable to water, as in water diuresis which may reach as much as 20 ml per min. If, however, a normal secretion of the pituitary anti-diuretic hormone is reaching the kidneys, the collecting duct walls become permeable to water and the osmotic attraction from the hypertonic medullary interstitial tissue draws much or most of the water out of the tubule, leaving a much smaller volume, e.g. 1 ml per min to emerge from the kidney as urine.

Energy expenditure in urine formation

The essential constituents of urine and plasma are compared in Table 38.1. Proteins and sugar are retained in the blood, whereas urea and sul-phates are largely concentrated in their passage from blood to urine. A third group of substances, such as sodium salts, appear in the urine in lower or higher concentration than in blood, according to the needs of the organism. In order to concentrate substances in solution an expenditure of energy is necessary. This is comparable with the energy necessary to concentrate a gas, as in pumping up a tyre. A source of physical energy, namely, the arterial pressure, is available in the kidney, and one can imagine a machine which would use this energy for the formation of urine. But our knowledge of the structure and mode of action of the kidney is not consistent with its acting only as such a machine; for the most part, the urine is formed by a process of active secretory work, i.e. the performance of chemical work at the expense of energy derived from the metabolism of the cell. In the kidney the metabolism is mainly oxidative, and the kidney consumes oxygen at a high rate.

The oxygen consumption of the kidney is, however, not simply related to the osmotic work done in urine formation, for it is unchanged in diuresis due to administration of water or of "osmotic" diuretics, e.g. urea or mannitol. The arterio-venous oxygen difference is lower, about 2 ml/ 100 ml, than in other organs, and instead of varying inversely with the blood-flow, as would be expected if the oxygen consumption were to remain relatively constant, it is practically unaffected by changes in blood-flow unless this is reduced to quite abnormally low values. These unique features of the kidney like autoregulation of blood flow are still unsolved mysteries.

Historical Highlights in Renal Physiology

In 1842 Bowman, working in London, gave the first description of the main histological features of the kidney. From these he inferred that blood at a high pressure passing through the thin-walled glomerular capillaries would be likely to filter a watery fluid into the nephron. The tubules with cells resembling in appearance those in other glands with a well recognized secretory function, would be likely to add the main solid constituents of the urine to the watery fluids passing down from the glomerulus. In 1844, Ludwig in Germany proposed the *filtration-reabsorption theory*. This differed from Bowman's view in supposing that a much larger volume of glomerular filtrate contained the whole of the plasma solutes which eventually appeared in the urine, but are concentrated by transfer of most of the water and of some other substances to which the tubules were permeable, back into the blood. Cushny emphasized the osmotic work performed by the tubule cells in concentrating the urine by reabsorption of water, and later Richards and his school in America used micropipettes to obtain samples of glomerular and tubular fluid for chemical analysis and thus produced the experimental proof that the filtration-reabsorption theory provides an adequate explanation of the formation of urine in so far as most of its normal constituents are concerned. Many foreign substances, such as phenol red or diodone (diodrast), when injected into the blood stream appear in the urine, however, in much greater amount than can be accounted for by the filtration-reabsorption theory which confines tubular function to the withdrawal of substances from the lumen of the tubule and their return to the blood. It is now generally agreed that such foreign substances, if present, and a few normal constituents of urine, are transferred to the tubular urine direct from the blood in the peri-tubular capillaries by secretion into the lumen of the tubule. In the hands largely of Homer Smith and his school in America, the filtration-reabsorption theory, so modified, has led to the development of methods of assessment of the glomerular filtration rate and consequently of a quantitative determination of both the reabsorptive and secretory functions of the tubules.

Agreement on the main outline of the theory of renal secretion was reached in the late 'thirties after nearly a century of ingenious experimentation and often heated polemic. However, in the 'fifties, Wirz and his colleagues in Switzerland introduced the counter-current theory of tubular function which is widely accepted though not all its implications have yet been explored.

The word "secretion" means transfer across a membrane against an osmotic gradient. In renal physiology it was used only for transfers from blood to tubule fluid, "reabsorption" being used for transfers from tubule fluid back to blood. Both processes require the performance of chemical work, and are secretory processes in the general physiological sense.

GLOMERULAR FUNCTION

In the past the glomeruli were thought of either as secretory organs, concentrating some of the constituents of urine, or as organs of filtration producing something less than the volume of urine to which the more concentrated constituents were added by secretion during its passage down the tubules. A third view, which has now established itself was that the glomerular fluid was filtered at, perhaps, a hundred-fold the rate of urine formation and that the fluid contained all or nearly all the solid constituents in urine, some of which were concentrated by the reabsorption of water during passage down the tubules. Complete experimental proof that glomerular fluid is formed from plasma by a physical process of filtration would be provided if it could be shown (1) that the composition of the fluid is exactly that of protein-free plasma, (2) that the glomerular membrane has pores of such size that plasma protein and larger molecules cannot pass but smaller molecules can pass, and (3) that the hydrostatic pressure-fall across the membrane is enough to drive the glomerular fluid at the known rate across the membrane of known resistance. The first two lines of evidence have been provided by convincing experiments. The third is supported only by rather speculative calculations from indirect observations and it could still be argued that some active pumping assists hydrostatic pressure in driving fluid across the glomerular membrane. In the absence of evidence, this possibility is usually ignored.

Direct evidence that glomerular fluid has the composition of protein-free plasma was produced in amphibian kidneys by A. N. Richards and colleagues by introducing the point of a micropipette (7 to 15μ diam.) into the capsular space and slowly withdrawing fluid from it (Fig. 38.2). The glomerular fluid so obtained was almost free from proteins, and could not, therefore, be suspected of contamination with blood; it contained chlorides and glucose even when these were absent from the bladder urine collected at the same time. Owing to the extremely small amounts available (1 mm^3

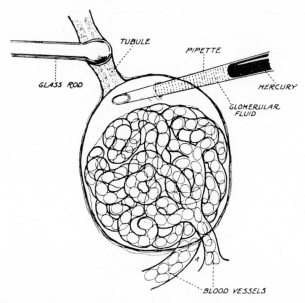

FIG. 38.2. Diagrammatic representation of Richard's method of obtaining a sample of glomerular fluid from Bowman's capsule in the frog.

A very fine pipette (7 to 15μ diam.) connected with a reservoir of mercury and filled with mercury up to its tip, is thrust through the wall of the capsule, and fluid is withdrawn from the capsular space by lowering the mercury reservoir. The tubule is blocked by pressing on it with a fine glass rod, so that no fluid can be sucked back into the capsule.

at the most), special methods of chemical analysis had to be devised; these have demonstrated the equality of the concentrations in plasma and glomerular fluid not only of all the chief normal constituents of urine such as urea, chlorides, and creatinine, but also of certain diffusible foreign substances, such as inulin. Here, then, is unequivocal evidence that in the amphibian kidney the glomerular membrane acts as a semi-permeable membrane, allowing crystalloids to pass through it, and preventing the passage of proteins. Similar observations on the composition of glomerular fluid were later performed on rats and dogs.

Functional pore-size of glomerular filter

Confirmation of glomerular filtration is shown by abolishing tubule function by cooling blood reaching dog kidneys. An increased flow of isotonic protein-free urine ensues. Poisoning with cyanide also increases urine flow.

The second property of the mammalian kidney indicating a filtration mechanism in the kidney is concerned with the nature of the filter. A filter implies a membrane which will allow the passage of particles below a certain size, but retain larger particles. An ultra-filter, such as the glomerular membrane, should allow the passage of molecules below a certain size, but retain larger molecules. The following table, 38.2 (after Bayliss, Kerridge

TABLE 38.2

Proteins excreted		Molecular Weight
Gelatin	. . . . .	about 35,000
Bence-Jones .	. . . .	,, 35,000
Egg albumin.	. . . .	,, 35,000
Haemoglobin	. . . .	,, 67,000
Proteins not excreted		
Haemoglobin	. . . .	about 67,000
Serum albumin	. . . .	,, 72,000
Serum globulin	. . . .	,, 170,000
Casein .	. . . . .	,, 200,000
Edestin	. . . . .	,, 200,000
Haemocyanin	. . . .	,, 5,000,000

Haemoglobin and serum albumin have molecules near the borderline and are believed normally to leak very slowly across the glomerular membrane, the amount that has leaked being reabsorbed by the tubules. If more than a small amount appears in the tubules, due to excessive concentration in the plasma or abnormal permeability of the glomerular membrane, the very limited reabsorptive capacity of the tubules will be exceeded and the protein will appear in the urine.

and Russell) shows that the kidney differentiates between molecules of different sizes in just such a simple physical way. Fig. 38.3 shows that the position of the filter in the kidney is in fact the glomerulus, since the protein with a sufficiently small molecule is shown to pass from the blood into the glomerular space.

The discrimination of the glomerulus between molecules of different size has also been shown in other series of compounds. For example, the dextrans, polysaccharides used therapeutically as blood substitutes, can be hydrolysed to any extent required to produce molecules of weights from that of glucose up to several millions, and the fractions of different molecular sizes have been separated and injected by Wallenius. In man and the dog, molecules of dextran exceeding about 47,000 in weight fail to be excreted in the urine. Molecules with a weight of 5,000 to 6,000 or lower

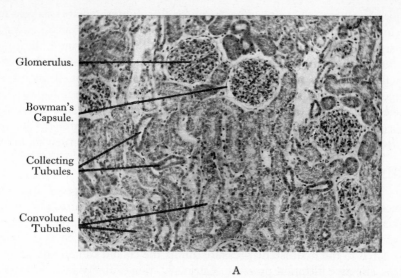

Glomerulus.

Bowman's
Capsule.

Collecting
Tubules.

Convoluted
Tubules.

A

Protein in
Capsular Space.

Blood Vessels.

Protein in
Tubules.

B

Fig. 38.3. Sections through isolated and perfused kidneys of dogs.
(Magnification × 140.)

A. Perfused with normal defibrinated blood for one and three-
quarter hours.

B. Perfused with normal defibrinated blood for one and a half
hours, and with blood containing egg albumin for half an hour. Note
the presence of protein in Bowman's capsule, indicating that the
glomerular membrane is permeable to proteins of relatively low
molecular weight (less than 70,000). (Bayliss, Kerridge and Russell.)

pass freely into the urine, whereas molecules of intermediate size pass more slowly. Human patients and animals with proteinuria allow the passage of larger dextran molecules (50,000 to 100,000) into the urine indicating an abnormally permeable glomerular membrane. Size as indicated by molecular weight is not the only property of molecules which affects their passage through membranes. The shape of the molecule and presence of electric charges are also concerned. Differences in these presumably account for the difference in the molecular weight of the proteins and polysaccharides which are just able to pass through the glomerular membrane.

Hydrostatic pressure

The third line of evidence required to complete the proof of filtration across the glomerular membrane is a relation between hydrostatic pressure across it and rate of formation of glomerular fluid appropriate to a purely physical process. The glomerular filtration rate should be fairly linearly related to the hydrostatic pressure minus the colloid osmotic pressure, i.e. the effective filtration pressure. Curiously, this evidence is far from manifest. In normal animals a large rise in arterial pressure, which might be expected to produce a corresponding rise in glomerular capillary pressure, raises the glomerular filtration rate very little. This is attributed to an altogether different mechanism discussed later under the heading "Autoregulation". In the isolated kidney of the dog, the control of autoregulation is less perfect than in the normal kidney and the glomerular filtration rate follows the arterial pressure changes more appropriately. An experiment of this kind is depicted in Fig. 38.4. How to calculate glomerular filtration rate from serum and urine creatinine concentrations and the urine flow will be described later under the heading "Clearances". An important property of the kidney is depicted in Fig. 38.4, namely that an increase in urine flow is accompanied by a change in its composition in the direction of that of the plasma; substances which are more dilute like chloride, or more concentrated like creatinine, in the urine than in the plasma, become less so in diuresis.

The pressure fall across the glomerular membrane has been calculated to be about 55 mm Hg in a dog kidney, more than half of which is devoted to overcoming the osmotic pressure of the plasma proteins. Under average conditions with mean arterial pressure of, say, 115 mm Hg, the glomerular capillary pressure may be about 75 mm Hg and the pressure in Bowman's capsule about 20 mm Hg. Micropipette measurements indicate pressures of 2 to 3 mm Hg in the distal tubules at resting urine flows but the pressure rises during diuresis.

Dilution of plasma proteins reduces the colloid osmotic pressure which itself opposes glomerular filtration. The glomerular filtration rate is, therefore, increased. This produces "dilution" or "saline diuresis", though this diuresis is augmented by an effect on the tubules. Glomerular capillary

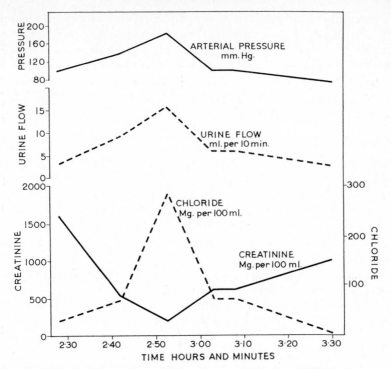

FIG. 38.4. The influence of arterial pressure on the isolated kidney of the dog.

Increase of arterial pressure produces a large increase of urine flow, and a change in its composition (decrease of creatinine concentration and increase of chloride concentration) such that the concentrations of the solutes move in the direction of those in the serum. Serum creatinine 75 mg per 100 ml. Serum chloride 760 mg per 100 ml (chloride estimated as NaCl). Temp. 37°C. (Gilson and Winton.)

pressure may vary although arterial pressure remains unchanged. For example, caffeine increases glomerular pressure by dilatation of the pre-glomerular arterioles (vasa afferentia).

PLASMA CLEARANCES

The interest in plasma clearances is due to their value in assessing both renal blood flow and glomerular filtration rate in unoperated man and other animals. Moreover, they can reveal which substances are excreted in greater or in less amount than that present in the glomerular filtrate and must, therefore, be partly "secreted" or reabsorbed in the tubules.

By *plasma clearance* is meant the volume of plasma which contains the same weight of the substance as is contained in the volume of urine secreted in a minute. Take, for example, the values of creatinine concentrations in plasma and urine given in Table 38.1. These would correspond to a resting urine flow of, say, 1 ml per min which, at the creatinine concentration of

0·15 per cent, would contain 1·5 mg. Since 100 ml. of plasma contained 1 mg of creatinine, equal amounts (1·5 mg) of creatinine would be found in either the 1 ml urine or in 150 ml plasma. The plasma clearance is then said to be 150 ml per min. The concentration in the urine divided by the concentration in plasma is called the *concentration ratio* or U/P ratio; and this, multiplied by the urine flow (F), (i.e. F × U/P) gives the plasma clearance.

Glomerular filtration-rate

Since equal volumes of glomerular filtrate and of plasma contain the same weight of a freely filtered substance, the *glomerular filtration rate* would equal the plasma clearance for a substance which is neither removed from, nor added to, during passage of the filtrate through the tubules. Creatinine appears to be such a substance in dogs, sheep, rabbits and some other animals. In them, the creatinine clearance is a measure of the glomerular filtration rate. In man, however, a little creatinine is added to the filtrate by the tubule cells and inulin is generally accepted as the best substance for measurement of filtration rate.

The choice of inulin for this purpose is justified by the following considerations. Inulin solutions, if pure, can be injected intravenously into man and other animals without harm and without affecting the circulation or the activity of the kidney. Inulin is not metabolized in the body. It is freely filterable through the glomerular membrane since its concentration in frog's glomerular fluid is equal to that in the plasma. The belief that inulin is neither reabsorbed nor secreted in the tubules is mainly based on the following observations: (*a*) The molecular weight of inulin is 5,200, and being a long chain polysaccharide, it diffuses at only about double the rate of haemoglobin. It is, therefore, unlikely to diffuse out of the tubules. (*b*) Inulin (mol. wt. 5,200) and creatinine (mol. wt. 112) have the same plasma clearances when measured at the same time in dogs and in many other species. It would seem that two substances with chemical natures and diffusion rates so widely different could not be treated exactly alike by tubule cells in either the process of secretion or of passive diffusion. (*c*) The inulin clearance is independent of its concentration in the plasma; whereas the clearances of most other substances which are higher or lower than that of inulin when their concentrations in the plasma are low, approach the inulin clearance progressively as their concentrations in the plasma rise (see Fig. 38.5). (*d*) In man and animals in which the creatinine clearance exceeds the inulin clearance, there are other substances, e.g. sorbitol and mannitol, whose clearances are identical with the inulin clearance. (*e*) Inulin cannot be excreted by certain fish whose kidneys contain no glomeruli ("aglomerular kidneys"). All constituents of the urine in these species must be secreted by the tubules and this emphasizes the incapacity of tubules to secrete inulin.

On the basis of these considerations there is now widespread agreement that the glomerular filtration rate in the normal kidney may be measured in terms of the plasma clearance for inulin. In kidneys damaged by disease or poison, in which abnormally low inulin clearances are found, the possibility of abnormal permeability of the tubules leading to loss of inulin by passive reabsorption must, however, be borne in mind.

The inulin clearance in man ranges in healthy individuals from 90 to 170 ml per min—the average is about 125 ml per min for men and 118 ml per min for women—all reduced to the standard size of 1.73 m^2 surface area, i.e. the area generally regarded as representative for men and women of average size. In a given individual, the inulin clearance is surprisingly difficult to change. In water diuresis, for example, an increase in urine flow from a resting value of 1 ml per min to nearly 20 ml per min which is about the maximum, involves little or no change in inulin clearance.

Renal plasma flow

The renal plasma flow could be measured in terms of the plasma clearance if a substance could be found which is completely removed from the plasma during a single passage from renal artery to renal vein. To obtain blood flow from plasma flow the haematocrit value would also be needed. Such a substance must be unable to diffuse out of the corpuscles during their passage through the kidney. With such an ideal substance, all of it would pass from the arterial plasma to the urine, leaving none in the venous plasma. Its *extraction-ratio* would be 1.0. The amount appearing in the urine in one minute would be the same as the amount in the arterial plasma passing through the renal artery in one minute. If its concentration in the plasma entering the kidney was also known, the volume of plasma traversing the kidney per minute could be calculated, that is, the plasma clearance would be equal to the plasma flow.

Substances approaching the required conditions are para-amino hippuric acid (P.A.H.) and the organic iodine compound known as diodone in England and iodopyracet or diodrast in America. If the plasma concentration of diodone is below the threshold above which the clearance begins to fall, the renal venous plasma, measured by catheterization of the renal vein, is found to contain only about one-tenth of that in the arterial plasma. The kidney has extracted, say, nine-tenths of the diodone, and so long as this extraction ratio remains constant, the necessary correction can be made in calculating the renal plasma flow. The extraction ratio fortunately appears to remain fairly constant in normal kidneys. It falls so far, however, in kidneys damaged by disease or poisons that the method often becomes inapplicable.

In resting normal men, the diodone (diodrast) clearance at low plasma concentrations averages about 655 ml per min, corresponding to a renal plasma flow of about 720 ml per min and a renal blood flow of nearly

1,300 ml per min. Taking the resting cardiac output at 5,000 ml per min, it appears that at rest the supply to the kidneys accounts for about one-quarter of the output of blood from the heart. The proportion of plasma entering the kidney which is removed by filtration in the glomeruli is known as the *filtration fraction*; this is 125/720, i.e. about one-fifth.

TUBULAR FUNCTION

Protein-free plasma, emerging from the glomerulus to enter the tubules at about 125 ml per min, is transformed into a very much smaller volume of urine leaving the further ends at, e.g. 1 ml per min. The main secretory work of the tubules is done in concentrating substances, such as urea, which are present in large amounts and which are relatively highly concentrated in the urine. Important also is the reabsorption of substances valuable to the body, such as glucose, which are present in plasma but normally absent in urine.

The reabsorptive function of the tubules has been unequivocally demonstrated by the experiments of A. N. Richards and his successors, already mentioned, in which a comparison of the composition of the glomerular fluid and bladder urine showed that, in suitable circumstances, glucose and chlorides might be present in the former, but absent from the latter. Moreover, the quantity of the glomerular fluid which they collected in a given time, multiplied by the number of glomeruli, was much greater than the volume of urine which appeared in the same time. Water, therefore, is reabsorbed, consequently substances which are not reabsorbed must appear in the urine in a higher concentration than in the plasma.

In man, 125 ml per min, that is, nearly 200 litres in 24 hr, are filtered in about two million glomeruli, producing about 1·5 litres of urine. On the average, therefore, each glomerulus filters 0·1 ml a day, nearly all of which is reabsorbed in passage down its tubule, of average length about 5·5 cm, and with reabsorptive surface greatly increased by microvilli (brush border) in the proximal segment.

Most products of metabolism, which appear more concentrated in urine than in plasma, are so concentrated because they are less reabsorbed in the tubules than is the water. Nevertheless, some substances are certainly concentrated beyond this level by transfer from peri-tubular capillary blood to the lumen by "secretion" by the tubule cells. Most striking of these are the substances already mentioned whose plasma clearances approach the total plasma flow through the kidney. If nine-tenths of such a substance, say diodone, which reaches the kidney in the plasma is excreted in the urine, and if this were derived entirely from the glomerular filtrate, the plasma emerging from the glomerular capillaries would contain only one-tenth of its normal content of water and the blood would be much too viscid to pass through the vasa efferentia. In fact, only about one-fifth of the water in the plasma is removed by glomerular filtration, leaving four-fifths in the plasma in the vasa efferentia. Direct secretion of some substances into the lumen of the tubule is, therefore, certain. Among other such substances are penicillin and the dye, phenol red, which cannot readily pass the glomerular membrane because much of it is bound to plasma protein. Many drugs are similarly protein-bound. Creatinine in some species, such as man, is secreted in small amounts; in others, such as the dog, concentrated only by the reabsorption of water. The plasma clearances of all "secreted" substances are higher than that of inulin but approach

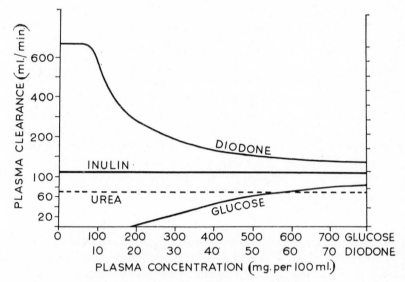

FIG. 38.5. Diagrammatic representation of the effects of plasma concentrations on plasma clearances in the human kidney.

 Glucose is "reabsorbed" up to a transport maximum, Tm = 350 mg/min.

 Diodone is "secreted" up to a Tm = 57 mg (Iodine)/min.

 Inulin is neither reabsorbed nor secreted in the tubules and the plasma clearance is little affected by the concentration in the plasma.

 Some urea diffuses passively out of the tubules in amount about proportional to its concentration in the plasma. (After H. W. Smith.)

this as their concentration in the plasma increases (Fig. 38.5). This is because there is a maximum quantity per minute which the tubule cells can secrete known as the "transport maximum" or Tm; whereas the amount contained in the glomerular filtrate per minute increases directly with concentration in the plasma. The filtered portion, thus, increasingly dwarfs the secreted portion of the substance appearing in the urine.

 Among substances which are reabsorbed, urea is quantitatively important. Its clearance is usually about one-half of that of inulin, and is independent of plasma concentration. The other half of the urea in the glomerular filtrate is passively reabsorbed from the tubule, the higher the urine flow the less, proportionately, being reabsorbed and the higher the clearance relative to that of inulin. Glucose is entirely reabsorbed in the tubules so long as the amount presented to the tubule cells by the content of the glomerular filtrate does not exceed the transport maximum which in man is about 350 mg per min. Below this its plasma clearance is zero. If the plasma concentration exceeds a threshold value, about 0·18 per cent for glucose, the excess which cannot be reabsorbed in the tubules appears in the urine, with measurable glucose clearances.

Proximal Tubular Activity

Micropipette samples of fluid from the glomerular capsule and from the termination of the proximal tubules have been obtained in frogs, rats and dogs. Further important evidence about tubule functions has been derived from microperfusion of individual tubules. A proximal tubule is punctured and filled with droplets of oil to prevent entry of glomerular fluid into the tubule beyond. This is perfused from a second micropipette and the modified perfusion fluid collected by withdrawing the first pipette and inserting it some way down the tubule. The glomerular fluid escapes through the hole left by withdrawing the first pipette but is replaced by perfusion fluid at, say, 20×10^{-6} ml per min in the segment beyond the oil by the second pipette.

In unpunctured proximal tubules, the glomerular fluid appears to lose by reabsorption practically all its content of glucose and about four-fifths of its volume of water. The total osmolar concentration remains unchanged but creatinine which is not reabsorbed from the tubules is concentrated about five-fold because of the reduction in the volume of water. Since the osmolar concentration does not rise, the reabsorbed water must contain all the sodium and other ions in about the same isotonic concentration as in glomerular fluid, or rather higher, to compensate for increased concentration of little reabsorbed substances like creatinine and urea. Confirmation of these views can be drawn from studies of drastic diuresis in larger mammals. One form of diuresis, osmotic diuresis, can be produced by substances which are not reabsorbed in the tubules, because if more water were reabsorbed, their concentration would increase and the total osmolar concentration of the tubular fluid would not remain the same as that of the glomerular fluid; the water, instead, flows on to become urine. Intravenous injection of large amounts of a powerful osmotic diuretic, such as a sugar called mannitol, may be followed by increase in the urine flow up to about one-third of the glomerular filtration rate. It is presumed that the flow down the later segments of the tubule is, then, so abnormally rapid that the composition of the outflowing urine will be practically the same as that of the fluid emerging from the proximal tubule, the distal tubule activity being swamped by the exceptional flood. Such urine has practically the same osmolar concentration as that of the plasma but it contains much more mannitol and much less sodium. Clearly, proportionately much more sodium than water is being reabsorbed, and since this sodium is being transferred from a weaker solution in the tubule to a more concentrated one in the plasma, it is inferred that reabsorption of sodium is an active process, known as a "sodium pump", which involves secretory work done by cells of the proximal tubule. The sodium ions transported by the sodium "pump" are accompanied by chloride ions, drawn passively out of the tubular fluid by the electrical gradient set up. In the proximal tubules, therefore, the secretory work necessary for reabsorbing the metabolically useful glucose and sodium chloride has the effect, indirectly, of also reabsorbing much of the equally useful water, leaving the unwanted creatinine, urea, and sulphates to be carried away in the urine.

The reabsorption of water in the proximal tubules is unaffected by the varying needs of the body and associated regulatory processes, but is decreased by osmotic diuretics. It has been estimated from indirect evidence that the average proportion of glomerular filtrate reabsorbed in the proximal tubule may be as much as 85 per cent in the larger mammals and this is referred to as the "obligatory reabsorption" of water; the fluid remaining corresponds in volume roughly to a maximal water diuresis. Further reabsorption of water in more distal tubular segments varies according to the requirements of the body and is referred to as "facultative reabsorption".

The Distal Tubular Complex

The loop of Henle, distal tubule and collecting duct form three anatomical segments which together convert the isosmotic effluent from the proximal tubule into urine. In overhydrated animals, the urine may equal this effluent in volume but will be much more dilute, nearly all the sodium chloride having been reabsorbed. In dehydrated animals, nearly all the water will have been reabsorbed but the urine that remains will be very concentrated, with a high content of sodium chloride, urea and other substances.

Micropipette samples of fluid from the first half of the distal tubule are hypotonic to blood, whether the urine is dilute as in water diuresis or concentrated as in antidiuresis. Here, or in the ascending limb of Henle's loop, therefore, must be a site of sodium chloride reabsorption. The distal tubule beyond, and also the collecting duct, must be practically water-tight in water diuresis. Since sodium chloride is still actively reabsorbed, a plentiful hypotonic urine is excreted. In antidiuresis, most of the water, as well as the sodium chloride, must somewhere be reabsorbed; removal of the water-tightness of the collecting ducts and distal tubules seems to be the essential action of the pituitary antidiuretic hormone (A.D.H.) (Chapter 32).

When A.D.H. thus renders the collecting ducts permeable to water, the water comes under the influence of an osmotic gradient due to earlier reabsorption of sodium chloride in or before the distal tubules. Water is therefore passively reabsorbed, but this would continue only to the point of producing isosmotic urine were it not for the high concentration, much higher than that of systemic blood, in the tissue fluid and capillary blood in the medulla, progressively increasing as the tip of the papilla is approached. This marked increase in osmolar concentration of the inner sections of the kidney, compared with the isotonic cortex, has been demonstrated in rats by experiments on the freezing points of the tissues, microscopically observed, as well as by equilibration with salt solutions of tissue slices taken from various parts of the medulla. A high osmolar concentration has also been observed in blood withdrawn by micropipette from blood vessels in the papilla of the golden hamster. Thus the capillaries in the medulla take part in the countercurrent concentrating process described below.

The concentrating process in the kidney can, therefore, be explained as a primary process which raises the osmolar concentration of tissue fluid and all constituent structures of the innermost zone of the renal medulla, and a secondary process of water passively reabsorbed from collecting ducts as they pass through this zone, leaving a correspondingly concentrated urine to emerge from the papilla. This primary process of osmotic concentration in the papilla is attributed to the active reabsorption of sodium chloride in or before the distal tubule, some of the salt remaining in the tissue fluid and raising its concentration, instead of being carried away in the blood. That the concentration is graded, becoming intensified toward the papilla, is consistent with its being produced by the countercurrent mechanism described below.

The present short account of the formation of urine as due to two active reabsorptive processes, the proximal and distal sodium "pumps", provides the bare bones of the explanation for the concentrating and diluting processes. Much is also known about the ways in which urine with great variations in content of its individual solutes is produced to meet the varying needs of the body, but much of this knowledge is still embarrassed by disputed interpretations.

The "Hairpin Countercurrent" System. Suppose that a tube is divided along the middle by a septum which has the property of actively transporting sodium chloride from the lower side A (Fig. 38.6) to the upper side D. A solution of sodium chloride is supposed to flow from left to right along channel D, and from right to left along channel A. Owing to the activity of the salt-transporting septum, the concentration of the solution in D will steadily rise, and that of the solution in A will steadily fall, as is indicated in the middle part of the diagram, sodium chloride being transferred from one side to the other. But if, now, we join one end of these two channels together by a U-tube, the solution entering channel A will be the same as that leaving channel D; all the concentrations of the solution in A will be raised, as indicated by the vertical arrows, and will become nearly the same as those in channel D. We now have what is called a "hairpin countercurrent system", the reason for the name being

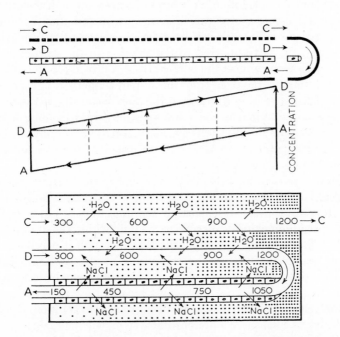

FIG. 38.6. Diagrams illustrating the action of the hairpin countercurrent system.

At the top is an idealized system whose action in producing a great increase in concentration at the tip of the hairpin is described in the text.

At the bottom is shown schematically the system as it exists in the kidney. A: ascending loop of Henle. D: descending loop of Henle. C: collecting duct. A is connected to C by way of the distal tubule, which actively re-absorbs NaCl, and allows water to pass from the tubular fluid to the blood so that the two become isotonic. The figures indicate the concentrations (milli-osmolar) of the fluid at various points within the loop of Henle and the collecting duct. The stippling indicates the corresponding increase in concentration of the interstitial fluid towards the tip of the loop.

clear from the diagram. The solution at the tip of the hairpin will be maintained at a much higher concentration than that of the solution entering and leaving it; this excess concentration may be much larger than that which could be created by each element of the septum, if there were no countercurrent, and it might increase indefinitely with increase in the length of the whole hairpin system.

The solution leaving the hairpin has the same concentration as that entering it, so that by itself, it cannot yield a concentrated product. Suppose, however, that we now add channel C (Fig. 38.6) which is separated from channel D by a membrane which is permeable to water, but not to any of the substances in solution. A solution flowing through channel C will lose water by osmosis into the hairpin system and thus become more concentrated; osmotic work will be done. Since the water removed from the solution in C is transferred to the solution in the hairpin system, it would be useless to connect the outflow from A directly to the inflow to C. This water must be removed from the system altogether, and not allowed merely to circulate within it. Further, the more water that is removed from C, the less concentrated is the solution within the hairpin, and the less effective it becomes in raising the concentration in C. For any considerable increase in concentration in C, the flow through C must be smaller than that round the hairpin.

Applying this idea to the kidney, we identify the hairpin system with the loop of Henle, the ascending loop being channel A, and the cells in its walls acting as the salt-transporting septum. These, however, do not transfer the sodium chloride directly to the fluid within the descending loop (channel D), but to the interstitial fluid, from which it may be supposed to diffuse passively through the thin walls of the descending loop as indicated in the power part of Fig. 38.6. Channel C may be identified with the collecting tubules whose walls must be supposed to be permeable to water, but relatively impermeable to all substances in solution. The loop of Henle, acting as a hairpin countercurrent system, will maintain a gradient of concentration in the interstitial fluid, increasing from the region of the convoluted tubules to the tip of the loop deep in the papilla. Such a gradient of concentration has, as already mentioned, been observed experimentally. As the urine flows down the collecting tubules it will lose water into the interstitial fluid and thus becomes more concentrated. This water must, of course, be carried away by the blood, or the whole process would soon come to an end. In the simplified system illustrated in Fig. 38.6, the water is shown entering the descending limb of Henle's loop, with the result that the fluid leaving the ascending limb becomes hypotonic. In the actual kidney, the process is somewhat different, owing to the presence of the blood capillaries which descend into the medullar, form loops, and return to the cortex. As in other low pressure capillaries, fluid will be drawn into the blood from the tissue spaces. The inner medullary blood flow is much lower than that in the cortex. Per gram of tissue, it is only about 2 to 4 per cent of the cortical blood flow in dogs. The conditions for effective operation of a hairpin countercurrent system and its associated passive diffusing channel are thus present in the renal medulla, so that the urine in the collecting tubules can become considerably hypertonic. In water diuresis, however, when the antidiuretic hormone is absent, the walls of the distal and collecting tubules appear to become impermeable to water although sodium chloride is still reabsorbed by the "sodium pump"; a plentiful hypotonic urine is, therefore, excreted (Fig. 38.8, p. 662).

ACID-BASE REGULATION

Metabolism of food produces sulphate, phosphate, bicarbonate and hydrogen ions (Chapter 29) which are eliminated in the urine. Most food, also, contains more potassium than sodium, so that there is relatively more potassium and less sodium in the urine than in the plasma.

Sulphate, phosphate and bicarbonate ions, like chloride ions, are drawn out of the fluid in the proximal tubules, in consequence of the active reabsorption of sodium ions; but they move more slowly, and a much greater fraction is left behind and excreted in the urine. This fraction increases with the amount delivered to the tubules whether the increase be due to increase in glomerular filtration or in plasma concentration of the anions.

Potassium and hydrogen ions are also reabsorbed from the fluid in the proximal tubules but in the distal tubules they are transported in the opposite direction, from plasma to urine, by a process of "ion exchange". The sodium ions reabsorbed by the distal "sodium pump" are mainly accompanied by chloride ions but, in part, exchanged for potassium and hydrogen ions destined for the urine.

There is an inverse relation between the amounts of potassium and hydrogen ions excreted, for example, urine becomes alkaline when potassium salts are administered, and respiratory alkalosis produces increased potassium excretion. Moreover, acidosis due to inhalation of carbon dioxide mixtures decreases potassium excretion. This inverse relation is explained by supposing that potassium and hydrogen ions compete for a common secretory process in the tubule cells. Other such competitive secretory processes in the kidney are well known, one of them involving among other substances diodone, para-amino hippuric acid, and penicillin. Therapeutic use was made of this limiting process during war-time scarcity of penicillin when it was conserved in the body by administering carinamide which competes for the same renal secretory process, so that it delayed the excretion of penicillin.

There are two ways in which the acid end products of metabolism can be excreted in urine without undue lowering of pH which in man never falls below 4·6. First, the urine is well buffered mainly due to its phosphate content, the Na_2HPO_4 being converted to NaH_2PO_4. Other substances, such as bicarbonate in the alkaline range and urea in the acid range contribute. Secondly, persistent excretion of acid urine stimulates the formation of ammonia in the tubule cells and the neutralization of acidic by ammonium ions.

AUTOREGULATION OF RENAL BLOOD FLOW

The blood flow through the kidney is very high, about 4 ml per min per g tissue. This compares with about 0·5 ml for heart muscle and brain, 0·1 ml for liver, 0·03 ml per min per g skeletal muscle and 0·15 ml in inner renal medulla. The blood volume in the kidney is also exceptionally high, about 24 ml per 100 g tissue compared with about 8 ml per 100 grams of the entire body.

In many isolated organs, the blood flow varies directly with arterial pressure. Unless the rise of pressure is due to vaso-constriction, doubling

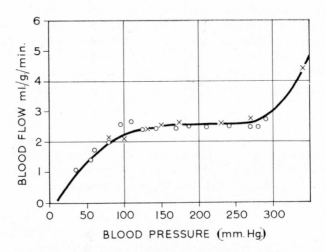

Fig. 38.7. Autoregulation of blood flow between arterial pressures of about 100 and 280 mm Hg in a kidney pump-perfused with blood from the carotid artery of the same dog.

Values obtained by continuous increase in pressure (circles) or by sudden increases in pressure (crosses) lie on the same curve, showing that the plain muscle of renal arterioles, unlike many other forms of plain muscle, does not contract after sudden stretch. (K. Thurau, K. Kramer and H. Brechtelsbauer, 1959.)

the arterial pressure will rather more than double the blood flow because the vessels dilate with pressure. In the kidney, however, the blood flow rises very little with increase in arterial pressure so long as the pressure is within the physiological range of 80 to 180 mm Hg. This control of blood flow is found in denervated and even in isolated perfused kidneys and is, therefore, called autoregulation.

Equally remarkable is the smallness of the rise in glomerular filtration rate when arterial pressure is raised, for example, by the carotid sinus reflex in unanaesthetized animals. This again is an autoregulatory affair and sheds important light on the site of the varying resistance controlling the blood flow which must, therefore, reside in the preglomerular blood vessels.

Vasoconstriction of, or near, the vasa afferentia seems the obvious explanation of autoregulation, especially since the phenomenon may persist when kidneys are perfused with cell-free blood substitutes which cannot alter their viscosity, at any given temperature. Nevertheless, the haematocrit of the blood in the kidney at normal blood flows is barely one-half that in the systemic circulation and this must mean that the cells pass through the kidney, probably through shunts, more rapidly than does the plasma. Some experiments indicating that increase in pressure increases this division into cell-rich and cell-poor fractions of renal blood suggest that autoregulation may, in part, be due to an effective increase in the viscosity of blood with rise in arterial pressure.

The participation of blood in the increasing osmotic pressure within the medulla, as the papilla is approached, has been mentioned. It is clear from our discussion of the countercurrent concentrating process that an enormous blood-flow such as 4 ml per min per g tissue would swamp the process. It has been found, however, that the medullary blood flow is only about 3 per cent of that of the cortex and, therefore, not so much more than the urine flow. Medullary flow is not subjected to autoregulation, as is the cortical flow and the increased medullary blood flow at high arterial pressure may, in part, account for pressure diuresis, since the increased blood flow limits the osmotic concentration in the tissues, and therewith, the withdrawal of water from the collecting ducts.

THE CONTROL OF RENAL SECRETION

Under normal conditions, the kidney does not contribute to the variation of peripheral vascular resistance which maintains steady systemic arterial pressure. The sympathetic nerves which supply the organ only come into action when the arterial pressure falls below 60–80 mm Hg when profound vasoconstriction and fall in glomerular filtration rate occur. This may be augmented by the effects of circulating adrenaline and noradrenaline under such conditions.

The effects on the secretion of urine of stimulation or blocking of various nervous structures may all be interpreted in terms of the changes induced either on the general arterial pressure, or on the calibre of the renal blood vessels, or on both. There is at present no sufficient reason for suspecting a direct nervous influence on the secretory mechanism proper, except for the anatomical fact that nerve fibres do supply the tubule cells. This is illustrated by the following experiment. If one kidney of a dog be completely denervated and the dog allowed to recover from the anaesthetic, the urine can be collected separately from each kidney through exteriorized ureters. The urine coming from the denervated organ is indistinguishable from that coming from its innervated fellow, both as regards rate of flow and composition. The increase of urine flow due to administration of water ("water diuresis") and its inhibition by exercise or stimulation of the skin are equal in both kidneys.

The degree to which circulating adrenaline and noradrenaline normally contribute to maintenance of the tone of renal blood vessels is uncertain.

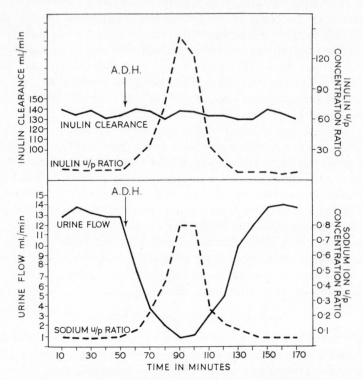

FIG. 38.8. Intravenous injection of 40 milliunits of antidiuretic hormone (A.D.H.) produces in a well hydrated man (1) antidiuretic action with no change in inulin clearance, i.e. glomerular filtration rate (scale on the left), and (2) increase in urine concentration of sodium and inulin (scales on the right in terms of urine/plasma concentration ratio). Plasma inulin concentration 25 mg/100 ml was kept constant by intravenous infusion of 1 g/hr; plasma sodium concentration: 325 mg/100 ml. (S. E. Dicker.)

Larger concentrations, due to injection, produce vasoconstriction which leads to fall in filtration and even anuria.

The antidiuretic hormone (A.D.H.) of the pituitary gland, as mentioned on p. 655, increases the permeability of the distal tubular complex and so increases the water reabsorption (Fig. 38.8). Secretion of the antidiuretic hormone ceases if the body is hydrated by fairly rapid drinking of two or more litres of water with consequent reduction of the concentration of the body fluids by 3 to 5 per cent. A water diuresis of very dilute urine ensues. Injection of hypertonic saline into the carotid artery stimulates secretion of the anti-diuretic hormone with consequent oliguria and a hypertonic urine. The control of A.D.H. secretion is normally through osmo-receptors in the hypothalamus, but secretion may also be evoked by pain, fright or by administration of nicotine or acetylcholine. Ethyl alcohol is the only substance, other than water, known to inhibit A.D.H. secretion but it can also be inhibited by hypnotic suggestion of drinking water and it is reduced or absent in the disease diabetes insipidus.

Aldosterone and to a less extent desoxycorticosterone from the adrenal cortex have a profound effect on renal function by promoting reabsorption of sodium and excretion of potassium. Aldosterone inhibitors, e.g. spiro-lactones, therefore increase sodium output and consequently act as diuretics.

The way in which circulating aldosterone is regulated is interesting. The extracellular volume—and thus sodium concentration in extracellular fluid—in some undefined manner acts on the juxta-glomerular apparatus causing it to release *renin*. The renin then reacts with angiotensinogen in the blood to form angiotensin which controls the secretion of aldosterone from the adrenal cortex.

Any substance which cannot leave the proximal tubules as rapidly as water does will reduce the reabsorption of water and act as an osmotic diuretic; for example mannitol, as already described, urea, sulphates, or an excess of glucose. The diuretics most widely used in medicine are, however, neither water, alcohol, aldosterone inhibitors nor osmotic diuretics but substances, such as chlorothiazide or organic mercury compounds, e.g. mersalyl, which appear to act by inhibiting chloride or sodium chloride reabsorption. Their diuretic action is sometimes rein-forced by combining them with one of the purine diuretics, aminophylline or caffeine, which may increase glomerular filtration by dilating the vasa afferentia and may also reduce tubular reabsorption.

Renal regulation of blood pressure (Renin)

A decrease in renal blood flow sufficient to give rise to ischaemia of the juxta-glomerular cells, which are in the walls of afferent arterioles next to the glomerular tuft, stimulates these cells to secrete renin.

Renin is an enzyme catalysing the conversion of the plasma protein *angio-tensinogen* into *angiotensin I* which rapidly turns into *angiotensin II* in the plasma. Angiotensin II has an action on the arterial pressure through two mechanisms. First, it produces peripheral arteriolar constriction; second, it stimulates the adrenal cortex to secrete aldosterone, which as described above, causes salt and water retention by the kidney, thus raising the arterial pressure as a result of increasing the extra-cellular volume. Angiotensin II is destroyed in the plasma by an enzyme, angiotensinase, after about 30 min.

Recent work casts doubt on the validity of this somewhat too-convenient theory on two grounds.

1. It is now possible to assay renin in the blood and it is found in normals and hypertensives that the concentration is too low to give rise to the effects observed.

2. The physiological effects of renin wear off (*tachyphylaxis*) rather rapidly. This is so because continued administration of renin uses up the available angiotensinogen in the plasma. It is not possible to produce a long-lasting elevation of arterial pressure by means of a continuous infusion of renin.

A similar series of substances have recently been found to affect systemic blood pressure when the blood supply to the placental site in the uterus is impeded.

MICTURITION

Urine is secreted by the kidneys continuously, but removed from the body only periodically. Meanwhile it collects and may remain for some hours in the bladder, which acts as a reservoir.

The urine passes from the kidneys to the bladder through tubes, the ureters, the walls of which contain plain muscle, and encourage the downward flow by peristaltic contractions. These contractions travel down the tube at about 2 to 3 cm per sec, and are repeated from about one to four times a minute. Consequently the urine enters the bladder in a series of squirts, as can be observed in man by looking through a cystoscope, a tubular instrument inserted through the urethra, which illuminates and renders visible the lining wall of the bladder. If, for any reason, the pressure inside the ureter is raised, its contractions become fiercer and more spasmodic in nature, a change which is readily observed in the isolated kidney of the dog. Such spasmodic contraction of plain muscle produces intense pain, and is illustrated in human disease by renal colic, which is an attack of severe pain and other symptoms due, for example, to passage of small stones from the kidney, blocking and distending the ureter and so evoking spasm of its wall.

Evacuation of the bladder is effected by contraction of the plain muscle in its walls, known as the detrusor muscle. The urethra is guarded by two sphincters—the external being of striated and the internal of unstriated muscle. If the external voluntary sphincter be held open by a catheter, the vesical contents are retained by the internal involuntary sphincter; even in such circumstances the subject can pass urine voluntarily by initiating a contraction of the detrusor muscle which induces relaxation of the sphincter. As the bladder fills, the intravesical pressure in man rises to about 5 cm water at a volume of 200 ml; the pressure is maintained at about this value until the volume of urine reaches 400 ml, after which further filling brings about a steeper rise in pressure, 20 to 30 cm water being reached when the volume is about 500 to 600 ml (Fig. 38.9).

The property of maintaining a constant pressure within the bladder through this range of volume was at one time attributed to an active relaxation of the muscle while the organ was being filled. The constancy is due, however, largely to the purely physical relation whereby, when a hollow organ is distended, and the length and tension of the muscle fibres in its wall are correspondingly increased, the pressure of liquid inside may hardly rise at all because the curvature of the wall becomes progressively less. A similar effect reduces the rise in pressure inside a toy balloon when it is blown up.

The bladder, like the alimentary canal, has a double autonomic innervation. Stimulation of the parasympathetic (pelvic) nerves induces contraction of the bladder but relaxation of the internal sphincter; the parasympathetic system contains the most important pathways for reflexes

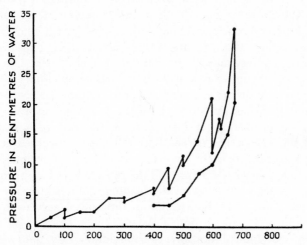

FIG. 38.9. Change in the pressure in the bladder of a man during filling and emptying.

Upper Curve. Water was slowly run into the bladder, and the pressure was observed after the addition of each 50 ml. The inflow was stopped at intervals, so as to allow time for the pressure to approximate to its final value, as shown by the short vertical lines.

Lower Curve. After 700 ml had been run in, the bladder was allowed to empty, 50 ml at a time. The pressures were all lower, indicating that the true equilibrium values had probably not been reached during either filling or emptying.

The pressure is not strictly constant over any range of volumes, but does not vary much between 100 ml and 400 ml. (Denny-Brown and Robertson.)

concerned in micturition including both afferent and efferent elements in the arcs. Stimulation of the sympathetic (pre-sacral or hypogastric) nerves causes contraction of the internal sphincter; relaxation of the bladder wall may follow intravenous injection of adrenaline in man. It is uncertain to what extent the sympathetic system normally affects the bladder in man.

The desire for micturition is set up when the volume of urine in the bladder reaches 200 to 300 ml, and a certain tension in the muscular wall is reached. When the tone of the bladder is increased, e.g. by cold or conditions of emotional strain, this critical tension may be reached with a relatively small volume of urine in the bladder. Up to a certain point, the sensation from a full bladder can be suppressed from a conscious level in the cerebral cortex, and, on the other hand, it is possible, by introspection, to become aware of small quantities of urine in the bladder.

Voluntary micturition is brought about by impulses passing from the cerebral cortex by way of the spinal cord and parasympathetic nerves, to the bladder. The detrusor muscle contracts strongly, raising the pressure in the bladder to 100 cm water, and simultaneously a reciprocal relaxation of the internal sphincter occurs. Voluntary effort to restrain micturition may considerably reduce the pressure within the bladder. Thus we have an example of involuntary muscle under the control of the will. Once micturition has begun, certain reflexes play a part in its completion. (1) Stretching of the bladder wall brings about reflex contraction of the bladder and this reflex can be abolished by cutting both the pelvic nerves, transecting the spinal cord, or cocainizing the interior of the bladder. It is unaffected by division of the hypogastric nerves. The reflex arc concerned is along the pelvic nerves to a centre in the hind-brain and back again along the pelvic nerves. (2) The flow of water through the posterior part of the urethra also brings about reflex contraction of the bladder, the reflex arc involving the centre in the hind-brain. Transection of the central nervous system only interferes with reflex micturition if the section is below a plane passing from the inferior colliculi dorsally, to the middle of the pons ventrally.

Diseases of the spinal cord involving the posterior columns may prevent the sensations from the bladder reaching consciousness, although micturition can still be carried out voluntarily. When the pyramidal tracts are interrupted, voluntary micturition is impossible, although the patient may be quite aware of a full bladder. When the voluntary control of micturition is impaired, retention of urine may result in over-distension of the bladder, and reflex passage of small quantities of urine at irregular intervals; this condition is known as "retention with overflow".

CHAPTER 39

THE CONTROL OF BODY TEMPERATURE

HEAT is continually produced in the course of the various chemical reactions of metabolism. This heat must be lost to the surroundings and, except over short periods of time, the rate of loss must be equal to the rate of production and a state of *heat balance* maintained; if this were not so, the body temperature would rise or fall indefinitely. The metabolic rate, and thus the rate of heat production, may vary over a wide range in different circumstances; and a man may live in surroundings which are cold or hot, dry or wet, and lose heat readily or only with difficulty. He is able, nevertheless, to preserve heat balance with his temperature almost unchanged.

The processes by which the body temperature is prevented from rising or falling unduly are of two kinds. First, the rate at which heat is lost from the skin is increased or decreased as necessary ("physical" regulation). In man, this is done partly by wearing appropriate clothes, but as in all warm-blooded animals it is also done automatically. Like any other hot object, the body cools at a rate which depends on the difference between the temperature of its surface and the temperature of the air and other surroundings. It cools more rapidly also if it is wet than if it is dry, heat being absorbed by the evaporation of water, and the rate of cooling depends on the difference between the wetness of the body and the wetness (humidity) of the air. Physical regulation, accordingly, is exerted in two ways: (*a*) by raising or lowering the skin temperature through control of the *rate of blood flow through the skin* and thus the rate at which heat is brought out to the surface of the body; and (*b*) by increasing the wetness of the skin, and thus the rate of cooling, by the *secretion of sweat*. Secondly, if the body temperature falls, in spite of all that can be done to reduce the loss of heat, the metabolic rate is increased, either deliberately by taking muscular exercise, or involuntarily by *shivering* ("chemical" regulation). The temperature of the skin, therefore, and at times that of a large part of the limbs, are subject to considerable variation. What is ordinarily referred to as the "body temperature", which remains nearly constant, is that of the "core", the internal organs of the abdomen, the heart, the brain, and the blood within these organs, although they are not all necessarily at exactly the same temperature. The temperature of a thermometer placed in the rectum, or under the tongue, is usually taken as a measure of the body temperature.

THE TEMPERATURE REGULATING CENTRES

The various processes by which a man keeps himself in heat balance are controlled and co-ordinated by "centres" in the brain in response to signals transmitted from temperature receptors. Some of the signals must indicate the temperature of the "core", since it is this, primarily, which is regulated.

The results of changing the temperature of the blood flowing to the brain in the carotid arteries of an experimental animal are shown in Fig. 39.1; the changes in the temperature of the tongue give a qualitative indication of those in the temperature of the brain. A rise in the brain temperature

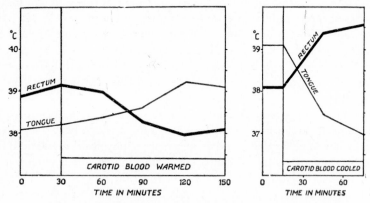

FIG. 39.1. The action of the temperature regulating centres.

    The effect on the body temperature of a dog, as measured in the rectum, of warming and cooling the blood flowing in the carotid arteries to the brain. The changes in temperature of the tongue are an indication of those in the brain. Note that the temperature of the rectum moves in the opposite direction to that of the brain, indicating the efforts of the regulating centres to counteract the warming and cooling of the blood supplying it. (From data by Geiger.)

is accompanied by a fall in the rectal temperature; and a fall in the brain temperature by a rise in the rectal temperature. These experiments indicate that there are structures in the brain which are sensitive to changes in the temperature of the blood and are capable of so altering the rate of heat loss from the body as a whole that the changes in the blood temperature would be counteracted. Transection of the brain stem at various levels in experimental animals has shown that co-ordinated temperature regulation ceases if the section is made posterior to the hypothalamus, so that the hypothalamus, and structures anterior to it, have no connection with the rest of the body: the "thalamic" animal has control of its temperature, but the "decerebrate animal" has little or none. More detailed studies, by localized electrical stimulation, and by warming and cooling small regions of the brain, show that the temperature receptors and the regulating "centres" lie close together in the anterior hypothalamus. It is probable that the organization of the receptors and regulating centres is essentially similar in man to that in the experimental animals studied.

The regulating centres will initiate responses leading to increased dissipation of heat, or to increased conservation or production of heat, only if they receive appropriate nerve impulses from temperature receptors. The body temperature cannot be regulated unless there is some change in temperature to initiate the regulation. The centres, however, receive nerve impulses from peripheral temperature receptors in the skin and the mucous membranes of the nose and mouth as well as from the central receptors. The temperature of the skin, as we shall see in more detail later, changes quite largely and rapidly in accordance with the temperature of the environment; the peripheral receptors, therefore, will "drive" the regulating centres appropriately even if there is no change in the temperature of the core. A man's body, moreover, has a considerable heat capacity, and appreciable amounts of heat must be gained or lost before there is a sufficient change in the temperature of the core to affect the regulating centres. Even if there were a sudden change in the rate of heat production, or in the temperature of the environment, the temperature of the central receptors would change only slowly, and the measures necessary to restore heat balance would be initiated gradually and after some delay. The peripheral receptors, however, will be affected more rapidly, and being very sensitive to changes in temperature, will immediately "drive" the regulating centres appropriately, thereby increasing the rapidity and precision with which heat balance is restored.

Normally, in a sedentary man, the temperature of the core varies from just below 36·5°C (98°F) to just below 37°C (99°F). Within these limits, there is a regular diurnal variation, the highest value being reached in the late afternoon, and the lowest in the early morning. In women, there may be a rhythmic variation with the menstrual cycle, the temperature being lower during the menstrual period and for some time afterwards. The body temperature rises and falls by about 1°C (2°F) in quite ordinary circumstances according to the temperature of the environment and the amount of clothing worn; on exposure to severe cold it has been known to fall as low as 22·7°C (73°F) with subsequent recovery. It rises during muscular exercise in proportion to the severity of the exercise as measured, for example, by the oxygen consumption, and may reach 39·5°C (103°F).

Fever

When an infection is accompanied by a fever, it seems that the temperature regulating centres become "reset", as one might readjust a thermostat, to a higher value of the body temperature. One feels cold, one's skin is cold and pale, one shivers, and the temperature rises to the new value, often as high as 40°C (104°F) and possibly as high as 44°C (112°F). On recovery from the infection, one's skin becomes warm and flushed, one sweats, and the temperature is brought down again.

The temperature centres are depressed by anaesthetics and by hypoxia. In temperate climates anaesthetized animals and men must be kept warm by adequate covering or an appropriate supply of heat. At high altitudes the air is cold and the partial pressure of oxygen is low; breathing oxygen is of great assistance in preventing a fall in the general body temperature and in preventing frost-bite of the extremities.

The amount of control which can be exerted over the rates of heat loss and of heat production, though large, are not unlimited. If the conditions are such that it is impossible to lose heat rapidly enough and the body temperature cannot be prevented from rising, the consequences are likely to be serious. The metabolic rate, like the rates of all chemical reactions, is increased by a rise in temperature. As the body temperature rises, the rate of production of heat will rise with it, and the temperature will rise even more rapidly. A vicious circle is established which will end in heat stroke and death. On the other hand, if in spite of all attempts to retain and produce heat the body temperature continues to fall, the temperature regulating centres, like other nervous structures, will become progressively less active. A time will come when the effort to maintain heat balance is abandoned; the person "basks in the cold", and unless he is soon removed from the cold environment and warmed, he will die.

Artificial Hypothermia

An individual's body temperature can be lowered by administration of a sedative to depress the hypothalamic controlling mechanism and immersing him in ice or ice-water. Chlorpromazine is usually used to depress the thermostat.

Deep temperature can be maintained at levels down to 27°C for up to a week if necessary without untoward effects. This technique of artificial cooling is used in heart surgery to enable the heart to be stopped for many minutes at a time since its metabolism is considerably reduced at lower temperatures. Also the requirement of the remainder of the body, including the brain, for oxygen is reduced.

Small laboratory animals, such as mice and rats may be cooled in a similar manner, down to near freezing point, and held in a state of suspended animation for long periods. Provided re-warming is carried out so that the circulation commences before brain temperature begins to rise, the cooled animal is apparently normal afterwards.

CONTROL OF THE BODY TEMPERATURE

All animals, including man, regulate their temperatures partly by means of appropriate behaviour. When warm, they keep quiet and seek shady and windy places; when cold, they move about or seek sunny and sheltered places, curling up so as to reduce the amount of surface exposed. But we are here concerned with the less elaborate "reflex" processes which come more strictly within the scope of physiology.

Blood Flow through the Skin

An ordinary man feels comfortably warm when the temperature of his skin lies roughly between 25°C and 35°C, although there are large individual variations. If he were at rest, and had no clothes, the air temperature would have to lie between about 20°C (68°F) and about 32°C (90°F), higher in dry windy conditions, when heat is carried away more rapidly, than in moist still conditions. In these "neutral" environments (neither hot nor cold) control of the body temperature is carried out entirely by control of the skin circulation. The excitation of the "40°" receptors in the skin falls progressively as the skin temperature falls, and that of the "30°" receptors rises reciprocally (Chapter 24, p. 416), whereas outside the "neutral" conditions, only one or other kind is excited.

If the rate of blood flow through the skin is large, heat is brought out rapidly from the core to the surface of the body, the surface temperature is well above that of the environment and the rate of heat dissipation is large. On the other hand, if no blood were to flow through the skin and superficial layers of the body, heat would reach the surface only by conduction through the layers of tissue, the core, in effect, having retreated away from the surface and become surrounded by an insulating layer; the temperature of the skin would approach that of the environment and the rate of heat loss would be small. The flow of blood through the superficial layers cannot be stopped entirely, however, at least for any considerable period of time, since the tissues continue to use oxygen. But the cold blood returning to the heart from a cold skin flows in veins, the *venae comites*, which form a network round the arteries carrying the blood from the heart; there is an exchange of heat, the venous blood being warmed and the arterial blood cooled (this has been observed experimentally). Heat is thus retained within the core even though the skin receives an adequate supply of blood. If the environment is warm, most of the blood flowing through the skin returns to the heart by way of the superficial veins and the "counter-current" heat exchange system is largely by-passed.

The magnitude of the vasomotor control over the vessels of the skin may be judged from the changes in skin temperature in different environments. The temperature of the bare skin is most accurately measured in terms of the rate at which it radiates heat to an appropriately calibrated radiation thermopile held a few millimetres from the skin and protected from draughts. Alternatively, and rather less accurately though often more conveniently, thermo-couples may be attached to the skin by adhesive tape or thrust just below the surface of the skin; this method must be used if the skin is covered by clothing. The greatest changes in skin temperature occur in the arms and legs, particularly in the fingers and toes, and the smallest on the head and the trunk. Different parts of the skin thus often have different temperatures, and the thermal insulation provided by the superficial layers varies from part to part. In cold conditions heat is lost more rapidly from the head and trunk than from the arms and legs. When a man moves from warm surroundings, with a maximum flow of blood through the skin, to cold surroundings, with a minimum flow, the average thermal insulation round the whole core increases about five-fold. An average man can thus maintain heat balance, by control of his skin circulation in spite of a five-fold change in the difference between the body temperature and the air temperature, for example, or of a five-fold change in the rate of heat production by metabolism. (There are large variations between different individuals.)

The effectiveness of this control is illustrated in Fig. 39.2. A subject was placed in a well-stirred water-bath, maintained at different temperatures

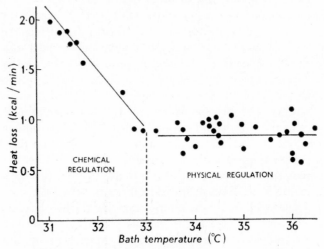

Fig. 39.2. Temperature regulation in a water bath.

A subject lay in a well-stirred water-bath, maintained at different temperatures on different occasions, and the rate of heat loss to the water measured. Since his temperature was constant during the measurement, this must also have been his rate of heat production. It was constant at temperatures between 36·5°C and 33°C, the range of "physical" regulation, by control of the cutaneous blood circulation. It rose steadily as the temperature was reduced from 33°C to 31°C, "chemical" regulation, by increase in the metabolic rate, being added. (Burton and Bazett, from Burton and Edholm, "Man in a Cold Environment", Edward Arnold (Publishers) Ltd.)

on different occasions, and the rate at which heat was transferred from the subject to the bath was measured. At all temperatures between 33°C (91·5°F) and 36·5°C (98°F), this subject was able to keep his rate of heat loss almost unchanged, in spite of the fact that the difference between his body temperature and the temperature of the bath varied by a factor of nearly ten.

Local and Reflex Actions

These changes in the rate of blood flow through the skin are brought about: (*a*) by direct local action on the calibre of the blood vessels; and

(b) by reflex control of the calibre by varying excitation of the vasomotor nerve fibres supplying them.

The immediate effect of exposing some part of the body, say a hand or foot, to a different environment, hotter or colder than before, is a vaso-dilatation or a vasoconstriction in the part exposed. The rate of blood flow through the hand, for example (almost entirely through the skin circulation) as measured by the rate of heat dissipation in a calorimeter (Chapter 29,

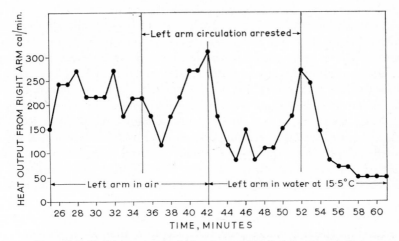

FIG. 39.3. Reflex vasoconstriction in one hand, following cooling of the opposite arm.

The subject's right hand was placed in a water calorimeter at time 0, and the rate of heat elimination calculated from the rate of rise of temperature of the water, after 25 min had been allowed for a steady state to be reached.

Vasoconstriction is indicated by the reduction in the rate of heat output. It occurred: (a) at the 42nd min when the left arm was placed in cold water, even though the circulation through this arm had been arrested and (b) at the 52nd min when the circulation was restored and cool blood entered the general circulation. (From Pickering, 1932, re-drawn. *Heart*, **16**, 118.)

p. 501), falls progressively as the temperature of the water is reduced, down to about 10°C. The consequent effect on the temperature of the skin, particularly on the tips of the fingers, when the hand is placed in cold water, is well shown in Fig. 39.3 below. Again, the blood flow through the forearm, as measured by venous occlusion plethysmography (Chapter 7, p. 79), depends on the temperature of the water within the plethysmo-graph. If the temperature lies between about 15°C and 20°C, the rate of blood flow is small, and little affected by temperature; but if the temperature is greater than 25°C, the rate of blood flow increases rapidly with rise in temperature, by about five-fold at 35°C and twenty-fold at 45°C. These measurements indicate that the blood flow through the muscles of the arm must be affected by temperature, as well as that through the skin.

A large part of the local vasomotor response, at least to cold, remains after removal, or blocking, of the sympathetic nerves and is produced either by an axon reflex or by a direct action on the blood vessels. The existence of *reflex* vasomotor control, through the temperature regulating centres, is shown by the response to change in the general body temperature or to change in the skin temperature of some other part of the body. In the experiment illustrated in Fig. 39.3, the rate of heat dissipation from the subject's right hand was measured in a calorimeter at a temperature of about 29°C. To begin with, his bare left forearm was in moderately warm air. On immersing this arm in water at a temperature of 15·5°C, there was an immediate vasoconstriction in the opposite hand, as shown by the decreased rate of heat dissipation to the calorimeter. This must have been due to a nervous reflex, set up by the temperature receptors in the cold arm, since the blood flow through this arm had been arrested before it was cooled, by inflating a sphygmomanometer cuff on the upper arm to 200 mm Hg. The converse effect, of a reflex vasodilatation when some part of the body is warmed, may also be demonstrated in a similar manner, though not so regularly as the reflex vasoconstriction.

When blood was readmitted to the cold arm, and on returning to the general circulation cooled the central receptors, the blood vessels of the hand were again constricted, and remained so for a considerable time. In the absence of circulation through the cold arm, the heat loss from the body was not increased appreciably; there was no "drive" from the central receptors towards increased conservation of heat, the "drive" from the peripheral receptors was over-ridden and the vaso-constriction was transient, lasting only some seven minutes.

This interaction between signals from peripheral and central receptors is demonstrated, also, by the experiment illustrated in Fig. 39.4. When the subject held his hand in ice-cold water, stimulation of the peripheral temperature receptors led to an immediate constriction of the vessels of the nasal mucosa, as shown by the fall in temperature. The total effect of the reduction in heat loss produced by such vasoconstriction (there may also have been an increase in the metabolic rate) was apparently excessive; the rectal temperature rose slowly, and the vessels in the nasal mucosa dilated again. Later in the experiment the rectal temperature fell, and the mucosal vessels constricted more profoundly than before, the central and peripheral receptors now acting in conjunction.

When some part of the body, say a hand or foot, is placed in a very cold environment (air or water at a temperature below 10°C), the tissues, particularly of the fingers and toes, may become so cold that there is risk of serious damage. This is avoided by the phenomenon known as "*cold vasodilatation*", produced by a direct local action on the blood vessels. Although protective locally, this increases the rate of heat loss unless compensated by vasoconstriction elsewhere. As may be seen in Fig. 39.4, after the subject's hand had been in ice-cold water for about twenty minutes, the skin temperature on the finger began to rise, indicating that the blood vessels were opening up again. The rectal temperature fell, and

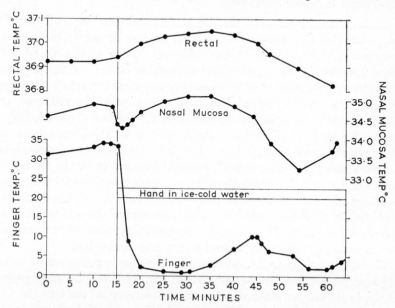

FIG. 39.4. Temperature regulation during extreme cooling of one hand.

The temperatures of the left index finger just beneath the skin, of the nasal mucosa, and within the rectum, are plotted against time. (Note the different scales on which the temperatures are plotted.)

After a control period of 15 min, the whole left hand was immersed in ice-cold water, producing extreme vasoconstriction in the finger, as shown by the great fall in temperature. After 20 min in the cold water, the temperature of the finger began to rise, owing to the onset of "cold vasodilatation".

The fluctuations in the temperature of the nasal mucosa illustrate the vasomotor changes produced by interaction between the peripheral receptors in the cold hand and the central receptors responding to the rectal temperature. (From Aschoff, 1944, re-drawn.)

the blood vessels of the nasal mucosa became constricted in compensation. The vasoconstriction extended, also, after some delay, to the blood vessels of the cold hand, and its temperature fell again. Such a "hunting" process, of alternate vasoconstriction and vasodilatation, may continue so long as the hand (or foot) remains in the very cold environment.

The release of a profound vasoconstriction in the skin, either as a result of "cold vasodilatation" or more particularly of a sudden change to a warmer environment, is likely to lead to a rather sudden drop in the general blood temperature, owing to the initial return of cold blood from the skin. It is not uncommon for people to feel much colder, and even to start shivering, on first coming into a warm room after having been out in the cold.

Reactions to Cold: Shivering

We have considered so far the effects of exposing only a small part of the body to cold environments. When a large part, or the whole, of the body is so exposed, the rate of heat loss may well be too great even when the blood flow through the skin has been reduced as far as possible everywhere. The first, and normal, reaction of an ordinary civilized man is then to put on more clothes. The effective thermal insulation of the stationary layer of air round the body can be increased, by this means, about six-fold, the limit being set by the fact that if the clothing is too thick one cannot move about; there is no such limit when a man is asleep. Fur-bearing animals have a comparable "pilomotor reflex", brought into action by the temperature regulating centres, by which the hairs are erected and the thickness of the air trapped between them is increased. When the thermal insulation provided by clothes or hair is sufficient, the temperature of the skin itself returns to the "neutral" zone, and further adjustment of the body temperature is made, as before, by control of the skin circulation.

If clothing is inadequate, the excessive heat loss is countered by increasing heat production. As may be seen in Fig. 39.2, this occurred progressively, in the subject studied, when the temperature of the water in which he was immersed fell below 33°C (91·5°F). The subject's body temperature was constant when the measurements were made, so that the rate of heat loss to the bath must have been equal to the rate of heat production by metabolism. When the temperature of the bath had fallen to 31°C (88°F) the subject had increased his metabolic rate some two and a half times.

The greater part of the increase in metabolic rate results from increased muscular activity; in the absence of obvious muscular exercise, there is greater "tone" and rigidity in the muscles, and individual muscle fibres contract in an inco-ordinated and asynchronous manner, producing the irregular tremors of *shivering*. This peculiar kind of muscular contraction is initiated by a "shivering centre" in the posterior hypothalamus; this has direct connections with the temperature regulating centres and is set into action by a sufficient fall in the general body temperature. Shivering may also occur, however, when the skin becomes cold, or when very cold air is breathed, without detectable change in the rectal temperature. Most people, by this means, can increase the metabolic rate to about three times the resting rate. By deliberate muscular exercise, however, the metabolic rate may be increased ten-fold, or for a short time, more than a hundred-fold.

That part of the increase in metabolic rate which is not due to muscular contractions is thought to be due to increased secretion by the thyroid gland and the adrenal cortex, the temperature regulating centres being connected with the adenohypophysis and increasing the secretion of T.S.H. and of A.C.T.H. (Chapter 32); the adrenal medulla also contributes by way of the sympathetic nerve supply. All these glands are known to secrete hormones which increase the metabolic rate of nearly all the organs and tissues of the body. They probably play an important part in the reactions to cold of some kinds of small mammal, but it is doubtful if they are of much importance in man.

Reactions to Heat: Sweating

The skin is always slightly wet as a result of the "insensible perspiration"; unless the air is saturated with water vapour, or the subject is immersed in water, there is always some loss of heat by the evaporation of water from the skin. The mucous membranes of the respiratory passages, also, are kept wet, and as pointed out in Chapter 12, the expired air is nearly saturated with water vapour at 37°C. Heat is lost by this route at a rate which increases with increase in the respiratory minute volume, and thus automatically with increase in the metabolic rate; but in man it makes only a small contribution towards preservation of heat balance.

The wetness of the skin, and the loss of heat by evaporation of water, are greatly increased by the onset of active sweating, which occurs when there is a rise in the general body temperature as is shown in Fig. 39.5. How large this rise must be depends on the skin temperature. In a cool environment, when the skin temperature is low, the rise in rectal temperature produced by a moderate amount of muscular exercise, for example, will bring about little or no sweating. In a warm environment, when the skin temperature is high, the same rise in rectal temperature will bring about copious sweating; if it is sufficiently warm, there may be sweating even without muscular exercise.

Sweat is produced by special glands in the skin which are innervated by fibres derived from the sympathetic system (Chapter 22). They are brought into action by means of impulses in these fibres, derived from "centres" in the spinal cord, which may act to some extent independently of the hypothalamic centres; a spinal man may sweat when his skin is heated. The amount of sweat secreted in a given time by, say, an arm or leg may be measured by collecting it in a waterproof bag in which the limb is enclosed. It is not possible, however, to estimate in this way the rate of sweating by the whole body, since evaporation is prevented and heat balance upset. In studying temperature regulation, the rate at which water is evaporated is of greater interest than the rate at which sweat runs off the surface of the body. This may be measured by weighing the subject at the beginning and end of the period, and correcting for the volume of fluid drunk, the volume of urine eliminated, and the loss of weight consequent on the loss in the expired air of the carbon of the food-

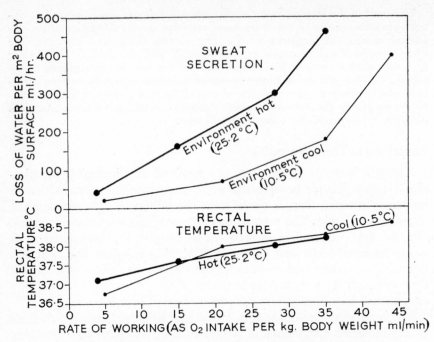

Fig. 39.5. Secretion of sweat during exercise in man.

Exercise was taken on a treadmill running at different speeds and with different gradients on different occasions. The severity of the the exercise was measured in terms of the rate of oxygen consumption. Two series of experiments were performed in environments with effective temperatures (p. 681) of 10·5°C (51°F) and 25·2°C (77·5°F) corresponding roughly in England to a mild winter day and a hot summer day respectively.

The rate of sweat secretion (measured as the rate of evaporation of water and including insensible perspiration) increased rapidly with increase in the metabolic rate, and was much greater in the hot environment (skin temperature about 34°C) than in the cool environment (skin temperature about 28·5°C). The skin temperature did not rise when exercise was taken.

The rectal temperature increased progressively with the severity of the exercise; it varied with the environmental temperature when the subject was at rest, but hardly at all when he was taking exercise. (Replotted from data of Robinson *et al.* in Newburgh "The Physiology of Heat Regulation", W. B. Saunders Co.)

stuffs metabolized—i.e. the difference between the weight of oxygen absorbed and the weight of carbon dioxide eliminated; this may be calculated from the metabolic rate. In extreme conditions a man may secrete 10–15 litres of sweat a day and, for a short time, evaporate water at a rate of 1 litre an hour.

The sweat glands secrete a vasodilator substance along with the sweat, so that there is a plentiful supply of blood, and thus of heat to evaporate the sweat. In parts of the skin which are particularly well supplied with sweat glands, this active vasodilatation largely replaces the passive vaso-dilatation, following inhibition of the vasoconstrictor nerves, which occurs in other parts of the skin.

There are two kinds of sweat gland, known as *eccrine* and *apocrine*. The apocrine glands, which occur chiefly in the axillae and pubic regions, are not concerned in temperature regulation, but probably have some secondary sexual function. The eccrine glands may be brought into action, not only by thermal stimuli, but also by emotional and mental stimuli, as in the "cold sweat" of fear and anxiety; the glands in the palms of the hands and soles of the feet, indeed, appear to respond only to such stimuli.

Some kinds of animal (dogs, for example) are not provided with sweat glands. They make use of the evaporation of water for dissipating heat by means of *panting*. When the body is hot, the respiration becomes very fast and shallow, so that a large amount of air passes over the surface of the tongue and outer respiratory passages. The amount of air which enters, and ventilates, the lungs is not increased, since there is no change in the composition of the alveolar air even after several hours of panting.

The rate at which heat is lost by evaporation of sweat depends not only on the rate of secretion, but also on the climatic conditions and on the access of air to the skin as affected, for example, by winds and clothing. In hot damp conditions the rate of secretion of sweat may exceed the rate of evaporation, much of the sweat may run off the skin and adequate cooling is difficult. When the atmosphere is dry, on the other hand, the rate of cooling may be large enough to counteract an actual gain of heat from an environment whose temperature is above that of the body. Indeed, a man may keep his temperature constant in an atmosphere with a tempera-ture as high as 120°C (250°F), sufficient to cook meat or to boil an egg, provided that the air is dry.

Sweat is not pure water, but is a solution containing, on the average, about 0·3 per cent sodium chloride—about one-half the concentration in plasma; there are very large variations in different circumstances, between different individuals, and between different parts of the same individual. It contains, also, most of the other constituents of the plasma except the proteins; lactate ions and urea, indeed, are usually present in greater concentration than in the plasma. Sweat which runs off the skin without evaporating is not entirely useless, since it washes away the dissolved substances which would otherwise be left on the skin, increasing the concentration of the sweat and reducing the rate of evaporation.

The loss of water by sweating results in the sensation of thirst, and the loss is made good by drinking. The loss of salt, however, may have important consequences. Failure to take in enough salt when recovering from heavy sweating will result in a dilution of the body fluids; ordinarily the excess water will be rapidly eliminated by the kidneys and the failure to restore the water balance may produce some discomfort but nothing more. If, however, the kidneys are for any reason unable to eliminate the excess water, a more serious condition of *water intoxication* may be produced. Even in the absence of renal insufficiency, this may occur when severe exercise is taken in hot surroundings and pure water is drunk while the exercise continues. Severe exercise largely inhibits water diuresis, partly owing to diversion of the blood from the kidneys to the active muscles and partly by an action on the neurohypophysis leading to a secretion of ADH. The consequent dilution of the body fluids then gives rise to the incapacitating condition known as "miners' (or stokers') cramp". (The condition was first observed in miners and in stokers of coal-fired boilers.) The necessity for taking an adequate quantity of salt along with the water (as occurs naturally in beer, for example) was in fact known empirically among miners and stokers before its *rationale* was understood.

The loss of substances other than salt in sweat is ordinarily of no consequence, since they would otherwise be excreted by the kidneys. If the kidneys are severely diseased, however, elimination of substances like urea by copious sweating may be of substantial benefit.

The salt concentration of the sweat depends on the state of the salt balance of the whole body. Prolonged existence in hot surroundings, with more or less continuous sweating, is apt to lead to some degree of chronic salt depletion; this is believed to account for the observed decrease in the salt concentration of the sweat as one becomes "acclimatized" to the environment. It does not occur if enough salt is taken to preserve the balance. The rate at which salt is absorbed from the sweat back into the blood stream, like the rate of sodium reabsorption in the renal tubules, is regulated by means of the hormone *aldosterone*, elaborated by the adrenal cortex; the rate of secretion rises as the sodium content of the body falls.

CLIMATE AND ITS MEASUREMENT

It is often useful to be able to measure the properties of an environment which affect the ease with which people living and working in it can regulate their body temperatures. The comfort and efficiency of workers in factories and offices may be affected by the atmosphere in which they have to work; the nature and quantity of clothing, food and drink to be taken on expeditions to polar, mountainous or desert regions are decided by the nature of the climate to be expected.

The *temperature* of the air, other things being equal, determines the rate at which heat is lost from the body by conduction and convection; the *humidity* of the air determines the rate at which heat is lost by the evaporation of water. Both these quantities may easily be measured by means of dry and wet bulb thermometers, sheltered from the sun and the wind.

In given conditions of temperature and humidity, the rate of heat loss is greatly affected by the *wind speed*, which can be measured by instruments known as anemometers. The air in immediate contact with the skin (or the surface of any hot object) forms a "stationary layer", usually a few millimetres thick; beyond this, the air is in motion relative to the skin as a result of thermal currents (hot air is less dense than cold air, and so rises), movements of the person whose temperature is being considered, and above all, the presence of winds. Heat and water vapour must pass through the stationary layer before being carried away by the moving air; the greater the air movement, the thinner is the stationary layer and the more rapid is the passage of heat and water vapour; hair and clothing, conversely, increase the thickness of the stationary layer and decrease the rate of heat loss. In the absence of appreciable evaporation of water, and for a given difference in temperature between the skin and the air, the rate of heat loss in a 10 m.p.h. wind is about four times as great as it is in still air, and in a 50 m.p.h. wind about nine times as great. For this reason, the unpleasantness of being in warm moist air may be largely removed by stirring the air with a fan.

Lastly, heat may be lost, or not infrequently gained, by radiation to or from surrounding objects which absorb or emit heat, to interstellar space by night or from the sun by day. The surrounding objects will, in general, be at different temperatures, have different shapes and have surfaces of different radiating efficiencies; measurement of their effect on the heat balance of a man is not easy, and is necessarily somewhat empirical. The "solar heat load", however, can be deduced fairly accurately from the altitude of the sun and the amount of mist or smoke in the atmosphere.

In exceptional circumstances—at least in the ordinary life of civilized man—substantial amounts of heat may be lost to rain or snow which falls on the skin or clothing. If the clothing (or an animal's hair) becomes wet, moreover, the trapped air is replaced by water and the thermal insulation is greatly reduced. Wet clothing is better than nothing, however, since the water within it is trapped and delays the conduction of heat to the rain or snow which falls on the outer surface.

Various attempts have been made—without marked success—to combine all the relevant properties of the climate into one figure which defines its overall cooling (or heating) power. From such figures, however, it is possible to make useful estimates, for example, of the amount of clothing needed in a given climate by a man taking different amounts of exercise. An empirical figure called the "effective temperature" is defined as the temperature of a still atmosphere, saturated with water vapour, which feels, subjectively to an ordinary person, the same as the particular climate under investigation. It may be deduced from measurements of the temperature and humidity of the air and the wind speed (and also the effects of radiation for the "corrected effective temperature"), by means of charts constructed from empirical observations on human subjects.

Alternatively, one may use the readings of the *katathermometer*, suspended in the place where observations are to be made. This is an alcohol thermometer with a large bulb; the cooling power of the air is measured as the reciprocal of the time taken for its temperature to fall from 100°F to 95°F.

When dry, the katathermometer measures the rate of heat loss by conduction, convection and radiation; when the bulb is covered by a moist finger-stall, it measures also the heat loss by evaporation of water. The surface of a man is rarely completely wetted, and the cooler and drier is the air, the smaller is the fraction wetted. In ordinary circumstances, this fraction lies between 10 per cent and 50 per cent, and an appropriate figure between the two values obtained with the katathermometer should be taken as a measure of the cooling power of the climate.

Section 12
THE PHYSIOLOGY OF MUSCLE

CHAPTER 40

MUSCLE: INTRODUCTORY REMARKS

MUSCLES are of exceptional importance in the life of higher animals; they are involved either directly or indirectly in virtually every body function. Some forms of muscular activity, such as limb movements and speech, are more obvious than others because they affect the interaction of Man with his environment. Of equal importance are the less overt actions, such as the beating of the heart and the movements of the gut, that affect his internal environment. All these forms of muscular activity are under the partial or complete control of the central nervous system, which influences the muscle directly through its motor nerve supply, and in some cases indirectly through the actions of neurohumoral agents that are released elsewhere and brought to the muscle through its blood supply.

Muscular Contraction

The diverse functions performed by muscles in the body all depend on one essential feature of muscle as a tissue—its ability to convert chemical energy into mechanical work. The change in membrane potential (the action potential) that accompanies excitation of a muscle cell switches on energy-yielding chemical reactions within the cell by activating the appropriate enzymes. Some of the energy that is liberated is converted into mechanical work in an event known as *muscular contraction* and the remainder appears as heat. The word contraction is rather misleading in that no significant volume change takes place; the essential feature of the mechanical event is that the muscle tends to *shorten*, but if shortening is in any way restrained the muscle will also *develop tension*.

Experiments on Muscle

The behaviour of muscles in the intact animal has been studied extensively and much has been learned, for example, about how limbs are moved, how blood is pumped by the heart, and how the uterus expels the foetus during childbirth. The contractions produced by a muscle under these circumstances vary widely in strength and speed, due to the operation of control mechanisms that adjust the activity of the muscle (by neural and sometimes humoral means) to meet the functional requirements of the moment. Contractions that vary in this way are not satisfactory for studies of the basic mechanism of muscular contraction. If one is concerned simply with the muscle as a machine for converting chemical energy into work (as we shall be in the chapters that follow), it is desirable to remove the influence of the control mechanisms; the muscle can then be made to contract in a predictable way by the application of suitable external stimuli (e.g. electric shocks of selected strength, duration, and repetition rate). The simplest way of removing the influence of the control systems is to remove the muscle from the animal. Many small muscles will continue to function normally in an artificial environment for several days, provided that their nutritional and excretory needs are satisfied, so this procedure is often a practical proposition. In fact the bulk of our knowledge of muscle physiology has come from experiments on isolated muscles, especially those of the frog; and in recent years increasing use has been made of single muscle fibres, isolated from a whole muscle by careful micro-dissection. However, it is important to remember that less drastic methods can sometimes be used; for example, a muscle can be disconnected from a control mechanism that has only a neural component simply by cutting its motor nerve or by producing a reversible block of nerve impulse transmission (e.g. by applying pressure or local anaesthetic). Valuable information about the properties of human and mammalian muscles *in situ* has been obtained in this way.

Although muscles often undergo simultaneous changes in length and tension when they contract naturally in the body, it is customary to hold one or other parameter constant in experiments on isolated muscle. The conditions are described as *isometric* when tension changes are measured at constant muscle length, and as *isotonic* when the muscle shortens and the tension in it is constant. When the muscle contracts against a spring it shortens and develops tension at the same time; this is known as an *auxotonic* contraction. As almost all experiments on muscle involve measurements of tension or length changes (sometimes both), the physical principles underlying such measurements will now be outlined.

Measurement of Tension

Tension cannot be measured as such; it must first be converted into another physical quantity that can. A device that makes such a conversion is called a *transducer*—in this case a force or tension transducer. The usual procedure for measuring the tension produced by a muscle is to connect it to a strip of spring steel, as illustrated in Fig. 40.1*a*. Tension in the muscle produces a slight bending of the steel strip, which can be measured either by magnifying the movement of the spring with an extension arm (as shown in the Fig. 40.1a) or by using another transducer (e.g. a strain gauge) to convert the bending of the spring strip into an electrical signal. The transducer must be calibrated by applying known forces to the spring, and the simplest way of doing this is to hang known masses in the place of the muscle; due to the attraction of gravity a mass of M grams will produce a force of M grams weight (g wt), or $M.g$ dynes, where g is the acceleration due to

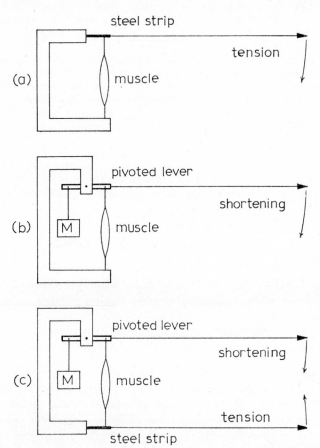

Fig. 40.1 Schematic diagrams of the apparatus used for measuring (a) tension developed in an isometric contraction, (b) shortening of the muscle in an isotonic contraction, and (c) tension and shortening in an isotonic contraction.

gravity (980 cm/sec²). The force exerted on the transducer by the muscle (i.e. the tension in the muscle) is usually expressed in grams weight.

Measurement of Shortening

The traditional method used for measuring the shortening of the muscle in an isotonic contraction is illustrated in Fig. 40.1b. The free end of the muscle is attached to a simple lever and an extension arm is used to magnify the movement for display purposes. If the magnification factor introduced by the extension arm is known, the shortening of the muscle can be determined from the movement of the pointer.

In an isotonic contraction the object is to measure the shortening of the muscle while the tension in it remains constant; such conditions are difficult to achieve in practice because there is no perfectly satisfactory way of loading the muscle with a pure force. The method most commonly used is to hang a mass (M g) on the lever, as shown in Fig. 40.1b. If the mass and the muscle are attached at points equidistant from the pivot, then the *load* on the muscle (= *tension* in the muscle = *force* opposing shortening) will be $M.g$ dynes (or M g wt). Because of the inertia of the mass the load on the muscle will only be constant when the lever is either stationary or moving at a constant speed. If the speed is increasing (i.e. lever accelerating) or decreasing (i.e. lever decelerating), the force on the muscle will be $M.g \pm M.a$, where a is the acceleration or deceleration of the lever. The inertial component, $M.a$, can be greatly reduced by hanging the mass close to the pivot on a compliant support. Fig. 40.1c is a schematic diagram of an arrangement for measuring tension and length simultaneously.

When a muscle shortens by an amount, x cm, against a force of $M.g$ dynes (or $M.g$ wt) the *work done* is $M.g.x$ ergs (or $M.x.g$ cm). Similarly, when the muscle shortens at a velocity, v cm/sec, its rate of working or *power output* is $M.g.v$ ergs/sec (or $M.v.g$ cm/sec). Note that 1 g cm $\approx 10^3$ ergs; 10^7 ergs/sec = 1 watt; and 746 watts = 1 horse power (h.p.).

CLASSIFICATION OF MUSCLE

Although muscles show wide variations in form, structure, and physiological characteristics, it is possible to divide them into a limited number of general types on either anatomical or physiological grounds.

ANATOMICAL CLASSIFICATION OF MUSCLE

Skeletal Muscle

Muscles with one or more skeletal attachments account for about 45 per cent of the body weight in man. They are responsible for all body movements, including respiration, and in general they are under voluntary control. The muscle cells (fibres) are of large diameter (typically 50μ) and they are very elongated; the ratio of length to diameter may be as great as 5,000 : 1. The fibres are multi-nucleate and they show prominent transverse striations when examined under the microscope. There are some striated muscles that do not have skeletal attachments (e.g. the muscles of facial expression); they have the same structure and physiological characteristics as skeletal muscle.

Smooth Muscle

Smooth muscle accounts for only about 3 per cent of the body weight, but it is found in the walls of almost every hollow tube and organ in the body (e.g. gut, ducts, blood vessels) and at many other sites. The muscle fibres are of small diameter (typically 5μ) and they are spindle-shaped;

the ratio of length to diameter rarely exceeds about 50 : 1. Each cell contains a single nucleus and there are no transverse striations. This type of muscle is sometimes referred to as *plain* or *non-striated* because of its histological appearance. Smooth muscle is innervated by the autonomic nervous system and in general it is not under voluntary control.

Cardiac Muscle

This type of muscle is the least abundant in the body (about 0·5 per cent of the body weight), but it is by far the most active. Although the heart has the functional characteristics of a single cell (e.g. activity spreads throughout the muscle) it is not a syncytium from the structural point of view. The myocardial cells are cylindrical in form, with a diameter of 10 to 20μ and a length : diameter ratio of about 5 : 1. The cells are arranged in columns that branch and anastomose. Cardiac muscle is like skeletal muscle in that it shows similar transverse striations, but it resembles smooth muscle in that its innervation is derived from the autonomic nervous system.

PHYSIOLOGICAL CLASSIFICATION OF MUSCLE

From the point of view of physiological properties we can divide muscles into single unit and multi-unit types. In a *single unit* muscle (e.g. the heart) activity spreads from cell to cell, and the muscle behaves as a single functional unit. A *multi-unit* muscle (e.g. any skeletal muscle) differs in that activity does not spread from cell to cell, and the muscle behaves as a collection of independent functional units. Smooth muscles are mostly of the single unit type, but there are some of the multi-unit type and a few with mixed characteristics. The examples given in the following diagram show how this physiological classification cuts across the more familiar anatomical divisions of muscle.

Anatomical Classification   Physiological Classification

SKELETAL		
SMOOTH	Pilomotor muscles Intrinsic eye muscles Nictitating membrane	MULTI-UNIT
	Intestinal muscle Uterine muscle Ureteric muscle	SINGLE UNIT
CARDIAC		

In the Chapters that follow skeletal muscle, smooth muscle, and cardiac muscle will be considered in turn. Each Chapter follows the same general pattern as far as possible. Attention has been concentrated mainly on mammalian muscle because of its particular relevance to human physiology, but where our knowledge of this type of muscle is incomplete, use will be made of information obtained from other sources.

CHAPTER 41

STRUCTURE AND FUNCTION OF
SKELETAL MUSCLE

STRUCTURE

The Whole Muscle

A typical skeletal muscle has a fleshy belly and a tendon at each end. The muscle fibres are organized into bundles known as *fasciculi*. In the human biceps, for example, there are 15,000 of these, each containing 20–60 fibres. In a muscle of the "strap" type the fasciculi lie parallel to its long axis, whereas in a muscle of the "pennate" variety they are arranged obliquely with respect to its long axis.

Almost all skeletal muscles contain specialized structures called muscle spindles, which contain a few poorly-striated muscle fibres known as *intrafusal* fibres. Muscle spindles are of great importance in the reflex control of movement (see page 333), but they make no *direct* contribution to the mechanical response of the muscle. *The information given in this Chapter applies only to the extrafusal fibres that make up the main bulk of the muscle.*

Muscle Fibres

Skeletal muscle fibres vary a good deal in size from one muscle to another. In humans the fibre diameter varies from about 10μ in muscles that produce finely controlled movements to about 100μ in muscles of coarser action. The fibre length shows even greater variation; for example in the human sartorius the fibre length approaches 50 cm, whereas in the muscles of the middle ear it is only a few millimetres. In all cases the ratio of the fibre length to diameter is very large compared with the corresponding values for smooth and cardiac muscle.

Each muscle fibre is enveloped in a delicate connective tissue sheath, which is intimately related to the plasma membrane of the cell, giving a composite structure known as the *sarcolemma*. The subcellular structure of a skeletal muscle fibre is extremely elaborate; there are internal membrane systems, known as the T-system and the sarcoplasmic reticulum, and each cell contains large numbers of nuclei, mitochondria, and myofibrils. The structure of the myofibrils, the T-system, and the sarcoplasmic reticulum will be considered in detail as these are peculiar to the muscle cell.

Myofibrils

Myofibrils are the contractile elements of the muscle. They consist of thread-like structures, about 1μ in diameter, which probably run the whole length of the fibre. A typical muscle fibre contains a thousand or more of these elements and they account for 70–80 per cent of the fibre volume. Individual myofibrils show transverse striations, and the characteristic striated appearance of a skeletal muscle fibre results from the remarkable fact that the striations of the thousand or so myofibrils are in register.

Nature of the Striated Appearance

When the *simple light microscope* is used to look for variations in *light absorption* (i.e. with the condenser aperture wide open), no striations can be seen in living muscle fibres. Striations are visible in fixed and stained material because consecu-

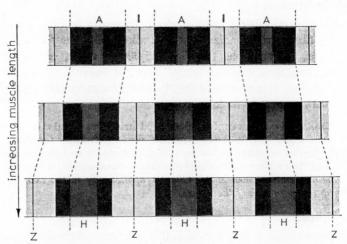

Fig. 41.1 Diagram showing the striation pattern of myofibrils from a skeletal muscle fibre. The three illustrations show how the striation pattern varies with the muscle length. When the muscle is stretched, the A bands remain unchanged in length, but the I bands and H zones increase in length in direct proportion to the amount of stretch. Note that the distance from the Z line to the edge of the H zone remains unchanged.

tive regions along the length of the myofibril vary in their affinity for basic dyes. If the microscope is used to look for variations in *refractive index* (i.e. with the condenser stopped down), living muscle fibres have a striated appearance, indicating that the protein concentration varies along the length of the myofibril. Great care is required in the interpretation of the striation pattern seen because this depends critically on the way in which the microscope is set up and focussed. It is often preferable to use a microscope that is designed to look for variations in refractive index, such as the *phase contrast microscope* or the *interference microscope*. If living muscle fibres are examined in the *polarizing microscope* the regions of high refractive index are found to be birefringent (anisotropic or A bands), and the regions of low refractive index are non-birefringent (isotropic or I bands).

The main features of the striation pattern are illustrated in Fig. 41.1. The *A bands* are birefringent, they have a high refractive index, and they

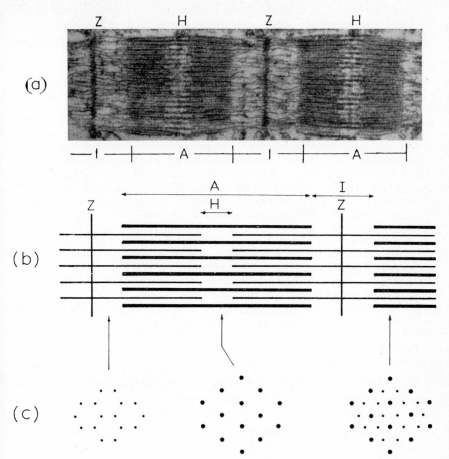

Fig. 41.2. Ultrastructure of the myofibrils of mammalian skeletal muscle. (a) Electron micrograph (magn. 26,000) of a longitudinal section of rabbit psoas muscle, showing the presence of two types of filament (H. E. Huxley). (b) Diagram illustrating the main features of the electron micrograph. The thick filaments (which are made up of myosin) are found in the A band, and the thin filaments (which contain actin and probably tropomyosin) extend from each Z line through the adjacent I bands into the outer parts of the A bands. The H zone is the part of the A band that does not contain thin filaments. (c) Diagrams illustrating the appearance of cross-sections of a myofibril at the levels indicated.

are heavily stained by basic dyes; whereas the *I bands* are non-birefringent, have a low refractive index, and do not take up basic dyes. The striation pattern shows additional features, which are illustrated in the lower part of Fig. 41.2. The I band is bisected by a narrow region known as the *Z line*, which has a high refractive index and which stains intensely. The

A band usually has a central region, known as the *H zone*, in which the birefringence, refractive index, and affinity for basic dyes are less marked. The Z lines divide the myofibril into units known as *sarcomeres*, which are typically 2 to 3μ in length.

As a result of research work done during the last 15 years, particularly with the electron microscope, we know why myofibrils have a striated appearance. It is due to the presence of extremely fine thread-like structures known as *myofilaments*, which are about two orders of magnitude smaller than the myofibrils. These cannot be seen in living muscle fibres because they are much too small to be resolved by any type of light microscope, but they can be demonstrated when thin sections of fixed and stained material are examined in the electron microscope (Fig. 41.2*a*). The A bands are found to contain "thick" filaments that are about 0·01μ (100 Å) in diameter and about 1·5μ in length, and the I bands contain "thin" filaments that are about 0·005μ in diameter and about 2·5μ in length. The thin filaments extend from the Z lines into the adjacent sarcomeres, where they overlap and interdigitate with the thick filaments in the outer parts of the A bands (Fig. 41.2*b*). The amount of overlap depends on the muscle length at the time of fixation. A transverse section through the outer part of the A band shows that the interdigitating filaments form a double hexagonal array (Fig. 41.2*c*). Transverse sections through other parts of the sarcomere show that the I bands contain only thin filaments, and that the H zone of the A band contains only thick filaments.

The filaments consist of aggregations of protein molecules. There is good evidence that the thick filaments are composed entirely of *myosin* (M.Wt $\sim$ 500,000), and that the thin filaments contain *actin* (M.Wt 57,000) and probably *tropomyosin* (M.Wt 53,000). The exact composition of the Z line is not known, but tropomyosin is a probable constituent.

When the resting muscle is stretched (see Fig. 41.1) and when the active muscle shortens (see Fig. 41.9*a*), the two sets of filaments are believed to slide past one another. This is known as the *sliding filament hypothesis*, but there is now so much evidence in support of this hypothesis that it is generally accepted as an established fact.

Sarcoplasmic Reticulum and T-system

When longitudinal sections of suitably fixed and stained muscle are examined in the electron microscope, structures known as *triads* are seen between the myofibrils at regular intervals along the length of the muscle fibre (Fig. 41.3*b*). In mammalian skeletal muscle these are found opposite the ends of the A bands (close to the A-I boundaries), but in muscles from other animals they are positioned differently with respect to the striation pattern. The central element of the triad is part of the T-system, and the elements on either side belong to the sarcoplasmic reticulum. The *T-system* consists of a network of branching and anastomosing tubules that extends over the entire cross-section of the fibre near each A-I boundary (Fig. 41.3*a*). The tubules appear to be invaginations of the plasma membrane and the space inside them is in direct continuity with the extracellular space through "pores" arranged around the circumference of the fibre. The diameter of the tubules is about 0·05μ and their volume has been estimated as about 0·5 per cent of the fibre volume. The *sarcoplasmic reticulum* (SR) is an entirely separate system of confluent tubes and spaces (cisternae), which seems to be homologous to the endoplasmic reticulum of other types of cell. This system is

(a)

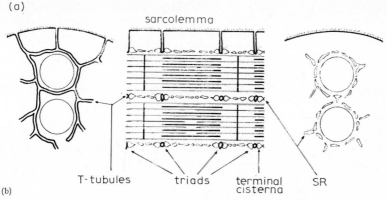

sarcolemma

T-tubules   triads   terminal   SR
                       cisterna

(b)

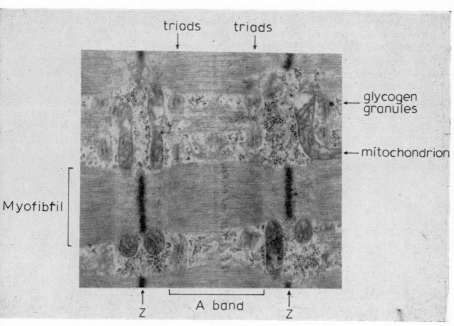

triads   triads

glycogen granules

←mitochondrion

Myofibril

A band

Z   Z

FIG. 41.3. Sarcoplasmic reticulum and T system of mammalian skeletal muscle. (a) Diagrams to illustrate the relations of these structures to the sarcolemma and two myofibrils located nearby. The middle diagram shows the main features of a longitudinal section, and the appearance of cross sections made at the levels of the left and right hand ends of the middle diagram are illustrated on the left and right, respectively. The left diagram shows that the T system consists of confluent tubules that form a network across the muscle fibre at the level of each A-I junction, and the right diagram shows that the sarcoplasmic reticulum forms an incomplete sheath of cisternae around each myofibril. (b) Electron micrograph (magn. 22,000) of a longitudinal section of human laryngeal muscle (Sally Page). Triads can be seen near the A-I junctions, and the fenestrated sheath formed by the sarcoplasmic reticulum can be seen in the A band region (upper centre) and crossing the Z line (top left).

mainly longitudinal in orientation and it forms an incomplete sheath around each myofibril. The volume of the SR has been estimated to be about 5 per cent of the fibre volume (i.e. about 10 times that of the T-system). Near the A-I boundaries of the myofibrils the SR is dilated to form terminal cisternae, which are closely applied to the tubules of the T-system, giving the structures known as triads in longitudinal sections of muscle. The T-system and the SR are concerned with a process known as *excitation-contraction* coupling, which is described in detail on p. 713.

EXCITATION

A muscle can be made to contract either by *direct* stimulation or by stimulation of its motor nerve (sometimes termed *indirect* stimulation).

Strength-Duration Relation

For all excitable tissues the stimulus strength required to produce a threshold response depends on the duration of the stimulus, and the relation between these parameters is hyperbolic in form. The curves for motor nerve fibres and skeletal muscle fibres differ as illustrated in Fig. 41.4*a* (curves N and M respectively). The strength-duration relation obtained by *indirect* stimulation is identical to curve N, but the relation obtained by *direct* stimulation is of the form shown in Fig. 41.4*b*. The left hand part of this curve is the same as curve N because strong brief shocks (sometimes called "Faradic" stimuli), which are too short in duration to excite the muscle fibres directly, stimulate intra-muscular branches of the motor nerve fibres and thereby excite the muscle fibres indirectly. The right hand part

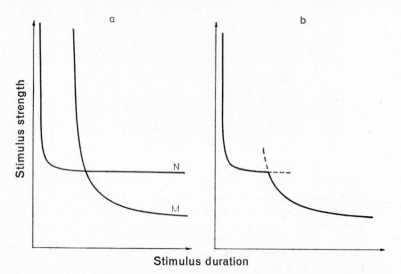

Fig. 41.4. Strength-duration curves. The graphs show how the stimulus strength required to produce a detectable response (threshold strength) varies with the duration of the stimulus: (a) for stimulation of motor nerve fibres (N) and muscle fibres (M), and (b) for stimulation of a whole muscle containing muscle fibres and intramuscular nerve fibres. The curve shown in (b) is a combination of the two curves shown in (a).

of the curve is identical to curve M because weak shocks of long duration (sometimes called "galvanic" stimuli) excite the muscle fibres alone. Thus direct stimulation of a *muscle* only results in direct stimulation of the *muscle fibres* when the stimuli are of the "galvanic" type (or when the muscle is curarized). In experiments on isolated muscles direct stimulation of the muscle fibres is preferred to indirect stimulation because the response evoked is less liable to fatigue, and because the delay between applying a stimulus and obtaining a response is reduced to a minimum (especially if multi-point stimulation is used to activate all parts of the muscle more or less simultaneously).

Strength-Response Curve

When a single muscle fibre is stimulated *directly*, its strength-response curve is of the form shown in Fig. 41.5a; the threshold and maximal stimulus strengths are the same showing that the fibre obeys the all or nothing law. When a whole muscle is stimulated *directly*, the strength-response curve is S-shaped and the

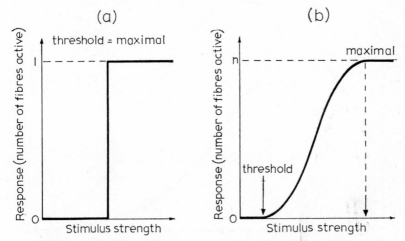

FIG. 41.5. Strength-response curves. (a) This graph shows how the response of a *single muscle fibre* varies with the stimulus strength. The threshold and maximal stimulus strengths are identical showing that the fibre obeys the "all or nothing" law. (b) A similar graph for a *whole muscle* containing n fibres.

threshold and maximal stimulus strengths are different (Fig. 41.5b). The curve has this characteristic shape because the muscle contains a population of fibres in which the threshold stimulus strength has an approximately normal distribution. The threshold for the whole muscle corresponds with the threshold of the most sensitive muscle fibres, and the maximal stimulus strength for the whole muscle is sufficient to excite the least sensitive fibres in addition to all the rest. In theory the strength-response curve is not a smooth curve as drawn, but a discontinuous line with as many steps on it as there are muscle fibres of different threshold; however, in a muscle containing thousands of fibres these steps are not detectable. When the muscle is stimulated *indirectly*, the number of theoretical steps is less because the smallest functional unit that can be recruited by a slight increase in stimulus strength is a nerve fibre, and this will bring another *motor unit* into operation. The number of possible steps is therefore equal to the number of motor units and not to the number of muscle fibres. This is of course the situation in the body where activation of the muscles is indirect.

CONTRACTION

The Twitch

This is the name given to the mechanical response produced by a single stimulus (direct or indirect). Fig. 41.6a shows the main features of a typical

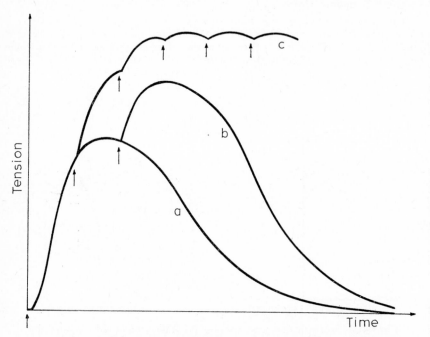

Fig. 41.6. Isometric myograms showing (a) the twitch response produced by a single stimulus; (b) summation produced by applying a second stimulus before the mechanical response produced by the first has disappeared; and (c) the tetanic contraction produced by a series of stimuli. The arrows show the timing of the stimuli in all cases.

isometric twitch. There is a *latent period* between the application of the stimulus and the first detectable mechanical response. Its duration depends on the method of stimulation. The minimum value (about 1 per cent of the twitch duration) is achieved by stimulating the muscle directly at several points along its length; this is the time required for the process known as *excitation-contraction coupling*. The latent period is prolonged when stimulation is indirect because of the additional delays introduced by nerve conduction and neuromuscular transmission.

The mechanical response consists of a *phase of contraction*, during which the tension rises to a peak, and a *phase of relaxation*, during which the tension declines to its initial value. The contraction phase occupies about one third of the total duration of the twitch. Mammalian skeletal muscles vary in their twitch durations; for example in a cat it is 0·2–0·3 sec for the soleus muscle and about half this value for the gastrocnemius.

Note that in some animals (e.g. amphibia, birds), the skeletal muscle fibres are of two distinct types, known as "fast" (or "twitch") and "slow" (or "tonic"). These differ not only in speed of contraction, but also in their structure, innervation, and electrical properties. The external ocular muscles of mammals contain fibres that closely resemble "slow" amphibian muscle fibres, and the intrafusal fibres found in muscle spindles have some features in common with them. Otherwise the fibres that make up all mammalian skeletal muscles appear to be of the "fast" amphibian type.

Summation

The surface membrane of the muscle fibre is refractory for a short time following the passage of an action potential, but it is important to note that the total duration of the action potential and refractory period (2–3 msec in mammalian muscle) is very short compared with the duration of the mechanical response. Because of this it is possible to excite the muscle for a second time before the mechanical response produced by the first stimulus has disappeared. If this is done a second mechanical response is added to the first in a process known as *summation* (Fig. 41.6*b*). The size of the combined response will depend on the timing of the second stimulus.

Tetanus

The summation mechanism can lead to an even greater mechanical response if several stimuli are given instead of just two (Fig. 41.6*c*). The type of mechanical response produced by repetitive stimulation is called a *tetanus*. This is said to be *fused* when the stimulus frequency is increased to the point where there is no detectable ripple in the mechanical response; otherwise the contraction is called an *unfused tetanus*. The fusion frequency for mammalian muscles at body temperature varies from about 50/sec for the slowest to about 500/sec for the fastest muscles.

MECHANICAL PROPERTIES

Mechanical "Model" of Muscle

From the mechanical point of view we can represent a muscle as a system with three components (Fig. 41.7): a *series compliance* (SC), a *parallel compliance* (PC), and a *contractile component* (CC). These can be tentatively identified with structures in the actual muscle, as indicated in the caption. This identification is probably an oversimplification, but the "model" shown is very useful in understanding the mechanical behaviour of a muscle at rest and during activity.

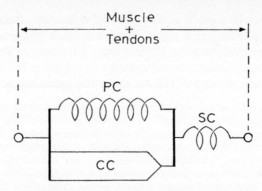

FIG. 41.7. A mechanical "model" of muscle. The mechanical components shown may be tentatively identified as follows: *Series
compliance* (SC) = tendons of muscle; *parallel compliance* (PC)
= connective tissue sheaths, sarcolemma; *contractile component*
(CC) = myofibrils. (This is probably an oversimplification in that
the myofibrils must contribute some series compliance.) Note that
the tension in the SC is always equal to the sum of the tensions in
the PC and CC.

Resting Muscle

The resting muscle has the mechanical properties of an imperfect elastic
body. The effect of stretching it is to produce passive (or resting) tension,
but the relation between tension produced and the muscle length is
non-linear (Fig. 41.8*a*); that is, the resting muscle does not obey Hooke's
Law. The resistance to stretch is due to the tendons (SC) and the connective tissue sheaths (PC), which behave like two springs connected in
series (Fig. 41.8*b*). Most of the extension takes place in the PC because it
is much more compliant than the SC (see Fig. 41.8*a*). The myofibrils (CC)
offer very little permanent resistance to stretch because the two sets of
filaments can slide freely past one another when the muscle is in the resting
state. However, this relative movement of millions of filaments gives the
myofibrils viscous properties, so in Fig. 41.8*b* the CC is shown as a viscous
element (dashpot) that damps the movements of the PC.

In experiments on the mechanical properties of active muscle one
customarily works at muscle lengths at which the tension in the PC (i.e.
tension in the resting muscle) is zero. The muscle then behaves as if it is
made up of only two components, the CC in series with the SC.

Active Muscle

When the muscle is stimulated the properties of the SC and the PC
remain unaltered, but the properties of the CC change dramatically. It is
transformed from a *passive* viscous element into an *active* element that is
capable of converting chemical energy into mechanical work. The transi-

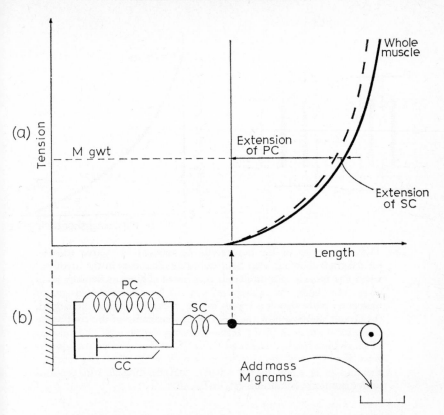

FIG. 41.8. Elastic properties of resting muscle. (a) Graph showing the relation between the tension in the resting muscle and its length. (b) Diagram illustrating how such a graph could be obtained. The muscle is depicted (in model form) at the length corresponding to zero tension. When a mass of M grams is used to stretch the muscle, the tension produced is M g. wt., and the muscle length increases as shown, part of the extension occurring in the PC and a smaller part in the SC. The CC is shown as a viscous element because it has viscous properties when the muscle is at rest.

tion is extremely rapid, requiring only a few milliseconds in a mammalian muscle at body temperature. In each sarcomere of the myofibril the two sets of filaments undergo a relative sliding movement due to the appearance of shearing forces between them when the muscle is excited, and an increase occurs in the amount of overlap between the thick and thin filaments in the outer parts of the A band (Fig. 41.9a). The Z lines are drawn together because the filaments behave as inextensible rods, and the sarcomere becomes shorter. The same thing happens in sarcomeres along the entire length of the myofibril. The velocity of shortening of the myofibril depends on the force that opposes shortening, as shown in Fig. 41.9b.

(a)   (b)

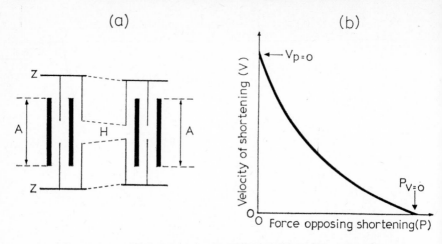

Fig. 41.9. Properties of the contractile component in active muscle. (a) Diagram showing what happens to the filaments in the myofibril when the muscle is stimulated. A relative sliding movement takes place, increasing the amount of overlap between the two sets of filaments. Note that the length of the A band remains unchanged. (b) Graph showing how the velocity of shortening of the contractile component varies with the force opposing shortening. The velocity of shortening has its maximum value (V_0 or $V_{p=0}$) when the force is zero ($P = O$), and the velocity is zero ($V = O$) when the force on the muscle is equal to the tension that the muscle can produce under isometric conditions (P_0 or $P_{v=0}$).

Isometric Contraction

It is important to distinguish between length changes in the whole muscle and length changes in the CC. The muscle does not shorten when it contracts under isometric conditions, but the CC shortens and stretches the SC (see Fig. 41.10a and c). The mechanical changes that take place in the muscle are illustrated by Fig. 41.10b, graphs A–C. Initially the force opposing shortening of the CC is zero ($P = 0$) so it shortens at its maximum velocity ($V_{p=0}$, graph A). However as the SC is stretched (graph B) the tension in it and in the CC will rise (graph C), and the velocity of shortening of the CC will then decrease (graph A) because of its force-velocity relation (Fig. 41.9b). If the muscle is kept in the active state by repetitive stimulation (tetanic contraction), the tension will rise to reach the maximum value that the muscle can produce at that length and temperature. The velocity of shortening of the CC is then zero ($V = 0$) and the maximum tension is designated $P_{v=0}$ (usually abbreviated to P_0). The time course of the rise of tension (graph C) depends on the total amount of series compliance (i.e. in the apparatus and the connections, as well as in the muscle) and on the force-velocity relation of the CC.

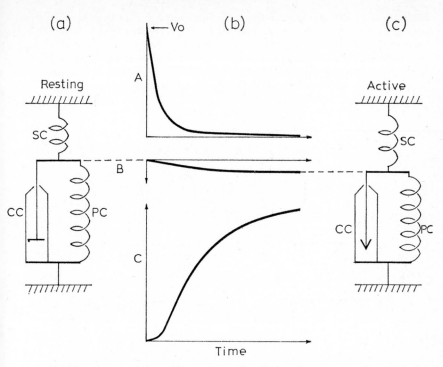

Fig. 41.10. Isometric contraction. (a) and (c) Diagrams showing how the CC shortens at the expense of the SC when the muscle contracts under isometric conditions. (b) Graphs showing how the following vary with time during the rise of tension in an isometric tetanic contraction:—

A, velocity of shortening of CC = velocity of lengthening of SC; B, shortening of CC = lengthening of SC; C, tension in CC = tension in SC = tension in whole muscle.

The tension that the muscle produces in an isometric contraction depends on the following factors:

(i) Pattern of Response

A twitch response differs from a tetanus (see Fig. 41.6) in that the CC does not have time to raise the tension to the tetanic value because the active state begins to disappear soon after the onset of the contraction. The tension reached when the velocity of shortening of the CC has fallen to zero (peak of twitch) is therefore less than the full tetanic value (P_0). The ratio of the peak twitch tension to the tetanic tension is about 0·5 in mammalian muscles at 37°C, and as one might expect from Fig. 41.10b it is very sensitive to the amount of series compliance.

(ii) Muscle Length

The symbol, L_0, will be used in this Chapter to denote the *mean body length* of the muscle (i.e. the length midway between the longest and the shortest lengths possible when the muscle is *in situ*). In general skeletal muscles show no appreciable resting tension at this length, so the tension measured during an isometric contraction at this length (or at shorter lengths) is therefore entirely due to the CC. At lengths greater than L_0 the muscle does show resting tension, and the tension measured during a contraction is therefore the sum of the contributions of the CC (active tension) and the PC (resting tension). Figure 41.11 shows how the total tension and the resting tension vary with the muscle length in muscles with well developed

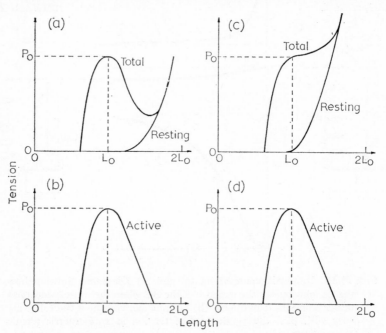

FIG. 41.11. Tension-length curves of resting and active muscles. The upper graphs (a & c) show how the tension in the resting muscle and the total tension in the muscle during an isometric tetanic contraction vary with the muscle length, when the muscle contains little connective tissue (a) or is rich in connective tissue (c). The lower graphs (b & d) show how active tension (i.e. total tension minus resting tension) varies with the muscle length; they are identical for the two types of muscle because the properties of the CC are unaffected by the properties of the PC. L_0 is the mean body length of the muscles, and P_0 is the tension developed at that length.

(Fig. 41.11c) and poorly developed (Fig. 41.11a) connective tissue sheaths. The tension produced by the CC can be obtained by subtracting the contribution of the PC (resting tension) from the total tension. Figure 41.11b and d shows that the tension developed by the CC varies with the muscle length in exactly the same way in the two types of muscle. (The dependence of tension production on the muscle length is thought to be related to the amount of overlap between thick and thin filaments in the A band of each sarcomere, for reasons given on pp. 713 and 715).

How much the length of a muscle fibre can vary in the body depends on the geometry of the joint (or joints) over which the muscle operates, and on the relative lengths of the muscle belly and tendon. However, the behaviour of the muscle at extreme lengths is of purely academic interest because such lengths are unattainable in the body.

(iii) Temperature

The main effect of temperature is on the time course of the contraction rather than on the tension developed. For example reducing the temperature of a mammalian muscle from 35 to 25°C has virtually no effect on the tension developed in a twitch or tetanus, but it doubles the duration of the twitch.

(iv) Muscle Size

The tension developed by a muscle depends on the number of tension-producing elements that are arranged in parallel and not on their length. The tension produced by a muscle will therefore depend on the cross-sectional area of its fibres; mammalian muscles at body temperature produce 3·0 to 3·5 kg wt per cm² of cross-section. It follows that for muscles of the "strap" type a short fat muscle of a given mass will develop much more tension than a long thin muscle of the same mass. Muscles of the "pennate" variety produce more tension than would be expected from the cross-sectional area of the *muscle*; this is because the total cross-sectional area of the *fibres* (taken at right angles to their long axis) may be much greater than that of the muscle.

Isotonic Contraction

The muscle shown in Fig. 40.1*b* and *c* is said to be *"preloaded"* because the mass that is hung on the lever is supported by the muscle at all times. Preloading has the unfortunate feature that the length of the resting muscle changes when the load is altered. This complication can be avoided by arranging for the load to be supported so that it does not stretch the resting muscle. An adjustable stop is used for this purpose, as shown in Fig. 41.12*a*, and the muscle is said to be *"afterloaded"* because it is not aware of the presence of the load until *after* the onset of the contraction. The length of the resting muscle can be varied by adjusting the position of the stop, and it simplifies matters if the length is set to L_0 because there is then no resting tension in the muscle.

When the muscle is stimulated (Fig. 41.12*b*) there is the usual latent period (phase A); then the CC starts to shorten, the SC is stretched, and the tension in the muscle rises. During this period (phase B) the length of the muscle does not change, and the tension rises with the same time course as in an isometric contraction. However, as soon as the tension in the muscle is equal to the force produced on the lever by the load (M g wt), the muscle begins to shorten (phase C); the tension then remains constant (i.e. *the conditions are isotonic*), and the length change that occurs in the muscle is precisely the same as that occurring in the CC. If the contraction is a tetanus, as in Fig. 41.12*b*, the muscle will continue to shorten until it reaches a limit that depends on the load and on the initial length of the muscle. When stimulation ends the load drops back on to the stop (phase D), and the tension then falls to zero as it does at the end of an isometric contraction (phase E).

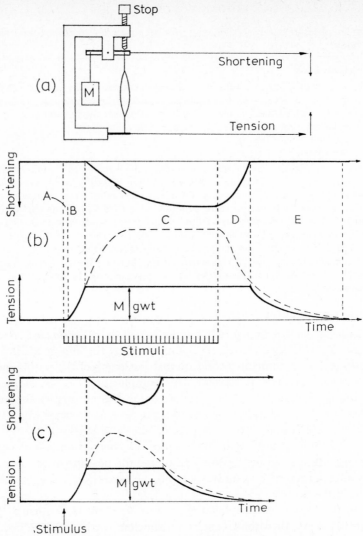

Fig. 41.12. Afterloaded isotonic contractions. (a) Schematic diagram of the apparatus used. The force opposing shortening is M g wt, but the tension in the resting muscle is zero because the load is supported by the afterload stop. (b) Tension and length changes in the muscle during an afterloaded isotonic tetanic contraction. There is a latent period (A) and then the tension begins to rise. During this phase (B) the conditions are isometric, but when the tension in the muscle reaches M g wt, the muscle shortens (phase C) and the tension then remains constant (i.e. the conditions are isotonic). When stimulation ends, the muscle cannot maintain its shortened state; the load drops (phase D) and the muscle is stretched. When the lever hits the stop, the conditions become isometric once again (phase E) and the tension then falls gradually to zero. The dashed line shows the tension changes that occur when conditions remain isometric throughout the tetanic response. (c) Similar curves showing the tension and length changes in an afterloaded isotonic twitch.

The performance of a muscle under isotonic conditions is determined by the following factors:

(i) Pattern of Response

The tension and length changes in an afterloaded isotonic twitch are shown in Fig. 41.12c. Because the active state begins to disappear very soon after the stimulus, the velocity of shortening (i.e. the slope of the shortening record) is slightly less than it is in a tetanic contraction, and the muscle does not have time to shorten as far. In other respects the twitch and tetanic responses are essentially the same.

(ii) Load

When the load (i.e. the force opposing shortening) is increased, the isometric phases of the response occupy more and more of the contraction-relaxation cycle; the load is lifted later and dropped earlier, and the muscle does not shorten as fast or as far. The relation between the velocity of shortening and the force opposing shortening is the same for the whole muscle (Fig. 41.13b) as it is for the CC (Fig. 41.9b). The *work done* (Fig. 41.13a) and the *power output* of the muscle are both zero when the force opposing shortening is zero (unloaded shortening) and when the muscle does not shorten (load $= P_0$ in a tetanus; load $=$ peak tension in a twitch). At intermediate loads the muscle produces power and does work, and the maximum performance is obtained when the load is $\frac{1}{3}$ to $\frac{1}{2}$ of P_0 in a tetanus and $\frac{1}{3}$ to $\frac{1}{2}$ of the peak tension in a twitch.

When the load drops during relaxation and the muscle is stretched (as in Fig. 41.12b and c), all the energy stored during the phase of contraction is dissipated as heat in the muscle. In order to obtain any net work from the muscle over the whole contraction-relaxation cycle, it is necessary to provide some means of supporting the load when it is lifted (e.g. a ratchet mechanism).

(iii) Muscle Length

Provided that the muscle is not stretched excessively, the *final length* that it will reach in an isotonic contraction against a given load is independent of its *initial length*. This means that if the length of the resting muscle is increased by altering the position of the afterload stop, the muscle will shorten more when it is stimulated and therefore do more work. This is a fundamental property of muscle, and it is of particular importance in cardiac muscle where it provides the basis of Starling's Law of the Heart ("the energy of contraction is a function of the initial length of the fibres", see Chapters 8 and 9).

(iv) Temperature

As one might predict from the effects of temperature on the time course of the isometric twitch, changes of temperature also have a marked effect on the velocity of shortening. Lowering the temperature of mammalian muscle from 35 to 25°C reduces the maximum speed of shortening (V_0) to about half, but it has no significant effect on the amount of shortening possible.

(v) Muscle Dimensions

A skeletal muscle fibre can shorten down to about 60 per cent of its body length in a tetanic contraction against zero load, but the velocity at which it does so (V_0) depends on the temperature and the species of animal; for example V_0 for human muscle at body temperature is about six muscle lengths per second. Long thin muscles shorten fastest (in cm/sec), but short fat muscles develop the greatest

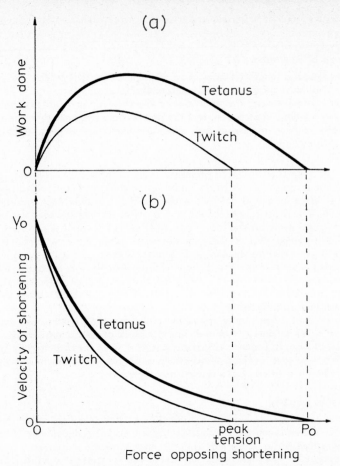

Fig. 41.13. Performance of the muscle under isotonic conditions. Graphs
showing how (a) the work done by the muscle and (b) the velocity
of shortening of the muscle vary with the force opposing shortening
in isotonic twitches and tetani.

tensions (in g wt). The maximum power output seems to be more or less independent of the shape of the muscle; it depends simply on the mass of tissue.

ENERGETICS

All spontaneous chemical reactions release "free energy"; that is,
energy that can be converted into work of one sort or another if the chemical reaction that releases it is coupled to a suitable "transformer". Muscles
contain transformers of various types: for example, the contractile mechanism can convert free energy into *mechanical work*; active transport mechanisms convert free energy into *osmotic work* or *electrical work*; and coupling

enzymes that allow an energy-yielding chemical reaction to drive another chemical reaction in the "backward" direction (i.e. the direction in which it would not proceed spontaneously) convert free energy into *chemical "work"*. Even more exotic transformations are possible in some situations; for example free energy is converted into light in firefly tails. The coupling between a chemical reaction that releases energy and the mechanism that utilizes it is never perfect. The *thermodynamic efficiency* of the coupling is defined as the fraction of the free energy released that is converted into work. The free energy that is wasted is degraded into heat immediately, but it is important to remember that the free energy that is successfully converted into work may also be dissipated as heat subsequently (e.g. when an ion that has been transported against a potential gradient diffuses down that gradient again).

Note that although any form of energy may be converted into heat, the reverse energy transformation is impossible in muscle, or in any other system where the temperature is essentially uniform. It can happen in a heat engine only because of the presence of large temperature gradients.

It has been known for a long time that isolated muscles (like intact animals) absorb oxygen and give off carbon dioxide, and that these processes are accelerated during activity. The oxygen is used in the oxidation of carbohydrates and other substances (e.g. fatty acids) to carbon dioxide and water. However, oxidative reactions do not provide the *immediate* source of energy for muscular contraction, active transport, and many synthetic reactions; the chemical reaction that is coupled directly to these processes is thought to be the hydrolysis of adenosine triphosphate (ATP) to adenosine diphosphate (ADP) and inorganic phosphate (P). This anaerobic reaction is associated with the release of about 10 kilocalories of free energy per mole of ATP breakdown. Rephosphorylation of the ADP formed can only be achieved if the necessary free energy (about 10 kcal/mole) is supplied by a coupled chemical reaction. Anaerobic processes can fulfil this role on a short term basis, but the eventual restoration of the *status quo* depends on oxidative processes, and these are therefore considered to provide the *ultimate* source of energy used by the muscle.

Energetics of Muscular Contraction

The following questions will be considered in this section:

(a) What chemical changes occur during contraction and recovery?
(b) What is the nature of the contractile process?
(c) How much free energy is released when a muscle contracts?
(d) What factors determine how much free energy is released?
(e) What is the efficiency of the muscle as a machine?

(a) What Chemical Changes occur during Contraction and Recovery?

The chemical reaction that drives the contractile process is the hydrolysis of ATP, but the ADP formed is rephosphorylated during the contraction and the subsequent recovery period by coupled chemical reactions. These will first be described in detail, and then the sequence of chemical changes that take place in the muscle during twitch and tetanic contractions will be considered.

Rephosphorylation of ADP

(i) *By the Lohmann Reaction*

Although a muscle contains sufficient ATP (2–4 micromoles per gram) for only a few contractions, it is impossible to detect any change in the ATP concentration in a normal muscle unless it is stimulated to the point of exhaustion. The reason for this is that the ADP formed is rephosphorylated extremely rapidly by the breakdown of phosphorylcreatine (PC) to creatine (C) in a coupled chemical reaction:

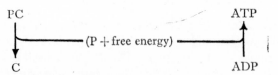

The substances ATP, ADP, PC and C can be regarded as the reactants in a reversible chemical reaction known as the *Lohmann reaction*:

$$ADP + PC \rightleftharpoons ATP + C$$
$$(0 \cdot 03) \quad (22) \quad (3) \quad (4)$$

The numbers in brackets give the concentrations (μmoles/g) of the substances in a resting frog muscle at $0°C$. This equilibrium is disturbed when the muscle contracts because the breakdown of ATP causes a reduction in ATP concentration and a rise in ADP concentration. The Lohmann reaction will proceed from left to right until equilibrium is re-established (Fig. 41.14a), and this happens extremely quickly because the enzyme that catalyses the reaction (creatine phosphotransferase) is very active. The importance of the Lohmann reaction can be demonstrated by stimulating a muscle that has been poisoned so that PC breakdown provides the only means of resynthesizing ATP (see p. 710). The concentration of PC falls as it is used to rephosphorylate the ADP formed during contraction, but because of the high equilibrium constant of the Lohmann reaction (~ 20) the ATP concentration changes very little until the store of PC is all but exhausted (Fig. 41.14b). A frog muscle at $0°C$ can produce about 100 twitches under these circumstances.

(ii) *By Oxidative Processes*

When oxygen is available two-carbon (2C) fragments from any source can be oxidized to carbon dioxide and water via the tricarboxylic acid cycle and the cytochrome chain. The oxidation of each 2C fragment is coupled to the rephosphorylation of 15 molecules of ADP. In skeletal muscle carbohydrate metabolism is the most important source of 2C fragments. Each hexose unit is metabolized in two stages: first it is broken down into two molecules of pyruvic acid via the Embden-Meyerhof pathway (the direct oxidative pathway appears to be unimportant in muscle) with the rephosphorylation of 9 molecules of ADP; the two molecules of pyruvic acid are then decarboxylated to give two 2C fragments, which are oxidized with the rephosphorylation of a further 30 molecules of ADP. Carbohydrate metabolism is accelerated by a rise in ADP concentration in the muscle, but the maximum rate of oxidative rephosphorylation of ADP appears to be limited in practice by the rate at which oxygen can be supplied to the muscle. Because of the very high yield of rephosphorylations per hexose unit (39), the glycogen store in the muscle can provide sufficient energy for many thousands of twitches under aerobic conditions.

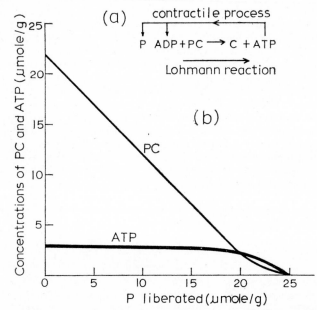

FIG. 41.14. The Lohmann reaction. (a) Diagram showing how the ADP produced by the hydrolysis of ATP in the contractile process is rephosphorylated by the Lohmann reaction. (b) Graphs showing how the PC and ATP concentrations in the iodoacetate-poisoned muscle change as more and more P is formed due to the hydrolysis of ATP. Note how the ATP concentration is maintained at the expense of the PC concentration (D. R. Wilkie).

(iii) *Glycolysis* (anaerobic breakdown of glycogen)

The splitting of glycogen into hexose units and the formation of pyruvic acid are anaerobic processes, but the coenzyme NAD is reduced to NADH by one reaction in the Embden-Meyerhof pathway. When oxygen is available the NADH is reoxidized via the cytochrome system with the rephosphorylation of 3 molecules of ADP per molecule of NADH (i.e. 6 molecules of ADP rephosphorylated per hexose unit). In the absence of oxygen the NADH is reoxidized by the reduction of pyruvic acid to lactic acid, but this reaction is not accompanied by any rephosphorylation of ADP. Thus when the conditions are anaerobic only 3 molecules of ADP are rephosphorylated per hexose unit. This is only 1/13 of the yield under aerobic conditions, so the effective energy store represented by the glycogen content is considerably diminished if the muscle is deprived of oxygen; in an isolated frog muscle at 0°C it is sufficient to permit about 1600 twitches, provided that the lactic acid produced can escape from the muscle into an adequate volume of bathing solution. If the lactate cannot escape (e.g. if the muscle is stimulated in an atmosphere of nitrogen), then the muscle ceases to respond to stimulation much sooner (after about 300 twitches) because the accumulation of lactic acid in the muscles reduces the pH to the point where contraction is no longer possible.

Measurement of Chemical Changes

Although it is possible to determine how the concentrations of certain cytochromes and coenzymes change in a muscle during and after a contraction (by spectrophotometry and related techniques) there is at present no way of continuously monitoring the changes in concentration of many other substances of interest (e.g. ATP, PC). The concentrations of these substances can be determined at any instant during the contraction-recovery cycle by rapidly freezing the muscle (to stop all chemical reactions) and then making an extract of it for chemical analysis. However, in order to determine the *change* that has taken place in the concentration of a substance it is necessary to know the value prior to the contraction, and this cannot be measured *on the same muscle*. The procedure used is to compare the concentration of a substance in a stimulated muscle with the concentration in an unstimulated (control) muscle, which is usually the corresponding muscle from the other side of the animal. Unfortunately pairs of muscles show appreciable random differences even when both are unstimulated. Studies of chemical changes therefore become very laborious because it is necessary to analyse large numbers of muscle pairs and to subject the results to statistical tests before any useful information can be obtained about the chemical changes that take place during muscular contraction.

Use of Poisons

If the muscle is kept in *oxygen-free nitrogen* the glycogen breakdown under anaerobic conditions can be determined from the change in either glycogen or lactic acid concentrations. If in addition the muscle is treated with *iodoacetate* (IAA), glycogen breakdown is impossible because the IAA blocks the enzyme triosephosphate dehydrogenase in the Embden-Meyerhof pathway, and because the direct oxidative pathway cannot be used in the absence of oxygen. In these circumstances the Lohmann reaction provides the only means of resynthesizing ATP, and the only net chemical change that takes place during contraction is PC breakdown. If the Lohmann reaction is prevented by *fluorodinitrobenzene* (FDNB), which poisons the coupling enzyme (creatine phosphotransferase), then ATP breakdown is the only net chemical change that takes place during a brief contraction.

Chemical Changes During and After a Single Twitch

ATP is hydrolysed during the contraction and the ADP formed is rephosphorylated very rapidly by the Lohmann reaction, which proceeds from left to right (Fig. 41.15a); these events are often referred to as the "initial" processes. It is important to realize that although the Lohmann reaction is extremely effective in maintaining the ATP level at the expense of PC, small changes in the ATP and ADP concentrations must occur. The rise in ADP concentration has an accelerating effect on oxidative phosphorylation and even on the earliest stages of glycogen breakdown, but the reactions involved are sluggish compared with the Lohmann reaction, and they only account for a small fraction of the ATP resynthesis that takes place *during* a twitch. At the end of a twitch the C, P and ADP concentrations are above normal and the PC and ATP concentrations are below normal, where "normal" refers to the values observed when the resting muscle is in a steady state (i.e. after a long period of rest). The normal concentrations are subsequently restored by glycogen breakdown, which occurs at an elevated rate in the period following a twitch because of the

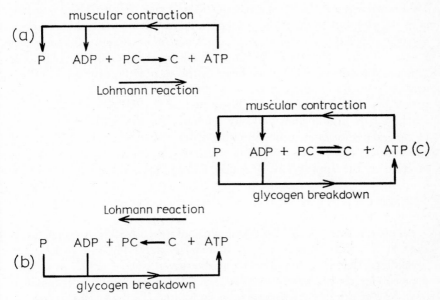

Fig. 41.15. ATP breakdown and resynthesis during contraction and recovery. (a) Chemical changes taking place during a twitch ("initial processes"). (b) Chemical changes taking place during recovery ("recovery processes"). (c) Steady state established during prolonged activity, in which the rate of ATP breakdown is matched by the rate of ATP resynthesis due to glycogen breakdown.

raised ADP concentration. The glycogen breakdown may be aerobic or anaerobic depending on the availability of oxygen. The ATP that is produced by the rephosphorylation of ADP is used to rephosphorylate creatine in the Lohmann reaction, which now proceeds from right to left (Fig. 41.15*b*). The rate of glycogen breakdown gradually falls as the concentrations of the reactants in the Lohmann reaction (in particular ADP) approach their normal values. Equilibrium is re-established eventually, though this takes at least 30 min following a single twitch of a frog muscle at 0°C. The events illustrated in Fig. 41.15*b* are often referred to as the "recovery processes".

Chemical Changes During and After a Tetanic Contraction

In a twitch there is very little overlap in time between the initial and recovery processes. This is not so in a tetanic contraction where glycogen breakdown makes an important contribution to the ATP resynthesis that takes place during the contraction. In fact if stimulation is continued for long enough glycogen breakdown will take over this function completely. This is almost certainly what happens during the sustained low grade contractions produced by postural muscles in the body. Initially the Lohmann reaction is of paramount importance, as it is in a twitch (Fig. 41.15a), but as the ADP concentration in the muscle gradually rises, glycogen breakdown is accelerated more and more. Eventually the point is reached where the rate of ATP resynthesis by glycogen breakdown is the same as the rate of ATP breakdown in the contractile process; ATP resynthesis by the Lohmann reaction then stops because it is no longer necessary. This state of affairs is illustrated by Fig. 41.15c. The Lohmann reaction is in equilibrium and any tendency for the ATP concentration to change due to fluctuations in either its rate of breakdown or its rate of resynthesis will be prevented by rapid displacement of the Lohmann reaction in the appropriate direction. When the contraction ends ATP breakdown by the contractile process ceases, and the ATP and PC concentrations are then restored to normal by recovery processes, as they are in a twitch (Fig. 41.15b).

When the rates of ATP breakdown and resynthesis are equal, as in Fig. 41.15c, the active muscle is in a steady state. The rate of glycogen breakdown that is required to support a given rate of ATP breakdown depends on the availability of oxygen. Under aerobic conditions it is only 1/13 of the rate under anaerobic conditions. However, the maximum rate of glycogen breakdown under aerobic conditions is limited by the rate at which oxygen can be supplied to the muscle, and if higher rates of ATP resynthesis are required the muscle has to fall back on glycolysis (which is a self-limiting process).

(b) What is the Nature of the Contractile Process?

Biochemical "Models" of the Contractile Process

The enzyme that catalyses the breakdown of ATP is a prosthetic group on the myosin molecule. If ATP is added to a solution of myosin (prepared by selective extraction of the protein from muscle), it is rapidly hydrolysed and heat is evolved because the free energy released is all degraded into heat. Hydrolysis of ATP also occurs with the evolution of heat when ATP is added to a solution containing both actin and myosin (known as an *actomyosin* solution), but in addition the physico-chemical properties of the solution change and a precipitate of actomyosin may be formed. These effects result from increased interaction between the actin and myosin molecules, which is brought about by the breakdown of ATP. A dramatic demonstration of the same phenomenon is possible if actomyosin threads are produced by extruding an actomyosin solution through a fine jet into a weak salt solution; when ATP is added to the system it is hydrolysed, and the actomyosin thread will either shorten or develop tension depending on the mechanical conditions. The analogy with contraction of the living muscle is obvious.

The Contractile Process in Myofibrils

The thick filaments consist of aggregations of myosin molecules, and the thin filaments are made up of actin and probably tropomyosin molecules. The two sets of filaments overlap in the outer parts of each A band (Fig. 41.9a), and the amount of overlap increases and when the myofibril contracts the amount of overlap increases because of a relative sliding motion of the two sets of filaments. Contraction appears to be a consequence of ATP breakdown at ATP-ase sites in the region of overlap where actin, myosin, and probably tropomyosin molecules are in close proximity. The shearing forces required to produce the relative sliding movement of the two sets of filaments are thought to depend on changes in actin-myosin interaction, but precisely how the free energy released by ATP breakdown is converted into movement remains obscure. There is evidence that the thick filaments have lateral projections that can form cross bridges between the two sets of filaments under some circumstances (e.g. in rigor, as described below), and it is thought that similar cross bridges may produce a relative sliding movement of the thin filaments with respect to the thick filaments by repeatedly breaking and reattaching at new sites further along the thin filaments.

Excitation-Contraction Coupling

The effect of excitation of a muscle fibre is to activate the ATP-ase sites in the myofibrils by the inward spread of some excitatory influence when the surface membrane of the fibre is depolarized. This inward spread is much too rapid to be explained by the diffusion of a chemical, and the likelihood is that it depends on the radial transmission through the T-system of either the action potential or an electrotonic potential created by it. The mechanism by which the electrical influence activates the ATP-ase sites is thought to be as follows. Myosin ATP-ase has the property that in the presence of tropomyosin-like proteins and actin its activity is critically dependent on the Ca^{++} concentration, which is extremely low in the resting muscle (about 10^{-8} M). Excitation is thought to activate the ATP-ase sites in the region of overlap by raising the Ca^{++} concentration to about 10^{-6} M. The Ca^{++} concentration is low in the resting muscle because most of the intracellular calcium is stored in small compartments (probably the terminal cisternae of the sarcoplasmic reticulum), from which it is released by the spread of electrical activity through the T system. This activates the ATP-ase sites and ATP breakdown continues until the Ca^{++} concentration is reduced to its resting level again due to active uptake of calcium by the sarcoplasmic reticulum. The decay of the active state in the muscle during a twitch and following the last stimulus in a tetanus probably occurs with the same time course as the fall in the Ca^{++} concentration.

Plasticizing Action of ATP and Rigor

In the resting muscle (see Fig. 41.8) the myofibrils offer very little permanent resistance to stretch because the thick and thin filaments can slide freely past one another. The lack of interaction between actin and myosin under these circumstances indicates that ATP has a "plasticizing action" when it is present, but not being hydrolysed because of the low Ca^{++} concentration. If all the ATP is hydrolysed, for example, by stimulating an IAA-poisoned muscle to exhaustion (see Fig. 41.14), a powerful interaction between actin and myosin occurs giving the myofibrils an almost "crystalline" structure. The result is that they become very inextensible and this state is known as *rigor*. (*Rigor mortis* is a similar condition that appears within a few hours of death as a result of ATP hydrolysis in the muscles.)

(c) How much Free Energy is Released when a Muscle Contracts?

When a muscle is poisoned with FDNB so that ATP breakdown is the only chemical reaction that takes place during contraction, all the free energy that is released is either converted into work or degraded into heat. It might seem at first sight that the free energy released could be measured as the sum of the work done and the heat produced by the muscle. Unfortunately it is not as simple as that because the breakdown of ATP is almost certainly associated with an *entropy change*, and this will entail a movement of heat between the muscle and its surroundings that is quite independent of the heat efflux due to the degradation of free energy. Depending on the magnitude and direction of this entropic heat movement, the heat produced by the muscle will be either greater or less than the heat efflux due to the degradation of free energy. As nothing is known about the entropy change that takes place when ATP breakdown actually occurs in the muscle, *it is not possible to determine the free energy released during a contraction*.

The entropy change that occurs when a reversible chemical reaction takes place in the forward (spontaneous) direction is matched by an equal and opposite entropy change when the reaction is driven in the reverse direction. Thus when a muscle is poisoned with IAA so that PC breakdown is the only net chemical change that takes place during contraction, the heat produced by the muscle is unaffected by the entropy changes associated with the breakdown and resynthesis of ATP as these cancel out exactly. However the situation is still complicated in that the heat produced under these circumstances depends on three things: (i) the wastage of free energy due to inefficiency in the coupling between ATP breakdown and the contractile process; (ii) the wastage of free energy due to inefficiency in the coupling between PC breakdown and ATP resynthesis; (iii) the heat movement due to the entropy change associated with the breakdown of PC; and their relative contributions are unknown.

However the sum of the energy appearing as heat and work, which is known as the *enthalpy change*, is worth measuring when ATP breakdown or PC breakdown is the only net chemical change occurring during contraction. The enthalpy change per mole of chemical breakdown $(-\Delta H)$ is a constant for a given reaction under given conditions (about 10 kcal/mole for ATP breakdown and for PC breakdown *in vivo*), and this figure can be used to calculate the amount of chemical breakdown (n, moles) from the enthalpy change, which must be equal to $n(-\Delta H)$ kcal. Furthermore the enthalpy change per mole of reaction $(-\Delta H)$ is probably proportional to the free energy released per mole of reaction $(-\Delta F)$ under all circumstances, and the proportionality constant $(Y = \Delta F/\Delta H)$ may be known one day.

The one situation in which the free energy released can be estimated with some confidence is when the initial and recovery processes are considered together. Uncertainties about entropy changes related to the breakdown and resynthesis of ATP and PC cease to matter under these circumstances because the ATP and PC are completely resynthesized, and the only net reaction that occurs (glycogen breakdown) is not associated with significant entropy changes when it takes place under aerobic conditions. The *total enthalpy change* (work done + heat produced during contraction + heat produced during recovery period) should therefore be equal to the *total free energy released* during contraction and recovery.

(d) What Factors Determine how much Free Energy is Released?

For reasons that have already been given, the free energy released cannot be determined, but the heat produced and the external work done by the muscle can be measured and the internal work done (by the CC in stretching the SC) can be calculated. The sum of the energy appearing as heat and work (i.e. the enthalpy change) can therefore be determined. It depends on the following factors:

   (i) the mechanical conditions,
   (ii) the pattern of response,
   (iii) the initial length of the muscle,
   (iv) the temperature.

(i) The Mechanical Conditions

When a muscle is stimulated the rate of release of energy rises rapidly to its maximum value before there is any appreciable mechanical activity. Subsequently the rate of release of energy at each instant depends on the mechanical conditions. The effect of the stimulus is thus not simply to trigger off the release of a fixed amount of energy; it is to switch on energy-yielding chemical reactions, and the amount of energy released depends on the length and tension changes undergone by the muscle during the contraction-relaxation cycle. For example, in twitches of a frog muscle at 0°C the total energy released is greater during an isotonic contraction than it is during an isometric contraction (Fig. 41.16).

(ii) Pattern of Response

When the muscle is kept in the active state by repetitive stimulation, the high rate of energy liberation that is reached soon after a single stimulus may or may not be maintained depending on the type of muscle. As no work is done during the plateau of a tetanic contraction, all the energy that is released during this phase appears as heat (the "maintenance heat").

(iii) The Initial Muscle Length

The energy liberation in *isometric contractions* at muscle lengths above L_0 decreases in exactly the same way as the tension developed (see Fig. 41.11). The explanation is thought to be that both the tension developed and the ATP breakdown depend on the number of sites of interaction between actin and myosin, and at lengths above L_0 the amount of overlap between the thick and thin filaments (and therefore the number of sites of interaction per sarcomere) decreases as the muscle is stretched. In contractions at lengths below L_0 the energy liberated does not

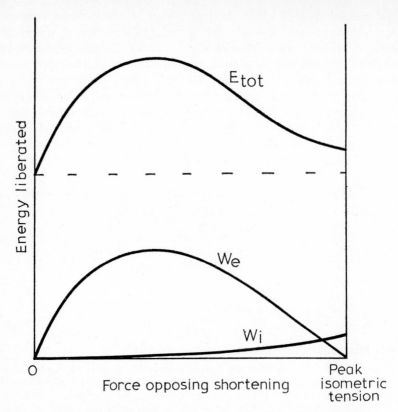

FIG. 41.16. Variation of work done and energy liberated with the force opposing shortening. Curve W_e shows how the external work done by the muscle in a series of isotonic twitches varies with the force opposing shortening; this has its maximum when the force is about one third of the tension produced in an isometric twitch (see Fig. 41.13*a*). Curve W_1 shows how the "internal" work done by the CC in stretching the SC varies with the force opposing shortening; this has its maximum when the conditions are isometric. Curve E_{tot} shows how the total energy liberated (as heat and work) varies with the force opposing shortening. If the total work ($W_e + W_1$) is subtracted from the total energy (E_{tot}), the quantity obtained (dashed line) is independent of the force opposing shortening. (It should be pointed out that this is almost certainly not a general property of muscle, but it is true for contractions of a frog muscle at 0°C.)

fall off in proportion to the tension, but it is not clear how actin-myosin interaction is altered when the H zone disappears and double overlap of thin filaments occurs in the centre of the A band. In *afterloaded isotonic contractions* the amount of shortening and the work done against a given load increase when the initial length of the muscle is increased; so does the energy released during the contraction.

(iv) Temperature

When the temperature of a frog muscle is raised the energy liberated in a twitch decreases slightly, but the *rate* of energy liberation increases because the duration of the twitch is reduced by an increase in temperature. The increased rate of ATP breakdown is associated with an increase in the velocity of shortening of the contractile component when the temperature is raised.

(e) What is the Efficiency of the Muscle as a Machine?

This is a complex question because free energy is released by several different chemical reactions during contraction and recovery, and it is used for a variety of purposes. The efficiency of the coupling between a chemical reaction that provides free energy and a reaction or process that uses it can be defined in very general terms as the fraction of the free energy released that is put to good use. During contraction and recovery there are four such couplings: (i) the contractile process, (ii) resynthesis of ATP by the Lohmann reaction, (iii) resynthesis of ATP by glycogen breakdown, and (iv) resynthesis of PC by the Lohmann reaction. It would be of great interest to know the efficiency of each of these couplings, but in fact the only thing that we can determine is their *overall efficiency* because it is only when the initial and recovery processes are considered together that the free energy released can be determined. Under these circumstances the free energy released is thought to be approximately the same as the total enthalpy change (i.e. work done + heat produced during contraction + heat produced during recovery). The overall efficiency can therefore be calculated as follows:

$$\text{Overall efficiency} = \frac{\text{work}}{\text{free energy released}} \approx \frac{\text{work}}{\text{work} + \text{total heat}}$$

For frog muscle at $0°C$, producing its maximum work output, the overall efficiency is 0.2–0.25 or 20–25 per cent, which compares rather unfavourably with other machines that utilize free energy released by chemical breakdown (e.g. diesel engine 40 per cent, fuel cell 50 per cent, accumulator 80–90 per cent). Unfortunately we do not know whether the main source of inefficiency in the muscle lies in the initial processes or in the recovery processes. It is possible that the efficiency of the contractile process alone compares quite favourably with that of the other machines quoted.

Energetics of the Resting Muscle

A continual expenditure of energy is required to keep the resting muscle in a state of readiness for activity. Some of this energy is used by active transport mechanisms to maintain electrical potential gradients and osmotic gradients that are always tending to collapse due to passive diffusion. Energy is also required for various anabolic processes. Although

ATP is often involved as an intermediary, the ultimate source of the energy used by the resting muscle is oxidative metabolism. All the free energy released appears as heat *sooner or later*; some of it is degraded into heat as a result of inefficiency in couplings, but the free energy that is put to good use is also dissipated as heat eventually; for example when ATP that has been formed by oxidative rephosphorylation of ADP is hydrolysed, and when substances that have been actively transported against a concentration gradient diffuse down that gradient again. This means that the rate of release of free energy in the resting muscle can be measured as the rate of heat production because the only net reaction taking place is oxidative metabolism and this is not associated with any significant entropy changes.

Technically it is difficult to measure the rate of heat production of a resting muscle because the rate is so low. It is easier to measure its oxygen consumption and then to calculate the corresponding rate of heat production from the known calorific value of oxygen. The rate of energy liberation required to maintain the *status quo* in resting muscle depends critically on the temperature (it is increased by a factor of 2·5 for a 10°C rise).

"Red" and "White" Muscles

Mammalian muscle fibres have a reddish colour because they contain cytochromes and myoglobin. The fibres can be divided into two main types (red and white) depending on the intensity of their red coloration. All mammalian muscles contain a mixed population of fibres, with red fibres predominating in "red" muscles and white fibres predominating in "white" muscles. The red and white fibres in a given muscle seem to have identical physiological properties; they differ simply in that red fibres are capable of much higher rates of oxidative metabolism than white fibres because they contain more cytochrome and myoglobin. The cytochromes are located in the mitochondria and they play a key rôle in the oxidative rephosphorylation of ADP. The myoglobin is present in the sarcoplasm and its most important property is that it greatly facilitates the diffusion of oxygen from the cell membrane to the mitochondria. (Myoglobin resembles haemoglobin in that it combines with oxygen, but it is not considered to provide a particularly useful oxygen store within the muscle fibre because myoglobin is present in low concentration and it does not give up its oxygen until the partial pressure has fallen to a very low value.)

"Red" muscles differ from "white" muscles in that they are active for a higher proportion of the time—their normal function in the body is either to contract frequently (e.g. diaphragm) or to produce sustained contractions (e.g. postural muscles). In a given mammal it is also true that "red" muscles usually contract more slowly than "white" muscles, but this is not so when mammals as a whole are considered, and the idea that slowness in contraction is linked with redness of colour seems to be fallacious.

MUSCULAR EXERCISE

Muscular exercise can vary enormously in character; at one extreme we have the spectacular performances of the playing field and gymnasium, and at the other we have the unimposing activities that occupy most of our waking hours. In all cases it is a complicated affair requiring the participation of almost all the systems in the body in one way or another. In this Chapter, only the aspects of the subject that concern the muscles directly will be considered.

When a muscle contracts in the body, for example in producing a limb movement, it is never the only muscle active. A co-ordinated limb movement requires carefully balanced contributions from prime movers, synergists, and antagonists. In a given muscle the number of motor units active and the pattern of excitation in each will vary throughout the course of a single movement. It is doubtful whether full activation of a muscle (i.e. tetanic contraction of all the muscle fibres) ever occurs in the body, even in the most violent limb movements. The muscle fibres that make up a motor unit are of course fully activated every time that motor unit fires, but the maximum rate of firing is far below the fusion frequency so the best that they can produce is an unfused tetanic contraction. It appears that the maximum performance that a muscle can be made to produce when isolated from the body (e.g. maximum tension developed, or maximum power output, or maximum work output) never constitutes a limit to its performance *in situ*.

Maximum Power Output during Muscular Exercise

All forms of muscular exercise make use of the body as a source of mechanical power. The maximum power that can be produced depends on the time for which it must be maintained, as illustrated by Fig. 41.17*a*, in which each circle shows the power produced by a champion cyclist during exercise of the duration indicated. The line shows the maximum mechanical power available from oxidative processes as calculated from the measured oxygen consumption of champion athletes, the known calorific value of oxygen, and the estimated overall efficiency of human muscle (20–25 per cent). The observed power output can exceed that available from oxidative processes because a limited amount of additional mechanical work can be obtained from anaerobic sources (phosphorylcreatine breakdown and glycolysis). In a champion athlete this *anaerobic reserve* amounts to about 0·6 h.p. × minute, and it can be used at whatever rate is demanded by the exercise. It is of particular importance in exercise of *intermediate duration* (up to 5 min) because oxidative processes are slow to get under way; the anaerobic reserve is used to boost the power output above the level that can be supported by oxidative processes. This is illustrated by Fig. 41.17*b*, in which the shaded area shows the estimated contribution of the anaerobic reserve to the work done by the muscles of a champion cyclist during a sprint lasting 1 min. When the exercise is of slightly longer duration (Fig. 41.17c) the relative contribution of the anaerobic reserve to the total work done is less because the oxidative processes have time to get under

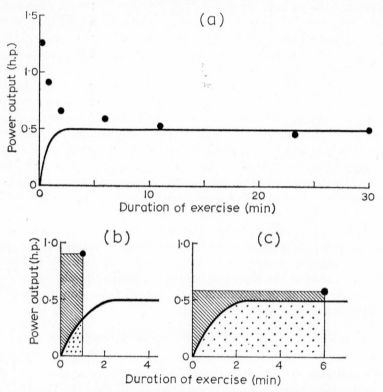

FIG. 41.17. Human power output. The points on these graphs show the power output maintained by champion cyclists during periods of exercise of the duration indicated (D. R. Wilkie). The curve shows the power output that can be obtained by oxidative processes; when the observed power output exceeds this, the extra power is provided by anaerobic hydrolytic processes. In graphs (b) and (c), the rectangles show the work done by the cyclists during exercises lasting 1 minute (b) and 6 minutes (c). The cross-hatched areas show the contribution of hydrolytic processes, and the stippled areas show the contribution of oxidative processes.

way. When the anaerobic reserve is utilized it creates what is known as an *oxygen debt*; this must later be repaid because the lactic acid produced as a result of glycolysis must be reconverted to pyruvic acid and then either oxidized (in skeletal muscle, cardiac muscle or liver) or used in the re-synthesis of glycogen (liver only). The phosphorylcreatine store also has to be replenished by oxidative processes. The oxygen consumption therefore remains high for some time after exercise ends, and the extra oxygen is used to pay off the oxygen debt incurred during activity.

In exercise of *long duration* (more than 5 min) almost all the energy comes from oxidative processes and a steady state is established, as illustrated in Fig. 41.15c. The maximum continuous power output is then limited by the rate at which oxygen can be taken up in the lungs and distributed to the active muscles through the circulation, but the anaerobic reserve can still be put to good use at any time if a higher power output is required than oxidative processes permit (e.g. in a sprint at the end of a long distance race). Champion athletes can produce a steady power output of about 0·5 h.p. for long periods, and ordinary healthy individuals can manage 0·2–0·3 h.p.

In exercise of *very short duration* (1 sec or less) the maximum power output depends on the mass of muscle that can be brought into use, the mechanical properties of the muscles (in particular, their force-velocity curves), and the matching of the load to the muscles through the skeleton. Weight lifting is a good example of exercise of very short duration; it involves a single convulsive movement of the limbs in which a power output of up to about 2 h.p. may be achieved. This power output is a good deal less than the muscles could produce if optimally loaded because the velocity of movement is very low.

Effect of Training

It is uncommon to find athletes who are exceptionally good at exercises of very different durations; thus a weight lifter rarely makes a good long distance runner and *vice-versa*. The reason is that by training, athletes specialize their bodies for different purposes, and weight lifting and long distance running provide extreme examples of this specialization. Weight lifting requires afterloaded isotonic contractions of the muscles involved (see Fig. 41.12), and in order to raise a heavy load off the ground very large tensions must be produced. The muscles of a weight lifter adapt to the requirement for large tensions by increasing their cross-sectional areas enormously. The muscle fibres increase in size (hypertrophy) but not in number. The ratio of myofibrillar protein to sarcoplasmic protein increases because a greater proportion of the cross-section of the fibres is occupied by myofibrils, which increase both in number and size. Similar changes can be induced in selected groups of muscles by means of the "isometric" training programmes that are currently in vogue.

Exercises in which sustained power outputs are required (e.g. long distance running) lead to a different type of specialization in the body. The muscles do not increase particularly in bulk, but their capacity for oxidative metabolism is greatly enhanced by increases in the number of mitochondria and in the myoglobin content. Concomitant increases occur in the vascularization of the muscles, and in the cardiovascular reserve (i.e. the ability of the heart and circulation to deliver oxygen to the tissues). These adaptive changes allow the muscles to produce greater sustained power outputs than would otherwise be possible, and to recover more rapidly after exercise.

It has recently been shown that repeated stimulation of an isolated frog muscle over a period of several hours leads to an increase in the activity of certain enzymes, notably of creatine phosphotransferase, which catalyses the Lohmann reaction. (see p. 708). It is not clear whether the increase is due to the activation of precursor already present or to adaptive enzyme synthesis over a short period of time. However, it is an extremely interesting observation, and it suggests that the characteristics of a muscle may be a good deal more "plastic" than had previously been realized.

CHAPTER 42

THE STRUCTURE AND FUNCTION OF
SMOOTH MUSCLE

THE point has already been made (p. 687) that smooth muscle can be divided into two main types, known as *single unit* and *multi-unit*. The smooth muscles of the alimentary tract and its associated ducts, the ureters, and the uterus are all of the single unit type, and these make up the main bulk of the smooth muscle in the body. The intrinsic muscles of the eye, the pilomotor muscles of the skin, and the nictitating membrane of the cat are examples of the multi-unit type. There are also some smooth muscles that seem to occupy an intermediate position; for example, the guinea pig vas deferens, which has mixed characteristics, and vascular smooth muscle, which may have mainly single unit or mainly multi-unit characteristics depending on the species and on its location in the body.

STRUCTURE OF SMOOTH MUSCLE

In many respects the two types of smooth muscle are identical in structure. The cells are spindle shaped, each containing a single nucleus, and they are organized into bundles that branch and anastomose freely, as illustrated in Fig. 42.1a. When smooth muscle forms part of the wall of a tube or hollow viscus, the bundles of cells may be organized into circular and longitudinal layers (e.g. intestine, bladder) or arranged in a complex helical form (e.g. blood vessels, uterus of higher vertebrates).

The cells vary a good deal in size; the largest are found in the pregnant uterus where their diameter reaches about 15μ and their length may be 500μ, and the smallest are found in the walls of blood vessels where the diameter is typically 2μ and the length 20μ. The cells contain no myofibrils, but myofilaments can be seen when fixed and stained material is examined in the electron microscope. All the filaments seem to be of the same type, and they are similar in appearance to the thin filaments seen in skeletal muscle. Biochemical investigations have shown that smooth muscle contains actin and myosin (in about one tenth of the concentrations found in skeletal muscle) and tropomyosin; it is therefore reasonable to suppose that the filaments present in smooth muscle consist of actin and perhaps tropomyosin, as do the thin filaments in skeletal muscle. There is some evidence that the myosin molecules may be dispersed amongst the myofilaments in dimer form. (Contraction could still take place by a sliding mechanism, with the myosin units forming floating cross links between adjacent actin filaments.) Smooth muscle cells also contain structures that are probably equivalent to the sarcoplasmic reticulum found in skeletal muscle, but they are very poorly differentiated in comparison.

Single unit and multi-unit smooth muscles differ mainly in the intimacy of the contact between adjacent muscle cells. This is closely correlated with the extent to which activity can spread from one cell to the next, and it will be dealt with in a subsequent section.

Innervation

With the exception of amnion muscle all smooth muscles are innervated to some extent. The terminal branches of the autonomic nerve fibres intermingle to form a fine-meshed plexus, known as the *autonomic ground plexus*, which is found amongst the muscle cells throughout the tissue. The terminal branches are of very small diameter ($0 \cdot 1$–2μ) and they tend to run in small bundles, each of which is enveloped by an extension of either the Schwann cell syncytium or its basement membrane. The junctions between nerve and muscle cells are not nearly as well differentiated as the neuromuscular junctions in skeletal muscles. Each terminal branch of an autonomic axon is thought to make lateral contacts with a number of muscle cells along its length. In the junction regions, where the axon is slightly dilated and where mitochondria and synaptic vesicles are relatively numerous, the Schwann cell sheath is usually attenuated and the basement membrane may also be absent (see below). However there is little or no specialization of the post-synaptic muscle membrane apart from the absence of pinocytotic vesicles.

From the point of view of their innervation single unit and multi-unit smooth muscles differ in several respects:

(i) Density of Innervation

In the single unit type the innervation of individual muscle cells by several axons is probably rare; in fact some muscle cells may not be innervated at all. In the multi-unit type the innervation is more dense, and it is likely that each muscle cell is innervated by more than one axon.

(ii) Junctions between Nerve and Muscle Cells

In the single unit type the axon usually retains its basement membrane in the junction region, and the gap between nerve and muscle cells is not less than about $0 \cdot 08\mu$. In the multi-unit type there is usually no basement membrane in the junction region, and the gap may be as little as $0 \cdot 007\mu$.

(iii) Type of Innervation

Most smooth muscles of the single unit (like cardiac muscle) have both excitatory and inhibitory nerve supplies whereas multi-unit smooth muscles (like skeletal muscle) usually have only an excitatory supply.

EXPERIMENTS ON SMOOTH MUSCLE

Although from the medical point of view smooth muscle is unquestionably of greater importance than skeletal muscle, our knowledge of it has always lagged behind that of skeletal muscle. The main reason for this is that smooth muscle is a rather intractable material to study experimentally. Its awkward features are as follows:

(i) Tissue Architecture

Because of the complexity of the tissue architecture (see Fig. 42.1a) it is impossible to isolate a smooth muscle in the way that one can a skeletal muscle, which is a discrete entity with tendons that can be used to couple the muscle to a mechanical

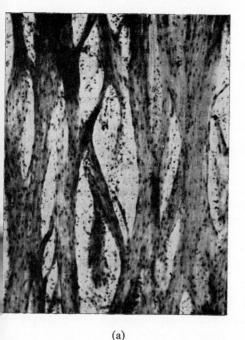
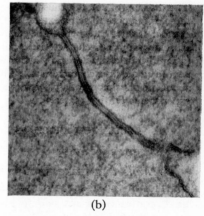

(a)   (b)

FIG. 42.1. Structure of smooth muscle. (a) Light micrograph (magn. 80) of pregnant rabbit uterus, showing branching and anastomosing bundles of muscle cells (A. Csapo). (b) Electron micrograph (magn. 100,000) of rat intestine, showing regions of close contact ("tight junctions") between muscle cells (T. Oosaki and S. Ishii). Note that the membranes of the cells fuse to give a five-layered structure.

recording system. The only way of making a preparation of smooth muscle is to cut out a strip of the tissue and then fix its ends with threads or mechanical clamps. This is rather an unsatisfactory procedure, but fairly reproducible results appear to have been obtained in studies of the mechanical properties of strips of cow mesenteric artery, strips of rabbit and rat uterus, and the condensed bands of longitudinal muscle (taenia) that are found on the surface of the guinea pig caecum.

However the problem remains that the damaged cells at the cut and clamped ends of the preparation have an unknown influence on the mechanical measurements.

(ii) Cell Dimensions

The small size of the cells in smooth muscle make it impossible to dissect out single cells for detailed mechanical studies, and it also makes it difficult to impale them satisfactorily with microelectrodes without causing extensive damage. In recent years, by using microelectrodes with very small tips (diameter about 0.1μ), it has been possible to obtain satisfactory measurements of the membrane potential of smooth muscle cells.

(iii) Spontaneous Activity

Spontaneous activity is a characteristic feature of the single unit type of smooth muscle, but it can be a great nuisance when the response of the muscle to controlled external stimulation is being investigated. It is possible to obtain stable electrical and mechanical baselines by cooling the preparation or by treating it with drugs that abolish spontaneous activity (e.g. adrenaline in some situations). The muscle can then be made to contract by electrical stimulation (direct or indirect) and by the application of chemical substances that depolarize the cell membrane.

(iv) Diversity of Characteristics

Smooth muscles differ from skeletal muscles in that their properties vary enormously. This means that the experimental observations made on one smooth muscle may not be applicable to another even if this comes from the same animal. The division of smooth muscles into single and multi-unit types has rationalized these differences to some extent, but all smooth muscles do not fit neatly into one or other of these categories. The *guinea pig vas deferens* is a good example of a smooth muscle with mixed characteristics; all activity in this tissue is neurogenic in origin (a multi-unit characteristic), but activity can spread from one muscle cell to the next (a single unit characteristic). The fact is that if one wants to know something about the physiology of a particular smooth muscle there is no substitute for actual experiments on that material.

EXCITATION PROCESSES IN SINGLE UNIT SMOOTH MUSCLE

Spontaneous Activity

The cells that make up a smooth muscle of the single unit type can contract in the absence of any activity in their autonomic nerve supply. Such contractions are said to be *myogenic* in origin, and they occur at a frequency that is the same for all the cells in a given tissue. The frequency varies from one smooth muscle to another; and in mammals the range is from about 1 to 10 per minute depending on the species and the location of the smooth muscle.

It is important to make a clear distinction between the behaviour of a smooth muscle (or a piece of smooth muscle) and the behaviour of individual cells within the tissue. A given cell has periods of activity during which it tends to contract in a rhythmic fashion and periods of quiescence, but the behaviour of the muscle as a whole depends on the extent to which the rhythmic contractions of the active cells are synchronized. (An apt analogy is provided by a large collection of identical clocks; they all tick at the same frequency, but the character of the sound that they generate *en masse* will depend on the degree of synchronization.) If large groups of cells contract and relax more or less simultaneously the mechanical activity of the muscle consists of *rhythmic contractions* at the same frequency as those produced by an individual cell. On the other hand if the cells contract asynchronously the mechanical activity of the muscle consists of a sustained contraction, known as *tone* or *tonus*, with little or no superimposed rhythmic component. This picture of spontaneous activity has emerged from microelectrode studies which have shown that the electrical activity of individual cells is essentially the same whatever the nature of the spontaneous activity produced by the whole muscle (i.e. rhythmic contractions or tone).

Spontaneous Variations of Membrane Potential

The variations of membrane potential shown in Fig. 42.2 are typical of those seen in microelectrode studies of individual cells in *guinea pig taenia*. When the microelectrode enters the cell (Fig. 42.2*a*) it reveals the presence

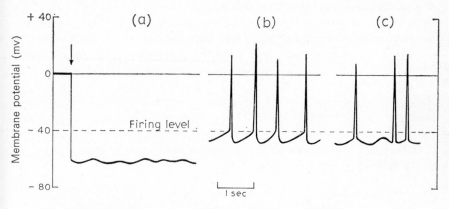

Fig. 42.2. Membrane potential variations in smooth muscle cells. These diagrams are based on microelectrode recordings from cells in guinea pig taenia. (a) Quiescent period: the membrane potential shows slow waves, but the mean potential is well above the firing level. (Arrow shows entry of microelectrode into the cell). (b) Active period: membrane potential changes in a cell showing pacemaker activity. (c) Active period: activity due to action potentials that have invaded the cell from adjacent active cells.

of a membrane potential, the inside of the cell being negative with respect to the outside. The alternation between periods of activity and quiescence, each lasting several minutes, seems to depend on very slow swings of membrane potential known as *pendular fluctuations*. Superimposed on these there are membrane potential variations of much shorter duration (0·5–1 sec) known as *slow waves*, which are most pronounced during the periods of activity. If the membrane potential falls to the threshold value ("firing level") during a slow wave then an *action potential* or *spike* is generated (Fig. 42.2*b*). The membrane potential is reversed during the spike, but the peak value reached is rather variable. During the repolarization phase of the spike, the slow wave is "wiped out" completely; a new slow wave then starts and the cycle may be repeated.

The potential changes shown in Fig. 42.2*b* are characteristic of a cell showing *pacemaker activity*, and they are reminiscent of those seen in the sinu-atrial node of the heart. Cells in which the mean membrane potential is too high to allow the slow waves to generate action potentials are quiescent from the mechanical point of view *unless they are invaded by action potentials from a nearby pacemaker cell*. Propagated action potentials (Fig. 42.2*c*) can usually be recognized because they do not necessarily coincide with the peak of a slow wave, and because they do not "wipe out" the slow waves in the way that so locally generated spikes do (cf. Fig. 42.2*b* and *c*). The sites of pacemaker activity change continually in the guinea pig taenia. Whether or not a given cell acts as a pacemaker depends on its mean membrane potential. If this is -60 mV or more (i.e. more negative) the magnitude of the slow waves is insufficient to reduce the membrane potential to the firing level, and the cell will be mechanically quiescent unless it is excited by a nearby pacemaker cell. On the other hand, if the mean membrane potential is -50 mV or less (i.e. less negative) the cell becomes a pacemaker because almost every slow wave will reduce the membrane potential to the firing level. Note that the slow waves occur all the time (even when the cell is mechanically quiescent); they reflect the intrinsic ability of the cells to show pacemaker activity.

Other smooth muscles vary in the character of their spontaneous activity, as the following examples show:

Ureter

The smooth muscle in the wall of the *rat ureter* bears a particularly close resemblance to cardiac muscle. Action potentials of the "plateau" type are generated by a fixed pacemaker at the renal end of the ureter. These are propagated from cell to cell with the result that well co-ordinated contractions spread along the length of the ureter, delivering urine into the bladder in a series of spurts. This type of muscular activity is one form of *peristalsis*.

Uterus

Uterine smooth muscle is particularly interesting because its properties depend on the levels of hormones in the blood stream. When the uterus is *progesterone-dominated* (e.g. during pregnancy) most of the cells are quiescent and unresponsive to drugs, including oxytocin. There is some tone present as a result of asynchronous firing of scattered pacemaker cells, but the action potentials generated do not propagate far and no rhythmic contractions occur. When the uterus is *oestrogen-dominated* (e.g. during parturition) most of the cells become active, and the contractions that they produce are well co-ordinated because the number of pacemakers is limited and action potentials propagate for long distances within the tissue. There is a pacemaker site near the insertion of each uterine tube, but it is unusual for both to be active at the same time. The pacemaker cells produce slow waves that last for 10–20 sec, and each slow wave generates a long train of spikes. These spread through the muscle and produce rhythmic contractions that are tetanic in character and of great importance in labour.

Effect of Stretch on Spontaneous Activity

A smooth muscle of the single unit type actively resists extension because this causes an increase in the amount of spontaneous activity in the muscle. There is a general reduction of mean membrane potential and an increase in the frequency of slow waves, with the result that quiescent cells become active and the rate of spike discharge in active cells is increased. This property is particularly well-developed in the smooth muscle of certain vascular beds where it is thought to contribute to the autoregulation of blood flow (see Chapter 6).

Ionic Basis of Membrane Potential

In smooth muscle the nearest equivalent to the resting membrane potential seen in nerve and skeletal muscle fibres is the membrane potential observed during periods of mechanical quiescence. This has a maximum value of about -70 mV, which is rather less than the values found in other excitable tissues. It probably has the same ionic basis as the resting membrane potentials found elsewhere (see Chapter 17), but it seems to be influenced to a greater extent by the permeability of the cell membrane to chloride and sodium. The causes of the pendular fluctuations and the slow waves are unknown; variations in the permeability of the membrane to sodium *may* be the cause of either or both, but this has yet to be proved. The self-regenerative depolarization of the membrane followed by a reversal of membrane potential during a spike are probably due to the inward movement of sodium and other ions, including calcium. This entry of calcium ions may play a rôle in excitation-contraction coupling.

Spread of Activity from Cell to Cell

Because activity can spread from one cell to the next in a smooth muscle of the single unit type, groups of cells (and in some cases the whole muscle) behave as a *functional* syncytium. The extent to which activity spreads in a given muscle is influenced by factors that alter the mean membrane potential (e.g. amount of stretch, local concentrations of humoral agents), but basically it depends on the intimacy of the contact between adjacent cells in the tissue. For example in *amnion smooth muscle*, where activity spreads very effectively through the tissue, the cells are in close apposition over large parts of their surface. In the regions of close contact there is no intervening basement membrane, and there are areas where the outer layers of the adjacent cell membranes (each of which consists of three-layers) fuse to give a five-layered structure. In *intestinal smooth muscle*, where activity only spreads for short distances, the plasma membrane of each cell is covered with basement membrane except for small areas that occupy about 5 per cent of the cell surface; in these regions the plasma membranes of adjacent cells are in close apposition and their outer layers are fused to give a five-layered structure (Fig. 42.1*b*). (These small regions of close contact have a bridge-like appearance, and it used to be thought that cytoplasmic continuity existed between adjacent cells; this is no longer considered to be the case.) Thus in these smooth muscles, and in others that have been examined from this point of view, a very good correlation has been found between the fraction of the cell surface that is in close proximity to adjacent cells and the extent to which activity spreads from cell to cell. There is also a good correlation between this structural feature and the velocity with which activity spreads through the tissue.

Mechanism of Spread

Several possible mechanisms have been suggested (electrical, mechanical, neural, humoral), but electrical spread by a process known as *nexal-syncytial transmission* seems to be the most likely mechanism. A region of close contact between adjacent cells ("tight junction" or "nexus") is considered to have a low electrical resistance, so that from the point of view of current flow two cells linked by several tight junctions behave as a continuous structure. As an action potential in cell A (Fig. 42.3) approaches the junction region, the local currents associated with its leading edge flow from cell A, through the tight junctions into cell B, and then out through its membrane. The membrane potential in cell B falls progressively as the action potential gets closer to the junction, and if it falls below the

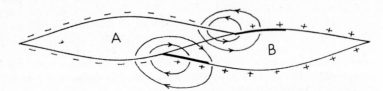

Fig. 42.3. Propagation of an action potentials from cell A to cell B by nexal-syncytial transmission. (See text for explanation).

firing level an action potential is generated in cell B. Thus propagation from one cell to the next is no different from propagation over the surface of a single cell.

STIMULATION OF SINGLE UNIT SMOOTH MUSCLE

Smooth muscle of the single unit type can be made to contract by direct or indirect electrical stimulation, and by the application of chemicals that depolarize the cell membrane.

Direct Stimulation

A strip of smooth muscle responds to a single stimulus by producing a twitch. The strength-response and strength-duration curves are similar to those obtained with skeletal muscle (see Figs. 41.4 and 41.5), but there is no well defined maximal stimulus because the strength-response curve does not show a plateau at large stimulus strengths. If the muscle is stimulated repetitively summation occurs and a fused tetanus can be produced.

Indirect Stimulation

The effect of indirect stimulation has been studied in detail in experiments on *rabbit colon*. The spontaneous activity in this tissue consists of slow waves with bursts of spikes that propagate for short distances. The application of a single shock to the *excitatory nerve supply* (cholinergic) produces a recognizable increment of tension, which is superimposed on the spontaneous activity. Microelectrode studies have shown that the arrival of an excitatory volley results in the appearance of a *junction potential*, which is of the same general nature as the endplate potential seen at the neuromuscular junction of skeletal muscle fibres. The effect of this in a particular cell depends on the timing of the junction potential with respect to the slow waves already present; if the cell membrane is sufficiently depolarized an action potential is generated. A single stimulus produces a detectable increment of tension because action potentials are generated more or less synchronously in a certain proportion of the cells. Repetitive stimulation at a low frequency (below 1 per sec) gradually increases the proportion of cells that respond synchronously, with the result that the muscle produces well co-ordinated rhythmic contractions (this process is known as "driving" the tissue). If the frequency is raised above 10 per sec the mechanical response has the appearance of a fused tetanus, but electrical records show summation of junction potentials leading to a maintained depolarization of the membrane with no superimposed action potentials. The application of a single stimulus to the *inhibitory nerve supply* (adrenergic) has no detectable effect on the spontaneous activity of the muscle, but repetitive stimulation leads to its complete cessation. Microelectrode studies have shown that all action potentials and slow waves are abolished, and the membrane potential is stabilized at a value well above the firing level. A similar effect can be produced by immersing the tissue in a solution containing adrenaline.

Chemical Stimulation

Smooth muscles produce a maintained contraction, known as a *contracture*, when the cell membranes are depolarized by immersing the muscle in solutions containing suitable neurohumoral agents or a high concentration of potassium. (Most mammalian skeletal muscles only produce a twitch-like response in these circumstances.)

MECHANICAL PROPERTIES OF SINGLE UNIT SMOOTH MUSCLE

Spontaneous activity is not suitable for detailed studies of the mechanical properties of smooth muscle. If it is abolished (see p. 726) then direct stimulation can be used to produce twitch and tetanic responses. The mechanical properties of smooth muscle are basically the same as those of skeletal muscle, but there are important quantitative differences, viz:

(i) Speed of Contraction

Smooth muscles vary enormously in this respect, but they are all much slower than skeletal muscle. For example the maximum unloaded shortening velocity (V_0) of a typical skeletal muscle is about 2,000 times that of *cow mesenteric artery* muscle, and about 20 times that of *guinea pig taenia*.

(ii) Tension Production

The maximum tension that a smooth muscle can produce (P_0, kg wt/cm^2) is only about half the corresponding value for skeletal muscle.

(iii) Operational Range of Muscle Lengths

In isometric contractions smooth muscle can produce tension over a much wider range of muscle lengths than skeletal muscle; similarly in isotonic contractions it can shorten through much greater distances. Whether this is due to differences in the architecture of the tissue or to fundamental differences in the contractile mechanisms of the two types of muscle is not clear at present. The wide operational range of muscle lengths may well be of importance in the normal functioning of smooth muscle *in situ*, as it is not restricted by skeletal attachments in the way that skeletal muscle is.

(iv) Force-velocity Curve

The force-velocity curves of smooth muscle and skeletal muscle (see Fig. 41.10b) are similar in shape, but the curve for smooth muscle is more convex towards the origin; this suggests that smooth muscle may be more economical in the maintenance of tension (i.e. requires a lower rate of energy expenditure to maintain a given tension), but this prediction has yet to be tested experimentally. The maximum work and power output are produced when the muscle shortens against loads of 0·3 to 0·5 P_0, as in skeletal muscle, but the maximum power output is much less because of the lower velocity of shortening of smooth muscle.

ENERGETICS OF SINGLE UNIT SMOOTH MUSCLE

Actin and myosin are present in smooth muscle, and the properties of actomyosin solutions suggest that ATP breakdown provides the free energy used in the contractile process. ATP and PC are present in much smaller amounts than in skeletal muscle, and it is possible to detect breakdown of both substances when smooth muscle (*cow mesenteric artery*) contracts under anaerobic conditions. The explanation of this seems to be that the recovery processes are not as effectively stimulated by a rise of ADP concentration as they are in skeletal muscle. It seems likely that excitation-contraction coupling is brought about by the movement of ions that activate the actomyosin ATP-ase (probably Ca^{++}) from the extracellular fluid into the cell during the action potential. How the activating ions are removed from the sarcoplasm during relaxation of the muscle is not clear at present.

MULTI-UNIT SMOOTH MUSCLE

Multi-unit muscles account for a small proportion of the smooth muscle in the body and they have not been widely studied. In fact the only one that has been investigated in any detail from several points of view is the *cat nictitating membrane*. This shows structural features that can be correlated with its physiological properties. Each muscle cell has a complete covering of basement membrane, so regions of close apposition between adjacent cells do not occur. However, the terminal branches of autonomic nerve fibres are found in close contact with the muscle cells (with no intervening basement membrane at most junctions), and multiple innervation of a cell by several axons appear to be common. The gap between adjacent muscle cells usually exceeds 0.1μ, whereas the gap between nerve and muscle cells in the junction regions may be as little as 0.007μ. These findings are what would be expected from the essential properties of a multi-unit muscle; i.e. (i) all activity is neurogenic in origin, and (ii) activity does not spread from one muscle cell to the next.

The application of a single shock to the motor nerve supply to the nictitating membrane (cervical sympathetic) produces a twitch response from the muscle, and repetitive stimulation produces a tetanus. Casual observations indicate that the mechanical response of the muscle is slow compared with skeletal muscle, but its mechanical properties have not been examined in any detail.

CHAPTER 43

THE STRUCTURE AND FUNCTION OF
CARDIAC MUSCLE

THE function of cardiac muscle is dealt with in detail in Section 3. The purpose of this short chapter is to summarize the essential properties of cardiac muscle for comparison with those of skeletal and smooth muscle.

Structure

Cardiac muscle is no longer considered to be a syncytium from the structural point of view. Although light microscope studies indicated that it consists of branching and anastomosing fibres, electron microscope studies have shown that the "fibres" are in fact columns of cells, each 10–20μ in diameter and 50–100μ in length, and that the "intercalated discs" are the closely-apposed surface membranes of adjoining cells. There is no intervening basement membrane between the adjacent cell membranes and in some regions their outer layers are fused to give a five-layered structure (as in single unit smooth muscles. Each cell has a centrally placed nucleus, but in most other respects the cells are very similar to skeletal muscle fibres. They contain myofibrils in which there are myofilaments arranged in eactly the same way as those in skeletal muscle fibres. The sarcoplasmic reticulum is also very similar, though the T-system is found at the level of the Z lines in myocardial cells, not near the A–I boundaries. The other main difference is that myocardial cells contain many more mitochondria.

Excitation

Although it is clear that the heart is not a syncytium from the structural point of view, it is certainly a *functional* syncytium. The intercalated discs contain many "tight junctions", and action potentials are thought to spread from one cell to the next by nexal-syncytial transmission (see Fig. 42.3). Cardiac muscle continues to contract rhythmically when deprived of its autonomic nerve supply because all activity in the heart is *myogenic* in origin. Action potentials are generated by pacemaker cells in the sinu-atrial node, and from there they propagate throughout the entire muscle (i.e. it behaves as a single unit). Although pacemaker activity is confined to the sinu-atrial node in the normal heart, this potentiality is present in all regions of the heart; this is demonstrated very dramatically by the "Stannius ligature" experiment, which shows that each chamber of the heart is capable of contracting spontaneously, rhythmically, and independently of the others. The rate of firing of the pacemaker is influenced by the excitatory and inhibitory nerve supplies of the heart. The cardiac action potential is peculiar in that following the peak there is a period lasting almost as long as the mechanical response during which the membrane potential remains close to zero (the "plateau"). During this period and for a short time afterwards the muscle cell membrane is in a refractory state; the practical consequence of this is that it is not possible to produce summation of mechanical responses and a tetanic contraction in cardiac muscle in the way that one can in skeletal muscle (see Fig. 41.6).

Mechanical Properties

The contractions of the intact heart are difficult to study from the mechanical point of view. However, the papillary muscles that join the chordae tendinae of the valve cusps to the inner walls of the ventricle make satisfactory preparations for this purpose. The velocity of shortening, work done, and power output all depend on the force opposing shortening in much the same way as in skeletal muscle. The relation between tension developed and the length of the muscle is also similar, though resting tension is found at shorter sarcomere lengths in cardiac muscle. The essential difference between cardiac muscle and skeletal muscle is that its performance is markedly influenced by a number of factors (e.g. neuro-humoral agents, drugs such as digitalis, interval between contractions) that have no significant effects on skeletal muscle. It has therefore been necessary to introduce the concept of "myocardial contractility" to describe the contractile state of the heart (see Chapter 8).

Energetics

The immediate source of energy for the contractile process in cardiac muscle appears to be the breakdown of ATP, and PC. Rephosphorylation is probably achieved entirely by oxidative processes. Studies of minced heart muscle have shown that its preferred substrates are lactate, pyruvate, and other substances which provide a ready source of two-carbon fragments that can be fed directly into the tricarboxylic acid cycle. The virtual dependence on oxidative processes for the resynthesis of ATP seems very reasonable in a muscle that is continuously active and therefore has little opportunity to repay an oxygen debt.

Section 13

THE REACTIONS TO INJURY

INTRODUCTION

In order to keep alive we must be in close contact with the outside world—with the air, water, food, and all kinds of solid objects which it contains. It is a matter of common knowledge that in doing so we may suffer injury. Our skins and the mucous membranes of our noses, mouths and throats may be damaged by cuts and grazes, or by excessively hot or cold materials; but for the most part, these injuries are of little consequence. Even if an injury is sufficiently deep to open a blood vessel, little real harm is done provided that the shed blood clots properly; if it does not, the loss of blood is inconvenient, to say the least, and may become so great as to be fatal. Clotting, or *coagulation*, of the blood, then, is the first of the reactions to injury which we shall consider.

The surrounding world, also, contains large numbers of micro-organisms, protozoa, bacteria, and viruses. These may enter the body through the skin and the mucous membranes, particularly if damaged; some of them become parasites, multiply in the body fluids and cause disease. The various processes by which such an invasion is opposed form the other group of reactions to injury which we shall consider. These reactions are brought into play, also, by the presence in the body fluids of different kinds of "foreign" material, many of which are not micro-organisms, or any kind of living organism, and not necessarily injurious. As a result of studying these reactions, we have learnt that each individual is not only unique in its physical structure and appearance, but also in its chemical composition: cells of one individual, if transferred to another, are treated as "foreign", potentially injurious, and destroyed. One cannot, in general, replace organs or tissues lost by one individual by those taken from another individual, although there are a few exceptions. Fortunately, the red blood cells are among these exceptions, and are less "unique" than are those of other kinds of cell; those of any individual may be placed into one or other of a small number of groups. The blood of one individual may be "compatible" with that of another, so that blood lost by one may be replaced by that of the other.

Chapter 44

THE COAGULATION OF BLOOD

WHEN a blood vessel is opened and the blood flows over the surrounding tissues, it normally sets to a jelly in the course of five to ten minutes. It is then said to have *clotted* or *coagulated*. If the clot is collected and washed free from red cells, it is found to consist of an interlacing network of fine white fibres of protein material to which the name *fibrin* is given. If a blood clot is allowed to stand, it slowly shrinks (retraction or syneraesis) and a pale yellow liquid called *serum* is squeezed out. Serum closely resembles plasma, but lacks a protein constituent which can be precipitated from plasma by half-saturation with sodium chloride. This protein is called *fibrinogen*, because it changes into fibrin during the process of clotting. If precipitated fibrinogen is redissolved in 2 per cent sodium chloride, and a little fresh serum added, a clot is formed in much the same way as it is in plasma. Fresh serum therefore contains a substance which induces fibrinogen to clot; this substance is known as *thrombin*.

Thrombin is an enzyme, and may be isolated in a moderately pure state by extracting fresh serum with alcohol, or by various other more elaborate procedures. Unclotted blood treated in the same way yields no thrombin, so that thrombin does not exist in circulating plasma, but is formed some time after the blood is shed. Plasma, therefore, must contain a substance which can change into thrombin under the proper conditions. This substance is known as prothrombin. It is ordinarily formed continuously in the liver, an adequate supply of a special vitamin (vitamin K—see p. 540) being necessary. If the supply is inadequate (owing to an inadequate diet, for example) there is partial failure of blood clotting.

There is a deficiency of vitamin K, also, when, owing to disease, the bile duct is obstructed; it is then not properly absorbed from the alimentary canal. The formation of prothrombin is impaired, as might be expected, when the liver is damaged as a result of disease or poisons such as chloroform. In all these types of inadequate liver function, however, the failure of blood clotting does not result only, or even chiefly, from an inadequate supply of prothrombin, but also from an inadequate supply of factors V and VII (see below, p. 742).

A failure of blood clotting, generally similar to that produced by inadequate liver function, is produced by administration of a substance known as *dicoumarol*. This is a derivative of the substance coumarin, which is responsible for the odour of new-mown hay; dicoumarol may be formed from it if sweet clover is improperly cured before being stacked. Animals eating this hay then develop a haemorrhagic disease.

Mechanism of Clotting

Since blood does not normally clot in the circulation, we infer that the conditions necessary for the conversion of prothrombin into thrombin, and the initiation of the process of clotting, are: (1) the contamination with tissue juices which takes place as blood flows from a wound, and (2) the contact with foreign surfaces such as the skin and the vessels in which the blood is collected. In these conditions, it appears that a substance called *thromboplastin* is released. This is most probably a second enzyme, and is present in extracts of most tissues, since the addition of such extracts to blood increases the rate of clotting. But it is derived particularly from very small cellular elements normally present in the blood, called *platelets* or *thrombocytes*. These are round or oval disc-shaped bodies, 2 to 3µ in diameter, with granular cytoplasm, but no nucleus. They are believed to be derived from large multinuclear cells of the bone marrow called mega-karyocytes. Cytoplasmic processes of these cells become pinched off and pass into the blood as platelets. Normal blood contains from 250,000 to 450,000 platelets per mm³. Within a few seconds after blood is shed its platelets agglutinate, that is, clump together, and then, more slowly, disintegrate. Consequently, in smears of normal blood the platelets are to be seen only in clumps, often consisting of as many as thirty or forty plate-lets. The clumping of platelets at the site of bleeding in small vessels tends to plug the wound in the vessel and thus helps to restrain haemorrhage; their subsequent disintegration releases thromboplastin, and so hastens blood clotting. If the early stages of clotting are observed by means of an ultra-microscope, needles of fibrin are seen to form in the immediate neighbourhood of clumps of disintegrating platelets, and to grow out from these centres until the whole of the blood is enmeshed in the network.

Agglutination and disintegration of platelets proceeds rapidly when blood is in contact with some kinds of "foreign" surface—such as glass and other substances which are wetted by blood—and only slowly if blood is shed through a cannula into a receptacle, made of a suitable plastic such as polythene, or coated with silicone or paraffin wax; these surfaces are chemically inert and are not wetted by the blood. If the platelets disinte-grate rapidly, clotting is rapid; if they remain intact for some time, clotting is delayed, but can be brought on rapidly if disintegrated platelets are added.

A further condition for the conversion of prothrombin to thrombin, and for the release of thromboplastin from the platelets, is the presence of calcium ions; if these are removed from freshly shed blood, by precipita-tion as calcium oxalate, by combination in an un-ionized state as calcium citrate, or by "chelation" with ethylene diamine tetracetate (EDTA) clotting does not occur.

It is probable that prothrombin is not converted into thrombin directly by the substance called "thromboplastin" (also known as *thrombokinase*); and the thromboplastin of tissue extracts is probably not identical with that of the platelets (at one time called *cytozyme*). The name "prothrombinase" has been given to the substance derived from tissue extracts which is responsible for the formation of thrombin; it has not been established that this same substance appears in the platelets in the absence of tissue extracts. This, however, does not affect the essential nature of the sequence of reactions which brings about clotting.

The process of blood clotting, then, may be regarded as resulting primarily from the interaction of three substances normally present in the blood—fibrinogen, prothrombin and calcium ions—with a fourth substance—thromboplastin—released from the platelets as a result of their disintegration. This release, moreover, is accelerated by the presence of thrombin, which thus indirectly accelerates its own formation from pro-thrombin; the reaction sequence is autocatalytic, and once started, proceeds at a progressively increasing rate. This accounts for the fact that even in the presence of all the factors necessary for clotting, there is a delay of several minutes before any change occurs, and then there is a rapid appearance of the clot. The whole reaction sequence is summarized, schematically, in Table 41.1.

TABLE 44.1

The Clotting of the Blood

Precursor (in liver)

(vitamin K)

Prothrombin (in blood)   Platelets (in blood)

⎡Damaged⎤ (Foreign   ⎸(Ca⁺⁺)
⎣Tissues ⎦ Surfaces) ⎸(Thrombin)

Thromboplastin

(Thromboplastin)

Prothrombin ⎯⎯⎯⎯⎯→ Thrombin
(Ca⁺⁺)

(Thrombin)

Fibrinogen ⎯⎯⎯⎯⎯→ Fibrin
(in blood)   (clot)

The fact that the circulating blood does not clot spontaneously and continuously may be very reasonably attributed to the stability of the platelets, and the consequent failure of prothrombin to be converted into thrombin. But there is good reason to believe that there is a second line of defence in the presence of naturally occurring anti-coagulant substances, the most important of which is *heparin*. This acts both in preventing the formation of thrombin from prothrombin, and in antagonizing the action of thrombin on fibrinogen. Heparin was originally isolated from the liver (hence the name), but was later shown to be contained particularly in the mast cells of the reticulo-endothelial system (see p. 747 & 749). These cells are present in considerable numbers in the connective tissue which surrounds the small blood vessels, and it is possible that they release heparin into the blood stream.

Prevention of Clotting

Shed blood can be preserved in the fluid state in the following ways:

(1) By defibrination. The blood while clotting is stirred with some object, e.g. a bundle of feathers—to which fibrin will adhere. The fibrin is thus removed as it forms and the red cells are left suspended in serum.

(2) By precipitating the calcium by the addition of sodium or potassium oxalate (0·1 to 0·3 per cent).

(3) By removing calcium ions by the addition of sodium citrate (0·2 to 0·4 per cent), fluoride or EDTA. Since calcium ions are necessary not only for the change of prothrombin to thrombin, but for the disintegration of platelets, oxalate and citrate solutions can be used to preserve platelets intact.

(4) By cooling the blood to 0°C, which retards clotting almost indefinitely and preserves the platelets.

(5) By preserving blood from contact with surfaces which it wets.

(6) By the addition of heparin.

(7) By the addition of certain azo dyes, e.g. chlorazol fast pink, which are thought to act partly as antithromboplastins.

(8) By the addition of hirudin, a material obtained from leech heads which acts as an antithrombin.

(9) By the addition of suitable concentrations of amost any neutral salt, e.g. one-seventh saturation with $MgSO_4$.

Blood clotting is of great value when localized near bleeding points due to injury or surgery. If, however, clots become detached from such points, or arise spontaneously, and travel as emboli in the blood circulation, they become a great danger. Often they lodge in the lungs (pulmonary embolism). Moreover, clots may form in diseased blood vessels and by blocking them, may impair vital functions, as in coronary thrombosis or cerebral thrombosis. In embolism or thrombosis, dicoumarol or more commonly synthetic anticoagulants are administered. When blood is passed through external apparatus and back into the body, as in many kinds of physiological experiment on animals, or when an "artificial heart" is used to maintain the patient's circulation during operations on the heart, clotting is likely to be initiated by the materials used in the apparatus. In these circumstances, heparin is injected to prevent the undesirable clotting.

Blood withdrawn from a donor, for subsequent transfusion to a patient who needs it, is ordinarily prevented from clotting by the use of citrate, heparin being relatively expensive. Citrate, however, cannot be used to prevent clotting in the whole of the blood in the circulation, since the complete removal of calcium ions would have disastrous effects on a great many of the bodily functions. It may be desirable, on the other hand, to promote clotting in order to check haemorrhage when blood vessels have been opened during surgery or as a result of accident; it is usually suffici- ent to provide a large area of "foreign" surface by applying a swab of cotton, but in severe cases the swab may be soaked in a solution of thrombin. Certain surgical procedures involve the use of a gelatin sponge for this purpose, having the advantage that it is subsequently re-sorbed and can be left *in situ*.

Haemophilia

The problem of checking haemorrhage may become really serious in certain persons, known as "bleeders", who suffer from an inborn disease in which blood clotting is so slow that haemorrhage from a relatively trivial wound may be profuse enough to be dangerous. *Haemophilia* is an hereditary defect which is manifested almost exclusively in males, but inherited through the mother. A person suffering from this disease—or more strictly, group of diseases—is found to lack none of the primary components of the clotting reactions (as summarized in Table 44.1). Detailed study of these reactions, however, and progressive purification of the known components, both in normal blood and in the bloods of haemophilic subjects, has revealed the existence of several additional *"factors"* which must be presumed to take part in the formation of thrombo- plastin and in the conversion of prothrombin to thrombin. These "factors" appear, ordinarily, to be associated with the globulin fractions of the plasma proteins, and it is not easy to demonstrate their presence. The haemophilias result from genetic deficiencies, such that one or other of these factors is not synthesized, and the clotting reactions do not proceed as they should.

Additional Clotting Factors

At least six of these additional factors have been described, and there may be more, since the nomenclature has been extremely confused, and the problem is complicated by the presence of anti-coagulants and inhibitors which oppose their actions. They have been identified by means of the Roman numerals from V upwards, with the exception of VI (given originally to a factor which was later found not to have a separate existence); the first four—and the most important— factors are those substances already recognized as essential for blood clotting, and given in Table 44.1. Many names have also been given to them describing their origins and supposed functions. Factor V is labile, disappears from oxalated plasma on storage in a refrigerator, and is consumed when fresh plasma clots. Factor VII, on the other hand, appears or becomes activated, when plasma clots, and thus accentuates the autocatalytic nature of the whole process. Factors V and VII were discovered in normal blood by means of these and other specific properties: they are necessary, in addition to tissue extracts and calcium ions, for the formation of thrombin from prothrombin.

Other factors have been discovered by study of the haemophilias, the commonest of which is known as "true haemophilia" or "haemophilia A", and others are known by the names of the patients who were first found to be deficient in factors not previously recognized. To give two examples only, it has been found that factor VIII is lacking in patients with "true" haemophilia, and factor IX is lacking in patients with a type of haemophilia first observed in a man with the name of Christmas (it is thus called the "Christmas factor"). Factor V and factors VIII and IX must be present, in addition to calcium ions, for the formation of thromboplastin from the platelets.

Blood clotting may be defective, also, owing to a reduction in the number of platelets in the blood (*thrombocytopenia*), or, very rarely, owing to a lack of fibrinogen. These deficiencies may be congenital, or may result from disease.

Measurements of Clotting Time

The clotting time of normal blood may vary from four to sixty minutes, depending on the method used to measure it. To get consistent results, the following conditions must be controlled: (1) *Temperature.* Clotting time increases as the temperature decreases. (2) *The manner of obtaining the blood.* Blood drawn from a vein clots more slowly than blood from a skin puncture, which allows more contamination by tissue juices. (3) *Agitation of the blood.* Agitation hastens clotting. (4) *Cleanliness of apparatus.* The cleaner the apparatus, the slower the clotting.

A simple method is to collect a few drops of blood from a puncture in the lobe of the ear on a clean watch glass, which is then covered by another watch glass to limit evaporation. The fluidity of the drop is tested from time to time by gently tipping the watch glass. The time from the shedding of the blood till the first signs of clotting appear under these conditions is about 4 to 8 min at 20°C, for normal human blood.

Detection of abnormalities in the clotting reactions starts by the use of such simple procedures. But if clotting is found to be abnormally slow, more elaborate procedures must be used in order to establish the nature of the defect.

The Dale-Laidlaw apparatus consists of a short glass capillary whose ends are partly sealed to retain a small lead shot. Blood, introduced by capillarity, fills the tube which is then rocked to and fro at intervals. The shot ceases to move when clotting occurs and provides an accurate end-point. Normal clotting times with this method range from 5–15 minutes.

Bleeding Time

Blood loss is also controlled by a mechanism involving the contraction of vessel walls. A ragged tear of a blood vessel (as opposed to a clean, sharp incision) stimulates its smooth muscle directly and the opened end is completely or partially closed off. Capillary bleeding is controlled in this way very rapidly and as a rule the haemorrhage is arrested well before clotting has had time to be effective. Even in haemophiliacs, in the absence of clotting, haemorrhage from *small* vessels is rarely dangerous.

The bleeding time is measured by making a small (standard) incision into the skin of a finger, continuously blotting the resultant drop of blood with a filter paper, until the bleeding stops. The normal bleeding time is 2 to 5 min.

Prothrombin Time

It is useful to know the amount of prothrombin in the blood, and there is a well-defined relationship between prothrombin *concentration* and the prothrombin *time*. The latter is found experimentally by immediately treating a sample of the patient's blood with oxalate to prevent conversion of any prothrombin into thrombin (see p. 739). An excess of calcium ions and tissue extract is mixed with the oxalated blood and the time from mixing to coagulation is measured. This is the prothrombin time, the precise value depending on the conditions of the test, being usually about 10–15 sec.

Thrombosis and Embolism

A clot, formed abnormally in any blood vessel is termed a *thrombus*. If such a clot is friable, or occurs in a site where the blood-flow past it is able to break off parts of it, these *emboli* are carried in the circulation until they lodge in a narrow part of the system, usually blocking the vessel as a result. For instance, emboli formed as a result of a clot in the great veins or the right side of the heart, pass into the lung causing "*pulmonary embolism*". These thrombi are usually started in two ways. The intimal lining of the heart or the vascular system becomes "rough" as a result of disease (atherosclerosis, infection or trauma) thus triggering the deposition of platelets at the site, followed by the formation of a clot as already described. When blood is stagnant (*stasis*) the minute quantities of thrombin always being formed reach a local concentration high enough to start the clotting process.

An example of the first mechanism is *coronary thrombosis* where platelet and fibrin deposits gradually narrow the lumen of the coronary artery or one of its branches. Eventually, the vessel suddenly collapses and the ventricular muscle is deprived of its blood supply—often with fatal results.

The second mechanism occurs as a result of blockage of blood flow in any part of the body. It is seen commonly in bedridden patients (often after abdominal surgery or parturition) when the legs are immobilized or kept in the flexed position for long periods of time. Large clots can then occur during the course of an hour or two with the considerable risk that they will be carried to the heart and then to the pulmonary arteries, blocking them. If both arteries are blocked, death is immediate unless "*pulmonary embolectomy*" (clot removal) can be carried out in the operating theatre. Smaller clots may occlude only part of a lobe of the lung and a clinical picture of pain, difficulty in breathing and coughing blood (*haemoptysis*) ensues.

Anticoagulants

The injection of 1 mg/Kg (patient's body weight) of heparin prolongs the clotting time to about ten times the normal value, having an action lasting for four or five hours. It is destroyed by an enzyme called *heparinase*. Overdosage of heparin, as revealed by massive, uncontrollable haemorrhages, can be neutralized by giving *anti-heparins* (e.g. protamine or hexadimethrine bromide)—substances which combine with heparin, inactivating it.

Heparin is used in clinical practice for the prevention of clotting when the patient is being maintained on kidney machines or heart lung machines.

Synthetic anticoagulants, such as dicoumarol, having a longer action than heparin, are used in cases of arterial or venous thrombosis where the prolonged depression of the ability of the blood to clot is required. They act by competing with Vitamin K, in the prothrombin formation system.

Chapter 45

DEFENCE REACTIONS

Disease

The study of disease processes is relevant in the consideration of the normal physiological working of the body. The basic reactions to various types of injury, infection or deficiency are themselves physiological; moreover the changes brought about by diseases often help to reveal the true nature of physiological mechanisms.

We may, for the purposes of this book, consider *disease* to be a departure from the normal in the functions and/or structure of some part of the body. These departures may be due to *congenital* (inborn) causes, to *trauma* (physical injury), to *deficiency* (nutritional, metabolic or due to the malfunction of endocrines), to *infection* with micro-organisms and to *poisoning*. In most of these instances, damage occurs to the cells of the body; their function is impaired, they may die or the affected cells may recover.

Inflammation

Cells, comprising living tissue, when acted upon by noxious influences in their environment, react in a specific manner. As we go higher in the phylogenetic scale we see that this reaction becomes more complex and that complicated mechanisms have been developed in order to combat the injury.

This reaction to injury is called *inflammation* and is an integral part of the majority of diseases. It may be rapid in its evolution, i.e. *acute*, or it may be of slower or continuous development, i.e. *chronic*. The ingress of micro-organisms into tissues, particularly when these are *pathogenic* (i.e. cause disease) must be countered and the organisms destroyed or removed; in addition the injury caused by them must be repaired. Thus the natural history of the inflammatory process involves two distinct, but related parts, the *defence reaction* and *repair*.

The changes occurring in inflammation can easily be studied under the microscope and varied as this reaction is, the main features of the process are constant and it is generally believed that the way in which infection is overcome is fundamentally similar in very many diseases.

Localization

Successful resistance to infection entails that it must be localized—if the distribution of the infecting agent is widespread, the risk to life is increased.

It is usual for the infection to be "walled off" by a fibrin barrier formed in lymphatics and in interstitial spaces (much like a blood clot).

This barrier can be demonstrated experimentally by observation of its formation under the microscope or by injecting trypan blue (*a*) into the region when it remains there or (*b*) into the surrounding tissues when it fails to penetrate into the area.

Antibodies also accumulate in the infected area. The response of the tissues depends markedly upon the nature of the infecting organism. Some bacteria characteristically cause spreading infections and it can be shown that these do not elicit the rapid production of fibrin in the tissues. For example the *streptococcus* releases an enzyme, *fibrinolysin*, which is responsible for the delay in formation of the fibrin barrier.

Leukotaxine

Inflammation is characterized by capillary dilatation, increased capillary permeability leading to fluid exudation and the emigration of leucocytes into the tissue spaces. The stimulus leading to these events is thought to be the release, by the noxious agent, of a polypeptide called *leucotaxine*. Histamine has similar effects to this substance but can be separated from it in terms of other pharmacological actions. The "triple response" produced by mechanical or chemical injury to the skin (Chapter 7, p. 94) results largely from the action of histamine, or histamine-like substances and may be regarded as the basic reaction also underlying the inflammatory reaction. The mast cells of the reticulo-endothelial system, and basophil leucocytes contain a precursor of histamine and may well be the main source of the histamine released in tissues damaged by wounds or by bacterial toxins. It is, however, agreed that the major factor involved in the chemotaxis of leucocytes is a substance other than histamine itself.

REACTIONS TO "FOREIGN" MATERIALS IN THE BODY FLUIDS

When "foreign" or abnormal substances or living organisms enter the body, they are removed, and any deleterious actions produced are opposed, by a number of processes which are often referred collectively to as "defence reactions". Particulate matter, whether living or dead, is removed by absorption (*phagocytosis*) in certain kinds of *leucocyte*, which circulate in the blood, and in certain tissue cells belonging to the *reticulo-endothelial system*. Certain substances, usually but not necessarily associated with, or derived from, "foreign" organisms, react in various ways with substances already present in the body fluids of the animal or person invaded (or specially formed in response to the invasion), the reactions being of an unusual nature and called "immunity reactions"; they were first studied in connection with the fact that after a person has recovered from certain kinds of disease, he may subsequently be unharmed by—or immune to—further attacks by the particular micro-organism which causes the disease.

White Cells or Leucocytes

These are usually classified into three groups: the granular cells (sometimes called *Polymorphs*, but now often called *Granulocytes*), the *Lymphocytes* and the *Monocytes*.

The *Granulocytes* are called "polymorphs" (polymorphonuclear leucocytes) because in stained smears of blood their nuclei are seen to be divided into two, three or four lobes by deep indentations. They are sub-divided, according to the staining reactions of their granules, into:

Neutrophils, with very fine cytoplasmic granules, showing no striking affinity for acidic or basic stains (the name "polymorph" is often restricted to this group of granulocytes);

Eosinophils, with very coarse granules, stained bright red by eosin, the nucleus being nearly always bi-lobed; and

Basophils, with coarse granules having an affinity for basic dyes and hence stained blue by the stains commonly used for blood.

The red bone marrow is the normal site of production of granulocytes and in it can be recognized immature granular cells in two developmental stages. The younger are known as myeloblasts and the older as myelocytes. Myeloblasts have no granules, but myelocytes have granules in which the tendency to become eosinophilic, basophilic or neutrophilic can be easily seen. The nuclei of the myelocytes, however, are only slightly indented. These immature forms of granular blood cells may appear in the circulating blood in blood diseases, called *leukaemias*.

The *Lymphocytes* of normal blood are the smallest of the white blood cells, the small forms having about the same diameter as a red cell. They are characterized by an almost round, densely staining nucleus surrounded by a narrow zone of cytoplasm free from granules. The lymphocytes are produced in the lymphoid tissue from larger cells with pale nuclei.

The *Monocytes* (*transitional cells* or *large mononuclears*) have large oval or bean-shaped nuclei; both nuclei and cytoplasm are pale staining.

Normal human blood contains 5,000 to 10,000 leucocytes per mm^3. When the number is lower than normal, a state of *leucopenia* is said to exist—as, for example, in typhoid and influenza. Most general infections, on the other hand, are accompanied by a striking increase in the number of circulating leucocytes, a condition known as *leucocytosis*.

The White Cell Count

The number of leucocytes per cubic millimetre of blood (the *White Cell Count*) is estimated in the *haemocytometer* in much the same way as is that of the red blood cells (see Chapter 10, p. 134). The blood is diluted 20-fold, in a special pipette, with a fluid which contains acetic acid to dissolve the red cells, and suitable stains for the white cells. A drop of the suspension so formed is placed on the special microscope slide, forming a layer exactly 1/10 mm deep. When the cells have settled, the number lying within a square 1/16 mm^2 in area is counted. These squares are formed by lines ruled at the corners of the area containing the much smaller squares used for the red cell count. Several counts are made, and the average count is multiplied by 160 (the cells counted came from 1/160 mm³ of suspension) and by 20 (the dilution factor) to give the number of cells per cubic millimetre of the original blood.

The estimation of the proportion of each type of leucocyte in a particular sample of blood can be done on any properly stained blood smear, and is known as the *Differential White Count*, approximate values for normal human blood being:

$$
\left.
\begin{array}{l}
\text{Granulocytes} \left\{
\begin{array}{ll}
\text{Neutrophils, 70 per cent} \\
\text{Eosinophils,} \quad 1 \ \ ,, \ \ ,, \\
\text{Basophils,} \quad \ 0{\cdot}5,, \ \ ,,
\end{array}
\right. \\
\text{Lymphocytes} \qquad \quad \ 24 \ \ ,, \ \ ,, \\
\text{Monocytes} \qquad \qquad \ \ 4 \ \ ,, \ \ ,,
\end{array}
\right\}
\begin{array}{l}
\text{Of total white} \\
\text{cell count.}
\end{array}
$$

The leucocytes are motile, and can creep over surfaces and make their way out of the blood into the tissue fluids, through interstices in the blood vessels. The lymphocytes, in particular, circulate from the blood stream into the tissue spaces, whence they are carried to the lymph nodes with the lymph, and then back again into the blood stream by way of the thoracic duct.

The Reticulo-endothelial System

The loose, or reticular, connective tissue which surrounds the blood vessels, for example, and provides support and attachments for the abdominal organs, contains, besides the fibroblasts which are responsible for the reticular structure, other kinds of cell called mast cells, plasma cells and macrophages. The same, or very similar, kinds of cell are found in the endothelial lining of the sinusoids of the liver, spleen and bone marrow, and in the lymph glands. These cells, in their various locations, constitute the "*reticulo-endothelial system*", and they are closely related to the leucocytes of the blood. The whole subject is very confused, but it is thought that the basophil leucocytes may well be identical with the mast cells of the reticulo-endothelial system; and lymphocytes seem, in certain conditions, to develop into macrophages, with monocytes perhaps as intermediate stages.

Phagocytosis

The most important of the cells which ingest bacteria and other foreign particles, living or dead, are the macrophages of the reticulo-endothelial system. When dyes, such as trypan blue or lithium carmine, or particulate matter such as indian ink, are injected intravenously, they are taken up for the most part by these macrophages, particularly by those in the liver known as Kupffer cells. When there has been a local invasion of bacteria, as in an infected wound of the skin, there is a great accumulation of neutrophil granulocytes (polymorphs), which leave the blood stream in the infected region, ingest the bacteria, and release proteolytic enzymes—perhaps as a result of their own disintegration; these enzymes break down cells which have been killed by the infection. The liquid known as pus is made up of these broken down cells, together with the remains of the leucocytes, and possibly some erythrocytes; it is sealed off from the body fluids in general by the proliferation of fibroblasts, which form the scar tissue.

IMMUNE REACTIONS

Foreign substances, when introduced into the body, act as *antigens*, and lead to the development of *antibodies*, which react with them in various ways. If the antigen is a protein in solution—such as a serum protein of a different kind of animal—the antibody which is formed precipitates the antigen, a reaction which can be easily observed in a test-tube; the antibody is thus termed a *precipitin*. Antigens, however, may also be present on, or released by, living cells such as bacteria or red blood cells. The corresponding antibody will then: (*a*) make these cells stick together in clumps, or agglutinate, when it is called an *agglutin*; or (*b*) lead to their destruction or lysis, when it is called a *lysin* (or more specifically, for example, a *bacteriolysin* or a *haemolysin*); or (*c*) neutralize the poisonous (toxic) effects of the substances released by bacteria, when it is called an *antitoxin*. Antibodies of all kinds seem to be produced chiefly by lymphocytes; but at the site of an infection there is a great accumulation of eosinophil granulocytes, and these also may play some part in the antigen-antibody reactions.

The antigen-antibody reactions are highly specific, most kinds of antibody reacting only with one particular kind of antigen; serum proteins from different species, which cannot be distinguished by chemical methods, can be distinguished by the way they react with an antibody prepared against one of them.

It is the presence of the antibodies formed in response to an invasion of bacteria, or other micro-organisms, which is responsible for the subsequent failure of further infection to produce the disease—an immunity which may last for many years. Many of these antibodies can be prepared artificially, or the animal or man can be induced to develop them itself without having to undergo the full rigours of an actual attack of the disease; their study has consequently become an important part of medical science, known as *Immunology*.

Antibody Formation

Antigenic substances trigger the division of the lymphocytes which give rise to appropriate antibodies. It is this ability of the body to produce an unlimited selection of these molecules which is responsible for the resistance to disease. The main antibody molecules found in the circulation are the gamma globulins, of which there are more than 10,000 different kinds, although they all have similar structural properties and a molecular weight of 150,000. They are made up from a long chain of amino acids and it is the sequence in which the various acids are arranged that leads to the infinite variety of antibodies which are found.

Each gamma globulin molecule consists of four sub-unit polypeptide

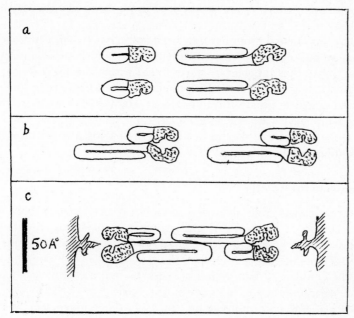

FIG. 45.1. Gamma globulin antibody molecules consist of four polypeptides, 2 L-chains and 2 H-chains (a). These form half-molecules
(b) which combine to form the whole structure of the antibody (c).

The white parts are identical and are the linking portion of the
molecule; the stippled parts are the folded regions, having variable
amino acid sequences, which form zones interacting with and inactivating the antigen.

chains (Fig. 45.1). Two are the same and have a molecular weight of 25,000; these are the light or L-chains. The remaining two are of double the molecular weight and are the heavy or H-chains. The L- and H-chains are folded in a way enabling them to interact to give half-molecules which in turn combine forming the complete gamma globulin molecule. Part of the chain structure keeps the whole molecule together, whilst the remainder is available for folding into different shapes which dovetail into, and interact with, a specific antigen to inactivate it.

Where Do Antibodies Originate?

The *Clonal Selection* theory of the immune response was originated by Macfarlane Burnet. It is based on the idea that when certain cells having the property of antibody synthesis meet antigen, they multiply forming specific colonies (*clones*) of cells manufacturing the specific antibody.

The *Instructional* theory supposes that each of the antibody-forming cells contains the antigen, which then behaves like a "template" from which antibody molecules are synthesized to fit, much like the way a lock and key do.

Direct experimental proof has now been found by Nossal, that the clonal selection process occurs *in vivo* when lymphocytes respond to antigens. It was first shown that antigens are never found within the antibody-forming cells. Later, using a new method for the detection of marker chromosomes in isolated, single, antibody-forming cells he established that non-antibody-forming lymphocytes are able to stimulate the initiation of *germinal centres*, acting as sources of long-lasting memory cells having a specific reactivity for an antigen, when this is injected.

Antigen-sensitive Cells

The antigen itself first acts on a special target cell of lymphoid origin termed the *antigen-sensitive* cell. Only about 1 in 20,000 to 1 in 50,000 of the population of lymphoid cells exposed to antigen respond in this way. If two distinct antigens are applied, the total number of responding cells is exactly doubled, a fact which appears to indicate that each antigen affects a separate group of antigen-sensitive cells.

Following antigenic stimulation, each of the antigen-sensitive cells divides sequentially about eight or nine times (mitotically) producing a clone of progeny. During the first day or two these daughter cells remain close together and form a recognizable antibody-forming focus.

By using a highly immunogenic protein, flagellin (prepared from *Salmonella typhi*) labelled with radio-iodine, the distribution and fate of injected antigen can be followed in detail. Two types of antigen capture occur in the lymph nodes as revealed by electron micrographic autoradiographs. In the medullary part of the node, macrophages ingest the antigen into a vacuole and it then becomes enclosed in a membrane to form a lyzosomal structure. In the cortical region, the antigen is trapped in lymphoid follicles, and following this, lymphoblast cells make their appearance in the form of typical germinal centres. Such a germinal centre created by the trapping of an antigen is still capable of dealing with other unrelated antigenic materials in the same way, so that it appears that one centre can manufacture a number of different strains of memory cell for different antigens, simultaneously.

Lymphocytic Transformation

Micromanipulation methods and the examination of marker chromosomes, so that labelled lymphocytes in an injected dose can be traced, have shown that donor lymphocytes eventually turn into large plasma blast cells which produce the antibody molecules.

SUMMARY OF THE BASIC FEATURES OF THE IMMUNE RESPONSE

(1) The antigen–antibody reaction is specific, and is due to chemical groups on the antigenic molecule, especially polar groups.

(2) The number of antibody molecules produced very greatly exceeds the number of antigenic molecules introduced into the body.

(3) A *second* dose of antigen evokes a larger and faster antibody response, than did the first. This can be considered as a type of memory and is termed the *anamnestic response.*

(4) When antigens are introduced at an early stage in the individual's development, the immune response is absent or small. This is called immunological tolerance.

(5) The immune response, in normal conditions, is to foreign molecules. The body can distinguish between "non-self" and "self". *Auto-immune diseases* occur when this recognition of self-markers breaks down and an immune response develops to an individual's own cells.

Immunosuppression can be artificially induced with drugs such as azathioprine (Imuran) or X-irradiation, and consists in a damping down of the normal development of immunity.

Complement

Suppose a specific haemolysin has been produced in one animal by repeated injections of the red cells of another animal; if serum containing the specific haemolysin is heated to 56°C its haemolytic power is lost. The addition of fresh serum from almost any normal animal, however, restores the haemolytic power. Since the added normal serum would not, by itself, have haemolysed red cells, it is evident that two factors are concerned in this type of haemolysis, (1) a specific antibody which is stable to heat (thermostable), and (2) a non-specific factor which is destroyed by heat (thermolabile), known as the *complement*; this is present in any normal serum. Red cells which have been treated with *heated* serum (containing the antibody which would have haemolysed them if the complement had not been destroyed) are said to be sensitized, because, if they are introduced into a solution containing the complement, haemolysis follows immediately.

Not all types of reaction between antibodies and antigens require complement for their completion, but nearly all antigen-antibody compounds have the property of absorbing complement, and thus making it inactive or *fixed.* Complement fixation can be used as a test for the presence of either antibody or antigen. The most famous of these complement-fixation tests is the *Wassermann reaction*, which is a test for the presence of the syphilitic antibody in the blood of a patient suspected of suffering from syphilis. A standard amount of antigen and a standard amount of complement are added to the heated serum of the patient. If the syphilitic antibody is present, it reacts with the antigen; complement is fixed, and sensitized red cells added subsequently are not haemolysed. Curiously enough, the standard antigen used in the Wassermann test has nothing to do with syphilis, but is prepared from an alcoholic extract of heart muscle. Presumably this empirical antigen, unexpectedly discovered in the course of controls on the Wassermann reaction, has the same chemical configuration as some antigen in the causal organism of syphilis, for exhaustive tests have only confirmed the usefulness of the reaction in the diagnosis of syphilis.

Anaphylactic Shock

If a single injection of an antigen is followed after an interval of about 10 to 14 days by an injection of a second dose of the same antigen, the consequence is a profound, and often fatal, collapse, due to a very low blood pressure resulting from dilatation and increased permeability of the capillaries; in some animals, asphyxia is induced by intense constriction of the bronchi. The first dose of the antigen clearly rendered the animal hypersensitive, instead of immune, the hypersensitivity being associated with a *low* content of antibodies in the blood. A widely supported view of the mechanism of anaphylactic shock supposes that the free circulating antibodies due to the first injection are sufficient to "neutralize" only a part of the second dose of antigen; the remainder of the antigen reacts with antibodies which are attached to tissue cells. This reaction damages the tissue cells in some way, leading to the production of histamine, which is known to produce, when injected intravenously, a train of events very like anaphylactic shock. If the animal in the hypersensitive state is given a series of injections of the antigen, each too small to produce shock, it will, in time, become desensitized, presumably because an adequate supply of circulating antibodies is developed.

On rare occasions a condition resembling anaphylactic shock results from an intravenous injection of an antitoxin. This is usually due to the patient being hypersensitive to the horse serum from which most antitoxins are prepared.

Allergy

There is a mild type of anaphylactic response, with much less violent manifestations of hypersensitivity, known as an "allergic reaction". This may follow the consumption of mussels, lobsters, strawberries or several common foodstuffs by certain persons who are said to be "sensitive"; or it may follow contact of the skin or mucous membranes of the respiratory passages with the pollen of certain grasses (in "hay fever"), the hairs of certain animals, or even the close presence of these animals. The nature of the reactions produced depend on the nature of the antigen (or "allergen"), and may vary considerably from one person to another. Characteristic reactions are nettle-rash and urticaria—i.e., the eruption of wheals on the skin; congestion and excessive irritability of the mucous membranes of the nose and pharynx; and constriction of the bronchioles, producing asthma (Chapter 12, p. 166).

CHAPTER 46

THE BLOOD GROUPS

IT is well known that the effects of severe loss of blood are usually best countered by transfusion of blood from another individual. Early attempts at such transfusion often had disastrous results, owing to the fact that the injected red cells may clump together (*agglutinate*) in large masses which block certain of the capillaries in the body (Fig. 46.1); the cells then haemolyse, and the liberated haemoglobin is in part converted to bilirubin, with consequent jaundice, and in part excreted by the kidneys; the secretion of urine is impaired, or may even stop. When such effects follow the transfusion, the blood of the donor is said to be *incompatible* with that of the recipient. This incompatibility was explained when it was discovered that human serum may contain antibodies which act on the red cells of certain other individuals, making them stick together (agglutinins) or break up (lysins); these are termed "naturally occurring" antibodies, since they have not been formed in response to the presence of known antigens. To be susceptible to the agglutinins, the red cells must contain agglutinogens (i.e. antigens) with which the agglutinins react. The experimental facts were found to be explicable by the hypothesis that two kinds of agglutinogen, A and B, are to be found in human red cells. In some bloods the red cells contain agglutinogen A, in others they contain B, in others both A and B together, and in still others they contain neither. Thus blood can be classified into four groups according as their cells contain the agglutinogens, A, B, AB or O. Similarly, it is postulated that there are in human sera two agglutinins, α and β, which react respectively with agglutinogens A and B. Obviously, in any normal blood, the corresponding agglutinins and agglutinogens which would react with each other cannot be present at the same time. Consequently, only in O blood are α and β agglutinins to be found together. In A blood only β agglutinin is present, in B blood only α, while in AB blood neither α nor β is present.

The blood of a particular man can be easily assigned to its proper group if samples of serum from blood of groups A and B are available as is indicated in Fig. 46.1, which shows the effect of serum from each group on cells of each of the other groups. In blood transfusion it is always desirable to use a donor of the same group as the recipient, but in emergency it is considered allowable to use any donor whose cells are not agglutinated by the serum of the recipient. The donor's cells are exposed to the full effect of the recipient's serum, whereas the donor's serum is diluted by the greater volume of the recipient's blood, and hence is not likely to harm the recipient's cells. As can be seen in Fig. 46.1, cells of group O are not agglutinated by any type of serum; people with blood of group O are thus called *universal donors*. Similarly, serum from group AB will not agglutinate cells of any group; people with blood of group AB are thus called *universal recipients*.

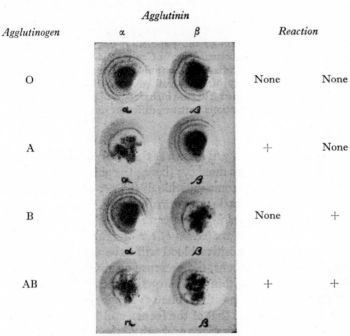

Agglutinogen	Agglutinin		Reaction	
	α	β		
O			None	None
A			+	None
B			None	+
AB			+	+

FIG. 46.1. The Agglutination of Red Blood Corpuscles, and the Four Blood Groups in Man.

Four large drops of serum of group B (containing agglutinin α) and four large drops of serum of group A (containing agglutinin β) were placed on the slide. To each of the top two drops was added a small drop of blood of group O; to the second two, a drop of blood of group A; to the third two, a drop of blood of group B; and to the bottom two, a drop of blood of group AB. Agglutination only occurred when the agglutinogens on the corpuscles met the corresponding agglutinins in the serum. (Lattes' "Individuality of the Blood".)

More detailed and extensive studies of blood groups have shown that the matter is much more elaborate and complicated than was at first thought. Agglutinogen A consists of two parts or varieties A_1 and A_2; and there may be agglutinogens on human red cells which may be classified into at least ten groups or systems, in addition to the ABO system, and to which identifying letters and names have been given. These are of little consequence in transfusion, since normal human sera rarely contain the corresponding agglutinins; they are responsible, however, for the fact that on rare occasions two bloods are found to be unexpectedly incompatible.

Blood groups are inherited according to Mendelian laws, the presence of each of the agglutinogens on the red cells being decided by the presence of a certain gene in the chromosomes of the individual concerned (compare Chapter 37., p. 631). They may thus be of practical value in proving non-paternity, in law suits concerning the paternity of illegitimate children. The chance of getting positive evidence is increased by the fact that all the agglutinogens—those which are of little importance in transfusion as well as those of the ABO group—are inherited, and their presence can be detected by appropriate immunological tests. The blood groups, indeed, are of considerable interest and importance in the study of human genetics.

Different races of people tend to have different blood groups. In the people of western and north-western Europe, for example, groups A and O are the most common, and the proportion of the population who are of group A becomes smaller as we proceed east across Asia; in Central Asia and India, group B is the most common, while the Indians of Central and South America may be almost entirely of group O. Study of the blood groups, therefore, particularly when those of the systems other than ABO are included, is of great value in anthropology, indicating possible inter-relations between different races of mankind.

Rhesus factors

The group of agglutinogens known as the *Rh factors* were first discovered on the red cells of Rhesus monkeys (hence the abbreviation), but they also occur on human cells in some individuals (85 per cent of Europeans). The corresponding agglutinins do not normally occur, even in the 15 per cent of Rh negative persons. *Injection of Rh positive blood into a Rh negative person will, however, lead to the production of the agglutinins.* A later transfusion, therefore, of more Rh positive blood will have serious consequences. As with the other agglutinogens, the presence or absence of the Rh factors is inherited. The foetus within a Rh negative mother may, by inheritance from the father, be Rh positive. The agglutinins are then formed in the mother's blood, pass into that of the foetus, and lead to destruction of the red cells, and usually miscarriage or death of the infant shortly after birth. The only remedy is to remove the agglutinins by complete replacement of the infant's blood with that from a normal person.

It is thus advisable before transfusion to test directly the donor's cells against the recipient's serum, and the recipient's cells against the donor's serum, a procedure known as the *cross agglutination* test. This is a precaution not only against errors in grouping, but also tests for the presence of the Rh factors and of the other agglutinins which may occasionally be present.

Rouleaux Formation and Sedimentation Velocity

Red blood corpuscles in plasma nearly always show a tendency to come together with their broad surfaces in apposition, thus forming aggregates which look like rolls of coins and hence have been named *rouleaux*. In practice it is never difficult to distinguish these orderly rouleaux of ten or twenty cells from the disorderly clumps of thousands of cells found in the agglutination reactions. The tendency to form rouleaux varies among different individuals and different species, and largely determines the suspension stability of the blood, i.e. the time required for the red cells to sediment down completely in blood (made incoagulable) which is allowed to stand. This is due to the fact that the rate at which a system of suspended particles settles increases with the size of the particles, other factors remaining constant. The formation of rouleaux may be regarded as a mild, and reversible, kind of agglutination; it occurs more readily when the concentration of fibrinogen or globulin in the plasma is increased, and it may be related to the presence of antibodies and to the occurrence of immunity reactions. An increased sedimentation velocity has been observed to accompany most inflammatory diseases, and also to accompany pregnancy; its measurement, therefore, is of diagnostic interest.

Sedimentation sometimes occurs so rapidly that a clear layer of plasma is left before coagulation begins; the clot is thus partly free from corpuscles and forms what is known as the *buffy coat* on the surface of the corpuscular mass. This fact has been known since the days of the Greeks, and very largely formed the basis of the practice of blood-letting as a cure for all diseases. It was thought that the buffy coat was formed by the foul matter in the blood that was responsible for the disease; the more blood one could remove, therefore, the quicker would the patient recover. Accidents sometimes happened, however, for instance through the physician mistaking the normal effect of pregnancy for evidence of a pathological condition.

Chapter 47

TRANSPLANTATION

A PIECE of skin, or even a whole organ, may be removed from an individual and transferred, or *transplanted*, to some other place in the same individual, where it may survive and retain its functions. But if it is transferred to another individual, even of the same species of animal, it will not survive, but, after a week or two, will be destroyed and removed just as if it were a "foreign" substance, and with the same kind of inflammatory reactions. This is due to the formation of antibodies which react with the antigens of the transplanted tissue. If the animal on which the skin, for example, is grafted has been "immunized" ("sensitized" would describe the phenomena better in this instance) by a previous graft from the same animal, or the injection of a suspension of living cells from this animal, the graft will be destroyed very rapidly, the necessary antibodies being already present. But if the donor and recipient of the graft are identical twins, i.e. have developed from the same fertilized egg-cell, and have the same genes in their chromosomes, a graft from one will "take" in the other. Studies of this kind lead to the conclusion that no two individuals (apart from identical twins) have cells and body fluids of precisely the same chemical composition, any more than they have precisely the same facial appearance or fingerprints.

Genotypes and Grafting

Some people live to a great age, appearing simply to "wear out". Most, however, in common with motor cars, washing machines etc., break down due to the failure of a certain part. This failure may have serious consequences, and even may result in death, if a vital organ is affected. Occasionally the loss of an organ can be made up for by the taking over of its functions by another (e.g. when one kidney is damaged) or by replacement therapy (e.g. injections of insulin in a diabetic).

Modern surgical techniques now offer the possibility of transplanting tissues and even organs from one person to another or, occasionally from other species to human beings. Apart from live transplants it is now also possible to insert artificial organs either temporarily or permanently into patients. The main problem to be surmounted in obtaining successful grafts is in overcoming the immune response which destroys the graft when it is introduced into the recipient. Most of the antigenic proteins found in red cells (p. 756) which lead to transfusion reactions are present also in the remaining cells of the body; in addition there are many others.

Thus foreign cells when grafted, set up immune reactions, e.g. the α and β agglutinins will kill off any cells containing type A or type B antigen, while Rh antigen in the graft itself will stimulate Rh antibody formation in the recipient, this antibody later attacking the graft. There are very many similar antigens, and the recipient can be looked upon as responding in just the same way to transplanted foreign cells as to pathogenic bacterial infection.

Types of Transplant

(1) *Autotransplants* are pieces of tissue or organs which are grafted from one part of the body to another. Considerable use is made of autotransplants in orthopaedic and plastic surgery (cartilage, bone, tendon and skin). Since the genotype is the same, reactions do not occur and provided that blood supply to the graft is adequate, all the grafted cells survive.

(2) *Homotransplants* are taken from another person (or animal of same species—in experiments). They survive for several days or weeks, then to be destroyed by the recipient's immune response. Even so, some homotransplants are useful, e.g. to act as a "scaffolding" for new bone formation as in bone transplants, or to overcome a temporary crisis, as in blood transfusions.

(3) *Heterotransplants* are grafts from one species to another and usually are destroyed even more rapidly than homotransplants.

Corneal Transplantation

Certain tissues which do not have cells (or the cells are not vital for the purposes of the graft) can often be transplanted from one individual to another successfully. Examples are cornea, tendon, fascia and bone. The first experiment in human corneal grafting was carried out in 1789 by a Frenchman, Pellier de Quengsy who used a glass disc set in a silver ring sewn into the cornea.

However, it was not until 1905 that a successful corneal tissue graft was achieved.

At the present time about 80 per cent of all grafts are successful (and of course the failures can be grafted again). The success of corneal grafts, in comparison with that of other organs, is due largely to the fact that the cornea is avascular, and hence the antigens of the cornea never reach the recipient in sufficient amounts to evoke an immune reaction which would cause the graft to be rejected, or to go opaque. Also the antigenicity is probably low.

An interesting new development is the "odonto-kerato-prosthesis" which consists of a plastic cylinder cemented within a very thin, ring-shaped, cross section of the patient's own tooth root. The tooth, since it is an autograft, is accepted by the cornea and the plastic cylinder acts as a pin-hole lens.

Immunosuppression

As we have seen, only homografts from an identical twin will survive, because only then are the antigenic proteins of both donor and recipient alike (since they are determined by identical genes from the single fertilized ovum). This of course limits the possibilities of organ transplanting on any useful scale, although the first successful skin-graft between mono-zygotic twins was carried out as long ago as 1920.

The stimulus of the experimental work on immunological tolerance carried out mainly by Medawar, has led to a great variety of attempts at the clinical transplantation of tissues and organs with increasing success recently. This success is wholly due to the new techniques of suppressing the immune reaction in the recipient, which have developed as a direct result of Medawar's work.

Mechanisms of Action of Immunosuppressives

Immunosuppressive agents reduce all components of the homograft immune reaction (onset is delayed; intensity is reduced and lymphatic proliferation is less). It is difficult to be certain about the rôle played in suppression by these mechanisms, because we are still ignorant of the manner in which the immune response itself is built up.

(a) Inhibition of mitosis

Reduced mitotic frequency has been shown to occur after administration of most immunosuppressive drugs. This is responsible for the reduced lymphoid activity and antibody output observed.

(b) Reduced antigen capture

Only cortisone has this effect. It impairs the whole defence reaction of the host (see p. 746 et seq.) including phagocytosis and hence uptake of antigen from the donor.

(c) Inhibition of DNA synthesis

Various drugs affect the different stages in nucleic acid synthesis, e.g. 6-mercapto-purine inhibits the first step in purine synthesis—the conversion of phospho-ribosylpyrophosphate to phosphoribosylamine. X-irradiation, the alkylating agents and antibiotics such as actinomycin C act on the end stages of nucleic acid synthesis.

(d) Alteration of nucleic acid bases

Antimetabolites (such as 6-thioguanine) mimic the natural metabolites and hence replace them in the ultimately produced nucleic acids. Thus in immuno-logically competent cells in which RNA has been altered in this way, antibody of impaired combining power, or of anomalous structure is produced.

(e) Destruction of cells

Many immunosuppressive agents give wholesale cellular destruction, although presumably the important factor here is the recipient's lymphocytic killing.

Azathioprine (AZT, Imuran) is believed to act by inhibiting purine synthesis at three stages in the pathway. (Incorporation of glutamine; conversion of inosinic acid to adenoyl succinic acid and in the subsequent conversion of this to adenosine monophosphate.)

The commonly used examples in clinical practice are azathioprine, actinomycin C, and prednisone. The disadvantage of using these drugs is that the patient's resistance to any infection is reduced or absent and a delicate balance must be achieved between dosage levels required to suppress the immune reaction sufficiently to prevent rejection of the graft and yet retain a modicum of protection from infectious disease.

Kidney Grafting

In 1954 the first successful human kidney transplantation was performed and the rapid restoration of this patient's health was a potent stimulus to further work. The homograft was from an identical twin. The current era in kidney grafting began in 1961 with the use of azathioprine as an immunosuppressive agent in a grafted patient who survived for 36 days, but who died from toxic effects because very little was known at that time about the optimum use of this drug. At the present time there are over a thousand patients who have had successful renal grafts. Numbers of centres have been set up in various parts of the world and the average one-year survival rate is about 70 per cent; for two years or more it is about 60 per cent.

This successful outcome is mainly the result of the realization that the patient with kidney failure can only be treated surgically if in good general health. Thus artificial kidney units have been established in conjunction with the transplantation units and *intermittent haemodialysis* is usually carried out for long enough beforehand to ensure that the patient is fit to receive the graft. Haemodialysis (developed by Kolff 25 years ago) consists in connecting the patient via a pump to a dialysing chamber in which blood circulates on one side of a cellophane membrane and the substances normally removed from the plasma by the kidney pass into the dialysate on the other side of the cellophane. The amounts of the various urinary constituents removed can be controlled by the composition of the dialysing fluid. For instance the dialysing fluid will be made up to contain the same amount of Na^+ and K^+ as does plasma (142 mEq/l; 5 mEq/l respectively) and no net exchange will occur. On the other hand the dialysate will not contain any urea or creatinine, whereas normal plasma does. Therefore the urea and the creatinine are extracted by the dialyser.

Intermittent dialysis is performed on patients by permanently inserting two plastic silicone cannulae into the arm or leg. One is to give access to an artery, the other to a vein and when the patient is not being dialysed the two are connected together to form an arterio-venous shunt having a continuous rapid flow within it. This prevents clotting, but such shunts are the main problem encountered in looking after the patients. The site must be kept scrupulously clean, it cannot be bathed and it must be protected from injury. Patients have to be connected to the machine for about 10–12 hr, two times a week and usually in order to interfere as little as possible with normal life, dialyses are performed at night. The patient comes in the late afternoon and remains on the machine until the next morning. (He has an evening meal, sleeps and has breakfast before going to work the next day!)

In "*peritoneal dialysis*" several litres of dialysing fluid are introduced via a catheter into the peritoneal cavity and removed a few hours later. Here, the peritoneal membranes act as the dialyser. This method is much less effective in terms of plasma clearance than haemodialysis. It also is liable to infection and the peritoneum eventually fibroses so that exchange does not occur.

The surgical technique of renal transplantation is well established. The renal vessels are anastomosed, extraperitoneally to the iliac vessels and the ureter is joined to the bladder. After the transplant, dialysis may still be required for a time. In some centres "*tissue typing*" (a process similar to blood grouping) is carried out to select compatible donors. A major problem is the provision of a large enough number of donors since the majority of grafts are now taken from cadavers.

Transplantation of Other Organs

The lung has not yet been successfully grafted but the operative problems are not great. In dogs and baboons lung transplants have been successfully performed. The liver is also a candidate for grafting although the surgical technique is demanding.* The heart has been successfully transplanted twice at the time of writing (out of a total of 21 attempts!) The surgical technique is not a problem and the amount of immuno-suppression required is less than in the case of the kidney. Endocrine glands have also been homotransplanted in humans. Parts of organs, such as heart valves or heart muscle can be transplanted with success.

* The liver must function normally after transplanting or the patient will die since no artificial liver is yet available.

EPILOGUE

THE functions of the various organs in the body have been described in the preceding chapters with rather special emphasis on the properties of the organs or physiological systems concerned. In living animals and man, however, an organ or tissue rarely increases or decreases its activity without affecting the activities of many other organs or tissues. These are all controlled by the nervous and endocrine systems so as to promote, as far as possible, the well-being and stability of the animal as a whole and the preservation of the species.

To a large extent this control is directed towards maintaining at steady values the volume, chemical composition (content of oxygen, carbon dioxide, glucose, salts, pH, etc.) and temperature of the body fluids (the "internal environment"), as already described in several chapters; any or all of these are likely to be disturbed by change of activity in one part of the body and restored by compensatory changes in other parts. It was this kind of regulatory process to which the term "physiological homeostasis" was originally given. The concept, however, may be extended to many aspects of our relations with the external world; for example, maintenance of the characteristic posture and orientation with respect to gravity. These, of course, are not necessarily constant. We are capable of movement and of adjusting our behaviour according to changes in the environment, and in general this involves co-ordinated actions directed towards maintaining continued existence in the "normal" state. If we are threatened by some object in the external world, our muscles are activated for self-preservation by taking evasive or hostile action as instinct, experience and instruction dictate; the consequent disturbance of the internal environment brings into play all the necessary restorative processes. These will include not only those involving, for example, the cardiovascular and respiratory systems, but also the acquisition, intake, digestion and absorption of food and water to replace the stores used up.

The first step in the maintenance of homeostasis is the detection by appropriate receptors of small changes in the various states and conditions of the external and internal environments. The messages, or "signals", which they originate pass to various parts of the nervous and endocrine systems where they are modified and co-ordinated and sent out again ("reflected") to various effectors, e.g., muscles and secreting glands, which can change the position and movement of the body and the physical and chemical states of the internal environment. The changes that result affect the receptors which originated the signals, that is, there is "feed-back" from the effectors to the receptors as well as "reflex" control of the effectors by the receptors. It is an important feature of such a system that the feed-back should be "negative", so arranged that any change which disturbs the steady state induces a response which acts so as to reduce the disturbance and restore the initial or "standard" conditions. The actions of the effectors then cease, or become stabilised, only when the receptors cease to originate signals, or originate some standard pattern of signal; they are continuously "monitored" and adjusted so as to conform to a co-ordinated pattern. Movement of a leg, for example, involves much more than the excitation and contraction of certain leg muscles; the nervous system "thinks" in terms of co-ordinated movements so that there is an appropriate and varying excitation of some muscles and inhibition of others, monitored by signals from many kinds of receptor. Likewise, secretion of the trophic hormones of the anterior pituitary gland is reduced or suppressed by the hormones which they cause to be secreted by the target organs; this negative feed-back, from target organ to anterior pituitary gland, keeps the amount of these hormones in the body relatively constant. Homeostasis is maintained, therefore, by the action of systems which are essentially the same as those known to engineers as "servosystems".

Imagine a man hunting or reaping for his food supplies; or, a more likely occupation for our readers, imagine him in some active game or sport. His eyes are directed so that the images of the object aimed at lie on the foveae—a good example of "automatic following" by means of a servosystem. His arm muscles are activated so as to direct, say, the arrow, reaping-hook or implement of sport until the pattern of signals from his eyes reaches the desired standard condition such that he will hit the prey, cut the corn or drive the ball. His leg muscles may be activated so as to produce the movements of running. There is thus a continuous adjustment of contractions of opposing muscles, while balance and posture are maintained by the excitation and inhibition of most of the other muscles in the body; all being controlled by combining information derived from the eyes, the receptor organs for balance (semi-circular canals, etc.) and receptors in the skin, joints and muscles themselves. Unless this control is smooth and accurate, brought about by well co-ordinated activity of many parts of the nervous system, energy will be wasted in checking needless movements and in failure to achieve the goal desired.

The active muscles use oxygen and glucose and produce carbon dioxide and heat more rapidly than they did when at rest. The flow of blood through them is increased and, through the action of the vaso-motor control system, that through the temporarily unimportant abdominal organs is decreased in compensation. The temperature regulating centres ensure that the flow through the skin is also increased so that the extra heat generated is dissipated. By the action of the "muscle pump" and the secretion of adrenaline, the output of the heart and flow of bood through the lungs are increased; more oxygen is removed from the lungs and more carbon dioxide delivered to them. The increased amount of carbon dioxide in the body, the decreased amount of oxygen, and other associated departures from the "standard" state, excite the respiratory centres; more air is breathed in and out of the lungs, extra oxygen is supplied and more carbon dioxide carried away. The fall in blood sugar concentration leads to a release of glucose from the glycogen stores of the liver. Water is lost from the body in the dissipation of heat, particularly if the exercise is severe enough to cause sweating; excitation of the osmo-receptors results in secretion of anti-diuretic hormone by the posterior pituitary gland and the kidneys excrete as little water as possible until the loss is made good by drinking. All these homeostatic processes, moreover, are adjusted continuously, mainly through the autonomic nervous system and secretion of hormones, as conditions change throughout the period of exercise and subsequent recovery. Nearly every organ of the body, therefore, is affected by any form of severe exercise; and, indeed, the exploration of the consequences of exercise on various organs has been one of the most fertile fields of experimental inquiry in physiology.

BIBLIOGRAPHY

THE books and review articles listed below have been chosen from the many available for the guidance of students who wish to penetrate more deeply into certain branches of physiology. A few of the larger textbooks have been included for reference purposes. Medical students mostly find them too comprehensive to read from cover to cover, but they are of great value for more detailed study of those parts of the subject found most interesting. Many of the best accounts of human physiology are to be found in the introductory chapters of monographs primarily addressed to readers with clinical interests, and a number of such monographs have accordingly been included. A few have been included more for the sake of their stimulating outlook than for their detailed accuracy. Readers should, therefore, carefully note the dates of publication and bear in mind the possibility that part of the content may have been superseded by more recent discoveries.

Students should make a habit of consulting volumes issued within the last ten years, and for review articles on recent developments, and for lists of references to modern papers should refer to current volumes of such periodicals as the Annual Reviews of Physiology. Current views on specialised topics will be found in articles in Physiological Reviews, Ergebnisse der Physiologie (some articles in English), Biological Reviews, Pharmacological Reviews, Harvey Lectures, and the Cold Spring Harbor Symposia.

GENERAL

PRINCIPLES OF HUMAN PHYSIOLOGY, by *E. H. Starling and C. Lovatt Evans*. 14th edn. Ed. by *H. Davson and M. G. Eggleton*. 1968. Churchill, London.
COMPARATIVE ANIMAL PHYSIOLOGY, by *C. L. Prosser and F. A. Brown*. 2nd edn. 1961.
PRINCIPLES OF GENERAL PHYSIOLOGY, by *L. E. Bayliss*. 5th edn. Vol. 1 "The Physico-chemical Background". 1959. Vol. 2 "General Physiology". 1960. Longmans Green, London.
THE WISDOM OF THE BODY, by *W. B. Cannon*. 1932.
ELECTRONIC APPARATUS FOR BIOLOGICAL RESEARCH, by *P. E. K. Donaldson*. 1958.
DYNAMIC ASPECTS OF BIOCHEMISTRY, by *E. Baldwin*. 5th edn. 1967. Cambridge Univ. Press.
APPLIED PHYSIOLOGY (*Samson Wright*). 11th edn. by *C. A. Keele and E. Neil* assisted by *J. B. Jepson*. 1965. Oxford Univ. Press.
CLARK'S APPLIED PHARMACOLOGY, by *A. Wilson and H. O. Schild*. 10th edn. 1968. Churchill, London.
HISTORY OF BIOLOGY: A GENERAL INTRODUCTION TO THE STUDY OF LIVING THINGS, by *C. Singer*. 1950.
SHORT HISTORY OF PHYSIOLOGY, by *K. J. Franklin*. 1949.
SELECTED READINGS IN THE HISTORY OF PHYSIOLOGY, by *J. F. Fulton*. 1930.

CELLS, MEMBRANES

BIOLOGICAL TRANSPORT, by *H. N. Christensen*. 1962. Benjamin, New York.
GENERAL PHYSIOLOGY, by *H. Davson*. 3rd edn. 1964. Churchill, London.
TRANSPORT AND ACCUMULATION IN BIOLOGICAL SYSTEMS, by *E. J. Harris*. 2nd edn. 1960. Academic Press, New York.
THE PERMEABILITY OF NATURAL MEMBRANES by *H. Davson and J. F. Danielli*, 2nd edn. 1952. Cambridge Univ. Press.

CIRCULATION, RESPIRATION

HANDBOOK OF PHYSIOLOGY, published by *American Physiological Society, Washington.* Section 2 "Circulation" and Section 3 "Respiration". Vol. 1. 1964.
THE LAW OF THE HEART, by *E. H. Starling.* 1918. Linacre Lecture.
CARDIAC CONTROL, by *R. F. Rushmer and O. A. Smith. Physiol. Rev.*, **39,** 41–68 (1959).
THE BLOOD VESSELS OF THE HUMAN SKIN AND THEIR RESPONSES, by *Thomas Lewis.* 1927.
THE ANATOMY AND PHYSIOLOGY OF CAPILLARIES, by *August Krogh.* 1929.
SYMPATHETIC CONTROL OF HUMAN BLOOD VESSELS, by *H. Barcroft and H. J. C. Swann.* 1952.
VENOUS RETURN, by *G. A. Brecher.* 1956.
REFLEXOGENIC AREAS OF THE CARDIOVASCULAR SYSTEM, by *C. Heymans and E. Neil.* 1958. Churchill, London.
CARDIOVASCULAR DYNAMICS, by *R. F. Rushmer.* 1961. Saunders, Philadelphia.
COMPARATIVE STUDIES ON THE ADRENERGIC NEUROHORMONAL CONTROL OF RESISTANCE. AND CAPACITANCE BLOOD VESSELS IN THE CAT, by *S. Mellander. Acta Physiol. Scand.* **50,** Suppl. 176, 1–86 (1960).
RESPIRATION, by *J. S. Haldane and J. G. Priestley.* 1935.
THE LUNG, by *J. H. Comroe and others.* 2nd edn. 1967. Yearbook Publishers, Chicago.
RESPIRATION. A PROGRAMMED COURSE, by *O. C. J. Lippold.* 1968. Freeman, San Francisco.

CENTRAL NERVOUS SYSTEM

THE CONDUCTION OF THE NERVOUS IMPULSE, by *A. L. Hodgkin.* 1964.
NERVE, MUSCLE AND SYNAPSE, by *B. Katz.* 1966.
THE BASAL GANGLIA AND POSTURE, by *J. Purdon Martin.* 1967.
HUMAN POSITION, SENSE AND SENSE OF EFFORT, by *P. A. Merton. Symp. Soc. Exper. Biol.* **18,** 387–400 (1964).
THE GREAT CEREBRAL COMMISSURE, by *R. W. Sperry. Scientific American.* (Jan. 1964).
THE VISUAL CORTEX OF THE BRAIN, by *D. Hubel. Scientific American.* (Nov. 1963).
THE STATES OF SLEEP, by *M. Jouvet. Scientific American.* (Feb. 1967).
THE SPLIT BRAIN IN MAN, by *M. S. Gazzaniga. Scientific American.* (Aug. 1967).
HANDBOOK OF PHYSIOLOGY, published by *American Physiological Society.* Section 1, "Neurophysiology", 3 vols. (1959–60).
THE ELECTRICAL SIGNS OF NERVOUS ACTIVITY, by *J. Erlanger and H. S. Gasser.* 1937.
THE IONIC BASIS OF ELECTRICAL ACTIVITY IN NERVE AND MUSCLE, by *A. L. Hodgkin. Biol. Rev.,* **26,** 339–409 (1951).
IONIC MOVEMENTS AND ELECTRICAL ACTIVITY IN GIANT NERVE FIBRES, by *A. L. Hodgkin.* Croonian Lecture. *Proc. Roy. Soc. Lond.* **B. 148,** 1–37 (1958).
THE TRANSMISSION OF IMPULSES FROM NERVE TO MUSCLE AND THE SUBCELLULAR UNITS OF SYNAPTIC ACTION, by *B. Katz.* Croonian Lecture. *Proc. Roy. Soc. Lond.,* **B. 155,** 455–477 (1962).
GENERAL PRINCIPLES OF NERVOUS ACTIVITY, by *E. D. Adrian.* Brain, **70,** 1–17 (1947).
THE PHYSIOLOGY OF NERVE CELLS, by *J. C. Eccles.* 1957. Cambridge Univ. Press.
THE INTEGRATIVE ACTION OF THE NERVOUS SYSTEM, by *C. S. Sherrington.* 1906. (Reprinted 1947) Cambridge Univ. Press.
THE SELECTED WRITINGS OF SIR CHARLES SHERRINGTON, Ed. by *D. Denny-Brown.* 1939.
REFLEX ACTIVITY OF THE SPINAL CORD, by *R. S. Creed, D. Denny-Brown, J. C. Eccles and C. S. Sherrington.* 1932.
ANATOMY OF THE NERVOUS SYSTEM, by *S. W. Ranson,* revised by *S. L. Clark.* 10th edn. 1959. W. B. Saunders, Philadelphia and London.
PHYSIOLOGY OF THE NERVOUS SYSTEM, by *J. F. Fulton.* 3rd edn. 1949.
PHYSIOLOGY OF THE NERVOUS SYSTEM, by *E. G. Walsh.* 1957.
INTRODUCTION TO CLINICAL NEUROLOGY, by *Gordon Holmes.* 1952.
CRITICAL STUDIES IN NEUROLOGY, by *F. M. R. Walshe.* 1948. Livingstone, Edinburgh.
SELECTED PAPERS OF SIR GORDON HOLMES, Ed. by *F. M. R. Walshe.* 1956.
THE FUNCTIONAL ORGANISATION OF THE DIENCEPHALON, by *W. R. Hess.* 1957.
THE CEREBELLUM OF MAN, by *Gordon Holmes.* Brain, **62,** 1–30 (1939).

THE CEREBRAL CORTEX OF MAN, by *W. Penfield and T. Rasmussen*. 1950.
THE ORGANIZATION OF THE CEREBRAL CORTEX, by *D. A. Sholl*. 1956. Methuen, London.
SOME PAPERS ON THE CEREBRAL CORTEX, by *G. von Bonin*. 1960. C. C. Thomas, Springfield, Ill.
BRAIN FUNCTION, by *M. A. B. Brazier* (Ed.). 1963. Univ. California Press, Berkeley.
THE PARIETAL LOBES, by *Macdonald Critchley*. 1953.
THE PHYSICAL BACKGROUND OF PERCEPTION, by *E. D. Adrian*. 1947. Oxford Univ. Press.
NERVOUS GRADATION OF MUSCULAR CONTRACTION, by *P. H. Hammond, P. A. Merton and G. G. Sutton. Brit. Med. Bull.* **12**, 214–218 (1956).
CONDITIONED REFLEXES, by *I. P. Pavlov*, translated by *G. V. Anrep*. 1927.

AUTONOMIC NERVOUS SYSTEM

PHYSIOLOGICAL CONTROLS AND REGULATION, by *W. S. Yamamoto and J. R. Brobeck*. 1965.
THE AUTONOMIC NERVOUS SYSTEM, by *J. C. White, R. H. Smithwick and F. A. Simeone*. 3rd. edn. 1952.
THE AUTONOMIC NERVOUS SYSTEM, by *A. Kuntz*. 1954. Lea & Febiger, Philadelphia.
AUTONOMIC NEURO-EFFECTOR SYSTEMS, by *W. B. Cannon and A. Rosenblueth*. 1937. Macmillan Co., New York.

RECEPTORS AND SENSATIONS

THE BASIS OF SENSATION, by *E. D. Adrian*. 1928.
RECEPTORS AND SENSORY PERCEPTION, by *R. Granit*. 1955. Yale Univ. Press, Newhaven, Conn.
RECEPTORS FOR SOMATIC SENSATION, by *G. Weddell*. in *M. A. B. Brazier* (Ed.). 1961. First conference on Brain and Behaviour. Washington.
SOME PRINCIPLES OF RECEPTOR ACTION, by *H. Davies*. 1961. *Physiol. Rev.*, **41**, 391–416.
THE CHEMICAL SENSES, by *R. W. Moncrieff*. 2nd edn. 1951.
PHYSIOLOGY OF THE EYE, by *H. Davson*. 2nd edn. 1963. Churchill, London.
VISION AND THE EYE, by *M. Pirenne*. 1948.
THE VERTEBRATE EYE AND ITS ADAPTIVE RADIATIONS, by *G. L. Walls*. 1942.
PHYSIOLOGY OF THE RETINA AND THE VISUAL PATHWAY, by *G. S. Brindley*. 1960.
PHYSIOLOGICAL MECHANISMS OF VISION AND THE QUANTUM NATURE OF LIGHT, by *M. Pirenne. Biol. Rev.*, **31**, 194–241 (1956).
THE VISUAL PIGMENTS, by *H. J. A. Dartnall*. 1957. Methuen, London.
SPEECH AND HEARING IN COMMUNICATION, by *H. Fletcher*. 1953. Van Nostrand, New York.
BIOPHYSICS AND PHYSIOLOGY OF THE INNER EAR, by *H. Davis. Physiol. Rev.*, **37**, 1–49 (1957).
THE PHYSIOLOGY OF HEARING, by *I. C. Whitfield. Prog. Biophysics*, **8**, 1–47 (1957).
MECHANICAL INTO ELECTRICAL ENERGY IN CERTAIN MECHANORECEPTORS, by *J. A. B. Gray. Prog. Biophysics*, **9**, 286–324. (1959).
SENSORY COMMUNICATION, Ed. by *W. A. Rosenblith*. 1961. Wiley, New York.

DIGESTION

HUMAN GASTRIC FUNCTION, by *S. Wolf and H. G. Wolff*. 1947. Oxford Univ. Press.
PHYSIOLOGY OF THE DIGESTIVE TRACT, by *H. W. Davenport*. 1961. Year Book Publishers, Chicago.
SECRETORY MECHANISMS OF THE GASTRO-INTESTINAL TRACT, by *R. A. Gregory*. 1962. Edw. Arnold, London.
THE STOMACH, by *C. Thompson, D. Berkowitz and E. Polish*. 1967. Grune & Stratton, New York.
ABSORPTION FROM THE INTESTINE, by *G. Wiseman*. 1964. Academic Press, London and New York.

METABOLISM, NUTRITION

NUTRITION—A COMPREHENSIVE TREATISE, by *G. H. Beaton and E. W. McHenry.* 3 vols. 1964–66. Academic Press, New York and London.

REQUIREMENT OF MAN FOR PROTEIN, by *D. P. Cuthbertson.* 1964. Min. Hlth. Rep. Publ. Hlth. Med. Sub. No. 111, H.M.S.O. London.

HUMAN NUTRITION AND DIETETICS, by *Sir S. Davidson, and R. Passmore.* 1966. 3rd edn. Livingstone, Edinburgh.

ENERGY, WORK, AND LEISURE, by *J. V. G. A. Durnin, and R. Passmore.* 1967. Heinemann, London.

THE PHYSIOLOGY OF HUMAN SURVIVAL, by *O. G. Edholm and A. L. Bacharach.* 1965. Academic Press, London.

CALORIE REQUIREMENTS, NUTRITIONAL STUDIES, 1957. Food and Agriculture Organisation of the United Nations, **15,** Rome.

RECOMMENDED DIETARY ALLOWANCES. Food and Nutrition Board. 1964. Publication 1146. *Nat. Acad. of Sci.* Nat. Res. Counc. Washington, D.C.

THE ELEMENTS OF THE SCIENCE OF NUTRITION, by *G. Lusk.* 1931. 4th. edn. Saunders, Philadelphia.

THE CHEMICAL ANATOMY OF THE HUMAN BODY, IN BIOCHEMICAL DISORDERS IN HUMAN DISEASE, by *R. Passmore and M. H. Draper.* 1964. 2nd. edn. Ed. *R. H. S. Thompson and E. J. King,* Churchill, London.

HUMAN ENERGY EXPENDITURE, by *R. Passmore and J. V. G. Durnin. Physiol. Rev.,* **35,** 801–40 (1955).

THE RESPIRATORY QUOTIENT, by *H. B. Richardson. Physiol. Rev.,* **9,** 61–125 (1929).

PRINCIPLES OF GENERAL PHYSIOLOGY, by *L. E. Bayliss.* 1959. Vol. 1 & 2. Longmans Green, London.

A SURVEY OF THE ENERGY TRANSFORMATIONS IN LIVING WATER, by *H. Krebs and H. L. Kornberg. Ergebn. Physiol.* **49,** 212–298 (1957).

ENDOCRINES

THE HORMONES: PHYSIOLOGY, CHEMISTRY AND APPLICATIONS, Ed. by *G. Pincus and J. V. Thimann.* Vols. 1–15. Academic Press, London and New York.

TEXTBOOK OF ENDOCRINOLOGY, 4th edn., Ed. by *R. H. Williams.* 1968. W. B. Saunders, London and Philadelphia.

HORMONES IN BLOOD, Ed. by *C. H. Gray and A. L. Bacharach.* 1967. Academic Press, London and New York.

THE THYROID HORMONES, by *R. Pitt-Rivers and J. R. Tata.* 1959. Pergamon, Oxford.

NEURAL CONTROL OF THE PITUITARY GLAND, by *G. W. Harris.* 1955. Edw. Arnold, London.

THE ANTIDIURETIC HORMONE AND THE FACTORS WHICH DETERMINE ITS RELEASE, by *E. B. Verney.* Croonian Lecture. *Proc. Roy. Soc.,* **B, 135,** 35–105 (1947).

THE PARATHYROID GLANDS, Eds. *P. J. Gaillard, R. V. Talmage* and *A. M. Budy.* 1965.

THE ENDOCRINE ORGANS IN HEALTH AND DISEASE (HISTORIAL REVIEW). 1936. Rolleston.

NATURAL HISTORY OF CHROMAFFIN TISSUE, by *R. E. Coupland.* 1965.

THE PITUITARY GLAND, Eds. *G. W. Harris and B. T. Donovan.* 1966. 3 vols.

NEUROENDOCRINOLOGY, Eds. *L. Martini and W. F. Ganong.* Vol. I, 1966; Vol. II, 1967.

HYPOTHALAMIC RELEASING FACTORS AND THE CONTROL OF ANTERIOR PITUITARY FUNCTION, by *G. W. Harris, May Reed and C. P. Fawcett. Brit. med. Bull.* **22,** 266–272 (1966).

REPRODUCTION

REPRODUCTION AND SEX, by *G. I. M. Swyer.* 1954.

PHYSIOLOGY OF THE MAMMARY GLANDS, by *J. L. Linzell. Physiol. Rev.,* **39,** 534–576 (1959).

HUMAN REPRODUCTION AND SEXUAL BEHAVIOUR, Ed. by *C. W. Lloyd.* 1964. Lea & Febiger, Philadelphia.

REPRODUCTIVE PHYSIOLOGY, by *A. V. Nalbandov.* 2nd. edn. 1964. Freeman, San Francisco.

RENAL FUNCTION

THE PHYSIOLOGY OF DIURETIC AGENTS, *Annals N. Y. Acad. Sci.* **139,** 273–539 (1966).
SOME RECENT DEVELOPMENTS IN THE PHYSIOLOGY OF THE KIDNEY, by *R. O. Berliner. Internat. Acad. Pathol.* Monograph **6,** 60–68 (1966).
PRINCIPLES OF RENAL PHYSIOLOGY, by *Homer W. Smith.* 1956. Oxford University Press.
MODERN VIEWS ON THE SECRETION OF URINE (Cushny Memorial Lectures), Ed. by *F. R. Winton.* 1956. Churchill, London.
PHYSIOLOGY OF MICTURITION, by *O. R. Langworthy, L. C. Kolb and L. G. Lewis.* 1940.
CONTROL OF ALDOSTERONE SECRETION, by *J. O. Davis. Physiologist* **5,** 65–86 (1962).
THE KIDNEY: AN OUTLINE OF NORMAL AND ABNORMAL STRUCTURE AND FUNCTION, by *H. E. de Wardener.* 3rd. edn. 1967. Churchill, London.

BODY FLUIDS

THE BODY FLUIDS, by *J. R. Elkington and T. S. Danowski.* 1955.
PASSAGE OF MOLECULES THROUGH CAPILLARY WALLS, by *J. R. Pappenheimer. Physiol. Rev.,* **33,** 387–423 (1953).
THE LYMPHATIC SYSTEM, by *C. K. Drinker.* 1942. Lane Memorial Lecture.
LYMPHATICS AND LYMPHOID TISSUE, by *J. M. Yoffey and F. C. Courtice.* 1956.
PHYSIOLOGY OF THE CEREBROSPINAL FLUID, by *H. Davson.* 1967. Churchill, London.
THE FUNCTIONS OF BLOOD, Ed. by *R. G. MacFarlane.* 1960. Academic Press, New York.

MUSCLES

THE CONTRACTION OF MUSCLE, by *H. E. Huxley. Scientific American,* **199,** 67–82 (1958).
MECHANICAL AND ELECTRICAL ACTIVITY IN INTESTINAL SMOOTH MUSCLE by *N. Sperlakis and C. L. Prosser. Amer. J. Physiol.* **196,** 850–856 (1959).
TEXTBOOK OF GENERAL PHYSIOLOGY, by *H. Davson,* 3rd. edn. 1964. Churchill, London.
LIVING MACHINERY, by *A. V. Hill.* 1927.
THE STRUCTURE AND FUNCTION OF MUSCLE, Ed. by *G. H. Bourne.* 1960. Vol. 1 "Structure". Vol. 2 "Biochemistry and Physiology". Vol. 3 "Pharmacology and Disease".
PHYSIOLOGY OF VOLUNTARY MUSCLE, Ed. by *W. D. M. Paton. Brit. Med. Bull.,* **12,** 161–236 (1956).
PRINCIPLES OF HUMAN PHYSIOLOGY (Starling and Lovatt Evans). 14th. edn. 1968. Chapters on Muscle by *D. R. Wilkie,* Churchill, London.

TEMPERATURE REGULATION

PHYSIOLOGY OF TEMPERATURE REGULATION, by *J. D. Hardy. Physiol. Rev.,* **41,** 521 (1961).
PHYSIOLOGY OF MAN IN THE DESERT, by *E. F. Adolph.* 1947. Interscience Publishers.
MAN IN A COLD ENVIRONMENT, by *A. C. Burton and O. G. Edholm.* 1955. Edw. Arnold, London.
THE SWEAT GLANDS, by *J. S. Weiner and K. Hellmann. Biol. Rev.,* **35,** 141–186 (1960).
HUMAN PERSPIRATION, by *Y. Kuno.* 1956. C. C. Thomas, Springfield.

REACTIONS TO INJURY

HUMAN BLOOD COAGULATION AND ITS DISORDERS by *R. Biggs and R. G. Macfarlane.* 3rd. edn. 1962. Blackwell, Oxford.
BLOOD GROUPS IN MAN, by *R. R. Race and R. Sanger.* 4th. edn. 1962. Blackwell, Oxford.
THE HOMOGRAFT REACTION, by *P. B. Medawar.* Croonian Lecture. *Proc. Roy. Soc. Lond.,* **B.149,** 145–166 (1958).
A MODERN BASIS FOR PATHOLOGY, by *Sir Macfarlane Burnet. Lancet,* **i,** 1383 (1968).
FURTHER OBSERVATIONS ON RENAL TRANSPLANTS IN MAN FROM CADAVERIC DONORS, by *R. Y. Calne and others. Brit. Med. J.* **ii,** 1345 (1966).
RENAL DISEASE, by *J. S. Cameron. Brit. Med. J.* **ii,** 933 (1966).
PREVENTION OF RHESUS ISO-IMMUNISATION, by *C. A. Clarke. Lancet,* **ii,** 1 (1968).

INDEX

Figures in **heavy type** refer to pages in which illustrations or tables occur.

A band, myofibril containing, **691**

Abdominal muscles, action in respiration of, 167

ABO blood group, reactions of, 756–**757**

Acclimatization, high altitude, 225–227
to heat, 680

Accommodation, eye showing, 435
mechanism in nerve of, 272–273
nerve showing, 246

Acetoacetic acid, amino-acids forming, 511

Acetylcholine, arterial pressure and leg volume affected by, **550**
coronary blood flow affected by, 84
denervated muscle affected by, 289–290
medullary chemoreceptors affected by, 198
motor end-plate affected by, **282**–283
pacemaker and action potentials affected by, 113
Renshaw cell stimulation by, 303
tests in use for, 398, **399**
vasodilator action of, 70

Acetyl coenzyme A, citric acid cycle involving, 525
metabolic importance of, 508

Acetylene, pulmonary blood flow measurement by use of, 75

Acid-base balance, renal regulation of, 659

Acidity, HbO_2 dissociation curve affected by 142

Acidophile adenoma, effects of, 581–582

Acidosis, protein food inducing, 513

Acids, titration curves of weak, **149**

Aconitine, auricular fibrillation induced by, 129–130

Acromegaly, cause and nature of, 581–582

Actin, distribution in plain muscle of, 723
position in myofibril of, 692

Action potential, measurement in giant axon of, **251**–252
Na and K permeabilities of membrane change during, 267–271

Active state, muscle twitch and, 701

Active transport, intestinal absorption involving, 490

Actomyosin thread, ATP action on, 712–713

Acute hypoxia, respiration in, 223–**224**

Adams-Stokes attack, nature of, 129

Adaptation, receptor units showing, 407, **416**
temperature receptors showing, **416**

Addison's disease, cause and symptoms of, 561

Adenohypophysis, control of secretion of, 578–581
diabetes mellitus relation to, 523
gonadotrophic hormones secreted by, 602
hormones secreted by, 575–576
hypothalamus control of hormonal pattern secreted by, 580
parts of, **573**–574

Adenosinediphosphate, rephosphorylation of, 708–710

Adenosinetriphosphate, ACh synthesis involving, 400
breakdown in plain muscle of, 732
cardiac muscle oxidative resynthesis of, 735
energy liberation in metabolism and, 527
chromaffin granules in adrenal medulla containing, 553
mechanisms in muscle for maintaining, 708–710
plasticizing action of, 713
sodium pump dependence on, 266

Adrenal cortex, control of, 561
diabetes mellitus relation to, 524
female pseudo-hermaphroditism resulting from androgens secreted by, 636
menstrual periodicity control by, 598
structure and functions of, 557–562

Adrenal glands, origins of, 552

Adrenal medulla, control of, 555–**557**
innervation of, 385
structure and function of, 553–557

Adrenalectomy, effects of, 559–560

Adrenaline, actions of, 388, 554
arterial pressure and leg volume affected by small doses of, **550**
blood sugar affected by, 520
cardiac output relation to venous pressure affected by, 123–**124**
carotid sinus reflexes involving secretion of, **57**–58

Jacksonian fits, nature of, 357
Jaundice, red blood cell fragility in, 9
Joint receptors, respiration affected by stimulation of, 213
Joints, position sense dependence on, 328
Jugular pulse, heart block effect on, 109
Junction potential, plain muscle stimulation inducing, 731

Katathermometer, use of, 681–682
Ketogenic amino-acids, nature of, 511
Ketone bodies, theories of formation of, 516–517
Ketonuria, occurrence in diabetes mellitus of, 522–523
Ketosis, cause of, 516
Kidney, O_2 consumption by, 643
parathyroid action on, 570
structure of, 639–**641**
transplantation of, 763
Knee jerk, mechanism of, 332
Kreb's cycle. See Citric acid cycle
Krebs-Ringer solutions, types of, 28
Kupffer cells, nature of, 749

Labour, events in, 616–**618**
Labyrinths, importance in posture of, 338
receptors in, 414–**415**
Lactation, dietary allowance recommended for, **534**
factors affecting, 620
Lactic acid, blood buffering affected by production of, 160–161
production in muscle of, 709–710, 712
respiratory quotient affected by production of, 500
utilization by tissues of, 519
Larynx, afferent nerve supply to, 166
Latent period, crossed extensor reflex, 323
flexion reflex, 323
skeletal muscle showing, **696**
Lateral geniculate body, receptive fields of neurones in, 346
visual pathway involving, **343**
Law of Conservation of Mass, Fick principle and, 73
Law of Mass Action, titration curves of weak acids and, 149
Lead poisoning, parathormone treatment of, 571
Leech muscle, ACh test on, 398, **399**
Lengthening reaction, nature of, 336
Lens, change during accommodation in, 435
Leucocytes, types of, 748
Leucocytosis, infection and, 748

Leucotaxine, actions of, 747
Leukaemia, white blood cells in, 748
Limbic system, autonomic nervous system relation to, 394
Limulus, photoreceptor activity in compound eye of, 438
Lipids, metabolism of, 514–517
Lipoid soluble compounds, membrane permeability to, 5
Liquor folliculi, nature of, 589–**590**
Lithium, sodium replacement in action potential by, 271
Liver, amino-acids deamination in, 510
bile salts secretion by, 484
blood reservoir function of, 90–91
glucose production by, 517–518
Load compensating reflex, respiratory muscles and, 196
Local anaesthetics, nerve block by, 277
Locke's solution, composition of, **26**
Locomotion, internal organization of, 339
nervous control of, 315–316
Loewi, chemical transmission of vagus effect on heart shown by, **395**
Lohmann reaction, nature of, 708, 709
Long acting thyroid stimulator, nature of, 567–568
Loop of Henle, hairpin countercurrent system in, 657–**658**
Lumbar puncture, nature of, 23, 24–25
Luminosity curves, photopic and scotopic, **425**
Lungs, birth effect on, 171–173
buoyancy of collapsed, 175
changes in blood involved in liberation of CO_2 in, 159
mechanism of gaseous exchange between blood and, 182–187
respiration affected by afferent impulses from, 210–**212**
structural unit of, **164**
viscous resistance in, 169–**170**
water loss from, 543
Lung movement, sounds associated with, 173
Lung volumes, measurement of, **174**–**175**
Luteinizing hormone, action of, 602–**603**
Luteotrophic hormone, action of, 602
Lymph, formation and flow of, 20–23
Lymphagogues, types of, 21
Lymphocytes, antibody production by, 750, 752
characteristics of, 748
Lymphoid tissue, glucocorticoids action on, 560

PRINTED IN GREAT BRITAIN BY THE WHITEFRIARS PRESS LTD.
LONDON AND TONBRIDGE